An epic sourcebook for *Rifts®*, *Phase World®*, *the Minion War* and the entire Megaverse®

Dedication

In memory to our clan elder and my grandmother, *Jean Brown*. The bells in St. Peter's are ringing again, and your family will always think of you when they do.

To the second generation of *Browns*, my cousins. I grew up with Deanna and Chad who were like my sister and brother. Later on Matthew came along and he was the little brother who we would often abandon in the sand pit. Sorry Matthew, here's your public apology that is long overdue.

My cousin Jeffery who of all my cousins actually had an interest in RPGs and still to this day reads my books.

The sweethearts of the family, Melissa and Jackie, and then my much younger cousins, Timothy, Kaitlin, Scott, and Jacob who I would often wrestle with at holiday gatherings. Someone would always end up crying, but would inevitably come back for more. These days they are much too old to wrestle and I'm sure I would be the one crying once they took revenge for years of charlie horses, dragon bites and the occasional rug burn which Timothy always reminds me of, but your sister was involved in that too!

Finally, to my cousin Sara who we do not see often enough.

In all of you I see your parents and the values and traditions that have been passed down. How lucky I am to be part of such a large and loving family.

– Carl J. Gleba ~ 2017

The cover, by *John Zeleznik*, depicts a pair of modern Atlanean adventurers travelling to an alien world via a Rift. A Voyager leads the way.

First Printing – July, 2017

Palladium Online: **www.palladiumbooks.com** – also visit us at **facebook.com/PalladiumBooks**

Rifts® Secrets of the Atlanteans™ – A Rifts® Dimension Book, is published by Palladium Books Inc., 39074 Webb Court, Westland, MI 48185-7606. Printed in the USA by McNaughton & Gunn.

Palladium Books® Presents:

Rifts® Dimension Book™ 15: Secrets of the Atlanteans™

Written by: **Carl Gleba**

Additional Writing & Ideas: **Kevin Siembieda**

Editors: **Alex Marciniszyn**
Kevin Siembieda
Wayne Smith

Proofreader: **Julius Rosenstein**

Cover Illustration: **John Zeleznik**

Interior Artists:
Kent Burles
Scott Johnson
Kevin Long
Ramon K. Perez
Benjamin Rodriguez
Charles "Chuck" Walton II

Art Direction: **Kevin Siembieda**
Typography and Layout: **Wayne Smith**

Based on the RPG rules, writings, characters, settings,
concepts and Megaverse® created by **Kevin Siembieda**.

Special Thanks to the ultra-imaginative *Carl Gleba* whose brilliant ideas and adventure hooks always inspire me to do more, to *John Zeleznik* for another dynamic cover, to *Chuck Walton* for his artistry and friendship, *Ben Rodriguez* for banging out a zillion tattoos, *Andrew Cook* for everything, and to the core team and warriors at Palladium Books, *Alex, Wayne, Kathy, Julius* and newcomer *Scott*, all of whom work tirelessly to help bring you new worlds to explore.

– *Kevin Siembieda, July 2017*

Contents

Quick Find Index

Ancient Atlantis

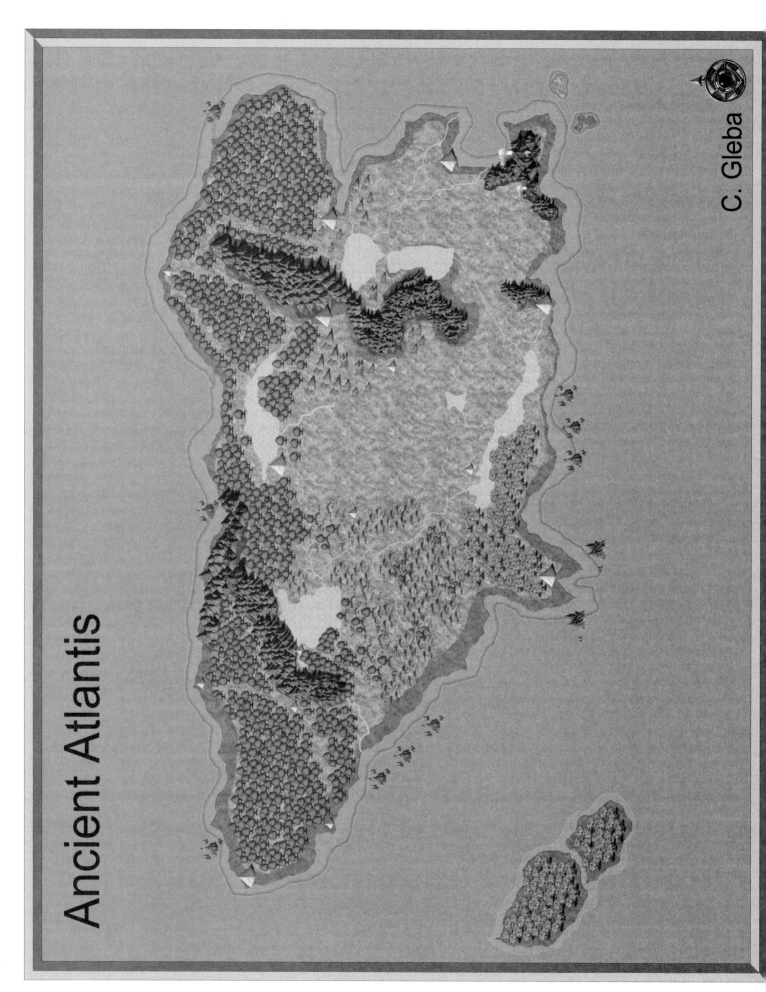

C. Gleba

Secrets of the Atlanteans

The island of Atlantis vanished long ago, but despite the loss of their homeland and being cast adrift through endless dimensions, Atlanteans managed not just to survive, but to thrive. Their traditions, technology, and culture still exist today.

Atlanteans have made the sum of the Megaverse their home. Traveling across dimensions as wandering paladins, scholars, healers, and warriors of light. They are a noble people known to fight supernatural evil and oppression wherever they find them.

What few people realize is that the Atlanteans have many secrets. As a society, they are scattered across the infinite cosmos. To encounter a single Atlantean is rare, a group of them rarer still, and finding an Atlantean city is almost unheard of. Few people have been able to tell the tale of seeing an Atlantean city and talk about their advanced healing centers or their vast knowledge of medicine, magic and traveling the universe. While there are many wonderful and enlightening secrets that the Atlanteans are willing to share, there are some dark secrets that are kept hidden from outsiders and even from their own kind.

Many of those secrets are about to be revealed.

Carl J. Gleba ~ 2017

Who are the Atlanteans?

Atlanteans are considered, by many, to be one of the first great civilizations on Earth. Their culture has its roots on an island continent in the middle of the Atlantic Ocean and was old long before the fabled Babylonian and Egyptian civilizations began to rise. At the time, the physiology of Atlanteans was the same as any human of the period, but their culture was far more advanced and steeped in magic. No one knows exactly where they originated or how they arrived on Atlantis, nor how they learned and mastered the secrets of the pyramids and magic. Even Atlantean history does not go back that far. Many Atlanteans believe they rose from a human tribe somewhere in the Mediterranean and were dimensionally Rifted to the island continent of Atlantis. This may well be true; Atlantis was a place of magic and probably a hotbed of dimensional activity as it was covered with ley lines and nexus points.

The early Atlanteans learned how to tame the ley lines by building stone pyramids. Atlantean records tell of small, "primitive" stone pyramids that would calm the ley lines, abate the random Rifts, and control storms. As their mystic knowledge of *Stone Mastery* evolved, so did their pyramids improve. New, better, larger stone pyramids replaced the old, and eventually, grand cities blossomed around them. As the Atlanteans' learned how to control magic, it became the *dominant technology* of their civilization. Magic enabled them to control the weather, grow bet-

ter crops, build, and meet the many needs of their people. This prosperity gave Atlanteans more time to experiment with magic, and in so doing, they learned how to open portals to new worlds via the Rifts.

It is ironic, but Atlantean mastery of ley lines and magic, combined with their curiosity, drove them to explore other worlds more than their own. Soon Atlanteans were visiting alien worlds and other dimensions. With new worlds to explore and new knowledge to be gained, Atlanteans all but forgot about the rest of Earth. Only a few excursions were made to other parts of the planet, where they found stone age people and cultures. To these primitive people, Atlanteans were seen as unusual strangers and met with fear and distrust. Others mistook them to be gods. For Atlanteans, these simple cultures offered little to interest or challenge them, so they spent their time on alien worlds.

As a civilization, Atlantean knowledge of science and magic easily surpassed that of Lazlo and Tolkeen of Rifts Earth, and in some ways, may have rivaled the knowledge of the Splugorth. No one else of that era could compete with them. Had the Atlanteans so desired, they could have conquered their home world, but their attention was drawn elsewhere. They had more alluring places to explore. Distant, alien worlds beckoned and Atlanteans answered the call. During the height of Atlantean society on Earth, travel to other worlds was commonplace. And it may have cost them their place on Earth.

On Rifts Earth, today, True Atlanteans are known as a people who have lost their ancestral home on Earth. Their island nation, once thought destroyed, returned to Earth only to fall into the clutches of the monstrous Splugorth and their inhuman minions. The Atlantean people are scattered and spread throughout the Megaverse. Some have managed to settle on other worlds where they live among the indigenous people, while others have tamed alien worlds for themselves, and many remain transdimensional wanders. Nomads who move from place to place and dimension to dimension in search of adventure, knowledge and purpose.

True Atlanteans are known as fierce and brave warriors willing to fight and put their own lives on the line to save others, restore justice, avenge the wronged and destroy supernatural evil. Among these heroes are dedicated groups of True Atlanteans who travel the Megaverse hunting their most hated enemy, *vampires* and all manner of *undead*. Their reputation throughout the Megaverse is that they are friends to those in need and an enemy to the forces of darkness and supernatural evil. These noble paladins and Champions of Light challenge tyrants and evildoers, slay monsters, hunt vampires, help the innocent, free the downtrodden, fight for justice, teach and counsel others, inspire and share bits of magic.

Despite their reputation as heroes and monster slayers, even heroes of renown are usually willing to help with mundane tasks such as farm work, chopping wood, tending to cattle and doing whatever they can to help. Nothing is beneath most True Atlanteans. And while it is the heroes and warriors who grab the headlines, many are scholars, teachers, healers, artists, writers, practitioners of magic, and diplomats who try to solve problems with words, high ideals and noble deeds.

As a rule, Atlanteans are a proud, yet humble people, haunted by their past hubris which doomed their beloved Atlantis. It is a past that keeps them grounded and soulful thinkers who have learned to look before they leap and try to see the big picture. Though never afraid to take a stand and fight, most use words,

ideas, strategies and tactics over force and violence whenever they can. It took tragedy and a long time for Atlanteans to learn humility, and to put others first. All Atlanteans are proud of their ancestry, but many would say that as a people, they have come a very long way since the days of Atlantis on Earth.

Atlantean Society

Atlantean culture, before the loss of Atlantis and their civilization, was a democratic society. They believed in freedom of expression, morality, fairness, and the accumulation of knowledge. Family has always been at the core, and most Atlanteans not only wanted to better themselves but their family's standing.

Social status in old Atlantis often fell into economic classes of the lower middle class, upper middle class and the wealthy. For Atlanteans, there were no poor, not really. There were lower middle class (30%), the majority upper middle class (65%), and the wealthy and powerful (5%). Thus, family standing was an important matter of perception and influence within Atlantean society. Accomplishment, such as being appointed to represent the local province on the governing council, or the family's children going to a prestigious university, or being selected as an Ambassador to a new dimension, and so on, set families apart. It was less about wealth and more about what accomplishments and prestige the family had to its credit that elevated a family clan. Local communities would have large gatherings where numerous families would meet to discuss who had accomplished what. In the end it was friendly rivalries that propelled Atlantean society to improve itself as a whole. That remains true to this day, despite being scattered all over the Megaverse. The tradition of family accomplishment and corresponding prestige continues, and compels many to greater and greater feats of heroics, derring-do and acts of charity.

The Island Continent of Old

Ancient Atlantis was an island nation. Temperatures were moderate, on par with Greece or Spain, the soil good for crops, and the land a mix of forest, lowland plains and forested mountains. Only the northern mountains would receive some snow during the winter, while the rest of the island received seasonal rain. Weather influenced Atlantean dress and style. In ancient Atlantis during the warm summer months, loose-fitting clothing was favored. Women often wore colorful, light dresses or skirts with loose-fitting blouses. Having access to other dimensions, it was easy to obtain cotton, silk and exotic fabrics, as well as dyes and pre-made, colored clothing not normally available on Earth. Most women preferred their hair long, and for many generations it was the fad to not cut the hair and let it grow to below the waist. This has changed with a more pragmatic approach for dimensional travel and modern styles.

Men of the time wore short leggings or kilts. Long pants were almost unheard of back then, and only worn in the winter months. Men preferred open vests or loose-fitting shirts. They too enjoyed colorful clothing, though most seemed to wear solid colors where women wore clothing with patterns or prints as well as solid colors. Men let their hair grow long, but it was trimmed and narrow in the back, worn loose or pulled into ponytails and braids or as dreadlocks. Most were clean shaven. Full beards were a rarity, but some grew large sideburns (muttonchops), goatees or mustaches. Even before changing their genetic structure, True Atlanteans seemed endowed with a full head of black or dark brown hair, with baldness being very rare.

Modern Atlanteans. Since the days of the *Coming of the Rifts*, modern True Atlantean attire varies from clan to clan and place to place, often based on one's environment. As most Atlanteans left Earth with little more than the clothes on their backs when Atlantis fell to destruction, fashions would change considerably. Some clans and families within the clans hung on to the old styles, while others adopted new ones or those of the alien people and worlds they would encounter. Even today, some clans wear the traditional long hair and ponytails and clothing of the past, while others wear animal furs and leather, and others wear modern clothes and fabrics from plastic and ceramics to alien wonder-fabrics. Whatever style strikes their fancy is what they wear. However, boots, capes and cloaks, long and short, never seem to go out of fashion for True Atlanteans.

Atlantean priests and **practitioners of magic** tend to wear robes with vest-like upper body pieces, ornate belts and girdles, or strips of cloth that may hang from the shoulders or waist, bracelets and armbands. Many favor *Egyptian style* mantles and necklaces around their necks as well as magical talismans and armlets or leather bands. But again, True Atlanteans wear a wide range of clothing from ultra-modern to what may look like the garb of an ancient culture, particularly those with an *ancient Egyptian* or *Persian flair*.

Modern and ancient dress. Some wear a combination of modern and ancient styles of clothing and equipment. Say, modern boots, pants and belt with a holster for an energy weapon, the body protected by a Naruni force field, or partial to full high-tech body armor, but some also wear an ancient-style leopard or wolf fur cape and leather or metal vambraces on the forearms, or something that resembles a traditional Native American or Mayan vest, shirt or jacket. Along those lines, True Atlanteans traditionally like to wear gold jewelry, talismans, amulets, charms, bracelets, vambraces, mantles and ornamentation.

Only **Undead Slayers** and **Tattoo Defenders** seem to have changed very little from their past. They wear leather breeches and vests to allow them quick access to their tattoos, although most combine them with Mega-Damage leathers and light armor to wear mixed with modern weapons and equipment, amulets and talismans.

The Vampire Scourge

Today, True Atlanteans are seen as heroes and noble sages filled with wisdom and insight. Atlanteans were not always that wise. Or heroic. In fact, some might have considered them arrogant and naive to not have thought that building bridges to other dimensions and alien worlds would not be fraught with danger.

Generations of dimensional travel was a boon to Atlanteans. They traveled to many worlds, met many people and learned a wide range of magic and science. They made friends with the likes the *Chiang-Ku dragons*, and made acquaintance with the *Minions of Splugorth, Prometheans* of *Phase World* and the people of *the Three Galaxies*, among others. Of course, there were some dangerous encounters along the way, but there would be one that would change the Atlantean culture forever.

During their exploration of the Megaverse, they opened a portal to a world that was dark and foreboding. At one point, there must have been intelligent life on the planet because there were ruins of massive cities that appeared to have been devastated by nuclear war or other holocaust. Much of the world appeared this way, but the damage was clearly done hundreds or even thousands of years in the past. Even the sky of this dead world let in little sunlight.

Atlanteans spent years exploring what they called the **Fallen Earth** – as they believed this world to be an Earth-like cousin to their beloved home world in another dimension. At one point, the world must have been a paradise and home to an advanced civilization. The Atlanteans found signs of advanced technology, advanced medical facilities and even the capability to travel in spacecraft.

One discovery surprised and excited the explorers more than any other: a large, metallic dome two miles (3.2 km) in diameter. The dome was made of an unknown material that channeled magic out and away from whatever was inside of it. When it was touched by one of the Atlantean team members, a telepathic message was delivered to everyone on the team. It was a desperate plea for help.

The being inside claimed to represent the sole survivor of this planet. It was starving to death and too weak to move. It needed help or it would die. Even its thoughts seemed weak. The being claimed to have been put into the dome with others to protect them, but only she had survived, and not for much longer. She appeared intelligent and suffering. More Atlanteans were brought in to devise a way to free the creature trapped inside. All members of the group felt a strange sensation and assumed it was from being touched by the psychic emanations of the being inside the dome. It made them all the more compelled to free her before it was too late. Some stories suggested there were at least a thousand Atlanteans on hand to rescue the being. Only a few argued against the idea, and they were ignored.

What the Atlantean explorers could not know was that the dome imprisoned a monster – *a Vampire Intelligence!* When they finally broke into the dome, hundreds of them became the first victims of the starving monster that had been locked inside. The rest fell under its thrall and were turned into vampire servants. A few were made into *Master Vampires,* the rest into *Secondary Vampires,* but all were made to serve the Vampire Intelligence and spread its essence to new worlds. The creature had indeed been on the verge of dying, trapped for millennia at great cost to the people of this dead world. A people who decided it was better to destroy their entire race than let the vampire plague spread to other worlds. It was the least they could do for having unwittingly exposed their planet and other worlds to the horror of vampirism. Now, thanks to the blind folly of the Atlantean explorers, the **Endless Hunger** had been set free again, and this time it would not need spaceships to reach new worlds. It had Atlantean stone pyramids and the Rifts. The Atlantean rescuers, turned into a small army of vampires, used the pyramid they had erected nearby to send vampires to a dozen worlds, including Earth. For the first time, Atlantis was being invaded by supernatural evil that they themselves had unleashed.

On ancient Earth, the vampire invasion began with a whimper in the night. As always, the vampire infestation began quietly and unnoticed. The people of Atlantis had heard of vampires and dealt with the occasional extra-dimensional invader, but had never encountered the undead in large numbers nor as the target of a full-blown invasion. The goal of the vampires was, of course, to create more their kind. Enough undead to give the Vampire Intelligence the ability to come to Earth and raise an unstoppable legion of vampires to claim the planet. Ancient Earth was fairly rich in magic and filled with human prey to feed upon, so it was a good target.

When the Atlanteans finally realized what they were dealing with, they and their *Lemurian allies* launched a massive counterattack. First, all stone pyramids were disabled to keep the monsters from escaping the island nation to other parts of the planet, as well as to prevent them from traveling to other worlds via the ley lines and Rifts controlled by the pyramids. It was too late. Vampires had already scattered around the globe as well as upon an undetermined number of worlds via Atlantean stone pyramids. It was a mistake they vowed to rectify.

It would take decades to cleanse the Earth of known vampire threats. A crusade joined by the Atlanteans' greatest ally, the people of Lemuria. The problem was that the undead could go into hibernation and hide for as long as needed. Still, the Atlanteans were relentless in their mission. When they felt they had purged all (or most) of the undead from their own world, they prepared to go on the offensive across the dimensional vale to hunt vampires wherever they had inadvertently allowed them to spread.

Their first stop, the Fallen Earth, but the Vampire Intelligence was gone. Worse, they learned that legions of vampires were spreading across a number of the worlds the Atlanteans had visited prior. The Atlanteans were more determined than ever to hunt down and destroy every vampire and the thousands of undead each had created in turn. More than that, having witnessed firsthand the harm a single vampire could do, and how vampirism spread like a plague, they vowed to wipe out the undead wherever they found them. Thus, the **Atlantean Undead Slayer** and vampire fighting magicks and weapons were developed. They would stop what they had unleashed and make things right as best they could for however long it took. (It may even be that the Pandora's Box myth might originate from tales of the Atlanteans' mistake, distorted as it was passed down through the ages back on Earth after Atlanteans were gone.)

Were Atlanteans responsible for unleashing the vampire menace upon the Megaverse? No, of course not. Vampires are a demon plague that has haunted mortals across the universe for ages, long before the Atlanteans ever existed. However, they did unleash a particularly aggressive Vampire Intelligence, and which used Atlantean technology/magic to spread its horror to other worlds, and that was damage enough. The noble Atlanteans intended to correct that mistake and resolved to make all undead pay the ultimate price.

The Vampire Crusades would last generations. Some would argue that they continue to this day, as most True Atlanteans consider the undead and demonkind, in general, to be their mortal enemies and destroy them whenever they are encountered. Any True Atlantean who does not take direct action against the undead brings shame to his family. Thus, all Atlanteans are vampire hunters by legacy of birth, and every one of them is taught at least the basics of how to fight and kill the undead.

It was during the period of the Vampire Crusades that True Atlanteans may have made some rash decisions that would compound their cultural guilt. First, the Atlanteans of the time believed they had freed the source of all vampires upon the Megaverse. Not true. It was an ancient and powerful being, but it was not the first or only one of its kind.

Second, finding and destroying vampires and the godlike monsters that create them became a cultural obsession. In their zeal and unwillingness to let any undead escape their wrath, the Atlantean Undead Slayers sometimes slaughtered entire villages, including the innocent. Anyone suspected of being a vampire, willing servant or vampire collaborator was put to death. Entire villages, cities and sometimes even entire worlds were destroyed to stop the vampire plague. Like the planet they had dubbed *Fallen Earth*, they would consider decimating an entire planet. If a world could not support humanoid life, the vampires would eventually starve and perish. It was as a terrible last ditch option in a scorched earth campaign, but it was proven to work.

Third, the Vampire Crusades became such a cultural obsession that it drove the Atlanteans to alter their own genetic structure. It took many years of experimentation in alchemical magic, but Atlanteans found a way to tweak their DNA enough to make themselves immune to being transformed into the undead. This made them the perfect vampire hunters. Of course, there were other consequences for this alteration of their genetic makeup, but it was all acceptable if it enabled them to right their terrible wrong.

What kind of consequences? The kind that have an impact on a people who rely so heavily on magic. For one, with the exception of Tattoo Magic, Atlanteans are insulated from all types of *physical transformation*. They cannot be metamorphed or physically altered by magic. This change to their DNA also makes it impossible for the so-called *True Atlanteans* to have children with anyone other than with fellow True Atlanteans. Though they started out human and still look every bit human, they cannot mate and bear offspring with humans. They are a new and different breed of human. Not so distant cousins who shared a common lineage before taking a sharp turn. This is one reason it has taken True Atlanteans so long to rebound from the disaster of Atlantis vanishing.

When all was said and done, the Vampire Crusades officially lasted for fifteen generations. How many True Atlanteans died fighting the undead and demons during the Crusades is unknown, but it was thousands. Perhaps hundreds of thousands. The Atlanteans were becoming a people obsessed. It might have destroyed them were it not for friends like the Lemurians, the Chiang-Ku and Prometheans who helped snap them out of their consuming madness.

It would take many more generations before True Atlanteans were finally able to put their tragic mistake behind them, but not the guilt. Most realized what had happened would shape their destiny. Offering aid and trying to help others is at the core of all True Atlanteans. Not recognizing the evil that had tricked them into setting it free into the Megaverse was a mistake that would not be repeated. Every generation of True Atlanteans since is trained to recognize and battle the undead, and they often stand against other evil supernatural beings. Over the eons, this has turned True Atlanteans into a symbol of *redemption and hope* for the living, and a symbol of *retribution and doom* to vampires. All True Atlanteans live with the shame and guilt of their ancestors, but now do so with heads held high, knowing that they have made up for the sins of their forefathers and serve as the vanguard against vampirism and the undead.

Most Atlanteans tell their children tales and parables about the Great Mistake, the Vampire Scourge and the Vampire Crusades. Even those scattered across the Megaverse far from home are taught these stories. Many of the tales are personal, with an ancestor at the center of the story. Some are tragic, some have happy endings, but all serve as a reminder of what the Atlanteans have become and why. These stories are sacred and secret, told only to Atlantean children and seldom to outsiders. The guilt is for them and them alone to bear, their shame is not to be shared with others. Thus, what drives Atlanteans to fight vampires and supernatural evil remains one of their greatest secrets.

Marks of Heritage

It is well known and acknowledged that it was the *Chiang-Ku dragons* who taught True Atlanteans the secrets of Tattoo Magic. What is not known is that ancient Atlantis was a safe haven for this rare species of dragon and friends to the people of the island nation.

Information about magic tattoos was shared freely and known across Atlantis, but not initially embraced by everyone. Atlanteans prided themselves on their perfectly sculpted bodies and it was not common for Atlanteans of old to cover themselves with tattoos. That slowly changed as Atlanteans increased their excursions across dimensions and to alien worlds. By the advent of the *Vampire Crusades*, magic tattoos had become a requirement. Having a tattooed warrior or even a few Atlanteans with one or two tattoos often made the difference between life and death for the vampire slayers. As the number of supernatural enemies increased for Atlanteans, magic tattoos became the great equalizer – a magical weapon carried on one's own body.

The Aerihman Clan receives the credit for establishing the tradition of the **Marks of Heritage**. It was the Aerihman who rallied the people and called for retribution against the "Vampire Scourge." These valiant warriors were the first to take responsibility, as Atlanteans, for unleashing the Vampire Intelligence from the dead world. They would redeem the name of their people by hunting this monster and the undead it created and spread like a plague. They would make things right, and beckoned all Atlantean clans to join them in this crusade. Representatives of every clan joined them in what many consider the Aerihman clan's greatest moments in history.

Before going off on the crusade, the Aerihman warriors received a pair of magic tattoos that represented their clan, gave them a weapon and protected them from the mind control powers of vampires. It also served to identify them when they fell in the field of combat. People would know the clan that fought against the devouring darkness to the end. Fellow Atlanteans going off to war in the Vampire Crusades followed the Aerihman's lead with similar tattoos.

Many children and clansmen honored their brave family members by getting the same tattoos. Fighting in the Vampire Crusades would quickly become a badge of honor and redemption for all Atlanteans, and wearing the tattoos a way to proudly display their respect and to honor of their fellow clansmen, many of whom would fall in combat. So it was that the tradition of the *Marks of Heritage* began. The Vampire Crusades also mark the time when True Atlanteans stopped being dimensional explorers and observers, and became members of the collective people of the Megaverse – human and otherwise.

Rules for the Marks of Heritage. All Atlantean clans use the Heart Pierced by a Stake (no blood drops) and a Flaming Sword as their Marks of Heritage. Two symbols identifying them as the eternal enemy of the undead and as True Atlanteans.

To differentiate between the various True Atlantean clans, the exact type of sword (broadsword, bastard sword, falchion, short sword, scimitar, etc.) and the design of the hilt varies. For example, one may be very simple, another covered in filigree or wrapped in a leafy vine or thorns, or the hilt may have a lion or wolf's head or wings, or some other design element such as a diamond shape, triangle, spike, etc., for which the clan is known or has a special meaning for it. This may include a clan crest.

A Flaming Sword (magic weapon, on the left wrist) gives the Atlantean a weapon that is always at his or her fingertips and is the symbol of Atlantis burning with justice and a commitment to do good.

The Heart Pierced by a Wooden Stake (protection, on the right wrist) makes all True Atlanteans impervious to the mind control powers of vampires when activated.

The tattoo is placed on an Atlantean child at age 5 or 6 and the child learns to activate these magic tattoos for self-defense and the protection of the innocent shortly thereafter. Channeling P.P.E. and the use of magic tattoos is something all True Atlanteans raised within their society understand.

Most True Atlanteans receive 2-4 additional magic tattoos in their lifetime, with the Cross (turn dead) or Eye of Knowledge (language) tattoos being two popular selections. Within Atlantean society, only the legendary "Tattooed Men," like the *Undead Slayer*, may have a body covered in magic tattoos.

The Janus Experiment

The End of the Atlantean Golden Age

The Janus experiment was what the Atlanteans envisioned as their next step in dimensional exploration. With stone pyramids, Atlanteans were able to visit dozens of alien worlds and dimensions. Planet hopping and going to different dimensions was becoming commonplace. Allies were found throughout the Megaverse, especially after the Vampire Crusades. With new allies, trade relationships were formed. Like today's modern businesspeople who hop on a jet at a local airport to travel to another city, Dimensional Pyramids were used to open portals to other worlds – doorways though which the Atlanteans could simply step through and be on another planet, usually at another stone pyramid or location rich in magic. For people this was fine, but for trade goods it would often take significant effort and magic energy to get them from a manufacturing location to a pyramid, through the pyramid, and to the intended destination. The Janus Experiment would eliminate the pyramid as the middleman.

The idea was to create a string of pyramids that would alter the dimensional fabric just enough so that Atlanteans could use their Ley Line Phasing ability and, with but a thought, jump dimensions without even needing a pyramid. The ability to travel to literally anywhere in the Megaverse with a mere thought not only appealed to many Atlanteans, but in their arrogance, they thought it would work without a flaw. This method of magical travel would also solve another problem. When pyramids open *dimensional Rifts*, the Rift sends ripples along the mystic grids

of the Megaverse, alerting supernatural creatures to the opening where potential prey can be found and new worlds can be accessed. The process behind the Janus Experiment would have no ripples and give all Atlanteans a newfound freedom to travel across the Megaverse.

Hundreds of small-scale tests were conducted. Again and again these tests worked without any serious problem. The few kinks and hiccups were quickly ironed out. All that was needed was the ability to save and harness P.P.E. and the power to teleport between dimensions. That is where Atlanteans combined two of their creations.

For centuries, clean energy was provided by Power Pyramids (described in the Pyramid section of this book). **Power Pyramids** were the perfect combination of power plant and P.P.E. storage depot. For safety reasons, Power Pyramids and Dimensional Pyramids were built as separate structures and never combined into a single structure. Again, Atlanteans, complacent and confident in their mastery of pyramid technology, assumed they had all the problems licked. Small-scale experiments proved successful when creating the hybrid Power/Dimension Pyramids. After several decades of work and preparation, the Atlanteans were ready for a revolution in dimensional travel. The **City of Atlantia** would become the proving ground for the new technology. Success seemed self-evident. When the hybrid system went online, the city was able to connect to several dimensions. For six months Atlanteans could, with a mere thought, phase to one of a dozen different worlds without need of a magic spell, ritual or stone pyramid. It was an astonishing, landmark achievement. All of Atlantis was thrilled with the success. The public was eager to have this power available all over the continent. Plans were put into place to turn Atlantis into a dimensional hub like no other.

A few years later, Atlantean techs were ready. All of Atlantis held their breath waiting for the system to go online. At the appointed time, the sun appeared to go black like a solar eclipse. Atlanteans could feel the vibrations in the air as the dimensional energies began to pour through the hybrid Dimension/Power Pyramids across the land. Different worlds and dimensions could be seen flashing before the populace of Atlantis in the sky above like a sort of spectacular fireworks display. It signaled a new dawn for Atlanteans and perhaps all of humanity.

Then came a darkness that did not abate. It grew at a fast pace. Then came the thunder. Thunder as loud as sonic booms was heard halfway around the world. Pyramids began to crackle and glow with mystic energy. Mild earthquakes shook the island and wild storms appeared out of nowhere to race down ley lines and rumble above Stone Pyramids and nexus points.

It took a while before anyone realized it, but the darkness that had blocked out the sun was not an eclipse. It was a massive Rift bigger than had ever been seen before. It unleashed thousands of creatures upon the unsuspecting nation. Atlantis was under attack! They would later learn that the Rift had stretched to the continents of South America and Africa.

Fear and panic gripped the people of Atlantis. At first, they thought the Vampire Scourge had returned, but this was something different. Little did they know in that moment that their fate had been inexorably sealed.

The Atlantean pyramid sorcerers worked furiously to get the situation under control, but to no avail. The pyramids burned hot like nuclear reactors running out of control and getting ready to melt down. Massive amounts of P.P.E. were being drawn from the ley lines of Atlantis and the very core of the planet. The energy was being sent into the Rift through the hybrid Dimension/ Power Pyramids, but to where?

All over Atlantis, defenders were fighting alien creatures in the streets. Fortunately, the defenses of Atlantis were formidable, and they were able to quickly rally and stave off the demonic invaders. However, unless they closed the giant Rift, they would keep coming and it would be only a matter of time before a greater threat like a Splugorth or other Alien Intelligence or dark god would come through. Minutes stretched into hours as Atlantean techs struggled to gain control of the Mega-Rift. Finally, after 36 long hours, the Atlanteans behind this experiment had one last idea to try. If the Rift could be overloaded with a massive infusion of P.P.E., it might shut down everything and close the Rift. It seemed too dangerous to consider, but they were desperate, and the plan should work.

The Atlanteans opened the floodgates of all the stone pyramids on Atlantis. The massive release of P.P.E. was enough to destabilize the huge Rift. Atlanteans cheered as they watched it close, but not without immediate consequences. Stone Pyramids across the continent were destroyed. Some exploded, some melted into mounds of molten rock, others crumbled into rubble, while still others just seemed to vanish into the dimensional void.

The epicenter of the dimensional disaster was the city of Atlantia. It had the first series of experimental stone pyramids to bridge dimensions. The largest pyramid was a work of art, with a marble exterior which only accentuated its beauty. In a flash, the city of Atlantia and its entire population disappeared from the continent, never to be heard from again. Where the city once stood was only a massive hole. Even today, legend has it that the fabled city still exists someplace, somewhere in space and time, giving many young Atlantean heroes and explorers hope to rediscover it in their travels.

Though the dimensional super-Rift had been closed, Atlantis' problems were far from over. Many cities remained under siege by supernatural forces. Many of these creatures were destroyed or repelled, with many fleeing across the sea to Europe, Africa and the Americas. Atlantis remained charged with unstable dimensional and magical energy, resulting in all kinds of dimensional anomalies. The worst effect, **time shifts**, would go unnoticed for a long time. Little did Atlanteans know that 40 years had passed during the catastrophe that seemed to them, only a few weeks of chaos. To the rest of the world, Atlantis was gone in a flash. Vanished overnight as if swallowed up by the ocean. Anyone not on the island would have no reason to suspect Atlantis still existed, only out of phase with time and Earth's dimensional vibrations. Atlanteans had no clue as they were consumed with dealing with the problem and disaster relief.

Each time the island continent would time shift, a new round of disasters swept the continent and other nearby locations on Earth. Just as a new generation thought they were safe and things were settling down, a new time shift would unleash storms that would devastate whole populations on neighboring continents to the west and east. Storms and floods would wipe entire cities away. Also unknown was that each time shift made the continent of Atlantis less and less stable in our dimension. Atlanteans knew they had to do something, but they thought they had time.

Atlantis would shift in time and space approximately eight times. Each shift caused chunks of Atlantis to disappear. By the fourth shift, Atlanteans figured out what was happening, but not

in time to save everyone. It was only a short time before the entire continent was swept away that Atlanteans had begun evacuation en masse. Some would use the few working Dimensional Pyramids to escape to other worlds, others escaped by sea and went to distant lands on Earth. Others were swept away to random dimensions in the turmoil of its last days. The rest would perish in the ensuing dimensional upheaval.

The Mass Exodus of Atlantis. The disaster of the super-Rift would herald the end of a golden era for Atlantis. It took years after the super-Rift was closed for Atlanteans to assess what damage had been done to their civilization, and none had yet realized the worst was yet to come. Some cities on Atlantis were still fighting legions of supernatural horrors that had come through the super-Rift. Others experienced destructive seismic activity eroding and toppling the cities that remained whole, while the rest of the island suffered from freak storms and strange dimensional anomalies. When communications were established with Atlanteans who had not been on Atlantis during the catastrophe, word came back to the people there that the continent of Atlantis had disappeared forty years prior. It was incomprehensible. They knew they were still alive and present, yet to the outside world, there was no Atlantis. It was only then that the survivors on Atlantis realized the catastrophe had placed the entire island continent in a dimensional flux, tearing it from its dimensional moorings and propelling it forward in time, out of sync with the rest of reality. They were still present, for the moment, but unseen. Out of step with the rest of the world. Their destruction inevitable.

The damage across Atlantis was extensive and getting worse as the earthquakes and dimensional storms increased in severity and frequency. Many cities were left with no power, magic energy ebbed and flowed unpredictably, and the levels of magic energy were minuscule compared to what they had been before the catastrophic event.

Things were bad. People were injured, sick and dying. Clean water was becoming a rare commodity, food even rarer. Whole families fled their homes, sometimes traveling hundreds of miles to get to a working stone pyramid. Even magic and ley lines were not acting as they should. Magic teleports were risky with the whole island charged with dimensional energy. Ley Line Phasing was impossible as Ley Line Storms surged across the island day and night. Panic gripped the once proud populace.

Atlanteans who had the means and opportunity had begun to abandon the island continent in droves. There was little communication and coordinated evacuations were impossible at most locations. With the majority of stone pyramids fried and shut down, tens of thousands took to the sea in ships, boats, and even makeshift rafts. Half would never make it to land. Many sailing vessels were lost due to overcrowded vessels on rough seas. Others vanished in strange storms and mist that swept them to other dimensions. Of those who made it to land, they often carried with them only the clothes on their backs. The lucky ones had a few bundles of possessions and what essentials they had managed to take with them. Atlantean refugees who had expected to use magic to survive and rebuild were dealt another terrible blow. The catastrophe had drained Earth of magic energy. With magic energy virtually nonexistent on Earth, their great mystic knowledge and powers were all but gone. The refugees were left vulnerable to the elements and the primitive people on other continents. People who were not welcoming of strangers they perceived as rivals, invaders or sorcerers.

On Atlantis, others fled to the handful of cities managing to survive and to the few Dimensional Pyramids that still functioned. In fact, with the magic energy of Earth syphoned away by the super-Rift, it was only the power reserves at the surviving stone pyramids that enabled Atlanteans to continue to work magic and to open portals to distant worlds and dimensions. These pyramids could not handle the demand to save everyone, but Herculean efforts were made to save as many as possible. A lottery was devised to allow families to escape Atlantis and travel to other planets and dimensions where they would be safe among Atlantean colonies on alien worlds, or among trusted alien allies. This effort was hampered, however, by plummeting levels of magic energy, shifting dimensional energies and more time shifts. Every time the continent of Atlantis drifted in time and farther from its original dimensional foundation, all manner of chaos erupted. With each time shift, the continent became more unstable. On the fourth time shift, a large portion of the island disappeared, taking with it tens of thousands of Atlanteans.

Chaos and panic were constant in the last months of life on Atlantis. There is no accurate count of those who died, but it is safe to say that it was at least half the population – millions of people. Between the storms, anomalies, seismic activity and risks at sea, those who managed to escape to other worlds were the luckiest. It was they who would form the foundation of the *Atlantean Clans* known today on Rifts Earth and across the Megaverse, and mark the Atlanteans as dimensional nomads with no place to call their true home.

The Atlanteans who survived on Earth were absorbed into other cultures, and are undoubtedly responsible for ancient megalithic structures such as Stonehenge, the pyramids of Egypt, the pyramids of the Americas, and a few other places. Inevitably, some were hurled through time, coming to a new continent hundreds or thousands of years after Atlantis vanished, but all shared the same fate of being absorbed into other cultures, or falling victim to them. Undoubtedly, some Atlantean survivors are the source of certain myths and legends about alchemy, demigods and demon and dragon slayers. It is unlikely that any Atlanteans existed into the modern age of humankind, though it's possible that figures such as *Leonardo da Vinci* and *Nostradamus* might have been True Atlanteans out of step with time, or descendants of some. If others did exist, they would have existed in secret societies cut off from their cousins across the universe, for it was not until the Great Cataclysm, the resurgence of magic and the Coming of the Rifts that True Atlanteans and Atlantis itself reappeared on Earth.

The last time shift would send the remainder of Atlantis into a dimensional void where it would remain lost for thousands of years, until the *Coming of the Rifts*. Circumstances were just right and Atlantis was brought back to Rifts Earth, but not without consequences, again. The sudden appearance of the massive island continent created tidal waves and raised the water level around the world. It would only be a matter of a few decades in the Two Hundred Year Dark Age before the *Splugorth* would arrive to a pristine island covered in surging ley lines and with no signs of human inhabitation. The Splugorth did not need to conquer Atlantis, they just needed to move in.

The story of the Janus Experiment and vanishing of Atlantis is told to each new generation of True Atlanteans as a reminder that their people learned humility the hard way, via death and tragedy, and the loss of their home world. The secrets of the forbidden hybrid Dimension/Power Pyramid were destroyed, for in the wrong hands it could be turned into a deadly weapon of mass destruction.

Atlanteans were quick to realize what they had done to themselves and their exile was not punishment enough. For an untold number of years, supernatural terrors left on Earth would attack and torment humanity. It was only because of the draining of Earth's ley lines that many of the monsters would retreat to other dimensions while they still could. Atlanteans who would return to Earth millennia later, noticed the absence of magic energy and because Atlanteans relied so heavily on it, felt that humanity would never be able to achieve the potential that Atlantis had known. Magic, they believed, would be lost to humans on Earth forever. The ley lines drained to a meager trickle. So it was, the guilt-ridden Atlanteans abandoned Earth, leaving it for new generations of humans to develop as they saw fit under science and technology, while Atlantean survivors on other worlds would continue to hone their mystic power, explore the Megaverse and hunt vampires and demons for the betterment of all good and peace-loving people.

The Origin of the Megaversal Atlantean Clans

To this day, Atlanteans break down their society by place of origin on ancient Atlantis, and then family. Clan names represent the original birthplace for that family on the island continent of Atlantis. Thus, the names of provinces that once existed on Ancient Atlantis keep the memory of Atlantis alive; there were more than 200 provinces before Atlantis vanished.

Most Atlantean people in the past would identify themselves by saying "I am Cladus Arilious of the Skellian Province." After the sundering of Atlantis the homeland was no more, but Atlanteans continued to use the names of provinces from which the family clan originated, thus retaining their identities and keeping Atlantis alive in their hearts. In some cases, like the Aerihman Clan, the family name and clan/province name are the same. This actually occurs quite often. Every Atlantean family is associated with a clan. Not being associated with a clan is almost unheard of, and most Atlanteans can trace their lineage back more than 20,000 years. There are smaller groups and factions within the larger clans, but all know the clan and province from which they herald.

After the vanishing and presumed destruction of Atlantis, many families traveled together. Over time, they formed new clans and alliances for their mutual protection. Sometimes the clan name would come from the new settlement or merger, but in other cases, as with the Aerihman, the family name with the largest number of survivors in it, or a name that had the highest prestige, was chosen. Thus, the smaller families were absorbed into one of the larger clans. Due to the integration of several families into one, there are many families within the clan that are not blood relatives, which has allowed for marriage within the clan. Each clan keeps close tabs on bloodlines to avoid interbreeding. Because of this, *arranged marriages* are still a common practice, although Atlanteans tend to be forgiving if the arrangement does not work out.

For arranged marriages, the young couple often go through a trial period to determine compatibility. It is up to the couple to decide how far they take this trial period. Atlanteans tend to be tight-knit, so the betrothed often know each other prior to the arrangement of marriage; it is not like a blind date. Arranged marriages can be fixed at birth, or at a later time when children are older and the two families recognize a mutual benefit from such a union or desire to see true love form a lasting bond in matrimony. In the early days after the Atlanteans' exodus from Earth, arranged marriages were a necessity to keep the bloodline pure, but that tradition has become dated and observed less frequently. Its practice varies from clan to clan.

Today, clans are the norm for all Atlanteans. Size varies, with the smallest clans being 100-1,200 members, while the largest clans can number into the tens of thousands. The average clan size seems to be between 2,000 and 80,000 members.

Atlantean Life Today

Once youngsters are given their **Marks of Heritage,** they have a normal childhood with an emphasis on education, which includes basic combat and knowledge about the undead and other monsters and enemies of Atlantis. Atlantean children are educated from a very young age, typically as soon as they can talk and walk, starting at age two or three. By the time the child is ten years old, he knows how to use his Marks of Heritage tattoos and is able to read and write in at least three languages. Science, philosophy, art and mathematics are taught as well.

From ages 12-17, Atlantean children begin internships. Since it is not known what the child wants to become as an adult, they are exposed to a variety of occupations and corresponding skill sets. Some assist Atlantean Ley Line Walkers and Stone Masters, while others train at the side of Undead Slayers to learn about combat and hunting and slaying supernatural evil. Others are exposed to the arts or scholastic or scientific pursuits. Atlantean children are expected to be able to know by age 17 what they want to focus on in their life. Those who do not find a focus (i.e. select an O.C.C.) automatically become the equivalent of an *Atlantean Nomad O.C.C.*

By age 17 or 18, after they have undergone most of their formal training, the young Atlanteans begin the tradition of **the sojourn**. A sojourn can be as short as 2D6+12 months, but most are 4D6+6 years; sometimes much longer. At the beginning of a youth's sojourn, he travels with other young Atlanteans led by an adult to help guide and watch over them for the first year before being left on their own. It is often during the un-chaperoned sojourns that young Atlanteans go off on their own, or in pairs or small groups, and may meet and join other adventurers or mercenaries. This is expected and encouraged, as part of the Atlantean culture is the belief in expanding personal knowledge and experience. Some Atlanteans spend the rest of their lives on their sojourn. Others return after a number of years to settle down and raise a family, or to pursue a particular profession or life's mission. It all depends on the individual.

Since education, knowledge and self-discovery are founding principles of Atlantean society, most young Atlanteans are able to figure out their calling in life in a few years, but those who do not are also accepted and not looked down upon. The so-called Atlantean Nomads are just as valued and accepted as Undead Slayers. In fact, they, like the Undead Slayers, are often revered as wise men who have seen the Megaverse and explored life in ways that few people ever dare attempt. Atlanteans also acknowledge that they need Nomads just as much as they need warriors and magic practitioners. As long as the Atlantean, young and old, displays the clan's values, they are encouraged to find their own path in life, whatever it is, without restriction or expectation to meet convention.

Most True Atlanteans hold life, freedom and the pursuit of knowledge in the highest esteem. They tend to be empathetic to others and are noble in character. All share a disdain for the undead and supernatural evil, and consider it their obligation and duty to protect the innocent from such beings, and whenever possible, to destroy supernatural evil. Even the Sunaj hold on to this basic principle.

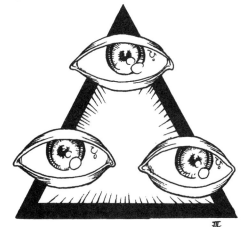

Notable Atlantean Clans

Clan Aerihman

Heroes, Undead Slayers (and the Sunaj)

Marks of Heritage/Clan Crest: On the right wrist is the traditional heart impaled by a wooden stake (Protection from Vampires). On the left wrist is a long sword enveloped in black flames with the hilt being a silver cross. The cross is an elaborate tattoo in silver and black with the words "Iuguolo Mortuuson" written on the horizontal section of the cross. It roughly translates to "kill all the dead." The origin of this is from the early days of the Aerihman when they battled during the Vampire Crusades. The Flaming Sword is an M.D. weapon in Mega-Damage settings.

Clan Estimated Size: Lord Aerihza estimates his total clan population to be 7.9 million True Atlanteans of Aerihman heritage. 4.7 million are located on Solaria, while another 1.3 are located on Argos. The rest are scattered across the Megaverse, with many in the Three Galaxies and some on Rifts Earth, plus those serving as Minions of Splugorth as the Sunaj also on Earth and scattered across the cosmos.

Clan Status: Infamous. The Aerihman are notorious for being aggressive, disciplined, warlike and secretive, as well as the sworn enemy of the undead and demons. Some of the Atlantean's greatest heroes throughout history are from Clan Aerihman.

Clan Notoriety: The Aerihman Clan is well known to all Atlantean clans as it has a long history that goes back millennia before the *Vampire Crusades*. Clan Aerihman is known for their aggression and warlike ways, past and present. Even today they are regarded with a certain amount of trepidation and concern by other True Atlanteans who know the Aerihman do not agree with the more peaceful culture of most other clans.

The Aerihman are in a sort of self-imposed exile, refusing to attend clan gatherings in the last century. It is a gesture of defiance directed at all the other clans for refusing to engage in a bloody campaign to try to take back Atlantis and reclaim Rifts Earth in the name of Atlanteans and humanity.

Through a network of contacts they have made it known that they are actively looking for the people responsible for killing 1,300 Aerihman. This is all a charade by their clan leader Lord Aerihza, who, as the head of the secret Sunaj Illuminati, is responsible for this terrible slaughter of his own people. For him, the end justifies the means, and their deaths serve a nobler,

greater purpose: a) to throw people off the trail of the Sunaj, and b) to turn their fellow Atlanteans to their way of thinking, especially when it comes to declaring war against the Splugorth of Atlantis.

Clan's Primary Homes: The Aerihman have large settlements on two worlds. Argos is the one known to most people, but Solaria is a closely guarded secret and has the larger Aerihman population of the two.

Alignment of the Aerihman Clan: Any, but typical is Principled (5%), Scrupulous (12%), Unprincipled (18%), Anarchist (25%), Aberrant (28%), Miscreant (10%) and Diabolic (2%).

Aerihman have a tendency to be ruthless and self-serving, especially in regard to what is best for their own clan. They are driven by their convictions to the point that too many are willing to do violence in the name of righteousness, justice and the Aerihman clan. Such ways are the danger of zealots who believe their views are best or the correct one, and need to be imposed upon others for their own benefit, whether they like it or not. Those who do not believe must be made to believe – or at least made to comply – by any means necessary, no matter how terrible. Those who do not acquiesce, must be pacified. (And to the Sunaj, subjugated or eliminated.)

Many Aerihman live by the clan's strong, if sometimes distorted, sense of honor, justice, and destiny, and are so driven, competitive, and sure they are right, they are willing to fight and kill their enemies, en masse if necessary. Anyone who stands in their way is regarded as a fool or obstacle to be removed. All of this is deemed necessary, in part, to avenge Atlantean honor, recapture Atlantis for Atlanteans, and to take their place as the rightful leaders of the people of Earth. They see Clan Aerihman as bold heroes who represent the future for all Atlanteans, because they have the will and discipline to take on the Splugorth to reclaim Atlantis and the Earth.

It is this sense of purpose and destiny that has come between the Aerihman and their Atlantean brethren in other clans. Most Atlanteans have given up on ever taking Atlantis. More importantly, they have moved on. Atlantis and Earth hold a special place in their hearts because it is their place of origin, but that was thousands of years ago. They see no reason to sacrifice the lives of god only knows how many Atlanteans and allies in a symbolic effort to reclaim Atlantis from the entrenched and supremely powerful forces of the Splugorth. This outlook is the chief source of contention and resentment between the Aerihman and all other Atlantean clans.

From the meekest to the most malevolent or maniacal, Aerihman clansmen are fiercely loyal to their clan and all like-minded clan members. They completely trust other Aerihman, take their word over others unless there is very strong evidence to the contrary, comply to the edicts of the clan, and believe the Aerihman clan is superior to any of their well-intended but weak and misguided Atlantean "brothers and sisters" from other clans. This makes Aerihman outspoken malcontents among the Atlantean people. The hard driven Aerihman are fine with following their own convictions without the support of their fellow Atlanteans, confident that history shall prove them right.

Clan Outlook on Rifts Earth: Earth is their home world and heritage. Most believe it is their destiny to some day reclaim Atlantis and Earth for all Atlanteans. They are willing to consider extreme measures to claim it and finally have one nation for all people. They cannot stand the idea that Atlantis is in the clutches of demons and monsters, and do not understand why other clans do not share their conviction on this.

Bonuses for Clan Aerihman: There is a much higher percentage of individuals with psionic abilities. Very early on, the clan put in place a eugenics program in which they engaged in deliberate, controlled breeding to increase the occurrence of psionics in their offspring. That campaign of careful selection via arranged marriages over several millennia produced impressive results. The practice is less formal but continues to this day.

Aerihman Clan Psionics: When creating a character who is member of the Aerihman clan, roll on the table below to determine the level of psychic ability; most are Minor or Major Psychics. This is subject to the approval of the Game Master and the desire of the player. For example, if the player does not want to play a Master Psychic, he can decline to do so and take the next step down to give his character Major psionic abilities and select an O.C.C. that is not a psychic.

01-20% No psychic abilities.
21-40% Minor psionic.
41-83% Major psionic.
84-100% Master psionic (can select an O.C.C. such as a Mind Melter, Mind Bleeder, Burster, Zapper, etc.).

Clan's Darkest Secret: The intensity of their disappointment and resentment toward other clans, and the existence of the shadowy Sunaj Illuminati. See the section on the Sunaj, pages 74 and 81, for more details.

Aerihman History

Of all the Atlantean clans, the Aerihman are noted for being the greatest warriors, vampire hunters, and the most militant. They have the largest number of **Tattooed Defenders** and **Undead Slayers** of any clan, and they produce the largest volume of Atlantean weapons and armor. They also have some of the largest and most densely populated Atlantean cities. Clan Aerihman keeps their population numbers a closely guarded secret, however, and only clan leader *Lord Aerihza* and a few of his top people know the clan numbers into the millions.

The Aerihman's military disposition comes from generations of warriors. Many clan members can trace their lineage back to before the *Vampire Crusades*. Hundreds of thousands of Aerihman took up the Crusade and lost many family members and clansmen in the campaign. They were especially hit hard when one of their early bases was overrun by the undead. According to legend, a Necromancer who commanded a legion of dead and was in league with vampires attacked without mercy. The clan took these attacks very personally and it is said to be one of the reasons they adopted the *cross* as their part of their clan's *Marks of Heritage*.

The Aerihman clan became very adept in waging war against many enemies, not just the undead, and have passed all they have learned on to future generations. As time would pass, it would be the Aerihman who would be the defenders of Atlantis whenever it was in danger. When the Atlanteans had to take a battle to another dimension, the Aerihman clan often led the way. So it is

that the Spartan-like Aerihman have always lived by a military standard and tradition. An Earth equivalent might be the Spartans and Athenians of ancient Greece; one wise and hardened to the ways of war, the other more peace-loving and attuned to the arts and scholarly pursuits. In this case, the Aerihman are the Spartans and the rest of the clans are the Athenians.

For the Aerihman, combat and aggression are instruments of defense and justice as well as power and acquisition. War is viewed as an inevitability not to be feared, but to be anticipated and fought for the best possible outcome. In that regard, the Aerihman use war as a weapon to get what they want. War and the threat of aggression are used to leverage and conquer enemies and rivals, to obtain new lands, dominate worlds and acquire power.

During the months of Atlantis' slow destruction, Aerihman leaders suggested going out into the world to conquer the rest of the Earth and claim it all in the name of Atlantis. They saw their destiny to be the rulers of Earth and shepherd the lesser people into civilization. Atlanteans were superior, after all, in every way. None of the primitive and fledgling civilizations of the era could stand against the combined might, magic and technological superiority of the Atlantean clans. The destruction of Atlantis, they said, was the hand of destiny pushing them to their inevitable place as world leaders — demigods even. The savages on foreign shores could be made into loyal servants of Atlantis. Atlanteans would be doing them a favor, raising them up out of barbarism, educating them and making them part of something grandiose. The continents that would later become known as Africa and Europe, the Aerihman would use as the launch points for global conquest and the creation of *New Atlantis*. Together with the other clans, they could reshape the world and make it a better place, despite the dropping levels of magic.

The Aerihman plan for world domination was squashed by the other clans who would not have it. The Atlantean majority believed they had peacefully convinced the Aerihman to give up such ideas, but that was not the case. It was only as magic levels dropped to almost nothing that the Aerihman clan decided abandoning Earth was, indeed, the smart, strategic maneuver, lest they be forced to completely forsake magic altogether. On other worlds where magic energies were strong, Atlanteans could advance magic and technology, and continue to explore alien worlds and dimensions, but they always planned to someday return to Earth. It was the smart and logical choice.

Over the millennia, rumors circulated among other clans which spoke of war parties within the Aerihman clan returning to Earth, and successfully conquering people and raising impressive city-states and civilizations. Such campaigns took place before the modern civilizations of China, Egypt, Greece and others rose into prominence. Forgotten civilizations that have since been wiped from the annals of known history on Earth. Stonehenge, the Sphinx, and some other ancient ruins, stone megaliths and ancient relics uncharacteristic of the era may be evidence of the existence of Aerihman True Atlanteans who returned to Earth. Of course, no one knows what evidence of these ancient campaigns may rest in the hands of the Aerihman themselves. Case in point, the following excerpt from a secret journal in a secured Aerihman archive reads:

"... the effort is lost. The enemies have managed to break our lines in several surrounding countries and our last stronghold is sure to be next. The human puppet in charge of our once impressive forces has faltered, despite

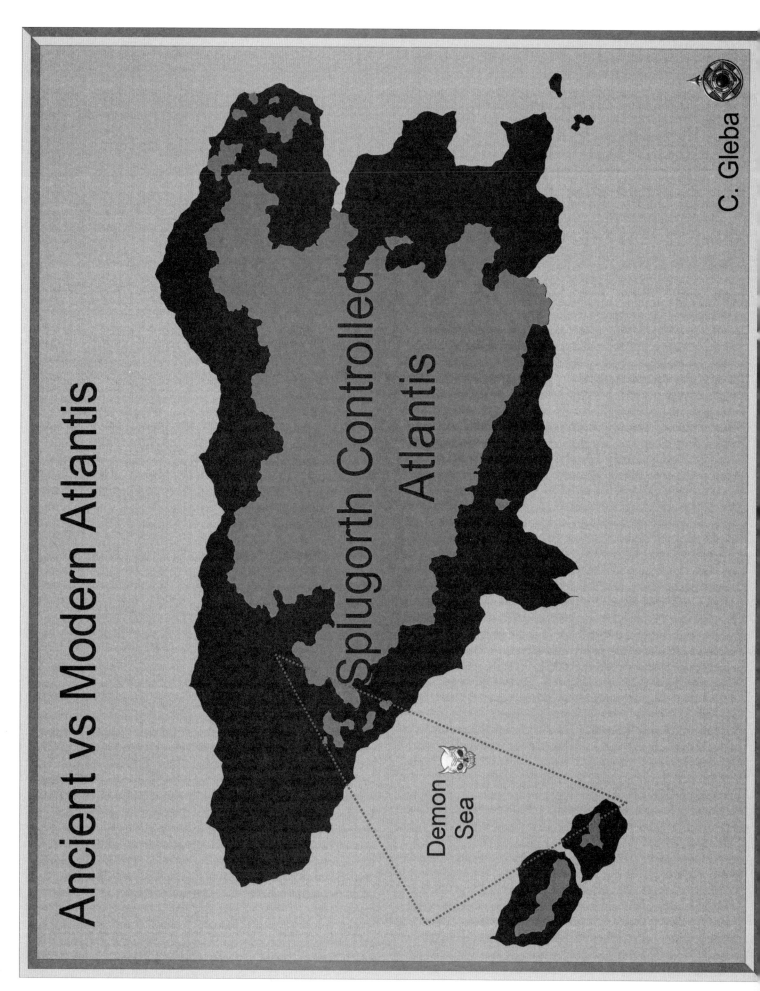

Ancient vs Modern Atlantis

Splugorth Controlled Atlantis

Demon Sea

C. Gleba

the superior technology we have given him. He and his leaders no longer take our advice. All is lost. It is simply a matter of watching it all play out as our perfect plan falls apart. Our effort on the other side of the world is also being pushed back. I could lie and blame others for my failure, but I will only speak the truth.

"Instigating war with an eye to global domination by our puppets was a mistake. I underestimated them and the others who have sworn allegiance to us. I would not have believed that these savages could have advanced so quickly in only a few decades. Not only did they manage to keep pace with the technology we had provided, they managed to outstrip us and push us aside. Now, they have the upper hand. Without magic to buoy our forces and enforce our will on this magic devoid world, I believe our time here is done. I will not dishonor my clan. I shall fight to the end and pay the ultimate price for my mistakes."

How many times members from the Aerihman clan may have returned and tried to reestablish Atlantean colonies, or outright conquer the people of Earth, is unknown. Myths and legends of ancient lost civilizations, and perhaps even some mythological gods, are likely to be testaments to such Aerihman endeavors. There is little doubt that the Aerihman clan and perhaps some of the Atlanteans who stayed on Earth and survived the disappearance of Atlantis, have had their hands in many civilizations throughout Earth history. Civilizations that may have existed for a thousand years or more until some grim fate befell them 8,000, 10,000, 20,000 years before the known ancient human civilizations rose. This would explain artifacts and ruins that had, in the 20th Century, been attributed to alien visitors from the stars. In a way, such speculation was correct, because these returning Atlanteans held little in common with their Earth cousins.

How far some members of the Aerihman clan would go to take back Earth is unknown. A few conspiracy theories among other Atlantean clans suggest the Aerihman were present on Earth before the Great Cataclysm, and wonder if an Aerihman accidentally or deliberately caused the Great Cataclysm that brought about the Coming of the Rifts and the return of magic with devastating results no one could ever have imagined. Evidence of this has never surfaced and it seems too extreme even for the Aerihman, but the theory is out there, and there are some who believe it to be true.

Such conjecture is based, in part, on this archived Atlantean audio communication, said to have been intercepted from an Aerihman operative present on Earth shortly before the Great Cataclysm. The identity of the speaker is unknown and the alleged communique has never been authenticated. Aerihman clan leaders insist it is a hoax or a deliberate fabrication created to implicate and smear the good name of the clan.

"...I have recently been promoted and am now in charge of my own Chromium Guardsman unit. Their machines and science rival our mightiest weapons. We could learn much from this technology and I am prepared to hand it over when the time is right. Our unit is being deployed to a hot zone in Central America. We have our people standing by on site, near the ley line nexus point, close to our deployment zone. With the planets aligning and the coordinated deaths of a few thousand enemy insurgents anticipated, we should have more than enough mystic energy to open a

Rift. After all these years, I yearn to finally go home. I don't know what I expected when I volunteered for this Earth assignment. These are not the primitive people spoken of in the past. They may know nothing of magic and mock the very concept of it, but they are an advanced civilization who have earned their place here. This is their world now."

No reply is known to have been given, and as noted, the authenticity of this alleged communication is highly suspect. Conspiracy theorists and clansmen hostile to the mighty Aerihman claim the date of this communiqué is just one or two weeks before the military clash believed to have triggered what humans call the **Great Cataclysm**. Could the Aerihman clan or a rogue Aerihman operative have accidentally (or according to some, deliberately) caused the disaster that led to the explosive return of magic and the Coming of the Rifts on Earth? What were the intentions? Did the Aerihman simply want the Chromium Guardsman technology or were the they trying to restore magic energy to the planet? This part of the conspiracy theory held by some, contends the Aerihman clan hoped that if the natural flow of magic was restored, it might entice other Atlanteans to return to their home world. Indeed, a pivotal point in arguments about forsaking ever going back to Earth to live was the fact that magic energy was too low to sustain their lifestyle. Could a rogue faction within the Aerihman clan have thought if magic could be restored, they would win other clans to their side about returning to Earth? It would give some Atlanteans a reason to return home. If so, it seem unlikely that even the most zealous and militant Aerihman would have deliberately devastated the entire planet and wiped out billions of human lives.

Certainly the transformation of Earth with overflowing ley lines and randomly opening Rifts unleashing monstrous invaders from a thousand different worlds could not have been the desired outcome. Since the universe was born, this type of phenomenon is rarely heard of anywhere in the Megaverse. Still, it might have been a much smaller, isolated Aerihman scheme that went terribly wrong.

No one is ever likely to know. Nothing further can be found in the Atlanteans' shared archives, and if the Aerihman are in possession of such evidence (if it hasn't been destroyed), they are not going to reveal their complicity in the deaths of billions of innocent people and creating the hotbed of danger that is Rifts Earth. Any complicity in this dimension shattering event, whether accident or intentional, would be one of the clan's darkest and most carefully guarded secrets. And the people of the Aerihman clan keep many secrets from their Atlantean brethren.

The conspiracy is likely to be pure fiction. Given birth by the simple fact that learning about Earth's cataclysmic transformation has only fueled the Aerihman's mad dream of reclaiming the Earth for all Atlanteans and returning to their rightful home. To them, the Great Cataclysm and the return of magic is a sign to all Atlanteans that it is time to come home. As if that were not enough, the reappearance of their beloved Atlantis is a clear sign of their destiny to reclaim it and all of Earth. According to the Aerihman, all these millennia spent traveling across the universe learning magic and fighting supernatural horrors have been leading up to the retaking of Earth. Humanity is all but obliterated. The undead have established a kingdom on Earth's soil, other demons and supernatural monstrosities enslave and prey upon their human kin. Atlantean Stone Magic can tame the ley lines and close the Rifts (at least in theory). If this is not the call of destiny,

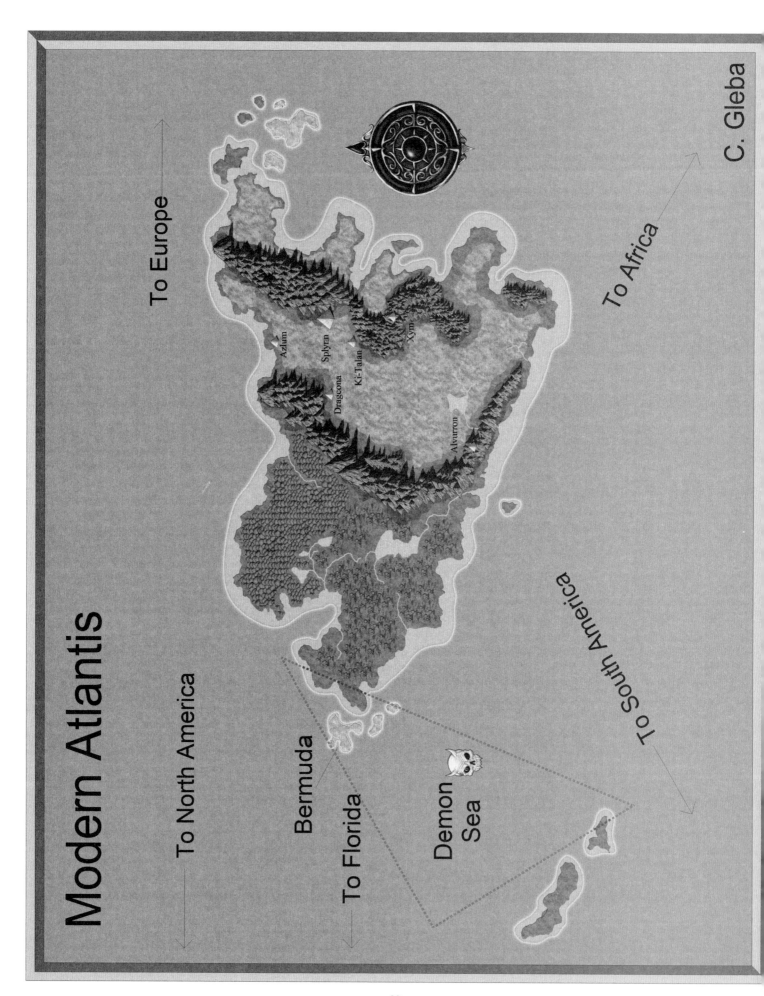

Modern Atlantis

To North America

To Europe

To Africa

To South America

C. Gleba

Bermuda

To Florida

Demon
Sea

Azlum

Splyan

Dragcona

Ki-Talan

Xym

Alvurron

the Aerihman do not know what is. By taking Earth, they will be rescuing and preserving their human descendants, destroying supernatural evil, and making the planet a safe, dimensional nexus that can contribute to interdimensional peace. Not to mention, be the greatest comeback story of the Megaverse. The Atlantean people would be, without question, the greatest, noblest heroes of them all!

This is their great purpose. This is their destiny! Only a blind man could not see it. A pronouncement they made to their Atlantean brethren when the Aerihman called together one of the largest clan gatherings in history. It would also be the last one they would ever attend.

When it was learned that an apocalypse had destroyed all of Earth's modern civilizations and that the beloved continent of Atlantis had returned, the Aerihman gathered their armies and called for all the clans to unite and return to Earth in a battle for the ages. Their purpose, to liberate their home world from the clutches of monsters and demons, make Atlantis their capital and to rebuild *their world* into a transdimensional paradise the envy of civilizations everywhere!

This meeting took place toward the end of what humans call the **Two-Hundred Years Dark Age**. The Aerihman insisted Atlanteans could tame the violent ley lines, control the spasming Rifts, rescue the human survivors and restore order in a storm of chaos. Naturally, the plan called for the eradication of certain evil invaders who had already claimed locations on Earth and were growing in power. This included the Vampires Kingdoms in Mexico, demon hordes across the globe, the devouring Xiticix, the dangerous Federation of Magic flirting with magicks and forces beyond their reckoning, and the insidious Splugorth who were turning Atlantis into a hub for their intergalactic empire of evil. The Aerihman already had a plan, were gathering their armies and would lead the other clans to victory.

The Aerihman leaders gave rousing speeches and already had the wheels of war in motion. Their generals were formulating strategies and tactics, gathering their forces from the far corners of the Megaverse and they knew – just knew – they would win this, the noblest and greatest military campaign of all time. Greater than the Vampire Crusades. The Aerihman people, civilians and heroes alike, were so euphoric and united over this and the fulfillment of their destiny, they never stopped to consider that other Atlantean clans might not agree to join them.

Matters were made all the worse by the euphoria of the Aerihman leaders and the people they represented. When the other Atlantean clans did not see things their way, the Aerihman leaders felt blind-sided and crestfallen. What had started as an ambitious plan to unite the clans and return home ended in a shouting match of epic proportions. Name calling and insults were hurled, fists were thrown and it all ended with screaming and hard feelings. The Aerihman were stunned by the attitudes of their fellow clansmen and ashamed of their cowardice and lack of identity. Their disappointment was beyond measure. Hot emotions turning into rage, disgust and resentment toward the other clans. The Aerihman were sickened by their brethren, flatly rejecting any arguments against returning to Earth.

While the Aerihman had always clung to their heritage and Earth origins, subsequent generations of the other Atlantean clans had changed and moved away from it. They saw themselves as citizens of the infinite Megaverse. They revered Earth as their home world and as their place of origin, but they had moved on. They no longer felt a burning connection to their birthplace or the people of Earth. They looked at the proposed war to recapture Rifts Earth for Atlanteans and saw a pointless campaign that would cost countless lives and would likely destroy everything they had built across the cosmos over the many past millennia. While all the clans agreed to send heroes and warriors to help champion the efforts of the heroes already there, and to battle supernatural evil, they would not commit the resources and manpower to wage a war campaign they saw as impossible to win. They lacked the Aerihman's conviction and questioned their strategies and tactics. Worse, the other clans saw *their destiny* written among the stars, not in an impossible war waged on Earth that would decimate their numbers and destroy all the good they were doing elsewhere.

To add insult to injury, the rest of the Atlanteans united only to condemn the Aerihman's plan and declared they would never join the Aerihman in any effort to try to invade and "liberate" Earth with the purpose of conquering it for the Atlantean people. That was just something they could not endorse. Worse, the united clans promised they would do everything in their power to stop any such action the clan might consider on its own. Their contention was the Aerihman's actions would bring down the wrath of the Splugorth and many other enemies, old and new, who might unite to destroy all Atlanteans. Outsiders seldom make a distinction between the many clans. All they would see is "Atlanteans," not the Clan Aerihman on its own, and would thus consider all Atlanteans everywhere the aggressor. And for what? A pipe dream about taking Earth in the name of Atlanteans? They would have no part of it, and would not let the Aerihman clan take action that would undo all the good they had all accomplished over the eons.

The gathering ended with the Aerihman declaring they would no longer attend any clan gatherings until the rest of them had come to their senses. That was roughly 120 years ago. Since then, the schism between the Aerihman and the other Atlantean clans has only grown wider. Both sides regularly find fault with the other's conduct and speak ill of the other. Sometimes to the point of spreading false rumors and innuendo, fist-fights and even the occasional duel in the name of clan honor.

In recent decades, the Aerihman people have come to the conclusion that their brethren have become weak and lost the vision and willpower they all once shared. For Aerihman leaders, something had to be done, but what? Decades of debates and arguments have accomplished nothing but create resentment. In the minds of some aggressive and warlike Aerihman leaders, an answer to this issue needed to be found and found soon. They asked themselves, how do you get rid of a growing cancer? The answer, you cut it out, even if some healthy tissue needs to be sacrificed. And so the Sunaj Illuminati was secretly born, and from it a growing number of influential Aerihman leaders who have hatched a secret agenda to "cleanse" their people of that cancer. The Sunaj Assassins and other zealots within its secret society are the willing instruments to bring about the necessary cleansing and desired change. Even if the blood of fellow Atlanteans must be spilled.

New Atlantis

The Aerihman's Adopted Home of Solaria

The Aerihman are spread out across several worlds and dimensions, but it is **New Atlantis**, hidden within the **Solaria dimension**, they now consider home. The Aerihman settled here thousands of years ago in secret and the clan does their best to keep this colony world hidden from outsiders, including other Atlantean clans. The irony is that the Solaria dimension is well known and well documented in many Atlantean archives. No one thinks to look here for life, let alone the Aerihman (or the Sunaj), because it is a hostile environment full of deadly floating gases and plasma that is supposed to be uninhabitable. Humanoid life cannot be supported in this toxic dimension – which of course, makes it the ideal place for the Aerihman clan to hide their new home world.

The Solaria dimension appears to consist of swirling columns and clouds of super-heated plasma and fire. Plasma storms constantly rage like swirling tornadoes of fire. There are, however, a handful of locations in Solaria where the temperature is moderate enough to support a breathable atmosphere. These locations take considerable time to find, and locating one with a ley line is very nearly impossible. The Aerihman hit the jackpot by finding a habitable zone with a massive *ley line triangle*. All they needed was firm ground to build upon.

As if by providence, it was discovered that matter floats while within the ley line triangle of the Solaria dimension. After years of planning and considerable resources, the Aerihman were able to Rift three small planetoids to the massive ley line triangle within Solaria where they wanted to build. The theory was that the ley lines would anchor the planetoids within the triangle and keep them from floating into nearby columns of plasma.

They were correct in a sense. The ley lines roped the planetoids inside the triangle and kept them from floating beyond the lines, but like placing a boat on the ocean, the three planetoids floated around within it. This was no good if the Aerihman were to create new worlds with working stone pyramids and reliable magic. For the pyramids to work, they needed be on a fixed position. In this case, one planetoid was intended to rest on each of the three ley line nexus points for maximum power.

The solution to anchoring the landmasses was dozens of giant, reaction control thrusters (RCTs) built into each of the planetoids at key locations. These thrusters are massive and not pretty, but they work. Since they draw their power from the mystic energy of the ley lines, the giant thrusters have an unlimited fuel source. The giant thrusters are constantly monitored, and over the years there have been enough RCTs assembled that if a few were to fail, there are still enough to compensate. However, if more than half of the thrusters fail, it is theorized the planetoid would drift away and eventually slam into one of the other two. If any of the planetoids collided into New Atlantis, the result would be devastating to the clan. Such a catastrophe is likely to knock New Atlantis out of its fixed location, making a future collision imminent. Worse, one or more of the planetoids might break free of the ley line triangle and slowly float away and into a pillar of plasma where it would be completely consumed and obliterated. Fortunately, the Aerihman reaction control thruster system has worked for millennia without the slightest hiccup.

The Aerihman clan is confident their unique location in such a vast and inhospitable dimension will keep their adopted home hidden and protected from enemies and rivals for eons to come. The existence of *New Atlantis* is little more than myth and legend. Few outsiders are ever brought to the dimension and seldom to New Atlantis. When they are, they arrive via a Rift or teleportation magic without a clue of the location of New Atlantis or that it is hidden in another dimension. The truth of the matter is most people born on New Atlantis don't know exactly where their home world is located. They don't need to when traveling via the dimensional portals of the Stone Pyramids on their home world. They just need to know New Atlantis exists, and that there are pyramids that they can return to at home.

Of the three planetoids brought in, only **New Atlantis** has been heavily reshaped and terraformed into a lush and habitable environment. The other two function as outposts and future colonies to be developed over time. Once the Aerihman figured out how to anchor the landmasses to the dimension along the dimensional ley line triangle, they decided to assemble and reshape the planetoid they intended to be their new home. In this case, they reshaped it in such a way as to resemble their beloved home of origin, the continent of Atlantis. Right down to making it a flat, floating landmass that can support life.

Stone Masters and mages have used their powers to raise mountain chains, create rivers and lakes, forests and meadows so as to accurately replicate the features of Atlantis, only on a much larger scale. The floating landmass is the shape of the lost continent, and any visitor with knowledge of Atlantis will feel immediately at home in the natural setting. So far, there are four major cities and several smaller towns and communities established on New Atlantis. These cities are home to the majority of the civilian Aerihman population and resemble traditional Atlantean cities with a mixture of ancient and modern buildings, magic and technology, surrounded by areas of forested wilderness and the occasional grassland and mountain range.

Also located on New Atlantis, away from the civilian population, are eight hidden **Sunaj compounds**. Each is a small city in and of itself. Two are detention centers, the rest are large, military-style compounds that serve as the base of operations for the sinister Sunaj and as military training centers.

Overall, New Atlantis is thriving. Though larger areas of this flat world are desolate and devoid of life, forests and scrub lands are starting to sprout up by themselves away from the key population centers as the artificial world becomes covered with life. Most of the water sources come from one of the Aerihman cities. It was found that to some degree, water will evaporate and fall back as rain, but very rarely due to the climate. The Aerihman had to be inventive and so there are some Dimensional Pyramids built with the sole purpose of importing water.

Over the last few thousand years, New Atlantis has become self-sufficient and can produce most of the Aerihman clan's basic needs.

Dimension of Solaria

Type of Dimension: Infinite Dimension.

Primary Dimensional Medium: Gas clouds, heat, fire and plasma fill the dimension which gives it the appearance of a massive plasma storm that never ends. Others have compared the dimension to the middle of a star and some have mistaken the dimension for the Elemental Plane of Fire.

Secondary Dimensional Medium: None/Artificial. There is no natural secondary medium. The Aerihman have imported a few planetoids to serve as a foundation upon which to build their new, secret empire. It is possible that there are other planetoids in Solaria and pockets that could be habitable, but if so, they remain unknown.

When someone arrives in Solaria, there is little reason to stay in this hellish dimension of toxic gas and fire. They float as if in outer space along the seemingly endless plasma streams and fiery gas clouds.

On New Atlantis and the other two planetoids, there is sufficient artificial gravity via the manipulation of the ley lines and magic through the stone pyramids, that any humans arriving there can function much as they would on Earth.

Dimensional Fabric: Weak, +20% to Dimensional Teleports.

Magic Level: High Magic Energy. While not as powerful as Rifts Earth, ley lines and nexus points are visible and the P.P.E. is easily accessible. The only known ley lines and nexus points are those currently under the control of the Aerihman clan. Leaving New Atlantis by following the ley lines is useless. Any ley line that extends beyond the formation of the giant triangle disappears after 2D6x10 miles (32 to 192 km) into a plasma cloud.

Dimensional Energy Matrix: Negative.

Time Flow: Time flows faster with a 4 to 1 ratio. This is one of the reasons the Aerihman chose Solaria. Because time flows faster in relation to the rest of the Megaverse, it allows the Aerihman clan to quickly increase their numbers and allowed them to recover faster than other clans.

Dimensional Quirks: There is a single, massive ley line triangle floating in Solaria. There may be other ley lines and triangles, but none are known. The three planetoids are anchored on each of the massive nexus points and therefore are connected to the three ley lines. This means that most of *New Atlantis* rests within the ley line and a portion of it on the nexus point, where ambient ley line magic energy is accessible on three quarters of the flat-world continent of New Atlantis. The fact that it is part of a ley line triangle makes magic very accessible and easily controlled via dimensional stone pyramids. Only areas around the outer edge of the flat, New Atlantis do not have any ambient magic energy.

Many of the easiest Rifts to establish in Solaria are linked to the Elemental Plane of Fire, suggesting the Solaria dimension has a connection to that dimension. Some Aerihman scholars have suggested that Solaria is actually a Parallel Dimension to the Elemental Plane of Fire with the odd quirk of having no Fire Elementals of any kind. Coincidently, any Elementals brought to Solaria want to leave immediately, even if brought in by a Warlock. If trapped on Solaria, the Elemental loses its physical form in 24 hours, leaving only its energy essence. The energy essence dies 24 hours later. It is just one of the weird properties of the Solaria dimension. Warlocks are able to see the Elemental in physical pain and only the most evil of them allow the Elemental to die in Solaria; most send the Elemental home long before it perishes.

Finally, scattered around the dimension are **null energy fields**. These fields seem to float randomly inside the dimension. The transmission of energy in these fields is nullified. So electrical devices, lasers, energy weapons, flashlights, radios, etc., do not work inside the null energy field. They go dormant as if the machine is out of juice. This includes cyborgs, power armor, robots and vehicles, all of which function at only 10% power when it comes to movement, while all other systems are offline for as long as they are trapped inside the null energy field. The field also impacts magic. Anyone using magic is required to spend double the usual P.P.E. amount to get half the usual outcome – reduce the spell's M.D., range, duration, modifiers, etc., by half, and double its P.P.E. cost to cast the diminished spell. The same is true of TW weapons and devices, and most other types of magic and magic items, including Bio-Wizardry, Biomancy, Elemental Magic and even Necromancy. Fortunately, null energy fields are rare and none have ever been spotted near New Atlantis or the floating ley line triangle it is attached to.

Neo-Atlantia
Aerihman Pilgrim Site

Neo-Atlantia is a small planet located in the *Corkscrew Galaxy* that was settled by the Aerihman a few hundred years ago. It is a small world the Aerihman took by suppressing resistance from an existing, indigenous population of humanoids. A clear breach of Atlantean protocol established thousands of years ago. The aggressive Aerihman have grown tired of their role as nurturers and believe they are better than other primitive beings. They believe Atlanteans need to embrace their superiority and lead the primitives through conquest and benevolent rule by their superiors, Atlanteans. The taking of Neo-Atlantia was the Aerihman quietly putting this philosophy to the test. When their fellow clansmen found out, however, the fallout was swift and decisive. They warned the Aerihman clan that conquest would not be tolerated and that Neo-Atlantia must be returned to its original and rightful inhabitants. And to ensure this took place, several other Atlantean clans would send observers to supervise the transition. With the amount of damage that the Aerihman clan had done in conquering the planet, it took fifty years to return the world back to its native population, mostly the way it had been. In a concession to Aerihman resistance to all of this, the clan was permitted to inhabit an isolated island in the southern hemisphere on Neo-Atlantia.

While Neo-Atlantia was a beautiful place to live, it lacked in ley lines and magic energy, so the Aerihman clan was not distraught over losing the planet. It was a matter of pride and being threatened and coerced by their Atlantean brethren that rankled the Aerihman. The clan did not appreciate being pressured by the other Atlantean clans into restoring the planet and leaving it all behind for the indigenous population. They would keep their little island colony outpost as an act of defiance and as a reminder that Atlanteans needed to wake up and take their rightful place in the Megaverse as benevolent conquerors and demigods. It would become an action that would cost the Aerihman clan more than they could have known, and introduce a new enemy of the Atlantean people, **the Sunaj.**

Accounts of the infamous atrocity tell how the Sunaj struck without warning and without mercy. Men, women and children were slaughtered. Their bodies left on display for all to see. Some were clearly tortured before being executed. The colony was ransacked before it was set on fire and razed to the ground. Less than two dozen survivors and some video footage would stand as evidence of the massacre at Neo-Atlantia. The attackers wore what would become the signature masks, capes and black garb of the Sunaj assassins.

The destruction of the Neo-Atlantia colony was the grand entrance for the enigmatic Sunaj. And they literally left a message carved into a portion of the scorched earth:

"This is only the beginning. The Sunaj will wipe out all Atlanteans from existence. We will not stop until this task is accomplished, even if it takes 10,000 years."

Attacks on other Atlantean colonies and holdings would soon follow, and continue to this day. Moreover, the Sunaj are found stirring up trouble, assisting pirates, monsters and other enemies of True Atlanteans across the Megaverse, and serve the Splugorth as their assassins and enforcers.

To this day, the origins and motives of the sinister Sunaj remain unknown. Everyone knows the Sunaj to be among the deadliest assassins in the universe, and as a fanatical organization of zealots dedicated to wiping out True Atlanteans. The reason for this unreasoning hate remains a mystery, especially to the Atlanteans themselves.

Given the history of Atlanteans, the Sunaj campaign of genocide seems almost certain to be fueled (perhaps with cash or the promise of power) by evil supernatural forces. Some portion of the Sunaj (their true numbers unknown) openly serve as the Minions of Splugorth in the role of assassins, bounty hunters, and special forces. It is a bond that seems to be built upon a mutual hatred of True Atlanteans. As such, the Sunaj, whether working for the Splugorth as minions or as hired assassins and independent contractors, are engaged in the systematic targeting and destruction of True Atlanteans. Picking them off whenever the opportunity presents itself (the Sunaj are *assassins* after all), raiding valuable Atlantean holdings, and killing anyone who gets in the way of their intended Atlantean targets.

What adds to the mystery of the Sunaj is that these obsessed killers seem to understand Atlanteans and their ways better than any enemy before them, and are able to seemingly vanish without a trace. To make matters worse, the Sunaj have, over the decades, allied themselves to an ever growing network of spies, criminals, cutthroats and organizations that hate True Atlanteans and want to see them destroyed, whether it is out of rivalry, hatred or revenge. As the reputation and network of contacts for the Sunaj grows, the assassins have become the go-to hit men to contact for eliminating problems involving Atlanteans. The Sunaj have become the de facto "Atlantean exterminators" across the Megaverse. ("Got a problem with an Atlantean, call the Sunaj.")

Sunaj assassins are so good at their job that even the Splugorth trust them enough to count them among their chosen, elite minions. A fact that only enhances the Sunaj's reputation among wicked supernatural beings and criminal organizations. This reputation insures that new information about Atlantean activities and new potential targets (people, heroes, convoys, spaceships, locations, meetings, etc.) are shared with the killers by mutual enemies of Atlanteans. This provides the Sunaj with excellent and ongoing intelligence about Atlanteans, their whereabouts and operations.

As for the Neo-Atlantia colony, the Aerihman clan has stated they have plans to restore and repopulate the colony someday, but for now, it is just a memorial. A sacred place that honors the victims who perished that day, and where many True Atlanteans make pilgrimages to honor the dead. The Aerihman clan who lays claim to the remote island has a small staff in place to maintain and protect the memorial. (Mostly secret Sunaj agents who secretly take notes on Atlantean clansmen who visit the memorial to track their whereabouts, plans and activities.)

The terrible secret behind the Neo-Altantia colony: The powerful Aerihman leader who secretly created, runs and fuels the Sunaj movement (all Sunaj are Aerihman Atlanteans) is having a hidden Sunaj base constructed underground on the island. A secret facility to better target, monitor and track the influx of True Atlantean pilgrims and follow them to other secret Atlantean enclaves, and help the Minions of Splugorth, pirates and anti-Atlantean forces hurt and destroy their Atlantean brethren.

Remember, the Aerihman extremists behind the secret society of Sunaj ultimately seek to wipe out the True Atlanteans who oppose their militant views on taking Atlantis back from the Splugorth. They believe if they can hurt the other clans enough, it will get them to change their minds. After all, if the Sunaj are a Minion of Splugorth, or being supported by the Splugorth from Atlantis, it makes the Splugorth a more immediate threat than their clansmen originally believed. If the Splugorth are protecting and sponsoring the Sunaj terrorists, that issue must be addressed, sooner or later.

Yes, all of this – the slaughter of the colonists, the creation of the Sunaj, their campaign of genocide against Atlanteans – is a part of a grand scheme to get the other clans to fall in line with the Aerihman clan's position on attacking Atlantis and reclaiming it from the Minions of Splugorth. The Sunaj see themselves as the hand of destiny for the Atlantean people. The selfless architects behind the scenes manipulating people and events so that the clans unite against a common enemy and seize their manifest destiny. They are self-righteous (and delusional) patriots who believe they seek only what is best for them and all Atlanteans.

In the end, it is all really about revenge, power and pride. And the power-mad scheming of one powerful and manipulative leader, **Lord Aerihza,** leader of the Aerihman clan as well as the secret leader of the Sunaj. This is his and his wife's dream of conquest and power in the name of their clan. Lord Aerihza and his Sunaj illuminati have been so clever and careful with this scheme that nobody, not even other Aerihman, let alone other Atlanteans, has any idea of what is taking shape in their own clan.

This grand deception gets even crazier when you realize that because True Atlanteans are famous demon slayers and champions of light, many evil and monstrous allies willingly hide and help the Sunaj without ever realizing the assassins are actually the hated Atlanteans themselves! The grand deception is further helped along by Sunaj assassinating Aerihman clansmen who are targeted for being too soft or willing to compromise, or who become a problem for Lord Aerihza and his cronies. By making it seem like ALL True Atlanteans are targets of the Sunaj without exception, but the Aerihman clansmen most of all, nobody suspects the Aerihman clan could possibly be the power behind it all.

The scheme seems almost too brazen and complex to work, yet for Lord Aerihza, all the pieces have brilliantly fallen into place and are working perfectly. The outpost on Neo-Atlantia was the perfect "sacrificial lamb" to give birth to the legendary Sunaj. Killing some of their own, in spectacular fashion, would steer suspicion away from the Aerihman clan. Just as important, the Sunaj leader knew such an extreme action would establish the Sunaj as a new, powerful enemy with an axe to grind against all True Atlanteans. He also knew such a bold attack would attract the favorable attention of the Splugorth, and endear the Sunaj to them. True Atlanteans are a hated nemesis of the Splugorth, so the enemy of Atlanteans was a potential ally and minion. The scheme went off without a hitch. The Sunaj became notorious overnight, and quickly caught the eye of the Splugorth. All it cost were a little over a thousand Aerihman lives in the island colony of Neo-Atlantia. Letting the Sunaj become a Minion of Splugorth was exactly what the Sunaj mastermind wanted. Such an alliance creates suspicion that the assassins were in league with the monsters from the very beginning, and that the Splugorth are the ones really responsible for the assault on Neo-Atlantia and all the other murders at the hands of the Splugorth. And not just any Splugorth, Lord Splynncryth and the Splugorth of Atlantis. How much more can the other Atlantean clans take before they declare war on Atlantis and give Lord Aerihza and many Aerihman what they wanted from the beginning: To take back Atlantis for Atlanteans?

See the section on the Sunaj O.C.C.s for more details about the assassins and their illuminati-like secret society. And remember, nobody outside the Sunaj organization knows they are Atlanteans within Clan Aerihman.

Argos

The recognized home of the Aerihman

The Aerihman clan also has a major colony on a small, habitable moon in orbit around a gas giant in the *Three Galaxies*. The moon is very earthlike and beautiful. The solar system is close to *the Threshold* in the Anvil Galaxy, just inside *the Halo*, and not near any commonly traveled space lanes.

There are many cities and towns, but the main city, **Argeleos**, is built around a large, strong, ley line nexus point with four connecting ley lines. The neighboring **city of Helaina** has a smaller population but is well known for its smaller ley lines and many Healing Pyramids and advancements in medicine and healing magicks.

The Argos colony is the oldest Aerihman settlement and was initially a military base that was set up during the Vampire Crusades. Thus, it is "known" among many other clans of Atlanteans and some of their allies – namely other vampire slayers and Champions of Light. That said, visitors are uncommon and not very welcomed, which is the way the Aerihman prefer it. Argos is now considered the "public" home of the Aerihman. If and when they have to meet with other Atlanteans and diplomats, Argos is where the clan receives visitors.

The Aerihman are in the process of building a space port from which space vessels can come and go with ease. All they have at present is a large landing field several miles from the main city.

Argeleos has a population of just under a half million Aerihman; the city of **Helaina** has 350,000. Most smaller communities range from a few thousand to 80,000. The majority of civilians in all cities know nothing about *the Sunaj* except what is known to everyone. Thus, only select individuals and insiders are agents of the Sunaj or know about *Solaria*.

The Argos Council of Elders was appointed by Lord Aerihza. While they are loyal to him, they are kept in the dark about the Sunaj and the clan leaders' secret plans to force a war with the Splugorth of Atlantis by killing Atlanteans. Those few on the Council who do know about Solaria, consider it a second home where the rest of the clan resides. The Argos Council of Elders is in effect, a puppet regime set up by Lord Aerihza with leaders he knows he can manipulate, dupe, and control.

If evidence were ever presented showing a connection between the Sunaj and the Aerihman clan, it would be brought to the Argos Council of Elders. Since they know nothing about the Sunaj or their plans, the Council would legitimately reject any and all accusations, work toward disproving such clearly fabricated evidence, and defend the honor of all Atlanteans by discrediting such "lies." Any sort of telepathic scan upon Council members reveals they are sincere, telling the truth and deeply insulted at the suggestion that any Atlanteans, let alone the noble and heroic Aerihman, could have any affiliation with such brutal killers. Even a captive Sunaj would not be known to the Council, who would reject the Sunaj as a Splugorth ploy intended to tear the clans apart and damage the reputation of Clan Aerihman, renowned for destroying demons and monsters, and protecting all the other Atlantean clans since the days of ancient Atlantis. This is exactly why Lord Aerihza keeps them in power (and in the dark). *Plausible deniability* is important when psychics and magic users versed in detecting the truth may come seeking answers.

Lord Aerihza, the secret head of, and mastermind behind, the Sunaj, is also the leader of the Argos Council of Elders, and he has a large residence in the city of healing. He travels between Solaria and Argos regularly. Aerihman secretly loyal to the Sunaj are in charge of pyramid operations on Argos, ensuring his comings and goings are undocumented and his privacy guaranteed, unless he wants his activities known. They also see to it that supplies and personnel for the Sunaj assassins are transported in secret to wherever they need to go. This conspiracy starts at the top and works its way down.

Clan Archerean

Clan Archerean resides on the planet Alexandria in the *Anvil Galaxy* of the Phase World dimension. The clan is not very large, but with the amount of Atlantean visitors that come to their city, they have one of the largest known concentrations of Atlanteans in the Megaverse with about 7-9 million at any given time. A number that swells during clan meetings. Alexandria is one of the few hubs where many Atlanteans gather to meet, reconnect, trade goods, and feel safe enough to spend time there for rest and relaxation. The Archerean clan settled on the planet after many years of travel and adventuring through the Three Galaxies.

The clan barely survived the vanishing of Atlantis. Most of their people resided on the western side of ancient Atlantis. Before they could fully prepare for their escape, seismic activity tore that side of the island continent to pieces. The families under the leadership of their Archerean magistrates managed to escape, but with only the clothes on their backs. To make matters worse, they traveled through several inhospitable dimensions. One dimension was home to a Vampire Intelligence with millions of undead. That mistake cost the Archerean refugees two thirds of their numbers. By the time they found their way to the Three Galaxies, there were fewer than 20,000 of them left. The world they arrived on was devoid of intelligent life and teeming with ley lines and pulsing with mystic energy. With the use of magic and ingenuity, the surviving Archereans were able to tame an area of the planet and reached out to friendly Atlantean survivors to join them in claiming the world for Atlanteans.

Alexandria

Home of the Archereans and Open to All Atlanteans

Today, the planet Alexandria has one of the largest known concentrations of Atlanteans anywhere. The reason it is so well known is because the early Archerean settlers actively sought out other clans for assistance. To truly tame and reshape the world, they needed more Stone Masters, Alchemists and bodies than they had. Always an amicable clan, the Archereans were happy to share their find with other Atlanteans regardless of their family clan affiliations. As a result, branches of many clans call the planet Alexandria home, and the planet has become a hub for Atlanteans to gather and conduct business. Many who call someplace else home have the equivalent of a "summer home" on Alexandria, and there are many sprawling estates, farms, ranches and areas of land claimed by specific Atlantean families, businesses and clans.

Obviously, with fewer than 10 million Atlanteans living on the planet, most of it is uninhabited. This is deliberate for security reasons, and also why surprisingly few outsiders are employed on Alexandria.

Arch City is the largest of the sprawling cities on the planet, with 6.7 million Atlantean residents, 2.6 million of which are Archereans. In addition to the Atlantean population, there are one million permanent non-Atlantean residents; there would be a hundred times that number if the clans allowed non-Atlanteans to settle on their adopted home world. The many pyramids located in the commercial/downtown, merchant and entertainment area of Arch City make it rather like New York City's Times Square and Grand Central Station for Atlantean travelers and visitors. Those who come to visit or engage in trade seldom travel outside the city, because it has everything one could want to see, do or purchase. An estimated 20 million people, Atlanteans and others, visit Arch City annually. Most staying 1-4 weeks at a time.

The other large cities are one-quarter the size of Arch City, with additional small towns and hamlets scattered across the planet. All are centered around ley lines and nexus points controlled by 3-12 stone pyramids to manage the magic and make life easier. Outside of the handful of cities, the smaller communities on Alexandria are spread out with most Atlantean inhabitants owning several acres of land to several hundred or a few thousand acres. The fact that there is so much remaining undeveloped wilderness is what attracts Atlanteans to the planet, and why most Atlanteans own large amounts of land which they largely preserve. Atlanteans appreciate nature and wildlife, so they enjoy having large gardens, horses, livestock, farms, parks, nature preserves and forested areas. Even the homes in population centers are fairly spread out with at least a few acres between them.

Marks of Heritage/Clan Crest: The right wrist has a Heart Impaled by a Stake. On the left wrist is a flaming claymore with the clan name running down the length of the blade.

Clan Estimated Size: Over the years, Clan Archerean has managed to rebound and increase their numbers. At the last census there were 3.6 million living on Alexandria, and another million wandering the Megaverse.

Clan Status: Well Known. All clans seem to know someone in the Archerean clan. This is because Clan Archerean has opened its adopted planet up to all Atlanteans and has become a trade center. They also work at trying to keep all the Atlantean clans united and in touch with one another. To that end, the clan has dispatched hundreds of Nomad Diplomats throughout the Megaverse to other Atlantean clans. The Archereans even try to keep in touch with the Aerihman. Without fail, every few months, an Archerean Diplomat tries to reach out to the Aerihman clan. The reply is always the same: The Aerihman are not interested in gathering at this time and will meet at a time and location of their own choosing when they are ready. The Archerean diplomat is then sent on his way, often without having left the Dimensional Pyramid where he arrived at.

Clan Archerean believes it is critical to the survival of the Atlantean people to remain in communication with the other clans. Atlanteans as a people have been hunted and slaughtered by evil supernatural creatures and hostile forces for generations. Their choice to be idealistic humanitarians, defenders of the innocent and monster slayers puts all Atlanteans in harm's way on a regular basis as well as makes them a target for all manner of evil and inhuman forces, not the least of which include the armies of demons, vampires and the Minions of Splugorth. This is why all Atlantean clans have comparatively small populations despite how long their civilization has existed.

Clan's Primary Home: Clustered. Clan Archerean reside on a planet in the Three Galaxies. They are limited to a single dimension and planet.

Clan General Alignment: Primarily good.

Clan Notoriety: Famous. Clan Archerean is known for their resilience and their culture of open friendliness, communications, and diplomacy. All Atlanteans are welcomed at Alexandria with open arms. Many families in Alexandria open their homes to visiting Atlanteans, and most families have 1D6+1 spare bedrooms for travelers to stay. Any Atlantean player character is likely to be able to stay at a family home for little or no cost, as if they were a visiting family member.

Clan Outlook on Earth: Accepted. The Archereans are content with their lives, do not take themselves too seriously, and do not dwell on the past, they look to the future. Atlantis holds no significance to them.

Bonuses for Clan Archerean: Characters from Alexandria, who are part of the Archerean clan, have access to skills found in the *Three Galaxies*. This includes space skills like Zero Gravity Movement & Combat, Pilot: Small Spacecraft and similar skills. Archereans who do not select a common Atlantean O.C.C. may select any O.C.C. found in the Three Galaxies. A few Archereans have even taken up the occupation of *Phase Mystics* found in Center on Phase World.

Also because Clan Archerean hosts an annual meeting of all the clans, any Archerean can expect to be well treated by their brethren by most Atlantean communities and individuals. Even the Aerihman show Archerean Atlanteans a certain level of politeness and respect. Visiting Archereans are often given a place to stay and provided with plenty of food for the duration at below normal prices. Most Archereans know that they can stay at least a month at a steep discount (half), before they have more or less worn out their welcome. However, most members of Clan Archerean are well versed in social graces and are polite, cordial, and respectful to their hosts, and do not push the limits of other clans' generosity toward them.

Clan Aurelous

Clan Aurelous is quite small compared to the other notable Atlantean clans. They are related to the Aerihman clan through several marriages and many think of them as a sub-clan of the Aerihman. The clan as a whole considers themselves to be healers and they are accredited with some of the best Healing Pyramids, holistic doctors and psychic healers of all Atlanteans. They roam the Megaverse, and when requested by another Atlantean clan, will usually agree to design and supervise the building of new Healing Pyramids, repairing and upgrading existing pyramids, and using their knowledge to heal and help others.

The Aurelous clan does not have a home dimension to call their own. Rather they have settled among various other clans and alien people. For example, a number reside among the Aerihman and quite a few live on Alexandria. A small group resides in Lazlo on Rifts Earth, another group in England, and another group lives on Wormwood.

The Aurelous thought that they were one of the fortunate clans to escape the cataclysm of Atlantis. They were one of the first groups of people to evacuate the island continent, and the entire clan was accounted for after their escape. They attended to thousands of wounded and injured Atlanteans and the entire Aurelous clan mobilized to establish triage centers around the Dimensional Pyramid on the distant world where they had fled. The Aurelous clan would have been seen as heroes to the Atlantean people had they not caught the notice of the Splugorth. The dimensional ripples from the pyramid alerted many supernatural menaces, but it was the Splugorth who first investigated. The clan did not have many warriors and with so many wounded, they were an easy target. Tens of thousands of Aurelous Atlanteans were taken by force and enslaved by the Minions of Splugorth. Nearly the entire clan was taken. If not for the Aerihman who rescued a small number of them, their entire clan might have been wiped out. There is little wonder why the Aurelous share such a close bond of camaraderie and allegiance with the Aerihman, more than any of the other Atlantean clans.

Even today, the clan is only at a fraction of its original numbers. Some of those who were rescued by the Aerihman settled on Argos and have raised families there. Their culture and beliefs are very similar to those of the Aerihman, and they hate the Splugorth even more than their kith and kin. Over the millennia that followed, Aurelous survivors and their Aerihman cousins did what they could to track down Splugorth slave compounds and try to free their captured kinsman and their descendants, as well as other slave races. Sadly, over time, the Splugorth's brainwashing was too complete to reverse and the rescue effort stopped. It is said that half of the Atlantean Tattooed warrior slaves in the service of the Splugorth are descended from the Aurelous clan. A statistic that haunts the free Aurelous clansmen and Aerihman alike. One more tragic secret seldom spoken of by any Atlantean, and certainly not by either clan closest to the nightmare.

Today, the clan still retains its healing prowess and expertise, and their knowledge and skills are coveted above all others when it comes to medicine and Healing Pyramids. As is their tradition, the Aurelous focus on the healing arts and pyramid construction (Stone Masters), but there are those who also become Tattooed Defenders, Undead Slayers, Nomads, Voyagers, and other occupations that fight and oppose the Splugorth and all evil supernatural beings. Like the Aerihman clan with whom they feel the greatest kinship, many Aurelous agree with the Aerihman's position on the Splugorth, taking back Atlantis, and taking a stronger leadership role among humans and other, less advanced people. Lord Aerihza has even considered secretly recruiting some Aurelous into the Sunaj.

Marks of Heritage/Clan Crest: The Aurelous clan can be identified by a Heart Impaled by a Stake on the right wrist, and on the left wrist, a flaming broadsword entwined down the length of the blade by a vine-like rose branch, its thorns dripping blood, and a white rose at the hilt. Written on a parchment over the vine is the clan name. The clan originally adopted the white rose because they were healers, not fighters.

Clan Estimated Size: 12,500 scattered among the Aerihman and various worlds and dimensions.

Clan Status: Little Known. In some circles, especially among Stone Masters and healers, Clan Aurelous are renowned for their healing capabilities and as the builders of the superior Healing Pyramids, but to most Atlanteans, the clan is all but forgotten. A footnote in history.

There are only a small handful of clans that the Aurelous consider themselves to have close ties with, and that includes the Aerihman and Archereans. At the moment, a quarter of the clan resides in the Aerihman settlement of Argos, another quarter on Alexandria, and the rest are scattered to the winds. Most Aurelous Atlanteans consider the Aerihman to be their closest friends and allies, and share many of their political and philosophical views, but others disagree and side with the Archereans, split 60/40.

Clan's Primary Home: Scattered, with no real world to call their own home, Aurelous reside in the communities of other Atlantean clans or wander the Megaverse.

Clan General Alignment: Fair mix.

Clan Notoriety: Science and healing and medicines. Those who know about the clan know them to be among the best healers and builders of Healing Pyramids of all Atlantean clans.

Bonuses for Clan Aurelous: All clan members are taught at least the basics in the healing arts. Characters from clan Aurelous will know the following skills in addition to any O.C.C. skills: Holistic Medicine, First Aid or Paramedic, and Identify Plants & Fruit or Brewing, starting at first level. The skills progress normally with each new level. Characters can opt, with the Game Master's approval, to forgo the three healing skills and instead add a +10% bonus (in addition to O.C.C./ O.C.C. related bonuses) to two different Medical or Science skills. Additionally, any Healing Pyramid built by or repaired by the Aurelous clan gives a +20% on each of the Advanced Healing options that are available. See Healing Pyramid, page 193, for more details.

Clan Bagh-Dach

More than a few clans are known to have warriors who have become living legends among Atlanteans and throughout the Megaverse. None, with the possible exception of the Aerihman, are as renowned as Clan Bagh-Dach. Many tales have been told of how a single Bagh-Dach warrior stood his ground against two dozen vampires, or the warriors who faced a Splugorth invasion, or the band of Undead Slayers who survived going to *Necropolon*, the dimension of the living dead. They not only possess some of the bravest warriors, but some of the most honorable and noble as well. As many heroic tales as there are to tell, so too are the tales of the noble warriors who sacrificed their lives for the greater good knowing it could save innocent lives. Indeed, when any Atlantean warrior, particularly a Tattooed Defender or Undead Slayer, arrives at a settlement just about anywhere, they are warmly greeted. Their reputation preceding them and their very presence inspiring hope and courage. When that warrior is a member of the Bagh-Dach clan, it is like having a rock star visiting. Virtually all Bagh-Dach Atlanteans are considered *Champions of Light* and regarded as the elite among heroes.

The legend of the Bagh-Dach does not begin in an auspicious way. There was no noble quest, crusade or deliberate war waged against evil. Their rise to greatness as unrivaled heroes and demon slayers was thrust upon them. It all started with a tragic accident.

Dimensional travel is unpredictable and dangerous. Exploring and mapping an entire world before colonizing it is nearly impossible. When the Bagh-Dach clan evacuated their people from Atlantis, they relocated to a planet that seemed Earth-like and appealing. What they could not know is that tucked away in a dark corner, the demons of Hades had established a secret base for creating the foulest of war machines. Hidden in a canyon, demons were summoning dark magic to create the dreaded **Demon Star** battle cruiser. A forbidden machine of mass destruction so rare and so powerful that many people prefer to believe it is a work of fiction designed to scare people like the boogey man, and not real at all. At the time, even those who had heard of the Demon Star and believed it was real, lived under the misconception that the dark secrets and magic needed for its construction had been forever lost many thousands of years ago. Yet here in the shadows, the denizens of Hades were building them. One Demon Star had been completed. Another was under construction. And the unwitting Atlanteans knew nothing of such things.

When the demons realized their desolate world in the middle of nowhere had been compromised by human refugees, they saw opportunity. Demons swarmed the unsuspecting Atlanteans with the intention of capturing and enslaving them all. The monsters would need to sacrifice thousands of humanoid lives for the many soul-devouring rituals needed to create a Demon Star. And here they were delivered, by fate, right into their laps.

The battles that ensued were fierce and bloody. The Bagh-Dach fought back valiantly, but the demons gave them no respite. Not only were the interlopers needed for human sacrifice, but the demons had to keep their secret Demon Star factory hidden from the outside world. That meant no Bagh-Dach Atlantean could be allowed to live. A quarter million Atlanteans perished in the conflagration that followed. In the end, 150,000 Bagh-Dach managed to slip away and escape, but not before tens of thousands of them perished in a bold siege in which they succeeded in destroying the factory and the Demon Star that was under construction. It was a victory that hurt the demons more than the Atlanteans could know. A disaster that would set the Demon Lord behind this plot back by several millennia.

The plight of the Bagh-Dach was not yet over. Though they did not realize it, the demons could not let them live. They had seen too much and the demons had to silence them before word about the creation of the Demon Star fell into the ears of the wrong people. So it was that the Bagh Dach Atlanteans were set upon by the remaining Demon Star, hunted and slaughtered without mercy. The demons' campaign forced them to splinter into smaller groups and family clans that scattered across the Megaverse. Out of necessity, the Bagh-Dach Atlanteans became warriors, Tattooed Voyagers and practitioners of magic. And even occupations like Nomads and healers learned how to use weapons and handle themselves in a fight.

The demons were relentless in their pursuit – driven by revenge and the need to protect their secret. Every bloody step of the way, the Bagh-Dach gave as good as they received, and with each battle, their heroics spread across the cosmos. As their legend grew, they met other heroes who joined their fight or who offered them sanctuary. This included the fabled Cosmo-Knights (who consider all Bagh-Dach their brethren in arms), other Atlantean clansmen, and even the Prometheans of Phase World who marveled at their bravery and took pity upon their plight (and who knew better than any that the demons' building of even a few Demon Stars was a portent of terrible danger yet to be revealed).

As the Bagh-Dach's numbers dwindled to a tiny fraction and other people finally came to their aid to hide and protect them, the remaining clansmen became more difficult to track and hunt down. In time, the demons gave up their pursuit, but by then, legend has it, fewer than 800 Bagh-Dach remained.

The members of the Bagh-Dach would never forget the genocide leveled at them. They had learned, first hand, the power of a Demon Star, and the cruelty of demons. From allies like the Cosmo-Knights, they became familiar with the terrible weapons and dark magicks possessed by demons. They also caught wind of rumblings about plans for something called the *Minion War*. All of it compelling the members of Clan Bagh-Dach to remain proactive in their private war against demonkind and protecting the innocent from them.

Today, many Bagh-Dach Atlanteans are scattered across the universe as wandering heroes and demon slayers. Others have settled on Phase World, Alexandria and elsewhere, but their official adopted home is rumored to be in a dimension called the *Plane of Sands*. It is there that you find the greatest number of Bagh-Dach trying to rebuild.

Marks of Heritage/Clan Crest: The Bagh-Dach clansmen have the classic staked heart on the right wrist, and a flaming long sword over a shield on the left. Individuals customize their flaming sword tattoo with a single word which seems to best represent them. Common words used are Honor, Courage, Freedom, Valor, or Liberty, but it can be anything that has meaning to the individual and his clan. Typically written on the flaming shield is the clan motto "Service before self," as a reminder that all clan members should do what they can to help others before themselves.

Clan Estimated Size: 32,000

Clan Status: Famous. Heroic demon slayers.

Clan Notoriety: Demon slayers and heroes. The Bagh-Dach clan is renowned for sending their warriors all over the Megaverse to fight the forces of evil, demons in particular. Some go out as small groups while others travel alone, and still others join other bands of fellow heroes and adventurers. They spend most of their lives wandering the Megaverse slaying demons, but many return home to visit and rest when they can. Of course, many go off and are never seen again. They are presumed to be fighting the good fight wherever they are needed, but they are more likely to have died on the battlefield of an alien world.

One notable member of the Bagh-Dach clan resides on Rifts Earth. *Sir Galahad* of Rifts England (his real name is *Argo Vinuh*) has been out of contact with his home for several years. While he would be greatly concerned about recent attacks on his people, his immediate responsibility is serving as a knight of New Camelot.

Clan's Primary Home: Half are scattered. The rest of the clan is clustered in a single dimension, the Plane of Sands.

Clan General Alignment: Primarily good.

Clan Outlook on Earth: As a whole, the clan has accepted what has happened to their former home. They have no interest in waging war over Atlantis.

Bonuses for Clan Bagh-Dach: Bagh-Dach seem fearless in battle, +2 to save vs Horror Factor. In addition to their tattoos, all warriors and adventurers from this clan possess one magic weapon, ideally a demon slaying weapon, and love Rune Weapons, and all types of magic weapons and items, as well as using captured Splugorth- and demon-made weapons against their evil creators. +10% bonus to Wilderness Survival and Dowsing skills in desert environments.

Plane of Sands

Home to the Bagh-Dach Clan

The Plane of Sands is a pocket dimension that can be accessed easily from either the Elemental Plane of Air or Earth. Being a pocket dimension, its size is limited, but has yet to be fully explored by the Bagh-Dach clan.

The dimension appears to be an endless desert filled with red sand, rust colored buttes and bluffs and the occasional mountain chain made of obsidian (volcanic glass that is not usable by Stone Masters). A bright red sun shines constantly, heating the desert to at least 100 degrees Fahrenheit (38 C), and sometimes much hotter. The sun shines for twelve days at a time, then there is a four day period of absolute darkness. The sun dims to the brightness of a full moon and during this "night" temperatures plummet to 40 degrees Fahrenheit (4.4 C). The extreme temperatures can be a challenge for those who are out in the elements.

There is the occasional oasis, but they are very rare. The Bagh-Dach clan has managed to terraform a few larger oases amid this massive desert using the few ley lines and nexus points available in this environment. Their settlements are very obvious with their Dimensional Pyramids crafted from the red stones found in the Plane of Sands. The Bagh-Dach settlements resemble a well manicured Mediterranean city surrounding 1-6 large pyramids. All of the settlements are enclosed by large, thick walls.

Despite the heat and desert all around them, all Bagh-Dach communities are green and full of life. Trees, plants and grass are everywhere. Imported from other worlds and kept watered and maintained by magic, each city is supplied with water via a series of aqueducts that come from one of the Dimensional Pyramids connected to an Elemental Plane of Water. Water rushes down the aqueduct system to replenish the city's supplies and to water its splendid gardens, farms and forest areas. Should the water supply get cut off, there are cisterns all over the city as well as in each home and building. Each community has one month's supply of water before a Rift is needed to provide more. There are also a few wells and springs in the mountains. At the moment, new aqueducts are under construction to deliver this water to the various Bagh-Dach settlements.

Type of Dimension: Pocket Dimension, 300,000 square miles (776,996 sq. km) in size.
Primary Dimensional Medium: Air is the primary dimensional medium.
Secondary Dimensional Medium: A massive continent covered with a large red desert.
Dimensional Fabric: Permeable, no bonus or penalty for dimensional teleports.
Magic Level: Low magic energy. There are ley lines and nexus points, but they are barely visible, even at night.
Dimensional Energy Matrix: Negative.
Time Flow: Normal time flow.
Dimensional Quirks: The Plane of Sands is missing the mystic elements of water and fire. This means spell magic or Elemental Magic where the focus is water or fire costs four times more P.P.E. to cast and ranges are reduced by half. Normal fire can be made in the conventional sense, but magically, it costs more to create. The same holds true of water which is why it is imported rather than created via magic or Techno-Wizardry. Typical waterworks for Atlanteans are created via magic, but the Bagh-Dach actually utilize plumbing in their pyramids and communities. See the pyramid section for more details on pyramid waterworks.

The last dimensional quirk is that Rifts are linked to the Elemental Planes of Earth and Air and the majority of random Rifts open to one of them. When a pyramid creates a Rift to one of these two Elemental Planes it costs half as much.

Clan Draco Amicus

Before Atlantis vanished, Atlanteans had a good relationship with Chiang-Ku dragons, but it was Clan Draco Amicus that managed to forge relationships with several other dragon species. Just like the many other Atlantean clans, the Draco Amicus are dimensional travelers who have made the Megaverse their home. During their travels, a large group of Clan Draco Amicus happened upon a great war in a far off dimension. Legions of dragons – all manner of dragons – were banding together in great flocks to battle bands of invading infernals. (This is not related to the Minion War and is not connected to it.) The Deevils were robbing the dragon nests of their precious eggs for nefarious reasons one can only guess at. The Draco Amicus were willing to assist the dragons and joined them in their war. They created numerous Dimensional and Healing Pyramids, and fought at their side. Some even joined some dragons on raids into the very pits of Hell. The Atlanteans and their stone pyramids tipped the balance of the war in the dragons' favor, and the Draco Amicus clan's years of fighting alongside the serpents earned them an honored place. Hence, the clan is forever

known as Friends of the Dragons. A friendship and status they have maintained for thousands of years.

The clan's relationship with dragons seems preordained, because in ancient Atlantis, they inhabited the Dragon Isles in the northeastern part of the island continent. Always ones to travel and explore, many were away in other dimensions when Atlantis vanished. A good thing too, because the Dragon Islands were among the first to be torn apart by dimensional anomalies. Unprepared, the clansmen on the islands did not have adequate time to flee, and perished in the first dimensional storms that shook the continent. Most of the clansmen who survived were away, journeying on distant worlds and alien dimensions. Of those back home, it is said that only a few hundred managed to make it to safety before Atlantis disappeared.

With the clan already scattered across the universe, they moved from world to world and dimension to dimension assisting beings in need, but never finding a place to settle and call their home. Only in the last thirty years has the clan found a dimension that appears uninhabited and safe for them to settle down. The dimension, christened Terra Orbis, has become the new home to the Draco Amicus clan. Already half of their people have moved to their new home, but the rest continue to wander among the stars, coming to Terra Orbis only to visit for awhile.

At least one third of the clansmen are Nomads and another third Tattooed Voyagers. The rest are a mix of occupations that range from Stone Masters, Tattooed Defenders and Undead Slayers to practitioners of magic, psychics, Wilderness Scouts, healers and scholars. They are capable fighters unafraid of battling the supernatural, but are among the least combat oriented of all Atlanteans. The Draco Amicus are also the least educated about Atlantean history after the continent vanished.

Marks of Heritage/Clan Crest: The clan has a heart pierced by a stake on the right wrist and a flaming scimitar on the left wrist.

Clan Estimated Size: 820,000

Clan Status: Hidden, at least until recently. Clan Draco Amicus is relatively unknown by the other clans, and vice versa. They know nothing about the clan gatherings at Alexandria, and are used to being independent dimensional wanderers. The only Atlanteans they know are those they may have stumbled across on their journeys. Fate carried the members of the Draco Amicus clan down a different path than the other Atlantean clans. As a consequence, the Draco Amicus do not know what happened to their clansmen. They know nothing about Phase World or the Three Galaxies, and have only recently heard about Rifts Earth. The latter has enticed a number of Draco Amicus to visit and explore the planet of their origins, but they have no interest in taking back Atlantis. Those who arrive during the Minion War will join the battle and fight against the demon invaders at the side of humans, D-Bees and dragons. They may even be able to rally bands of dragons to help fight, especially against the infernals of Dyval.

Clan's Primary Home: Clustered. Half of the clan is located in Terra Orbis, but they know there are other Atlantean clans out there, and they are trying to find them to reestablish contact. They know nothing about Alexandria, Argos, Phase World and the Three Galaxies or much of anything about the other clans or those places. Now that the clan has a relatively stable place to call home, they have started sending out their Nomad Diplomats to try and reestablish ties with other Atlantean clans. When contact

is established, it will be away from Terra Orbis, their new, hidden home.

Clan General Alignment: Predominantly good with some selfish.

Clan Notoriety: The clan is most notable for two things. One, having been MIA (missing in action) for thousands of years, and two, rumors about them and their relationship with dragons. Six dragons (two ancient, three adult and one 300 year old hatchling) are among their clan's council of elders and have lived and traveled with members of the core clan for more than one thousand years. The clan is also a notable group of humanitarians and they help and assist any group of good people in need they come across.

Clan Outlook on Earth: The clan has, long ago, accepted the fate of Atlantis and has moved on. Its reappearance and being claimed by the Splugorth means nothing to them.

Bonuses for Clan Draco Amicus: Draco Amicus are very comfortable around dragons and know how to deal with them without offending the creatures. Dragons who recognize members of Clan Draco Amicus are inclined to barter and trade with them, share information and possibly assist them in some small way. Many long-lived dragons remember, first hand, how the Draco Amicus helped to preserve some of the dragons' nesting grounds, a dimension only known to adult and ancient dragons, and these Atlanteans. The fact that the Draco Amicus have NEVER revealed the location of the dragons' nesting grounds nor betrayed them in any way these past many thousands of years, keeps the clan in their good favor and among the rare friends of dragonkind. Even hatchlings have a genetic memory of the clan's assistance in the Infernal War.

Characters who are from the Draco Amicus clan gain a +20% bonuses to Lore: Faeries and Creatures of Magic and are +2 to save vs Horror Factor when dealing with dragons. There is a 60% chance any dragon (80% if an ancient dragon) will recognize the clan crest or the family name, and give members of the Draco Amicus more latitude when dealing with them; i.e. not kill them or their associates the first few times the mortals annoy or accidentally insult the dragon, and not cheat them in business dealings.

Terra Orbis

The dimension of Terra Orbis is strange in that it appears to be an impossibly giant Dyson's sphere. A massive metal orb completely surrounding a star and drawing upon its energy. This Dyson sphere is so technologically advanced that much of the interior surface of the sphere is habitable and seems to contain thousands of biospheres, each containing a unique and different environment as if each held a world or environment unique unto itself. Some of them are habitable and some are uninhabitable, at least by human standards. This vast array of habitats, some as large as entire continents or small worlds unto themselves, makes you wonder if the sphere is a giant collection of different planets. But to what purpose, and what beings possess the technology to create something like this? One or more gods? The Cosmic Forge? The First? The Dominators?

A solid shell Dyson sphere would be a grand accomplishment in and of itself. Add in the thousands of biospheres each with its own unique environment, flora and fauna, and it makes it all the more incredible. Could this be a collection of worlds that belongs to a powerful deity or an advanced race of beings beyond human comprehension? Is it a preserve that salvaged an entire galaxy before it imploded? Is it a zoo or botanical garden on an unbelievable scale? (No intelligent life has been discovered by the Draco Amicus yet, but they have only scratched the surface of this vast sphere.) Could it be a giant pocket dimension contained inside a sphere? Is it a trap?

And where are the sphere's builders? Are they watching from a secret room? Are they dead and gone? Or have they only stepped out for awhile and will return soon? Whatever soon may be for the makers of a self-contained dimension like this. And how will they react when they discover Atlanteans have moved in like ants in the pantry? Will they be ignored? Exterminated? Captured and studied like lab rats? Tagged and released back into the wild to be observed and studied?

The Draco Amicus have asked themselves all these questions and more. It seems crazy to move half their clan inside this impossible and deeply mysterious environment and make it their home. Yet something about this place calls to them. Perhaps it is the impossible nature and pervasive mystery of it all that keeps the inquisitive Atlanteans transfixed by it, and attracted to stay. Terra Orbis could represent one of the greatest mysteries of the universe, and it is theirs' to unravel. It is a gift and challenge the Draco Amicus cannot resist, and so they stay.

After a decade of exploration inside the Terra Orbis Dyson sphere, the Draco Amicus discovered how to use what they have dubbed **gate rooms**. These giant chambers, each larger than a football field, have a dozen octagonal metal frames each on a different section of the walls. The gates vary in size from 10 feet (3 m) to 1,000 feet (305 m) in diameter. When powered up, the octagonal frame crackles with energy and creates a portal to another gate room elsewhere on the interior surface of the Dyson sphere near a different biosphere. Draco Amicus explorers were surprised and pleased when they figured out how to operate the gate rooms, and that they seem to work perfectly. Teams of explorers are able to travel through them with ease. So far, 47 different environmental biospheres have been identified, but only in the broadest of terms, as each one is like a continent or world in its own right. It would take many lifetimes to explore all the biospheres even for the long-lived Atlanteans. Given the size of the Dyson sphere and the limitations of the clan, they simply do not have the time and resources to explore the entire structure. That will take many generations.

For now, they are building their home base inside the tropical biosphere located near the gate room where they first arrived in the Terra Orbis dimension. This gate room appears to be a dimensional focal point. A stone Dimensional Pyramid has been constructed at this focal point to make dimensional travel more accessible for the clan. The pyramid was completed 15 years ago, and the two other pyramids are nearly completed. The city being built in the biosphere nearby is a work in progress, but already there are 317,000 Draco Amicus living there, inside a tropical paradise. Like most Atlantean cities, their homes and buildings are spread out and fit in nicely with the nature of their rainforest biosphere. In addition to the natural flora and fauna that existed in the alien biosphere when they first discovered it, the Draco Amicus have transplanted many of their favorite plants, fruits and crops from the many worlds they have visited. The weather is temperate with an average temperature in the 80s (27-32 C), and there is an abundance of natural food plants, including a type of coconut and banana-like fruits, among many others. The Atlanteans have a dozen fields where various other crops imported from

other worlds are grown, as well as some favored livestock. They are ever mindful to contain potentially invasive species from invading and undermining the original biosphere they now inhabit.

Fifty miles from their city is a freshwater ocean where several small Atlantean villages, ranches, farms and estates have been established. Many of the homes and structures are made of wood because it is natural and because stone suitable for building must be brought in from outside the Terra Orbis dimension. There are a few biospheres that could provide the necessary materials, as there seems to be an environmental biosphere with every conceivable environment. However, the Atlanteans are hesitant to disturb the other environments until they have had time to do much more exploration and evaluation of each, as well as the Dyson sphere itself. Even after 30 years, the clan estimates it has explored and mapped less than 2% of the interior.

The dimensional focal point for the dimension is what the Draco Amicus have dubbed the super gate room. This room, if it can be called that, covers a five mile (8 km) area and has over a hundred gates, each varying in size. At the center of this super gate room is a nexus with five connecting ley lines. All dimensional travelers arrive through this Rift and this is where the clan opted to build their Dimensional Pyramid. This super gate room still remains a mystery to the Draco Amicus and it is kept under heavy guard until they can figure out exactly how to close a few specific gates which appear to have been intentionally left on. Access to the tropical biosphere nearby is via an existing tram system that takes travelers there in less than five minutes.

The last structure to be identified by the clan consists of many sections of giant solar arrays each covering a thousand mile (1,609 km) area. Exploration into just one solar complex took six weeks and then they were only able to map out part of the overall complex. The countless solar panel arrays are what channel and harness the power of the star and feeds the millions (billions?) of internal mechanisms and gates of the sphere. The raw solar energy is channeled deep into the sphere and presumably distributed to where it is needed. The Draco Amicus have not been able to tap this energy source yet and still rely upon conventional means of power and magic.

It is theorized that there must be an army of robots inside the massive sphere that maintain and repair the internal workings and outer shell of the sphere. However, they have never come across one in the 30 years they have been inside the sphere. Nor have they ever encountered any inhabitants nor any other dimensional travelers. As far as they can tell, they are the only humanoid life forms living in Terra Orbis. If Terra Orbis is truly unknown to any other sentient beings – besides its maker(s) – it could be the ultimate refuge and perfect home for the persecuted Atlanteans. The question the Draco Amicus clansmen wrestle with is whether or not they should share Terra Orbis with their fellow Atlanteans and dragon friends. All things considered, the dimension and Dyson sphere could become the ultimate hidden home for all Atlanteans. For now it is a secret they keep to themselves.

Type of Dimension: Undetermined. Some believe it is Contained, while others argue that it could be Infinite. Until more of its mysteries are unraveled, the full nature of the dimension and exactly where it is located remains in question. There is a galaxy worth of biospheres, and nobody knows what exists outside the Dyson sphere other than complete blackness, as it contains all the star's light.

Primary Dimensional Medium: Artificial. Presumed to have been constructed by some kind of superior intelligence or unknown civilization.

Secondary Dimensional Medium: Land inside each biosphere. All of the 3,300 biospheres contain different environments and mimic different planetary conditions, many hostile to human life. The biospheres and key locations on the interior of the Dyson sphere are all interconnected by some kind of elaborate portal system which makes travel between the various spheres instantaneous. The technology that is responsible for the biosphere and this entire complex is beyond anything known to the Atlanteans, or anyone in the Three Galaxies for that matter. Trying to access and study the inner workings of the Dyson sphere needs to be done with considerable care and caution. The technology is so advanced and alien, it imposes a -60% skill penalty to applicable Electrical and Mechanical, and Science skills. Even the best minds of the Draco Amicus clan are stymied.

Dimensional Fabric: The dimension has a strong dimensional fabric imposing a -30% to dimensional teleports.

Magic Level: The level of magic energy is intermittent, similar to the Palladium and Heroes Unlimited dimensions. Ley lines and nexus points do exist and crisscross the interior of the Dyson sphere at certain locations. Some even go inside to the inner workings of the sphere. Only magic users who can see magic energy are able to see the ley lines and nexus points.

Dimensional Energy Matrix: Terra Orbis has a negative energy matrix, meaning that technology from Rifts Earth and the Three Galaxies will work just fine there.

Time Flow: Time flows at a normal rate in Terra Orbis.

Dimensional Quirks: The most notable of the dimensional quirks is that the dimension has a focal point and it is in the super gate room. Normally, the gate rooms create a portal to another sphere. This is where all dimensional travelers will arrive unless the Draco Amicus are manipulating the ley lines via the Dimensional Pyramid. The dimension also has another quirk that has been identified as the *multi-Rift phenomenon* via the gate rooms. Instead of the Rift jumping to different dimensions, it jumps to gate rooms near different biospheres within Terra Orbis. Rifting to another dimension or room is not possible from a gate room, but is possible via the Dimensional Pyramid.

Clan Equineous

Clan Equineous is one of the luckier clans because, though small when they escaped from Ancient Atlantis, they found a place to live only a few hundred years after their departure, and have not experienced any destructive events. Thus, they have lived a comparatively quiet and peaceful existence. Like most Atlanteans, at least one third of them are roaming the cosmos at any given time, but the rest are back home living the simple life.

Since the days of old, the clan has been the best at raising and training the best horses and other types of riding animals. They breed all manner of horses as well as exotic and monstrous animals that can serve as riding animals. There are some beasts of burden, but Clan Equineous prefer to raise and sell quality riding and racing animals. They have selected and returned home with beautiful, powerful and elegant creatures from across the cosmos and sell/trade them with their fellow Atlanteans as well as to numerous merchants on Phase World, around the Three Galaxies and elsewhere.

The clan is so devoted to their animals that they will not sell them to just anyone. Potential buyers are often grilled with questions to determine their experience, intentions, and ability to properly care for the creature. Essentially, the person who wants the animal is being assessed to see if he will respect it, take care of it and treat the animal well. They never sell animals for use in any sort of gladiatorial blood sport, nor to demons or beings known to be vicious and cruel. Most Equineous Atlanteans put the animal's welfare before making a sale. They are more concerned with selling the animal to a caring owner and giving it a good home.

Marks of Heritage/Clan Crest: The clan has a heart pierced by a stake on the right wrist and a flaming falchion sword on the left wrist, the hilt shaped as a horse's head.

Clan Estimated Size: 1.5 million.

Clan Status: The clan is very well known. They always show up at Atlantean gatherings often astride the most regal of riding animals, usually a Pegasus, Gryphon or other elegant or powerful creature from an alien world.

Clan's Primary Home: All of the clan, except those wandering about, is located in the dimension of Neo-Equineous.

Clan General Alignment: Primarily good.

Clan Notoriety: Famous for the quality breeding and training of horses and exotic riding animals. They also have a reputation for being very particular about whom they sell or trade their animals to.

Clan Outlook on Earth: The Equineous accepted long ago that Earth had to be left and probably for the better.

Bonuses for Clan Equineous: Any character from Clan Equineous gets the following skills, each with a +15% bonus. This is in addition to any O.C.C. or O.C.C. Related Skills. Horsemanship: Equestrian, Horsemanship: Exotic, Trick Riding, Breaking/Taming Wild Horses (-10% when applied to exotic animals), and Animal Husbandry. +2 on Perception Rolls regarding an animal's health, disposition/anxiety level, training and handling.

Neo-Equineous Dimension

The Equineous clan currently reside in the dimension of Neo-Equineous. After the disaster that struck ancient Atlantis, the Equineous clan were one of the last to leave. They stayed as long as was necessary to transport their prized stallions, herds of cattle and a host of animals. They had originally planned to take part in the Ark experiment (see 101 adventures at the end of the book), but the drawback was that they could only take 10% of their animals. Not willing to sacrifice that many animals, the clan decided as a whole to set out into the universe to find a new home. Neo-Equineous was found after an extensive search. It took a few hundred years, but it was worth it.

Neo-Equineous is a flat earth in this strange dimension, meaning that there are no planets and the infinite dimension consists of flat, floating continents in space. Each floating plate or continent has an atmosphere and weather, but a person could literately walk or ride off the edge and fall forever. The various floating continents nearest to the plate inhabited by Clan Equineous have different, hostile landscapes and conditions. A couple are frozen

like Antarctica, with glaciers, snow covered plains, and temperatures that never rise above freezing, and have a thin atmosphere. Another is a sand covered desert with a half dozen, tall, active volcanoes and a sprawling jungle in the center roughly the size of Canada, which is infested with many dangerous wild animals and giant flying insects. Another floating land mass is part stony scrub desert, like Arizona or Nevada, with a few large grassy plains. One of the largest floating continents is a mix of large grass plains and forest very reminiscent to the American Midwest on Earth, only its land mass is the equivalent of the entire surface area of the Earth. There are shallow lakes, rivers, and vast tracts of forests and even more open prairies. There are some low, rolling hills and a few mountain ranges – one that almost cuts the continent in half, and mountains along the western and eastern rim of the flat plate. This is the continental plate that the Equineous clan has made their home.

Dimension of Neo-Equineous

Type of Dimension: Infinite.
Primary Dimensional Medium: Vacuum just like outer space.
Secondary Dimensional Medium: Continent-sized, floating landmasses. Dozens of massive flat worlds float around in this dimension in orbit around a star. There are suns to provide light, except instead of planets, massive flat continents float around each sun. Some support life and others do not. They can vary just like a dimension full of planets. A neighboring continent floats overhead every 18 hours, and it becomes dark for 4-10 hours. The home continent to the Equineous clan has an 18 hour day of light and six hours of night.

Dimensional Fabric: Permeable, there is no penalty or bonus for dimensional teleporting.
Magic Level: Intermediate magic energy. Ley lines and nexus points are only visible to those who can see magic energy.
Dimensional Energy Matrix: None! Only magic and Techno-Wizard and similar systems operate in this dimension.
Time Flow: Time flows slower in this dimension. For every day spent on Neo-Equineous, two days have passed on Rifts Earth or Phase World.
Dimensional Quirks: Neo-Equineous has several dimensional quirks. First is the force of gravity. It is 20% stronger in this dimension. Also, magnetic fields are constantly in flux and changing, making devices like a compass or any instrument that requires a magnetic field useless. Many animals can sense magnetic fields and use them to navigate, but not here.

The dimension also has locations where dimensional fractures occur. Those that have been discovered, change between four other dimensions. One dimension is clearly the *Astral Plane*, another appears to be the *Plane of Mist*, another is the *Elemental Plane of Air* and the last one appears to be the *Shadow Dimension*. It is just the terrain that changes and not an actual Rifting event where people are transferred to another dimension. Each shift lasts for 1D4 hours.

Finally, there is a small ley line triangle where the Equineous have established a city with several pyramids placed along the triangle's nexus points and ley lines. Surrounding this area are hundreds of farms where different types of crops and livestock are raised.

Clan Marciniszyn

Clan Marciniszyn can trace it roots back hundreds of generations to long before the tragedy that took Atlantis away from them. The Marciniszyn clan is noted for its fierce loyalty to its fellow Atlanteans as well as for their hospitality. All Atlanteans know they can find shelter and get a hot meal from their Marciniszyn brethren. Visitors far and wide are welcomed at all Clan Marciniszyn cities, which explains why they are usually full of visiting Atlanteans and dimensional travelers. Most notable are Chiang-Ku dragons. It is a common belief that it was a member of the Marciniszyn clan who made first contact with the Chiang-Ku. As the story goes, a group of Chiang-Ku wounded from a great battle were weak, lost and on the run. An ancient clan elder named Alexii Marciniszyn befriended the wounded dragons and brought them to a Healing Pyramid and afterward welcomed them into his home, where his family treated them as their guests. When the Chiang-Ku asked how they could reward the Atlantean, he replied, "This day we have made new friends. That is enough for us." That seemed to impress the Chiang-Ku and ever since, as far as Atlanteans know, the Chiang-Ku have been steadfast allies.

The number of Chiang-Ku dragons found among the Marciniszyn clan is unparalleled, so the clan's tattoo artists have learned from the dragons and are some of the best in the Megaverse. Their tattoos are not simple images, but works of art. However, it takes twice as long for the Marciniszyn artist to create a work of tattoo artistry, and the side-effects of receiving this kind of tattoo last 50% longer. Despite the additional downtime, many Atlanteans, adventurers and travelers think it is well worth it.

Among Atlantean clans, the Marciniszyn are as well-known as the Aerihman or Archerean clans due to their artistic skills. Not just tattoo art, but all manner of artwork from paintings and drawings to sculpture and mosaics. Most Marciniszyn artists try to tell a story or depict a setting, person or emotion. They prefer realistic depictions rather than abstract works. Marciniszyn cities are filled with statuary, wall art, mosaics, and beautiful architecture. Every city has museums, libraries filled with books, especially illustrated books, as well as digital archives. Atlanteans travel far and wide to visit Marciniszyn cities and maybe get a tattoo. This has made their home dimension well known among Atlanteans.

Of late, Marciniszyn clansmen have been going missing, including six tattoo masters. Worst of all is the loss of their smallest city of Gaaree, and the 29,000 souls who once inhabited it. There were no survivors, so it took a week before it was discovered that the city had been laid to waste. The question is, how and by whom? The city, the majority of the buildings, including a handful of pyramids, homes, parks and trees, have been destroyed by some unknown means. Where the city once stood there is only a large, devastated swath of charged ruins. Naturally, the clan is very concerned and on high alert and searching for answers.

Marks of Heritage/Clan Crest: The clan has a heart pierced by a stake on the right wrist and a heavy rapier sword covered in orange flames on the left wrist.

Clan Estimated Size: 2.1 million.

Clan Status: Famous. The clan is well known among Atlanteans and travel to their home dimension is a common occurrence. They also have a presence at Alexandria and other Atlantean cities known for commerce and lively communities.

Clans Primary Home: The clan has settled in a single dimension.

Clan General Alignment: Principled (40%), Scrupulous (20%), Unprincipled (20%), Anarchist (10%).

Clan Notoriety: The clan is known for their tattoo art and their reputation as artists and humanitarians which has spread throughout many Atlantean clans.

Bonuses for Clan Marciniszyn: All clan members bear elaborate artistic tattoos in additional to magic tattoos, usually on their arms, chest, back and neck. Magic tattoos are seamlessly blended into the larger, decorative works. All Marciniszyn clan members with beautiful tattoo work get a +1 bonus to P.B. and +1 to their Horror Factor when facing their enemies. Known as warriors with the soul of an artist or poet, all Marciniszyn clansmen get the following skills, each with a +20% bonus and professional skill level. This is in addition to any O.C.C. or O.C.C. Related Skills. Art, Whittling & Sculpting, and Calligraphy or Photography.

Dimension of Goroth

The majority of Atlanteans in Clan Marciniszyn can be found in four major cities in the Dimension of Goroth. While Marciniszyn Atlanteans do explore the universe and go off adventuring and traveling, especially in their youth, of all the Atlantean clans, they are the least prone to decades of travel.

The dimension of Goroth is a forest plane with massive trees the size of skyscrapers. The Marciniszyn clan's cities are built among the trees, often up in them, creating a unique and wondrous city with ground structures as well as a network of massive tree houses. The trees are so tall and the forest so thick that there are vast highways up in the branches connecting the homes and businesses also cradled in the branches. The four big cities and another dozen small ones, like Gaaree, are scattered about the dimension, each thousands of miles apart. Travel from one to the other is best done via Dimensional Pyramids. As one might expect from the Marciniszyn artisans, the tree trunks are covered in ornate carvings, wooden statues and totem poles. To be part of the environment, most of the structures are made of wood and suspended above the ground up in the trees. Stone pyramids are always on the ground.

Type of Dimension: Parallel Dimension of three other dimensions. Goroth is parallel to Moroth, Soroth and Coroth. However, instead of trees, Moroth has naturally forming metal ore pillars and towers. Soroth has giant stone pillars, many of which are roughly hewn stone with what looks like wormholes that contain many natural openings, tunnels and caves. Finally, there is Coroth, the strangest of all. The pillars are organic and radiate life, but are not vegetation. Large blood vessels in the skin can be seen moving some kind of liquid, probably blood, from one location to another. The organic pillars are as tough as trees and can be climbed, but feel rubbery. Vine-like coils and clusters create bridges, blood vessels connect the various organic pillars. Because Coroth is so strange and different, travel there is restricted and those who visit report a constant uncomfortableness and eerie feeling (Horror Factor of 10) as if you were walking through the inside of some living creature. It is a very strange and unsettling experience, and some wonder if a place such as this is where the Eyes of Eylor grow. (Some wonder if there are Eyes of Eylor someplace in the dimension.) All other dimensional aspects are essentially the same except for the types of pillars.

Primary Dimensional Medium: None.

Secondary Dimensional Medium: Single large landmass. As far as the eye can see there are mega-sized trees. They are easily traversed via branches the size of bridges and highways. The habitable zone for Atlantean tree cities, homes and buildings is 200-1,000 feet (61-305 m) above ground. The habitable zone has normal weather, and temperatures that vary from 50 degrees Fahrenheit to 90 degrees Fahrenheit (10 to 32 C) depending on the weather, wind and time of year. There is no day or night in this dimension. Sunlight seems to emanate from above, through thick clouds that often create twilight-like conditions for 2D4 hours a few times a week, and there is considerable shade and dark areas under the thick canopy of upper tree branches. That shade and temperature difference (cooler toward the ground) creates a light fog on the ground and sometimes higher up into the trees, 1D6 times a week.

Dimensional Fabric: Weak, +10% bonus to dimensional teleports.

Magic Level: High Magic Energy. Ley lines and the occasional nexus point are found at all four of the clan's big cities and a few of the smaller ones.

Dimensional Energy Matrix: Negative.

Time Flow: Normal flow of time.

Dimensional Quirks: Oddly enough, the Element of Fire is missing from Goroth and in the other corresponding parallel dimensions, a single element is also missing. Moroth is missing water, Soroth is missing air, and Coroth is missing earth. Also, despite the numerous ley lines, there are four dimensional focal points on each world. These are massive Rifts each connected to 1D6+4 ley lines. Visitors who arrive via Rift are going to appear at one of these focal points unless they use a pyramid or Dimensional Teleport and know where they are going. Each of the four dimensions is linked to the others so most of the random Rifts cycle between these four dimensions.

Clan Navita

Clan Navita is most noted for their expertise in and with the Ocean. In the early days of Atlantis, the Navita coast along the southern part of the continent had tens of thousands of Atlanteans. One of the larger settlements, Navita, was a major seaport. The Atlanteans had a limited knowledge of the ocean and how to create large seafaring ships. They used magic as their primary method of travel to other continents. Among the seafaring Atlanteans, the Navita clan was the most skilled and daring. In fact, it was the sailors of Navita who first encountered the Lemurians. On that fateful day, a peaceful dialog was established and the two nations became friends, trade partners and allies. The people of Atlantis went so far as to build a large stone receptacle in the ocean to receive any of the Lemurian floating cities. Plans were in progress to building several more, but that would never happen as the initial stone dock was only completed a few years before the Janus Experiment and crisis that would make Atlantis vanish. It was fortunate the Lemurians were away at the time of the experiment or one of their cities would have no doubt been caught in

the dimensional turmoil created by the disaster and swept away with Atlantis.

Of all the Atlantean clans, none were closer to their Lemurian friends and allies. It was the Lemurians who taught the Atlanteans the ways of the ocean and showed them better ways to fish, sail and build ocean vessels. And most importantly how to respect the seas. The clan often worked hand in hand on creating watercraft for undersea exploration and exploring the ocean at large. While all Atlanteans loved travel and exploration, it was the Navita who held a passion for the ocean and sailing.

When the dimensional anomaly struck, the coastal communities were the first and hardest hit. The cities and fishing villages of Clan Navita were devastated by tidal waves and earthquakes. Hundreds of thousands perished. Unlike other Atlanteans, the members of Clan Navita knew exactly where they would relocate to survive. For years their clan had been visiting the water dimension they and the Lemurians called Oceania. It would become their new home.

Marks of Heritage/Clan Crest: The clan has a heart pierced by a stake on the right wrist and a cutlass sword radiating green flames on the left wrist; on the hilt, a dolphin.

Clan Estimated Size: 400,000

Clan Status: Known. The Navita have always tried to remain in contact with the other clans. An ambassador attends all clan meetings and the cities of Alexandria and Argos are frequent visits.

Clan's Primary Home: The entire clan lives in a single dimension called Oceania.

Clan General Alignment: Primarily good, but can be any.

Clan Notoriety: The clan is most noted for their study and expertise of the ocean. Several members are dedicated oceanographers and Ocean Wizards. The Navita are also known as the clan to first contact the Lemurians and to make an alliance with them. Today, thousands of years later, the Lemurians are remembered fondly and all Navita children are told of the Lemurians. Should the clan learn that Lemurians still exist, they would make an effort to try and reestablish contact with them.

Clan Outlook on Earth: The Navita accepted leaving Earth a long time ago and are content with living in Oceania and exploring the Megaverse. They have no love for the Splugorth, but see no reason to try to take Atlantis from them. Let sleeping dogs lie.

Bonuses for Clan Navita: All Navita clansmen get the following skills, each with a +15% bonus and professional skill level. This is in addition to any O.C.C. or O.C.C. Related Skills. Swimming, Boat Building, Sailing, and SCUBA or Water Skiing & Surfing. They also know about Lemurians and are likely to recognize one from stories and artwork even if they never met one before.

Navita's Dimension of Oceania

During the early days of dimensional exploration, Oceania was discovered. When the Navita found a dimension that was an infinite ocean, members of their clan along with some Lemurian allies were compelled to explore it. Early on in their history, Clan Navita had established a dozen smaller outposts complete with a number of stone pyramids. If it were not for the Atlantean colonies in this dimension, the Navita clan might have been wiped from existence when Atlantis vanished. The Navita clan shared their discovery with their fellow Atlanteans, but only they and the Lemurians found the water dimension the most inviting.

The dimension is as strange as they come. First, it is an endless ocean. The ocean is similar in composition to Earth's oceans, but a bit more on the salty and acidic side with a hodgepodge of additional chemicals mixed in. The water is not drinkable, but it does support an abundance of life and the Atlanteans (and Lemurians) use magic to purify and make the seawater safe to consume. Like Atlantis, there are a handful of small, forested, island continents and island chains where landlubbers can pitch camp. It is at these locations that the Navita established a few colonies. The Lemurians had also established a few colonies, but the elements and chemical composition of the water did not agree with them, and they abandoned their colony on Oceania long before disaster trapped them in a different ocean-limbo dimension.

There are all kinds of fish and sea life in the waters, including amphibians, reptiles, crocodile-like creatures, and aquatic dinosaurs on some of the small landmasses. The waters of Oceania also contain a host of deadly creatures such as the Armored Devil Fish (**Rifts World Book 3, England**), Trelque-huecuve (Monster Squid), Huecu – Demonic Manta Ray (**Rifts World Book 6: South America**) and all the creatures found in **Rifts World Book Seven: Rifts Underseas**, minus the Naut'Yll humanoids. Something the Navita have also discovered, and have so far been able to avoid, is two Splugorth Intelligences and their minions. There are two young Splugorth kingdoms, but both are several hundred thousand miles away, elsewhere in the dimension. The Navita have remained undiscovered as the two Splugorth are at war with each other, so their efforts and attentions are focused on each other for the time. The Navita are careful to keep their presence hidden from the Splugorth and their minions, and keep a watchful eye from a distance.

The main population center for the clan is a city called Navita Atoll, but over the years it has often been shortened to Navitoll. Navitoll is a natural atoll in Oceania. The main portion of the island is shaped like a large crescent moon and this is where the main Dimensional Pyramid, other pyramids and surrounding homes are built. The lagoon has been turned into a very large ship port and shipyards. Of late the Navita have been experimenting with stone ship hulls. They have heard rumors that stone ships exist in another dimension and they have sent envoys out to try and trade for the secrets.

Dimension of Oceania

Type of Dimension: Infinite.

Primary Dimensional Medium: Water, essentially the dimension is an infinite ocean.

Secondary Dimensional Medium: Air and islands make up the rest of the dimension. There are as many islands as there are stars in the sky. The islands vary in size, but rarely exceed the size of Hawaii.

Dimensional Fabric: Permeable, there is no bonus or penalty for dimensional teleportation.

Magic Level: High magic energy! Ley lines are visible as are nexus points.

Dimensional Energy Matrix: Positive energy matrix, so technology from the Three Galaxies and Rifts Earth will not function in Oceania. The Navita have come to rely heavily on Techno-Wizardry.

Time Flow: Time flows slower. Every day spent in Oceania means two days have passed on Rifts Earth.

Dimensional Quirks: The dimensional quirks found in Oceania seem to be tied to several of the strange anomalies found in Rifts Underseas. Shimmering Water, Dead Pools and Ley Line Storms, both above and below the sea, happen in Oceania. See **Rifts® World Book 7: Rifts® Underseas** for these anomalies and a variety of ideas for having an oceanbound game.

Clan Skellian

The majority of Clan Skellian currently calls the *city of Manoa,* located in the heart of South America on Rifts Earth, their home. During the collapse of Atlantis, most of clan Skellian left for other dimensions and worlds, but a small group stayed behind and made a new home in South America. There they erected a beautiful city with golden spires and stone pyramids that captured the fading magic energy to help maintain the Atlantean lifestyle, and enable them to maintain communications with their brothers and sisters in other dimensions. In short order, they made quick allies with a tribe of female warriors with superhuman abilities and dubbed them *Amazons.* They also befriended two monstrous looking but intelligent and peace-loving group of D-Bees, one the psychic *Shaydor Spherians,* and the other called *Ewaipanomas.* Unfortunately, the Ewaipanomas look so gruesome and demonic that most primitive humans attacked them on sight, assuming they were demons. It was not until the survivors of Clan Skellian found them and gave them refuge in their city of gold that the Ewaipanomas found a home on Earth. It is ironic that Clan Skellian proved to be the salvation of the Ewaipanomas, because it was the dimensional catastrophe caused with the disappearance of Atlantis that had yanked a few thousand Ewaipanomas from their native dimension and displaced them on Earth. The Skellians have searched for eons to find the aliens' home dimension without success, but have embraced them as honorary members of their clan.

This branch of the Skellian clan might have remained on Earth till modern times except for two reasons: the continued waning of magic energy and two visions of destruction. Magic energy was becoming nearly nonexistent on Earth. Not even Clan Skellian's network of stone pyramids along ley lines could stop it, and their City of Manoa was beginning to literally crumble down around them. Just as frightening were the premonitions of the Skellian psychics whose visions were confirmed by another alien refugee the clan had taken in. An alien species whose psychic abilities were greater than the Skellians'. Both *Shaydor Spherians* and Skellian psychics foresaw the coming of the Spaniard invaders and the death and destruction they would bring to the people of South America. As bad as this was, they also foresaw the *Great Cataclysm.* A disaster that would wipe out most of human civilization and reshape the planet. The Skellian clan of Manoa debated long and hard about their next course of action. They wanted to stay and try to change the course of the future. Many hoped that if they stayed, they could mitigate the death and damage the European invaders would cause and perhaps find a way to prevent the Great Cataclysm. It was their Spherian allies who convinced them this was pure folly.

The Shaydor Spherians assured them that in their vast experience, only small things could be changed when premonitions of sweeping events were revealed. They insisted the future for individuals and groups was not yet set in stone, but that the larger, more severe future event could not, in their experience, be stopped or significantly altered. The Conquistadors would come and conquer, just as the Great Cataclysm would happen and reshape the planet. It was Spherian belief that these life-altering events were already set in motion, which is how they could glimpse future events, and were meant to be. To try to stop or change them would be wrong even if it were possible, which it was not. However, they consoled, they were shown these visions of the future for a reason. They surmised it was so that they might survive for a purpose not yet clear to any of them. That their survival was one of the small things that could be changed.

The Skellian Council of Elders in Manoa felt they had a couple of options for their people's survival. They still had enough magic held in reserve for them to travel to other dimensions or worlds like many Atlantean clans before them. However, they and their Amazonian and Ewaipanomas felt their destiny remained somehow tied to the Earth. So it was the Skellians of Earth who decided to use all of their remaining magic energy to carry their entire city and population into a limbo dimension. The only thing connecting them to Earth being a few of the stone pyramids they were leaving behind. They theorized that if magic energy returned to Earth on the level they were seeing in their visions, it would be enough to reach them via the pyramids and return them to Earth when magic was back and after the worst of the destruction had passed.

The Spherians and Atlantean psychics could not say with certainty whether or not this was the right course of action, but the consensus was that it felt right. Those who wanted to stay behind could do so. And some did. The rest, city and all, vanished from Earth into a dimensional limbo. Those who stayed on Earth perished at the hands of the European invaders and the existence of the Skellians and their city of gold, the Amazons and Spherians became the stuff of myth and legend.

For five hundred years the members of Clan Skellian and their allies would wait in self-imposed exile inside that limbo dimension. They carried on as best they could and waited, but wondered if they had made the right choice. Some began to fear they would never see Earth again and would be lost forever inside the limbo dimension. The premonitions of the Spanish invaders and the Great Cataclysm had both seemed imminent and close together in time. Such is the unpredictable nature of psychic premonitions. The coming of the Spanish invaders happened a short decade after the city of Manoa vanished into limbo, but five centuries would pass before the Great Cataclysm and the Coming of the Rifts.

One day, life changed for the people of the city of Manoa when, quite literally in a flash of light, they found themselves back on Earth. Returned to the fertile Amazon valley in South America exactly where they had left centuries earlier The reappearance occurred during one of the early decades of the apocalypse. This was not the world as they remembered it. Earth had been thrown into chaos. The level of magic energy was off the charts and beyond anything the Skellians had ever imagined. Space and time was torn asunder at ley line nexus points and all manner of things came through dimensional Rifts that opened and closed on their own. Rifts Earth was still in the throes of transformation by unchecked magic and dimensional forces. The Skellian Atlanteans would face one challenge after another, and be forced to battle through the Two Hundred Years Dark Age. Tens of thousands of lives were lost, but through their combined resources and sheer force of will, they managed to come through it. In the process, they and their Amazon and Ewaipanomas allies created new legends about valiant heroes, warrior women and headless monsters who together, have carved out a kingdom in the Amazon jungles.

It has only been in the last hundred or so years that the Skellians of Earth have begun to try to reestablish contact with their fellow Atlanteans. This includes finding members of their own clan who had gone off to explore the Megaverse when the City of Manoa was whisked to the limbo dimension. They want them to know they have a home on Rifts Earth, and that all are welcomed. Today, the Skellians' City of Manoa is thought to be the largest settlement of Atlanteans on Rifts Earth. To the surprise of many other Atlantean clans, the city is intermixed with a few other species who are considered equal citizens and honorary brothers and sisters to the Skellian clansmen of Manoa. *The Ewaipanomas* and *Shaydor Spherians* (see **Rifts® World Book 6, South America** and **Rifts® World Book 2: Atlantis**, respectively) are the two D-Bee races, as well as the genetically augmented human females known as *Amazons* who also reside with the Skellian clan.

This is a contradiction that some Atlantean clans find odd. While many live on worlds with other people and champion the rights of all people, they do not typically live together in Atlantean cities as they do in Manoa. Moreover, Atlanteans tend to be arrogant in their assumption that they are older, wiser and superior to "Earthlings" and many other people and civilizations. This view is not shared by most of Clan Skellian. For thousands of years they have lived, fought and bled together with their alien allies, and see them as their equals without disparity. This has also made them very accepting of other races and they treat most everyone as equals unless proven unworthy. This strange attitude has branded the Skellian clan as a group of radicals or rogues who have "gone native" and are themselves, less civilized than other Atlantean clans. The Aerihman are adamant in this opinion, and many other clans agree. This means most Atlanteans don't see eye to eye with Clan Skellian. The fact that the clan has spent most of its existence on Earth has also created a sense of cultural guilt carried by most Atlanteans for having abandoned their home world and Clan Skellian for more than 10,000 years! This makes other Atlanteans feel guilty and uncomfortable around them and all too keenly aware of their cultural differences. Citing Skellians as different, rougher around the edges and a bit too crude and outspoken for their taste. This doesn't mean that Clan Skellian is any less heroic or noble. Some would argue it makes them more heroic and closest to their ancestral roots than any other Atlantean clan. It is ironic, but the members of Clan Skellian hold no resentment toward their fellow Atlanteans and welcome them as equals and family who have been apart for too long.

The only reason Clan Aerihman is making diplomatic gestures to the Skellians is because the clan would also like to reclaim Atlantis from the clutches of the Minions of Splugorth. The Aerihman also think they could use the City of Manoa as the base of operations for an Atlantean siege on Atlantis. The Skellians and their allies may be less "civilized" and technologically advanced than the Aerihman, but they are far from stupid and realize this. They will not let themselves be manipulated or used as pawns in another clan's scheme.

Moreover, they are not going to jeopardize everything they have fought so hard to preserve and build. The Skellians would like to reclaim their ancestral homeland of Atlantis for all Atlanteans and are willing to join that fight, but only if it makes sense and only after they have insured the security of Manoa. There are several hostile cities and groups around Manoa, and if not dealt with first, they could prove to be problematic for the long term survival of Manoa and its people.

South America, like the rest of the planet, has become home to numerous D-Bees, monsters, and evil supernatural creatures that threaten all peace-loving beings. The Skellians have developed a new form of tattoo magic called Monster Shaping Tattoos that enable Atlanteans to magically disguise themselves as other beings. Clan Skellian has not informed other clans of this new form of Tattoo Magic and may not do so for some time. Spies and intruders have already been detected in Manoa and there was an incident where a prominent Skellian Tattoo Master was almost kidnapped by one of the Splugorth minions known as the Sunaj. Clan Skellian was fortunate to prevent the kidnaping, but the Sunaj got away before more could be learned about them and their plot. Clan Skellian suspects that it is the Splugorth who are after the Monster Shaping Tattoo Magic. They do not suspect the Sunaj are really agents of the rogue Aerihman Illuminati.

Marks of Heritage/Clan Crest: Skellian clansmen have the heart impaled by a stake on the right wrist and a large flaming sword with a serrated blade near the hilt on the left wrist.

Clan Estimated Size: There are 58,000 Skellians who are permanent residents in Manoa, another 32,000 Skellians live in small villages and homesteads scattered around the city and elsewhere in the Amazon. An additional 19,500 Skellians are on missions across South, Central and North America, with the majority of those operating in and around the Vampire Kingdoms which they seek to undermine and destroy. Some of them have befriended Anti-Monsters, Lemurians, Shemarrians, humans, Cyber-Knights, and, of course, Reid's Rangers. Another 5,000 Skellian warriors and Nomads are exploring and scouting Africa where they help those in need like they do in the Americas, and work to ascertain the level of danger from supernatural creatures in that part of the world. They also hope to find allies in Africa to oppose the Splugorth of Atlantis and establish secret Atlantean bases of operation for future campaigns against the invaders of Atlantis. Another few hundred are scattered across the globe and 4,000 wander the Megaverse with the intention of making contact with other clans and securing resources and allies for a possible campaign against the Minions of Splugorth in Atlantis.

In addition, there are an estimated 6,000-8,000 Skellians who have become dimensional wanderers and have not been back to Earth in a few generations.

Because the Atlanteans of Clan Skellian embrace non-Atlanteans as members of their tribe, it is important to list the others who live in and around Manoa and who consider themselves members of Clan Skellian. Circa 110 P.A.

   520,000 Humans
   460,000 Amazons
   410,000 Ewaipanomas
   311,000 Shaydor Spherians
   145,000 Lizard Men (refugees from Lagarto)
       212 Dragons (various)
       117 Chiang-Ku dragons, specifically.

Clan Status: Known. The clan was effectively hidden for thousands of years, as most Atlanteans lost contact with the clan after they abandoned Earth. The fate of the Skellians unknown. However, Skellians were always known by the other clans as the one that stayed behind. And now the clan is reaching out to the others and there is talk among the clans.

Clan's Primary Home: The clan's primary settlement/home is Manoa in the Amazon jungle on Rifts Earth, but they are spread all over the globe and beyond, as described above.

Clan General Alignment: Mostly Principled (33%) and Scrupulous (50%).

Clan Outlook on Earth: They see Earth as their one and only home, but they also acknowledge and accept that it is completely transformed and still changing. They recognize that the planet is no longer home just to humans and that it is a transdimensional hub with a grandiose future that is not yet known. They hate the Splugorth and their Minions and would love to, one day, drive them off the planet and reclaim Atlantis for themselves. However, they also realize that may not be possible. Most Skellians are respectful of other Atlanteans, though they do not always agree with them. Skellians are strong-willed, courageous, independent and accepting of others. That said, there are hostile nations, mutants and D-Bees in South America that are becoming dangerous threats that may need to be dealt with harshly.

Bonuses for Clan Skellian: Members of Clan Skellian have exclusive access to the Monster Hunter O.C.C. and Monster Tattoos, but can be any Atlantean or Rifts Earth O.C.C. All Skellian clansmen get the following skills, each with a +20% bonus. This is in addition to any O.C.C. or O.C.C. Related Skills. Land Navigation, Tracking (people), Track Animals, and Lore D-Bees. They are also +2 on Perception Rolls involving demons and monsters.

Clan Skolos

Clan Skolos lived in the valleys of the mountain region of Ancient Atlantis. During the Atlantean golden age, some of the mountains in Atlantis were among the tallest in the world so Clan Skolos was used to difficult living conditions. The Janus Experiment caused Clan Skolos's home in the mountain valleys to phase and shift out of the Earth dimension. The clan unexpectedly found itself in an alien land on another world. A barren wasteland filled with massive glaciers and arctic weather. There were no apparent ley lines or nexus points to open Rifts and the dimension was all but impenetrable to the few Shifters in the clan. They were trapped and didn't know where. It took the clan a year before it located land away from the glaciers. While Stone Masters worked tirelessly to build shelters, people were dying by the handful each day due to the harsh conditions and freezing weather. Food and what little resources the clan was able to salvage from their transported city were stretched to the limit. Scouts were sent to find a less harsh environment, and a source of food or a ley line, but each expedition that returned (many did not) had no success. In the meantime, the few clan elders left set about with a bold plan, the creation of a bio-dome. If they were to survive in this frozen wasteland they had to stretch their skills to the limit. The first effort was to create a stone wall which would be the foundation. The second would be the glass enclosure.

Stone formed a latticework while chunks of quartz were shaped and made into thin, glass-like panels by Crystal Mages and Stone Masters. Scouts and warriors figured out which alien beasts were edible and spent long days hunting to provide enough food for everyone. With no magic ley lines available, it took more than five years to complete. In that time, half the population succumbed to the environment.

Today, the city of Paradise Eve is a testament to the resilience of Clan Skolos. The city is under a massive stone and quartz dome. The dome is over a thousand feet (305 m) high and the city covers a 5 mile (8 km) area. There are a dozen pillars that support the dome and many function as living places, like high-rises. Stairs and switchbacks circle around each massive pillar, some of them connected with stone bridges or catwalks. The only noticeable thing lacking in Paradise Eve are stone pyramids. There is no ley line in the city and so there was no practical reason to build a pyramid.

Paradise Eve is home to 112,000 Atlanteans. Each family has a modest home. Between the dome and various magical enchantments, the average temperature is 72 degrees Fahrenheit (22 C). The section of land that Paradise Eve is built on very fertile soil, making growing crops as easy as it was at home. The clan also discovered animals they could domesticate and eat. One such beast is the Shaggy Bison. Picture a buffalo the size of a wooly mammoth with just as much fur. It seems Paradise Eve was built on one of their feeding grounds. Fortunately, there was plenty of ground left around Paradise Eve, plus the creatures seemed to like the heat that the structure gives off. Large pens were constructed around the city and today the creatures are raised and used in a variety of capacities. Primarily they are a source of food, but they are also used as riding animals and can easily trek between Paradise Eve and the second city built by the Skolos, Salvation.

Compared to most Atlantean cities, Paradise Eve and Salvation are Spartan and primitive, and lack running water, electrical power and other amenities. The clan learned after discovering the Shaggy Bison that their blubber can be converted into useable oil. This oil warms the houses and lights the homes and streets. The Skolos have learned how to get the most out of the oil without having to needlessly slaughter thousands of Shaggy Bison.

The second city of Clan Skolos is Salvation, so named because it is built upon the nexus point of two faint ley lines. Located under a glacier, it took years to get to the Rift using a variety of magic and conventional means. Finally, when enough ice was removed from around the nexus point, a Dimensional Stone Pyramid was erected. From start to finish of a functioning Dimensional Pyramid, 46 years had passed. Now with a way off the frozen world, scouts came back with the shocking news that Atlantis was gone – just gone – and Earth was devoid of magic energy. Going home was a poor option. Many Skolos elected to leave the ice world to live among other people and scattered across the Megaverse. But half of the survivors made a startling decision. Now with access to other worlds, magic and resources, they would make their home on the ice world. Too many Skolos clansmen had died on the ice. This world had been christened in Atlantean blood, making it theirs now.

Today the glaciers still loom over the two cities, but there is no danger from them. The Skolos clan has built two modern cities enclosed in temperature controlled biospheres. Each with all the amenities you would expect, including sprawling parks, gardens, works of art and stone pyramids. The original settlement has been renamed *Paradise Eve* and a tunnel through the ice connects it with Salvation via bullet trains. This is a huge endeavor as the two cities are roughly 500 miles (800 km) apart. A maze of ice tunnels through the glaciers and under both cities provide hiding places and escape routes in case of attack. Life is good, and over the millennia there have been no enemy incursions. In part, because the location of the ice world is so secret that even Atlanteans from other clans do not know where it is located. Moreover, the planet's inhospitable environment is a deterrent in and of itself.

Marks of Heritage: The standard heart with a stake on the right wrist and a bastard sword seemingly made of ice radiating light blue flames on the left. Almost all add the Ice Dragon's Head Breathing Ice (Impervious to Cold) directly below or next to the sword as their next magic tattoo.

Clan Estimated Size: 76,000 Skolos live in Paradise Eve and 88,000 live at Salvation, and 2,000 live as primitive hunters on the surface in ice villages. An estimated 160,000 are scattered throughout the Megaverse in small groups and family units. Some of whom have become victims of the Sunaj and mysterious disappearances.

Clan Status: Hidden and relatively unknown. They have only in the last 20 years begun participating in the annual clan meeting on Alexandria. This is due to their isolation and being widely dispersed, and the time difference between the Skolos ice planet and the Three Galaxies.

Clan's Primary Home: A single dimension.

Clan General Alignment: Predominantly good and Anarchist, but can be any.

Clan Notoriety: The clan is notable for having one of the largest groups of Crystal Mages among all known Atlantean Clans. It was the Crystal Mages that helped fashion the quartz used in the dome of Paradise Eve.

Bonuses for Clan Skolos: Characters from Clan Skolos automatically know Hunting and Wilderness Survival with an emphasis on winter survival techniques, with a +20% bonus. This is in addition to any O.C.C. Related Skills and bonuses. Also, any member of Clan Skolos who has psionic abilities automatically has *Resist Cold* as an extra ability.

The Skolos Ice World

The Skolos Ice World is mostly a frozen rock with ice and snow covered mountains and glaciers as tall as mountains. The land is broken up with small and larger expansions of tundra covered in tough grass and scrub. The vegetation is brown or grey most of the time, but blossoms into a sea of green and color during its month of spring and 70-80 days of summer.

Type of Dimension: Infinite Dimension.

Primary Dimensional Medium: Combination Space/vacuum and gaseous. Where solar systems would be are instead large pockets of gas, essentially massive nebulas that can be light years across.

Secondary Dimensional Medium: Planets. Contained within the various gaseous sections are planets. The gases illuminate the planets and provide a marginal amount of heat and light. Each gaseous area also has a sun at the center, but the planets do not necessarily rotate around the sun. Most are stationary, mired in a section of the gas. Skolos, for the most part, experiences an eternal ice age. The sky is constantly dark with storm clouds. When the clouds do clear, no stars can be seen, just an eerie black and blue glow of the surrounding gases.

Dimensional Fabric: Impenetrable! Each planet has 1-4 nexus points where a Rift can form. Finding one can be very difficult.

Magic Level: Intermediate. Magic energy is not very high. Ley lines and nexus points are only visible to those who can see magic energy like Ley Line Walkers, Nomads and Voyagers. Ley lines are all but nonexistent, with only a dozen at most, found on a single planet.

Dimensional Energy Matrix: Negative.

Time Flow: Times flows slower. There is a 1 to 2 ratio for the movement of time. For every one day that passes in Skolos, two days pass on Rifts Earth and in the Three Galaxies.

Dimensional Quirks: No Aerodynamics and Multi-Rift. Conventional flight via jet or propeller where wings are required for lift is all but impossible. Magic flight and flight with a contragravity device can be achieved. Creatures of magic like dragons and supernatural beings can fly, but ordinary creatures like birds are essentially grounded.

The few Rifts that form in the dimension are multi-Rifts. Meaning that they constantly fluctuate between dimensions and worlds. There is no pattern or rhyme or reason to it. The Rifts jump between four dimensions, once each minute, so at most, a group would have four melee rounds (60 seconds) to try and jump through a Rift and all land in the same place. Fortunately, the Rift at Salvation is under the control of a Dimensional Pyramid.

Clan Tsitas

The Lost Clan

Clan Tsitas was once a well-known clan from an area that corresponds to where the current-day city of Splynn now rests. Prior to the Janus Experiment the clan was well known for their dimensional brokering services. They had numerous contacts throughout the Megaverse with whom they did business. Mostly it was in the exchange of knowledge and the trading of technology.

When disaster struck, it is generally assumed that most of the clan escaped and were able to survive among one of their many trading partners. This was indeed the case, and the clan thrived for many generations, but then vanished.

Just before clan's disappearance, they had made contact with the Archerean clan on Alexandria and were excited to know that other clans had survived. However, the Tsitas clan was in transition and promised to send a group of representatives as soon as they got settled. Then they vanished.

What few people know is that when the clan learned of Rifts Earth and the return of Atlantis, its people had found renewed purpose. They put out a call for all their people to unite and gather for an epic return to Earth – Rifts Earth. When they learned about the Vampire Kingdoms, they decided it was their destiny to purge the vampires from Rifts Earth or die trying. Approximately 40% of their clan were Undead Slayers, 10% Tattooed Defenders, and 10% practitioners of magic. If successful, they would declare the Vampire Kingdoms the new home for all Atlanteans, and the staging ground for a military campaign against the Minions of Splugorth on Atlantis.

The last word received from the clan was that they were planning to establish a beachhead somewhere in Mexico or New Mexico. (The reports on this communique are unclear on this matter.) That was in 72 PA. Not a single word has been heard from them since. More than 200,000 Atlanteans missing.

What happened to the clan is anyone's guess. Conjecture and every manner of theory and crazy rumor has been offered. The bottom line is the Atlanteans vanished and the vampires remain. There are no report or evidence of any sort of a military campaign leveled against the monsters, making the clan's disappearance all the more inexplicable. The only possible link to the clan's whereabouts or fate could be in *Arzno*. In 73 P.A., three dozen children were found wandering along the Rio Grande River. Most were youngsters, ages 4-9. All were traumatized with no recollection of how they got there or where their parents might be. A few of the oldest claimed they were Atlanteans come home to Earth to liberate the innocent from vampires and demons. Today, most still live in Arzno and the surrounding area. Most have two tattoos, one on each arm. Could these children (adults today) be the key to finding out what happened to Clan Tsitas?

Any young children who survived remember very little if anything about life as an Atlantean. The people who found and raised them have little to add. Young clan members who grew up in Arzno have connections there, but they know little to nothing about their Atlantean heritage. There may be clues among these now adults and other places along the Mexican border, but this is no easy investigation.

Marks of Heritage/Clan Crest: On the right wrist is a heart impaled by a stake and on the left wrist is a flaming bastard sword with four arrows forming a cross over the sword near the hilt.

Clan Estimated Size: At last count when the clan leaders visited Alexandria over 50 years ago, they reported that they were 220,000 strong. Today there are believed to be fewer than 6,000 – all of them Tsitas who were off adventuring on other worlds and dimensions when their clan vanished.

Clan Status: Unknown. The last clan member was seen about 50 years ago in Alexandria. Communications were last made in 72 P.A. Since then, no Atlantean has heard anything from this clan, not even any survivors.

Clan's Primary Home: A single dimension. The entire clan is believed to have resettled on Rifts Earth somewhere in the New West close to the vampire border or somewhere in Mexico.

Clan General Alignment: Most common alignments were Principled (10%), Scrupulous (20%), Unprincipled (30%), and 35% Anarchist.

Clan Notoriety: Other than the fact most of the clan has gone missing, they were also known as being uncharacteristically selfish and opportunistic as well as glory hounds and show boaters.

Clan Outlook on Earth: Regret. The clan decided to come back to Earth after many years of regretting the decision to leave. Unfortunately, they may have paid the ultimate price for that decision.

Bonuses for Clan Tsitas: Of the few thousand Tsitas Atlanteans who were not part of the Great Campaign, they live with regret and are haunted by the disappearance of their clansmen returning to Earth. Many are driven to find out what happened to their kinsmen and wonder if they are trapped or imprisoned somewhere by vampires or Splugorth. A number have come to Earth trying to find clues to what happened but have come up empty. Others have followed other avenues of investigation elsewhere in the Megaverse without success. The children are happy and don't remember their past, so they have been left with their adopted parents. From time to time, a few, now adults, have gone off with the occasional Tsitas Atlantean they believed to be a family member to rediscover their heritage.

All surviving Tsitas get the skills Lore: Demons and Monsters and Tracking with a +20% bonus. Many have rededicated themselves to hunting and destroying vampires and monsters.

True Atlanteans

The Atlantean R.C.C., Revisited

Physically, True Atlanteans might be considered supermen. Through science, medicine/genetic manipulation and magic, they have slowed the aging process to such a degree that the average Atlantean lives to be 500-600 years old. They are physically stronger (Augmented P.S.) and larger (6-7 feet/1.8 to 2.1 m) than humans, exhibit high intelligence, resistance to disease, and are adept in the ways of magic and dimensional travel. The Tattooed Men who hunt the undead and monsters possess Mega-Damage bodies. Most Atlanteans are so accustomed to dimensional travel and alien civilizations that they seldom suffer culture shock or psychological disorders, proving themselves well-suited for their chosen role as protectors of the Megaverse. In many cases, because of distortions in space and time caused by dimensional travel, stasis fields, and magic, an Atlantean adventurer may skip entire decades, skipping through time and passing through the ages without participating in them. The passage of a few physical years for such a dimensional traveler may be several hundred or even thousands of years for those left behind in a different time continuum on a particular world. Thus, Atlantean dimensional travelers out of sync with time and history, may be mistaken to be thousands of years old or even immortal, when the truth is they have lived a fraction of those years. Time is relative to the dimensional traveler.

Before the disappearance of Atlantis, the Atlantean people were the most advanced on Earth. Their civilization predates Stonehenge by at least 8,000 years, perhaps twice that. According to some, it was the descendants of survivors of ancient Atlantis who may have built Stonehenge and taught the Egyptians the secrets of pyramid building. Atlanteans displaced in time may have also appeared millennia later to teach the Maya the secrets of stone pyramid construction (and magic?), and might explain Earth legends of pale skinned men, prophets and gods appearing in South America, Japan and other distant lands.

The Atlantean civilization on ancient Earth had a long list of accomplishments. They had advanced in the ways of magic, medicine, architecture and engineering, as well as art, philosophy and literature. Even their science was advanced for the time, though it was not science as humans today know it. Atlanteans used magic in ways that incorporated scientific understanding and principles, so the two where tightly woven together.

True Atlanteans had always been a people who thirsted for knowledge and understanding of the universe and all things in it, including themselves. A trait that continues to this day.

Then and now, most Atlanteans care very little about physical possessions or the acquisition of wealth and power. Instead they value experiences, knowledge and interpersonal relationships. This is evident in their strong sense of family and clan unity, and their empathy with other life forms even when they are quite alien. Atlanteans search for enlightenment and a greater purpose. This compels them to strive to be the best they can be and makes them attuned to the needs of others. The thought of doing harm to others, whether it is for personal gain or ulterior motives, is alien and abhorrent to these people. As a result, criminal behavior and violence against their fellow Atlanteans has always been a rarity. Competition, both physical and academic, is almost always in the form of friendly rivalries with Atlanteans exhibiting respect and good sportsmanship toward those who may best them. This is not to say no Atlanteans are ever selfish or evil, because some most definitely are, but as a people and a culture, they strive to be better than that.

The catastrophic loss of Atlantis and how it affected not just their own people but many others, and how it reshaped the face of the planet, has taught Atlanteans to try to preserve, nurture and find harmony with the natural environment they inhabit.

This is why many people across the Megaverse consider Atlanteans to be a noble and heroic people. Many count them among the legendary Champions of Light, a classification of heroes dedicated to protecting all life and battling supernatural evil.

This different way of looking at life, progress and achievement conflicts with many other civilizations, including many human and D-Bee cultures. Which has made Atlanteans both heroes and outcasts. Their high ideals and constant search to better themselves lead some to be envious and others to assume Atlanteans think they are better than anyone else. This is seldom the case, though the confident, outspoken and virtuous nature of Atlanteans can be easily misinterpreted as such by those who are insecure and less virtuous. Atlanteans also have a reputation for being preachy, impudent and arrogant.

Their unique views and sense of history that have shaped their culture and attitudes can make Atlanteans seem to be arrogant know-it-alls who think they are superior to others. To make matters worse, many among the Aerihman, the largest and most influential of the Atlantean clans, do indeed believe they and all Atlanteans *are superior*. They also believe it is time they acknowledge and embrace this simple truth and take their rightful place as the benevolent rulers and demigods of lesser beings like humans. In many ways Atlanteans *are* superior to their human ancestors. A fact that makes some people uneasy. The backlash from all of this has created animosity and resentment leveled at Atlanteans among certain individuals, groups and people. In short, True Atlanteans have their share of enemies. Not just the undead and demonic beings they have sworn to destroy, but those who are envious of them as well as various criminals, despot rulers and business people who have seen the heroes' ideals and interference in their affairs threaten their criminal empires, tyrannical regimes or exploitive business operations. Awareness of these enemies has made the noble heroes secretive and very protective of their fellow Atlanteans.

As a general rule of thumb, Atlanteans are intelligent, usually see the larger picture, and think before they take action, espe-

cially actions that may have consequences for others. It is rare to encounter even a young Atlantean who does not stop and think to weigh his options and possible outcomes before taking action. It is unusual to find a True Atlantean behaving in a rash or immature manner. Nor are they rattled or perplexed when others do not see their point of view.

Most Atlanteans have a strong moral compass. They are compassionate, empathetic, open and sincere, but have strong convictions, speak their minds, say what they mean and do not hide behind words or political correctness. Most are up-front, direct and truthful, with what some would consider too little tact, but that is how Atlanteans are. If they believe someone is acting like an irrational idiot, or about to make a mistake, they come out and say so, or try to intercede. This sincerity and outspokenness contributes to the belief held by some that True Atlanteans are arrogant, when from the Atlantean's point of view, they are trying to do what is best or right. As Atlanteans get older some develop a much better sense of tact and diplomacy, but many never change.

One of the True Atlanteans' greatest convictions is that life is sacred and should be lived to the best of your ability. They believe every person has the potential for greatness if nourished properly and given the chance. After their own Atlantean people, they value their human ancestors most, but accept all sentient beings as their equals and as having value and purpose in the cosmic scheme of things. All life matters. The exceptions, of course, being vampires, demons and other evil supernatural beings who seek to torment, kill or enslave the innocent. Such primal and elemental beings have proven to be intractable and beyond redemption, so they are hunted and destroyed like the plague they are. Atlanteans learned this lesson the hard way during the Vampire Crusades, a part of history that still haunts them as a people. The undead and demonkind shall forever be the enemies of the heirs to Atlantis. It is why they fight the undead and travel the Megaverse as knights errant and educators.

True Atlantean R.C.C.

The following applies to all True Atlanteans whether they are a ditch-digger, scholar, adventurer, warrior or any of the specific O.C.C.s describe in the pages of this book.

Tattoos of Heritage: Two magic tattoos given to the Atlantean at around age five or six (protection from vampires and a flaming sword). Each tattoo can be activated the same as any magic tattoo; standard rules apply. Unless a so-called Tattooed Man, most Atlanteans acquire 1-4 additional magic tattoos and may adorn their bodies with ordinary, decorative tattoos.

Alignment: Any, but most Atlanteans tend to be one of the following alignment, unless specified differently under the clan description: Principled (30%), Scrupulous (35%), Unprincipled (15%), and Anarchist (10%). The *Aerihman clan* (and the Sunaj) is an exception, with more Anarchist and evil alignments than average (see clan description for details).

Attributes: I.Q. 3D6+4, M.E. 4D6+6, M.A. 3D6+4, P.S. 4D6+4 (considered Augmented Strength), P.P. 3D6, P.E. 3D6+6, P.B. 3D6+6, Spd 4D6+6.

Hit Points: P.E. attribute number + 1D6 per level of experience.

S.D.C.: Starts at 50 points plus those gained from O.C.C.s, physical skills, and magic tattoos. Each magic tattoo beyond the Marks of Heritage provides an extra 10 S.D.C. points (40 S.D.C. maximum).

Note: The average Atlantean is never allowed to get more than the two Marks of Heritage and a maximum of four additional magic tattoos. This is law and tradition dutifully followed by all Atlantean Clansmen, and strictly enforced by clan elders and clan Alchemists. Only the special combat oriented Atlantean O.C.C.s are allowed to acquire more magic tattoos. A process that makes them more than human with Mega-Damage bodies and Supernatural P.S. and P.E. to better fight the supernatural and other powerful enemies.

M.D.C.: The typical True Atlantean only has M.D.C. via Mega-Damage Capacity body armor, force fields, magic spells and other forms of physical or magical protection such as Armor of Ithan from a Techno-Wizard device, magic amulet, etc.

Atlanteans who possess M.D.C. bodies are limited those who receive *more than six* magic tattoos, something most ordinary Atlanteans avoid. Only Atlantean O.C.C.s such as the **Tattooed Defender, Monster Hunter, Undead Slayer, Voyager** and other so-called, **Tattooed Man O.C.C.s** (including the *Sunaj Assassin*), are M.D.C. beings when they visit Mega-Damage environments, due to the influence of their many Magic Tattoos. The number of magic tattoos and corresponding M.D.C. and bonuses are indicated under the appropriate O.C.C. description. For O.C.C.s that make the Atlantean into a Mega-Damage beings, Hit Points and S.D.C. points are added together (including bonuses from physical skills) and they become M.D.C. on a point for point basis. So if the combined Hit points and S.D.C. are 83 points, then the Tattooed Man has 83 M.D.C., and so on.

Each magic tattoo after the initial six provides an additional 11 M.D.C. to males and 13 M.D.C. to females.

As they increase in experience, they gain an additional 1D6 M.D.C. per level.

Size: 6 feet, 2 inches to 7 feet (1.9 to 2.1 m) roll 2D6 inches and add the result to 72 inches/6 feet for height. Most are lean and muscular with chiseled features.

P.P.E.: 3D6 P.P.E. points, with 10 P.P.E. being average/most common to start. Plus the average Atlantean has an additional 12 P.P.E. from the *Marks of Heritage* (six points each) and +6 P.P.E. for each additional magic tattoo. Maximum of four additional tattoos unless one of the specialized Atlantean O.C.C.s, which acquires the P.P.E. of that O.C.C. *Practitioners of magic* also gain a much higher level of P.P.E. as needed to power their mystic abilities and fuel their spell casting. The *Atlantean Nomad* tends to have a higher level of P.P.E., presumably due their strong sense of wonder about the Megaverse and their regular use of dimensional Rifts, stone pyramids and magic to travel to new worlds and dimensions.

Horror Factor/Awe Factor: 12 for the average Atlantean. Monsters fear all Atlanteans and humans tend to be awestruck when they realize they stand with or against a True Atlantean.

Disposition: Varies with the individual, but most True Atlanteans are confident, bold and headstrong, the latter, is especially true when young, under the age of 100. They tend to speak their minds and are not shy about expressing their opinions, ideas and feelings, which can get them in trouble sometimes. Atlanteans are also compassionate and empathetic toward others, and have a strong sense of right and wrong. All of this adds up to make them kind, merciful, honest, noble and brave people who stand up against evil and injustice, and help those in need.

Age: All True Atlanteans are long-lived. As a first level or low level player character, it is assumed the individual is young by Atlantean standards, 1D6+20 years old and probably looks like a 17-20 year old until he or she is 50 years old. See life span, below.

Life Span: 500 years on average, but some have been known to live to 800, 900 and 1,000. True Atlanteans' knowledge of medicine, science and magic has given them impressive longevity and healing abilities that make them long-lived and youthful in appearance even when well into their hundreds. Time warps caused by dimensional travel may make it seem as if the character is even older, skipping decades at a time. Most Atlanteans look to be 19-35 years old, which means they may be anywhere from 19-295 years old. An Atlantean who looks to be 40 or 45 years of age is likely to be 300-500 years old. One who looks to be a healthy and active person in his 60s or 70s, is undoubtedly 800+ years old.

Natural Abilities: In addition to those of humans, the life span of True Atlanteans is 10-15 times longer, and they heal quickly. Some Atlantean O.C.C.s create heroes with M.D.C. bodies in Mega-Damage environments via their magic tattoos.

Healing Abilities (special): Atlanteans recover Hit Points and S.D.C. (or M.D.C., as the case may be), at a rate of 2D6+10 points per 24 hour period of normal rest and recovery, or 1D6 Hit Points/S.D.C. (or M.D.C.) per hour of meditation at a ley line or nexus point; more at a Healing Pyramid.

Ley Line Phasing (special): All Atlanteans are taught how to Ley Line Phase. This is exactly like the Ley Line Walker's ability. It takes a full melee round (15 seconds) to Ley Line Phase and cannot be used during battle.

Impervious to Shape-Changing/Metamorphosis (special): True Atlanteans altered their genetic structure in such a way as to prevent themselves from being physically transformed by any means, including, but not limited to metamorphosis potions and spells, magic rituals, vampire transformation, Petrification, Turn to Mist, Growth or Reduction/Shrinking spells, potions, or via Splugorth Bio-Wizardry, microbes, parasites and symbiotic organisms, or any other form of magic or supernatural transformation including curses, wishes or other forms of enchantment. Atlanteans still can be tortured in Bio-Wizard Chambers, and while they cannot be transformed per se, they can be horribly scarred and disfigured. This is something the Splugorth often take great delight in doing.

Consider this an *automatic save vs transformative magicks*.

Being impervious to transformation is a two-edged sword as helpful magic potions and spells that physically transform the character for the purpose of disguise or power do not work on Atlanteans either. Turn to Mist, Metamorphosis spells, Featherlight (on self), Giant, Reduce/Shrink spells, etc.; if it physically transforms the body, it does not work. Healing magic works because it magically speeds up the natural healing process; so do Restoration and Resurrection because they are repairing the original body, not making it something non-Atlantean.

Operate Dimensional Pyramids (special): All True Atlanteans above the age of 13 (and all True Atlantean O.C.C.s) know how to operate the Stone Pyramids created by Atlantean Stone Masters and Minions of Splugorth for the purpose of healing, communications, teleportation, and dimensional teleportation. **Base Skill:** 25% +5% per level of experience. Note

that the average True Atlantean does not know exactly how Stone Magic works nor how to build pyramids, just how to operate them.

P.P.E. Recovery (special): 10 points per hour of rest or sleep. 15 P.P.E. per hour of meditation.

Recognize Vampires by Appearance (special): 10% per level of experience. There is a +10% bonus to recognize Secondary Vampires and a +30% bonus to recognize Wild Vampires. It is the cunning and powerful Master Vampire who remains most difficult to identify (-30% skill penalty) unless it is openly flaunting its power and demonic nature.

Sense the Presence of Vampires and Vampire Intelligences (special): True Atlanteans can sense the presence of vampires and Vampire Intelligences within a 1,000 foot (305 m) radius, but cannot pinpoint the exact location. Also see Recognize Vampires, above. **Note:** Atlanteans cannot sense other types of undead like zombies, etc., only vampires and Vampire Intelligences.

Sense Rifts and Ley Lines (special): As dimensional travelers for thousands of years, True Atlanteans are able to sense the presence of ley lines up to 5 miles (8 km) away, a nexus point up to 10 miles (16 km), and sense an open/active Rift up to 20 miles (32 km) away. They can tell when there is more than one ley line or nexus within their sensing range, but are unable to pinpoint the exact location. They do, however, know the general direction and whether it is close by or far away, weak or powerful, and if a Rift is opened.

Skills Known to Most True Atlanteans: Speak an ancient dialect of Greek (their native language) at 98% as well as *American* and *Dragonese/Elf* at 80% +1% per level of experience. They are literate in Greek at 98%, and literate in American and Dragonese/Elf at 60% +3% per level of experience. Meditation 80% +2% per level of experience. As dimensional explorers, all True Atlanteans know *Lore: Dimensions* at 30% +5% per level of experience (see **Rifts® Ultimate Edition,** page 126, for details on this skill).

Available O.C.C.s for Atlanteans: Any, but most lean toward those designated as *Atlantean O.C.C.s* described in this book and O.C.C.s related to magic, psionics, science, medicine and scholastic pursuits. Atlanteans NEVER consent to bionic conversion or cybernetic implants, and due to their unique nature, they can NOT become Juicers or Crazies. Any kind of Juicer or Crazy conversion process is likely (95%) to kill the Atlantean!

Experience Level: 1D10 or as set by the Game Master for NPCs. Player Characters, if allowed, should start at first level.

Attacks per Melee: As per Hand to Hand combat skill.

Damage: Augmented P.S. with bonuses from combat training, or as per weapon, magic, or psionics.

Bonuses (in addition to those acquired by attributes and skills): +1 on Perception Rolls regarding vampires and the undead (recognizing clues to their presence, servants, victims, etc.), +2 to save vs magic and disease of all kinds (in addition to P.E. bonuses), +4 to save vs Horror Factor (Atlanteans have see a lot in their travels and throughout their history). **Note:** O.C.C.s will provide additional bonuses. All bonuses are cumulative. Make sure you include the O.C.C. bonuses for your character too.

Vulnerabilities: Not being able to transform their bodies can have unforeseen consequences, and their outspokenness and reputation as heroes and Champions of Light can sometimes get them into trouble or make them targets. Furthermore, noble and caring Atlanteans may be too trusting and duped by evildoers who use their generous and heroic natures to trick and manipulate them. Their strong sense of justice and compassion for others may also make it difficult for them to walk away from people in need and sometimes compels True Atlanteans to take dangerous risks and go against the odds. This may be true even of characters with Anarchist or evil alignments.

Magic: Applicable only if a magic O.C.C. is selected.

Magic Tattoos: All Atlanteans have the **Marks of Heritage** and up to 1D4 additional magic tattoos; player's choice with the Game Master's approval.

At age five or six, all Atlanteans receive the Marks of Heritage. These are a pair of magic tattoos. The one on the right wrist is always the *Heart Impaled by a Stake tattoo* for protection from vampires. The second tattoo is placed on the left wrist and is always a flaming sword of some sort. The exact size, shape and style of the sword varies. The second tattoo is always *clan specific* and this is how many Atlanteans recognize other clan members when they meet them. A family name or crest is likely to be part of the tattoo on or under the weapon. The family crest is often elaborately drawn and one of the more beautiful tattoos on the Atlantean's body. In some cases, the crest is designed as a Magic Shield tattoo for additional protection and use in combat. See descriptions of some family tattoos in the section describing notable clans.

Psionics: Standard, basically the same as humans, complete with Master Psychics who can select psionic O.C.C.s such as Mind Melter, Mind Bleeder, Psi-Ghost, Burster, Zapper, etc. (See **Rifts® World Book 12: Psyscape** for a large range of Psychic O.C.C.s.) IMPORTANT NOTE: A player who rolls Master Psychic, but does not want to play a Master Psychic, may decline to play a Master Psychic. Knock the character down to a Major Psychic with 8 psionic abilities (do not select from Super-Psionics).

Standard Equipment: As per O.C.C.

Money: As per O.C.C.

Cybernetics and Bionics: If a True Atlantean loses a limb, he will strive to get to a Healing Pyramid where he can be made whole. If that is not feasible, he may settle for a *Bio-System*, organic, replacement. All Atlanteans are attracted to natural things and seldom seek out bionic reconstruction or cybernetic implants. Cybernetics and any mechanical systems built into the human body interfere with and reduce the potency of magic and spell casting. However, Atlanteans who do not use magic, other than a few tattoos, *may* consider as many as five cybernetic implants, but never bionics. Even partial bionic reconstruction is likely to make an Atlantean feel violated and despondent, or drive him completely insane.

Habitat: Atlanteans are dimensional travelers and can be found anywhere across the Megaverse, exploring or living among other humanoids.

Alliances and Allies: Other True Atlanteans, demon hunters, vampire slayers, Cyber-Knights, Cosmo-Knights, heroes, noble adventurers, Champions of Light and people of good alignment are all likely to be seen as potential allies. Atlanteans may ally themselves with anyone they deem worthy.

Rivals and Enemies: Atlanteans abhor the practice of slavery and stand up against cruel injustice and fight for what is right and good, so evildoers of every stripe can become an enemy. Vampires and all undead are the mortal enemies of all Atlanteans. Demons and all Minions of Hell, wicked supernatural beings, dark gods, evil Alien Intelligences and their henchmen and followers are also deadly enemies. Unknown to most Atlanteans, so are the *Sunaj*. No clan has yet realized that they are being systematically targeted for extermination by the Sunaj. So far, most Sunaj attacks seem to be random and unrelated, or part of a group of other villains such as criminals, dimensional raiders, slavers, Minions of Splugorth or attributed to the Minions of Hell. Those who have been killed by the Sunaj seldom show any evidence to link them to these mysterious assassins. Furthermore, most clans do not gather often enough for word of such targeted attacks, or a greater danger looming over them, to be recognized or for word to spread. Being scattered across the universe as they are makes it difficult to receive current news or recognize patterns connected to attacks on Atlanteans.

Optional True Atlantean Character Creation Tables

Roll percentiles or select the option that best suits the kind of Atlantean character you want to play. Of course, the Game Master has final approval.

Step 1: The Character's Clan

01-10% Clan Aerihman*
11-15% Clan Archerean
16-20% Clan Aurelous
21-30% Clan Bagh-Dach
31-40% Clan Marciniszyn
41-50% Clan Skellian
51-60% Clan Skolos
61-70% Clan Tsitas
71-80% Clan Equineous
81-90% Clan Navita
91-00% Clan Draco Amicus

Or your own clan. Game Masters can, or allow a player to, roll on the Clan Creation Table (elsewhere in this book) to create a new True Atlantean clan. In the alternative, pick any of the clans listed.

* At the Game Master's discretion, a True Atlantean player character from the Aerihman clan can be rolled up as any of the available Atlantean O.C.C.s and Tattooed O.C.C.s and, if the Game Master allows it, even as a member of the secret Sunaj order of assassins, including a *Sunaj Assassin, Shadow Assassin* or *Shadow Mage*. HOWEVER, we do not necessarily recommend this unless both the G.M. and the player are okay with it. If the G.M. says no to allowing a Sunaj as a player character, please honor his position. **Game Master Note:** Include a Sunaj player character with the utmost care and make sure its inclusion does not upset the balance of the player group or your campaign/story. And make sure the player knows he should NOT be actively disrupting or undermining the player group, without dire consequences (i.e. someone in the group, or the entire group, kills him).

As much as the Sunaj character may sincerely bond with and care about other members of the player group, at some point he is likely to find himself at odds with his teammates. G.M.s, make sure the player clearly understands that there may come a time when his Sunaj character may be faced with the terrible decision of choosing between the adventurer group or his duty to the Sunaj. He may even have to betray or sacrifice them in the name of the Sunaj cause. If the Sunaj player character should clearly side against the Sunaj or the Aerihman clan, and they find out about it, the character will be branded a traitor, a bounty placed on his head, and he will be hunted by the Sunaj for extermination.

Aerihman can be good guys and gravitate to warrior O.C.C.s and monster slayers. Though all Aerihman tend to be bold, aggressive and combat oriented, that is not always the case. Moreover, many Aerihman are heroic and trustworthy adventurers, heroes and monster slayers who know nothing about the Sunaj. Like everyone else, they believe these professional killers are aliens/D-Bees with an unreasoning grudge against True Atlanteans. The average Aerihman has no idea the Sunaj are part of his own clan or have anything whatsoever to do with Atlantis. Remember, the Sunaj leaders within the Aerihman clan are very secretive and only recruit members into the Sunaj who share their extreme agenda of clan domination. If a player character is Sunaj, he will go through great lengths to conceal his Atlantean heritage.

Step 2. Number of Worlds Visited

Why is this important? Because True Atlanteans are dimensional travelers by their very nature. Which means the character is likely to have visited at least a few different worlds not including where he was born. All Atlanteans know their *home world* and *home dimension*, as well as *Rifts Earth, Phase World*, and 1D4 additional planets or dimensions. This allows them to travel to these planets using Dimensional Rifts and magic stone pyramids. This knowledge is not all inclusive, meaning they do not know everything there is to know about each particular world. They just possess the most basic knowledge of the world, its people, technology, primary culture, etc., and where on that planet they are likely to find a stone pyramid, ley line network or other mechanism to create a dimensional Rift and come and go as they please. For more exact details, characters can roll on the *Lore: Dimension skill* to reveal additional information on what they may know about a particular dimension or planet and its inhabitants.

Step 3. Additional Tattoos for Non-Tattooed O.C.C.s

The average Atlantean can have up to four tattoos in addition to his two Marks of Heritage = **six total**. More than that transforms the character into a Mega-Damage being in M.D.C. environments. Such a transition is avoided by the average Atlantean. These 1-4 additional magic tattoos are sometimes acquired as a reward for years of service, a notable achievement, or a grand act of heroism or selflessness, and sometimes in trade for services that are dangerous. Game Master discretion in all cases. Game Masters, this is not applicable for Atlantean characters who are Tattooed Man O.C.C.s like the Undead Slayer and Voyager.

01-15% One additional Weapon or Weapon Modification tattoo.

16-30% One additional Animal tattoo.

31-45% One additional Monster tattoo.

46-60% One additional Power tattoo.

61-75% Two additional tattoos, one Animal and one Monster.

76-90% Two additional tattoos, one Power and one Weapon or Weapon Modification.

91-96% Two additional tattoos of choice. Two magic tattoos selected from the same category or one from two different types of tattoos, but two tattoos total. Select from Weapon, Animal, Monster or Power.

97-100% Three additional tattoos of choice. Three magic tattoos selected from the same category or one from three different types of tattoos, but three tattoos total. Select from Weapon, Animal, Monster, Power or Dimension. **Note:** As a rule, only the Nomad and Tattooed Voyager are able to receive Dimension Tattoos.

Step 4. Feelings about Atlantis

It is known by all True Atlanteans that Atlantis has returned to Rifts Earth where it has been completely occupied by the Splugorth and their minions. How does the character regard his homeland? Is it something that drives the character? Is he curious about his homeland and wants to see it? Or is Atlantis a distant memory or fabled place that the character has little concern about? Players should feel free to pick or roll randomly on the table below.

01-15% No feelings whatsoever. The Megaverse is my home. Earth is the place of Atlanteans' origins and a footnote in history that every Atlantean learns about, but nothing more. This character loves being a citizen of the endless Megaverse who never thinks about the ancient homeland. He's more interested in learning more about new worlds and people across the universe. To this character, Atlantis is an answer to a trivia question. He never thinks about it and has no interest in visiting Atlantis nor liberating it from the Splugorth.

16-30% No impact. You can't live in the past. It is a shame the ancient homeland was lost, vanishing in a dimensional disaster thousands of years ago. In recent centuries, Atlantis has reappeared but fallen into the hands of the Splugorth. Sad, but we came to terms with the disappearance of Atlantis generations ago. Home is where your family and friends are. Atlantis is just a name and place from our past. A piece of history and a hunk of ground that is a distant memory no living Atlantean has ever known.

The continent of Atlantis reappearing on Rifts Earth and being claimed by the Minions of Splugorth has no real importance or significance to this character, except as stories, legends and parables from ancient times to help you learn life's lessons. This individual spends his time exploring worlds, seeking enlightenment and knowledge, and helping others. Let the Minions of Splugorth have keep Atlantis. Atlanteans moved on eons ago.

31-40% Few feelings and little concern. There are greater issues than claiming a piece of ancient land on a distant planet because it's a piece of Atlantean history or heritage. Atlantis and Earth may have once been the home of Atlantean ancestors, but it's not home anymore, and hasn't been for a very long time.

This character focuses his energies on such things as exploration, the pursuit of enlightenment, helping others, killing vampires and supernatural menaces, finding new resources for his clan or any number of grand to personal goals. Does the character like the fact that the ancestral home is occupied by the Minions of Splugorth? No, but who cares? There are more important things to worry about and an entire Megaverse waiting to be explored.

41-50% Curious and would love to visit someday. Atlantis is a part of Atlanteans' fabled heritage. Someday it would be nice to walk on the soil where the forefathers once did. The character has heard many stories about ancient Atlantis and modern Atlantis under the control of the Splugorth, enough to be intrigued and to want to visit the homeland someday. Yes, the monstrous Splugorth are there and it is said the birthplace of Atlanteans is in the hand of monsters, but to stand where your ancestors once stood would be nice. Visiting Atlantis someday is definitely on this Atlantean's bucket list, but spilling blood to try to take it back from the Minions of Splugorth? Not worth the lives waging such a war would cost. It's just a symbolic piece of history. Let the sleeping Splugorth dogs lie and focus on better things.

51-60% Atlantis is a wonderland to be explored. This character dreams of visiting Atlantis to walk on the soil where the forefathers once tread. Such an adventure would be glorious. And challenging, because it would require walking amongst many enemies and monsters they have sworn to destroy. A visit to the Splugorth's Atlantis would require planning, disguise, and self-control. Still, to see the wonders of the Splugorth empire and one of their infamous Dimensional Markets would be glorious.

This character has a strong sense of history and is enamored with the notion of visiting the land of origin for all Atlanteans. To him, Atlantis is another magical alien world to be explored. The fact that it is part of Atlantean heritage makes it all the more alluring, even if it is in the hands of the hated Splugorth. For a curious Atlanteans Atlantis offers a treasure trove of exotic wonders, magic, aliens from many worlds, magic, forbidden knowledge and a place of danger and intrigue too exciting to resist. An adventure of a lifetime made all the more exhilarating because of its history and the danger of being discovered by the Splugorth.

However, waging war against the godlike Splugorth and their Minions from across the cosmos is pure madness. He can understand why the Aerihman clan might want to recapture Atlantis, but prays they never seriously enter into a war they could never win. Atlanteans lost Atlantis long ago. They have made a wonderful life as citizens of the infinite Megaverse. Be satisfied with that and forget the past.

61-70% Angry but pragmatic. This Atlantean hates that the Splugorth have Atlantis as one of their many conquests. Their keeping the name Atlantis is a clear and deliberate slap in the face of every Atlantean that has ever lived. Knowing the wicked creatures, it may have been done to provoke Atlanteans to take action against the Splugorth. All of this angers and disgusts this character. Though he would love to take the motherland back and turn it into the paradise and paragon of virtue it once was, he accepts it is not possible. At least not now, when the Splugorth empire is at its zenith.

Many Atlanteans share this sentiment. They have strong feelings of nostalgia towards the Atlantean homeland and it is a constant source of consternation that it is occupied by the Splugorth and a dimensional hub for wicked beings. If the Splugorth could realistically be removed from Atlantis, he would join that effort, but they cannot. Not at the moment. The Splugorth are too powerful and their minions too numerous. But should that day come, he is willing to fight the good fight. Meanwhile, this character is likely to visit Atlantis to investigate what the Minions of Splugorth

have done with the homeland, and to strike out at the monsters and visiting villains whenever the opportunity presents itself. This is likely to include undermining merchants and businesses, picking off Sunaj and other evil henchmen of the Splugorth, helping slaves escape captivity and flee the island continent, assisting heroes, stealing from the minions and giving the stolen weapons and magic to the people who oppose and fight them, and harassment of the enemy in any way possible, whenever possible.

Atlanteans with this attitude may take dangerous chances to help those being enslaved and abused by the Minions of Splugorth as well as carefully use the resources of Atlantis against its vile masters. These Atlanteans are pragmatic, however, so they plot and bide their time, do not engage in anything too crazy or foolish against the Minions of Splugorth, and tend to be careful when on Atlantean soil. They enjoy visiting the homeland as often as possible and like sticking it to the enemy, even if it is in small ways, at every opportunity. Every small triumph in the name of justice against an evil empire is a cherished victory.

Such Atlanteans do what they can to thwart the Splugorth, but they need a huge amount of convincing before they might even consider joining the Aerihman in all-out-war. This character may admire the Aerihman's moxie and love of Atlantean heritage, but they also believe victory is impossible and that the usually disciplined Aerihman are lost to emotion and lust for revenge that is blinding them to the practical truth. Leave Atlantis be until the time is right, which may be eons, then move against them. And if Atlantis is to remain forever in the Splugorth's clutches, so be it. It changes nothing about who Atlanteans are as a people or the noble path they follow.

71-80% Atlantis is a vital part of our heritage. It belongs to us! Atlanteans who carry this sentiment feel strong ties to the motherland. It is the birthplace of their people. It belongs to all Atlanteans and cannot be desecrated by monsters and the scum who serve them. Monsters and henchmen Atlanteans have clashed with on many occasions over the millennia and continue to oppose. Monsters who enslave and create dark magic that feeds on the souls and life force of the innocent and heroes alike. Something must be done.

A driving goal in life is to liberate Atlantis from the clutches of the Splugorth and reclaim it for all Atlanteans. These well-intended warriors are likely to visit the Splugorth's Atlantis at every opportunity to get the lay of the land, gather intelligence and plot acts of sabotage and insurrection against the Splugorth. Like the Atlanteans in #61-70%, these patriots kill minions, cause trouble and harass the Splugorth and their minions at every opportunity. They are careful so they can fight another day, but are much more brazen about their attacks and acts of sabotage. Every victory against the occupiers of Atlantis, large or small, is a welcomed one. Such characters have no compunction against stealing from and cheating the Splugorth and their underlings, and do anything they can to hurt them and their operations. It is a matter of pride and heritage to fight this guerilla war and inspire insurgency. This includes helping the *Liberated Underground* to freeing slaves and outright acts of violence, murder, and destruction against the hated enemy. They are mindful to try to keep collateral damage upon the truly innocent, such as slaves and adventurers, low, but this is war, and innocent people get hurt.

81-90% Atlantis has been stolen from us, but vengeance shall be ours. This character does not believe Atlantis can be successfully recaptured for Atlanteans, but does believe the

Splugorth and their servants must be punished for their crimes, not just against Atlanteans but all good people who suffer within their empire. A driving goal is to make life difficult for the Splugorth and their minions whenever and wherever possible, but especially on Atlantis. This could mean liberating a group of slaves, destroying random Splugorth Minion patrols, killing Slavers and Horune Pirates, and engaging in acts of sabotage, terror, espionage and assassination. These Atlanteans also work toward preventing the Splugorth from expanding their land holdings on Earth, as well as locating and recovering ancient Atlantean artifacts and magic items that can be used against the Splugorth and supernatural evil.

True Atlanteans with this outlook are already waging a war against the enemy. While they may not believe the Minions of Splugorth can be routed from Atlantis, they intend to make it their hunting ground and make the Splugorth and their minions pay, and pay dearly. This involves frequent targeted assaults, sabotage and harassment driven by burning hate and a lust for revenge. Hardened combatants, they seldom worry about collateral damage that might hurt others. To them there are seldom "innocent" people on Atlantis, so collateral damage is of little concern. When one of their attacks causes more damage and hurts more minions or Splugorth holdings than expected, it is welcomed. In war, there is death and sacrifice that is always paid with the blood of the innocent. Since revenge and payback is the driving motivation, such campaigns against the Minions of Splugorth are not limited to Atlantis, and take place all over Rifts Earth and across the Megaverse.

Should a military campaign that has a real chance for success ever be launched by anyone other than another army of monsters, this character will be in the streets doing everything he can to help. Many Aerihman share this attitude.

91-100% Atlantis is our birthright. We must fight to free Atlantis! Atlantis belongs to Atlanteans is the rallying cry of these Atlanteans. It is a piece of Atlantean heritage and their birthright that has been stolen. Justice demands Atlantis be delivered to the Atlantean people. This is the sentiment shared by the vast majority of people in the Aerihman clan.

These Atlanteans may engage in the campaigns of harassment and attacks as described in the previous two listings, above, but they have much bigger dreams. The ultimate goal is to destroy or forcibly compel the Splugorth and their minions to abandon Atlantis so that Atlanteans can forever reclaim their birthright and come home again. For them this isn't just about revenge or justice, it is their destiny. Such Atlanteans may go to extremes to accomplish this, and are always quick to join any operation to undermine and hurt the Splugorth and their minions. For many, especially among the Aerihman clan, their connection to Atlantis is powerful, even all consuming. Their need to liberate their homeland bordering on obsession. This obsession does not stop with Atlantis or the Splugorth. Their ire is directed at anyone who serves the Splugorth, anywhere across the universe. When Atlantis is won and once again in the possession of True Atlanteans, they intend to retake all of Earth, one continent at a time. Wiping out supernatural evil, their worshipers and henchmen to unite humanity and other mortals under their leadership. Then they will expand across the stars.

Individuals with this belief are constantly looking for ways to hurt and destroy the enemy from grunts to high-command to the Splugorth, themselves. They talk a good game and are likely to regularly speak ill of Splugorth and all who follow them, convince and pressure other Atlanteans and heroes to rally around this noble imperative, and destroy anyone who willingly serves the Splugorth, from Horune Pirates and Sunaj to Slavers and complicit associates. "We are monster hunters. Our homeland is occupied by monsters. We must free the continent and reclaim our birthright for generations to come."

Characters with this attitude hate the Splugorth with a passion and may go about reclaiming Atlantis in many ways. The ultimate goal is to raise an army comprised of others who despise the Splugorth and invade the continent. This may mean enlisting other nations of Earth, people from other worlds and dimensions, and perhaps even getting deities involved. If he is very lucky, maybe that day will have happen in his lifetime. This Atlantean is a zealot for the cause and tries to recruit others in taking real, measurable action against the Splugorth occupation of Atlantis. For too many (like the Sunaj), the end justifies the means, and this character is willing to do whatever it takes to recapture Atlantis, even if doing so would have long-lasting ramifications on Earth and beyond.

Atlantean Clan Random Generation Tables

Want to make an Atlantean clan of your own? Just follow the tables below. Game Masters can roll or select the options that work best for their game. As far as names go, I, Carl Gleba, typically use Greek names which are easy to look up on the internet. Of course, some names can just be made up. I also found it helpful to look at some Latin words which I found appealing as well.

Step 1: Clan Estimated Size

How big is the clan? Are we talking a small group under a hundred or is it thousands? A good rule of thumb is that most of the lesser-known Atlantean clans are small and generally a few thousand to several thousand strong. As the Game Master, if you are not satisfied with that, roll twice and add those numbers together or determine your own population.

01-15% Tiny Clan: 6D6+60 members. Roll once on the Number of Families table.

16-40% Small Clan: 2D6x100 members. Roll once on the Number of Families table.

41-80% Medium-Sized Clan: 2D6x1,000 members. Roll once on the Number of Families table.

81-95% Large Clan: 2D4x10,000 members. Roll once on the Number of Families table and double the number.

96-100% Very Large Clan: 2D6x100,000 members. Roll on the Number of Families table and multiply by five.

Step 2: Number of Families Making Up the Clan

Remember that most clans are made up of several families. This will determine just how many families comprise your clan.

01-20% 1D6+6 families.

21-60% 2D4x10 families.

61-95% 1D6x100 families.

96-100% 1D6x1,000 families.

Step 3: Clan Status

Clan status determines how well known a particular clan is to the average Atlantean. For instance, there are no Atlanteans who have not heard of the Aerihman clan, while most of the other major clans described in this book are known to each other and the majority (70+3D6%) of the smaller clans. The percentile numbers below are only for True Atlanteans. If the player characters are trying to track down a particular clan, this should give the Game Master a good gauge if the "typical" Atlantean citizen has heard of it. Otherwise, only an Atlantean Nomad, Clan Elder, or Clan Alchemist many know anything about the lesser clans, but may want a payment or a favor for them to share what they know; G.M. discretion.

01-20% Little Known. This is a clan that is hardly known to most Atlanteans. It could be because only a few survivors made it off Atlantis, or the clan has failed to make contact at any clan gathering in a few generations. They are not likely to be recognized by other clans and then there is only a 01-10% chance of the average Atlantean having heard of this clan. They have virtually no significance or influence among Atlanteans.

21-40% Hidden. This clan is either on the run, which is still possible from the days of Ancient Atlantis, or is in hiding from its enemies such as Vampire Intelligences, the Splugorth, the Sunaj, demons, etc. There are rumors about the Hidden clan, but none have been to a clan gathering or made contact with another clan in several generations. To determine if anyone has heard of this clan, roll 01-30%. They have little significance or influence among Atlanteans.

41-70% Known. Atlanteans have probably heard of this clan and made contact with some of its clansmen or seen them at a gathering. However, this clan is either only just rising into prominence or is has dealt with difficult times and is fading from prominence. Its representatives attend most clan gatherings and participate, but do not have a great deal of clout. There is a 01-66% likelihood of having heard of this clan.

71-90% Well Known. Clans that are well known often have a reputation of some sort. The reputation maybe be good or bad or focus on one particular element of speciality, such as being wonderful artists, or philosophers, musicians, or builders, or warriors or skilled practitioners of magic, or for some particular event probably involving besting or destroying a particular foe, or playing a key role in a particular battle or event. This reputation has spread, making them known to most Atlantean clans. This is in addition to being actively involved with numerous clans and attending or hosting a clan gathering. There is a 01-90% chance of having heard about and knowing things about this clan.

91-100% Famous or Infamous. Large or small, this clan's reputation precedes them as they are widely known for one reason or another, good or bad. This can stem from as far back as ancient Atlantis or much more recent events. It be could be a good deed, a misdeed, accident, act of bravery or heroics, an act of cowardice or betrayal, or other feat, occurrence or ability that has won the clan notoriety. There is a 01-90% of having heard of a famous or "Infamous" clan.

Step 4: Clan's Primary Home

It is generally accepted that at least 30% of any Atlantean clan is away, wandering the Megaverse. In some clans, that can be as high as 50%. That leaves the rest to set down roots and try to make a home somewhere. Most Atlanteans have settled over the years. This step determines where at least half the clan is located.

01-45% A single world in a familiar dimension same as Earth and Phase World. All clan cities and homes are located on a single planet.

46-65% Scattered among 1D4+1 worlds and two or more dimensions. The clan has outposts at a few locations. They have one known location or trade city, but the rest are secret, believing it is safest to be spread out among a few secret locations across the cosmos.

66-85% Clustered. The clan has settled among the outposts and cities of other Atlantean clans. These people are likely to be found among 2D4 different clans at numerous locations.

86-95% Dimensional Nomads. The clan has not opted to settle down and instead they are broken down into smaller groups or tribes and constantly on the move. They travel between 1D6 dimensions where they can stay for up to 2D6 months before they pack up and move again. Chances are these nomads travel to where they feel they are needed, or to explore, or to go where there is the promise of new experiences and adventure, or an opportunity to help their own clan or fellow Atlanteans, destroy a supernatural evil, or acquire a rare artifact, magic, etc. Other times it may be to hide and lay low, or just to rest or enjoy the beauty of a new world or dimension.

96-100% Scattered about the Megaverse! The clan is loose-knit and has individual and small groups all over the Megaverse on dozens, perhaps hundreds of worlds, Rifts Earth and the Three Galaxies among them. They do not have a home city, but may have a favorite gathering place, or 1D6x10% of them meet at clan gatherings to touch base and visit with their fellow clansmen. Instead, these individuals, pairs and small groups have adopted other worlds and local people (non-Atlanteans) as their home and have integrated themselves into other societies.

Step 5: Clan General Alignment

What is the clan's general alignment? Individuals can still be any alignment within their clan regardless of the clans' average alignment, and they remain a tight-knit family unit who loves and cares about each other. Remember, as a general rule, Atlanteans tend to be good and often hold themselves to high standards. Game Masters can use this step to determine if there are any "bad seeds" in the clan or anyone who could go rogue.

01-60% Lawful and good, with the best of intentions: 80% of the clan are Principled or Scrupulous while 18% are selfish, and 2% are evil.

61-75% Mostly good with some selfish: 65% good, 30% are selfish and 5% are evil.

76-90% A more even mix: 20% Principled, 20% Scrupulous, 20% Unprincipled, 20% Anarchist, 10% Aberrant, 6% Miscreant and 4% Diabolic.

91-98% Selfish Outlook: 2% are Principled, 20% Scrupulous, 25% Unprincipled, 35% Anarchist, 12% Miscreant, 2% Diabolic and 4% Aberrant.

99-100% Evil Outlook: 4% Principled, 6% Scrupulous, 10% Unprincipled, 20% Anarchist, 30% Aberrant, 20% Miscreant and 10% Diabolic.

Step 6: Clan Notoriety

What is the clan noted for or makes it stand out? Each clan is likely to have a primary and a secondary element of notability. So roll twice, and it is fine if you roll the same thing twice, because it just stresses the emphasis of that particular area of notoriety. Those in the list are broad areas of possibilities, and Game Masters should feel free to create and offer other, specific areas of notoriety. Just because a clan is notable for art does not limit it to painting. It can be sculpting, painting, drawing, musical composition, or any combination or creative endeavor.

01-05% Art. The people of this clan all share an understanding and love for art. This could be something specific like sculpture, painting, drawing, etching, carving, mosaics, pottery/ceramics, sequential art, tattoo art, animation/digital/holograms, 3D art, architecture, landscaping/topiary, etc., or all of the above. Most societies and cultures that appreciate art include most to all forms of art. A character from this clan may select an art skill (Art, Calligraphy, Whittling, etc., with a +10% bonus) as one of his O.C.C. Related or Secondary Skill selections even if it is not normally available to his O.C.C.

06-10% Music. This clan is renowned for one or several types/styles of music, and may be known for great symphonies, songs and musical compositions, and/or the making of top quality, precision musical instruments. Dance often goes hand in hand with music, so this clan may also be known for its dance, musical theater and performance arts. In addition to a deep love for music, most of these clan members exhibit some level of musical talent, even if an adventurer or warrior. A character from this clan may select a musical skill such as Sing, Dance or Play Musical Instrument (with a +10% bonus) as one of his O.C.C. Related or Secondary Skill selections even if it is not normally available to his O.C.C.

11-15% Scholastic. This clan is renowned for education and learning, probably with a focus in one or two areas (mathematics, history, philosophy, anthropology, creative writing, etc.). They are also likely to have wonderful and progressive schools and teachers. A character from this clan may select any Language, History or Lore skill (with a +10% bonus) as one of his O.C.C. Related or Secondary Skill selections even if it is not normally available to his O.C.C.

16-20% Science or Medicine. The clan excels in science and/or medicine with one or two standout specialities. For instance, the clan may excel in the science of healing, or genetics, or dimensional physics, or astronomy/physics, chemistry/pharmaceuticals (or more likely, holistic medicine or magic and psionic healing), or computers, or robotics, or engineering, space travel, or xenology or zoology, and so on. A character from this clan may select any Science or Medical skill (with a +10% bonus) as one of his O.C.C. Related or Secondary Skill selections even if it is not normally available to his O.C.C.

21-30% Wealth. The clan either has a knack for business and trade, or has easy access to a profit generating resource (natural or man-made) such as minerals, crystals, ley lines, industry, communications, dimensional/magic transportation, tourist trade ... something that is a reliable cash cow. A character from this clan starts out with twice as much money/credits and a vehicle or additional, quality weapon (G.M.'s discretion).

31-40% Magic or Psionics. The clan is noted for having many experts and masters versed in the magic arts or psionics, and use it in a way that has made them notorious. This could be that the clan has some of the best Stone Masters or Crystal Mages, or Line Walkers, or Shifters, or Techno-Wizards (or Techno-Wizard devices), or offer other magicks, potions, amulets, or magic items not commonly available elsewhere, and so on. The clan has an abundance – probably more than is usual – of magic practitioners or Master Psychics. All clan members have a good understanding of magic and/or psionics, and feel comfortable around it. A character from this clan may select any Magic or related Lore skill (with a +10% bonus) as one of his O.C.C. Related or Secondary Skill selections even if it is not normally available to his O.C.C. If a practitioner of magic, the character gets a bonus 3D6 P.P.E. If psychic, he gets a bonus 3D6 I.S.P.

41-50% Monster Slayers/Warriors. The clan is notorious for being monster hunters and/or protecting people from evil supernatural beings and dangerous creatures of magic such as dragons. While versed in finding, fighting and slaying all manner of monsters, the clan may have an area of specialty such as the undead, demons, Deevils, Minions of Splugorth, Entities, Elementals, dragons, werebeasts, and so on.

They are likely to have a large number of Undead Slayers, Tattooed Defenders and various combat oriented O.C.C.s, but the difference is they are not militaristic and do not gather in armies. Rather they stalk their monstrous prey as lone hunters, in pairs and small, elite squads and platoons. Hunting and battling the supernatural and monsters is just their thing. Many members of the clan wander the Megaverse to battle these creatures, rescue their victims and liberate people from their torment and tyranny. A character from this clan may select any W.P. (with a +10% bonus where appropriate) as one of his O.C.C. Related or Secondary Skill selections even if it is not normally available to his O.C.C.

51-60% Humanitarians. All True Atlanteans are known for their compassion and heroism, but this clan is famous for going above and beyond the call of duty. Members of the clan work very hard to live up to this reputation, and are known for their acts of mercy, charity and kindness. They are known to willingly send their own people into plague invested villages to offer healing or care, take dangerous risks and fight for the downtrodden and underdogs. All are gracious hosts, providing food, drink and assistance to those they meet, and will give those truly in need, the shirt off their back. A character from this clan may select any Communications or Domestic skill (with a +15% bonus) as one of his O.C.C. Related or Secondary Skill selections even if it is not normally available to his O.C.C.

61-65% Tragedy. The clan is known for a terrible tragedy that has befallen them at some point in their history. This is probably something terrible and sad, and could be anything from war or genocide to natural disaster, plague, or some other terrible event. While the tragedy is what everyone knows the group for, the clan has valiantly met the challenge, grown from it and has moved forward with grace and courage. A character from this clan may select any one skill from any skill category (with a +10% bonus where appropriate) as one of his O.C.C. Related or Secondary Skill selections, even if it is not normally available to his O.C.C.

66-70% Betrayal. The clan is known for something terrible they did. This could be some sort of betrayal, backstabbing, deceit, trickery, an act of treachery, the murder(s) of an important person/head clansman(s), or some other heinous act leveled against another clan, their own clansmen, a non-Atlantean ally or innocent people who had put their trust in them. To this day, the clan lives in the shadow of this dark deed (or several foul acts). Atlanteans from this clan carry that black mark wherever they go, and are looked down upon by their fellow Atlanteans and all who know about their great betrayal. Even characters of good alignment are looked at with suspicion and distrust. An honorable character from this clan needs to work extra hard to make amends for the betrayal and to prove they are good, noble and trustworthy.

A character who tries to be a shining example of goodness gets a bonus of +1D4 to M.A. attribute plus 12 S.D.C. if Principled alignment, +8 if Scrupulous. In the alternative, the character may be a ruthless cutthroat, assassin, thief, criminal or raider worthy of the treacherous reputation. Such a character may select any Rogue or Espionage skill (with a +15% bonus) as one of his O.C.C. Related or Secondary Skill selections even if it is not normally available to his O.C.C.

71-75% Explorers. The clan has a reputation for daring exploits and as pathfinders in exploration. Many people from this clan are fascinated with discovery and visiting and exploring new, exotic planets and dimensions. They love travel and adventure and are always ready to go on a new quest or expedition. They tend to be inquisitive, think on their feet and are such risk takers that they have been known to stowaway and jump ship at exotic or unknown locations. A character from this clan is +1 on Perception Rolls and may select any Wilderness skill (with a +15% bonus) as one of his O.C.C. Related or Secondary Skill selections even if it is not normally available to his O.C.C.

76-80% Something rare and precious. This could be lost knowledge that the clan has, a lost form of magic (Crystal or Shadow Magic, perhaps, or a magic from an alien world), a piece of forgotten Atlantean history, technology or relic from the past, or magic item, or some other unique treasure that has won them fame (or infamy). A character from this clan may select any Technical skill (with a +15% bonus) as one of his O.C.C. Related or Secondary Skill selections even if it is not normally available to his O.C.C.

81-85% Combat. This clan is known for its fighting prowess and military acumen. A character from this clan may select any Military or W.P. skill (with a +15% bonus where applicable) as one of his O.C.C. Related or Secondary Skill selections even if it is not normally available to his O.C.C.

86-90% A unique relationship. The clan is known for its association or alliance with a notable individual, group, organization, planet, specific race of people, philosophy or deity. The relationship can be good or bad, but the clan and these people/organization are tied together in such a way that the clan is known for it. A good example is the relationship *clan Skellian* has developed with the Amazon warrior women of South America and other D-Bee races in their home city. A character from this clan may select any Technical skill (with a +15% bonus) as one of his O.C.C. Related or Secondary Skill selections even if it is not normally available to his O.C.C.

91-95% Secretive. Secretive can mean that the clan has a specific secret to keep hidden or is secretive and distrusting of others, especially non-Atlanteans. In general, they hide the locations of their cities, and information about population numbers, strategic strengths and weaknesses, allies, magical resources, their plans and agendas, and other data from most everyone. In the alternative, the clan could also be hiding something that they are deeply ashamed of and are afraid that others might not accept or under-stand. The clan members may keep to themselves as a result, but are more likely to behave in a friendly manner, they just do not share their secrets or information about themselves. Tend to be distrusting and suspicious of others. A character from this clan may select any ONE Espionage or Rogue skill (with a +15% bonus) as an extra bonus skill in addition to those normally available to his O.C.C.

96-100% Nosy Snoops. This clan is notoriously nosy. They love uncovering secrets and are skilled investigators, detectives, interrogators and spies. A clan with this reputation may be subtle and gather the information exclusively for their own knowledge, or use it to influence and leverage others, or they may be notorious gossips who love to know everything going on, have their nose in everyone's business, and enjoy exchanging, sharing and spreading what they know and rumors. Most members of this clan are charismatic, affable and friendly. These snoops and finders of secrets are also surprisingly open and trusting of others, at least until they find something suspicious. They love mysteries, puzzles and intrigue, which can get them into trouble when they go snooping around the wrong person or place. May be notorious for revealing one or more big secrets or scandals outside their own clan, or for uncovering and sharing something important or beneficial for all Atlanteans or good people. They only show discretion and the ability to keep secrets about their clan. A character from this clan may select any TWO Communications or Espionage skills (with a +10% bonus) as extra bonus skills in addition to those normally available to his O.C.C.

Step 7: General Outlook on Atlantis

How does the clan feel about having lost Ancient Atlantis? They no longer have their home world as their birthright. Are they content being a displaced people who have adopted homes, or do they even care about their human ancestors on Earth or resent humanity and the current state of the planet? What follows is the clan's general outlook on this matter. It does not reflect every individual in the clan, but it is the common sentiment.

01-60% Acceptance. The clan accepted their fate and the tragic loss of Atlantis long ago. Its reappearance and the island continent falling into the hands of the Splugorth has not changed their feelings. This clan is focused on the future and not the past. They have been exploring and making their place in the Megaverse for thousands of years. While ancient Atlantis is thought of fondly, the past is the past, and Atlantis is pretty much a non-issue for this clan.

61-80% Indifferent. The loss of Atlantis through the misuse of magic is a part of every Atlantean's history and legacy. On one hand, the continent's reappearance on magic rich Earth is nostalgic and exciting. On the other hand, it is rather sad and tragic that it has fallen into the hands of the Splugorth, denying Atlanteans what some feel is their birthright. But for the people of this clan, it does not impact or affect them one way or the other. They could not care less about the fate of the land that was the birthplace of their people. They are content with the lives they have established over the centuries and have no strong feelings about Atlantis, one way or the other. There are more important things to do.

81-90% Regret. The clan feels regret for having ever left their home world. They believe they should have stayed on Earth, their rightful home. Knowing Atlantis has fallen into the hands of the Splugorth is a tragedy that eats at their hearts every day. The clan will not go against the collective will of the Atlantean people, nor move the clan back to Earth, but they wish Atlantis was theirs. They have no problem in voicing their regret or their opinion that someday, maybe Atlanteans should try to force the Splugorth from their homeland and make it a satellite outpost or dimensional hub for all Atlantean people.

91-100% Rebellious. The clan rejects the notion of deserting their home. Earth and Atlantis are their rightful home. They agree with the Aerihman clan that Atlantis is their birthright and destiny. Many members of this clan are willing to do whatever is necessary to reclaim their home and they are likely to be sworn enemies of the Splugorth and their minions. However, the actions the clan are willing to take may vary. Some just voice loudly that it is wrong to leave the homeland to the Splugorth and something needs to be done. Others are active subversives and freedom fighter who engage in raids, attacks and sabotage against the Minions of Splugorth on Atlantis and may work with the Aerihman whom they see as like-minded patriots. Others take action against the Splugorth and their minions wherever they are encountered as an act of defiance, protest or revenge. This is not open warfare or suicide attacks, but when the opportunity avails itself to cheat, hurt or kill the Splugorth, they take it.

True Atlantean O.C.C.s

Tattooed Defender (new)
Tattooed Monster Hunter, Revisited
Atlantean Nomad, Revisited
Tattooed Undead Slayer, Revisited
Tattooed Voyager (new)

Sunaj Assassin, Revisited
Sunaj Shadow Assassin (new)
Sunaj Shadow Mage (new)

Crystal Mage (new)
Stone Master Mage, Revisited

The following O.C.C.s are exclusive to True Atlanteans. Please note the distinction between the True Atlantean O.C.C.s listed in the pages of this book and the Splugorth Slave O.C.C.s for True Atlanteans described in **Rifts® World Book Two: Rifts® Atlantis**. Splugorth Atlantean O.C.C.s are *warrior slaves* and include the *Tattooed Man, T-Monster Man, Maxi-Man,* and *Tattooed Archer*. While an Atlantean character could be one of these O.C.C.s, it would make them a slave and servant of the Splugorth, or an escaped slave who hates the Splugorth but may be uncivilized, ruthless and more dangerous than True Atlanteans not bred in captivity. Free Atlanteans do not typically train in the Splugorth O.C.C.s., instead preferring to be one of the O.C.C.s presented here. Any of the Splugorth O.C.C.s may be made available as a player character at the Game Master's approval.

Note that while a True Atlantean character is most likely to be one of these Atlantean O.C.C.s, they can be almost ANY O.C.C. available to humans, from men-at-arms or adventurers to practitioners of magic and psychics. The choice is left to the player.

Tattooed Defender

Dimensional Pyramids located at ley line nexus points help to control the energy levels and the Rifts that can be opened up to the Megaverse. Unfortunately, dimensional travel via the Rifts, even with the control of a stone pyramid, is dangerous and a double-edged sword. While Dimensional Pyramids can open a stable Rift, they cannot contain the ripples that travel along the Megaversal grid of ley lines. These ripples travel to numerous dimensions and like the tug from a fly in a spider's webbing, alert supernatural beings to its presence and they are able to follow the ripples back to their source, i.e. the dimensional Rifts. While At-lanteans have made many friends in their travels, they encounter many more hostile creatures. A great many of them evil supernatural beings drawn to the open Rift and the magic needed to create it. Such demons, entities and worse have been problematic from the first days Atlanteans began to use ley lines and pyramids to open portals to other worlds. So it is that some O.C.C.s, like the *Tattooed Defender,* go back to ancient Atlantis.

If the *Undead Slayer* and *Tattooed Voyager* are special forces, then the *Tattooed Defenders* are the valiant foot soldiers in the thick of things. They hold the line and rush to face whatever new danger threatens Atlantean citizens or the innocent. Tattooed Defenders guard all stone pyramids and respond to all dimensional incursions by raiders, invasion forces, and supernatural monsters. Each clan has a select number of Tattooed Defenders responsible for guarding clan assets and resources, and protecting pyramids and its citizenry. When necessary, these scattered fighting forces can be gathered and mobilized as an army to defend against any invaders and any threats that comes their way. Tattooed Defenders may join forces with other Tattooed Men, mages, psychics, heroes and adventurers whenever necessary, but the majority are the front-line defenders and police of the Atlanteans.

When Atlanteans or other heroes need to be broken out of an enemy prison, rescued from some other danger, or when combat forces are needed for any manner of combat missions or police work, the job usually falls upon the Tattooed Defender. The skilled warriors may be sent out on missions across the Megaverse to follow a lead, conduct an investigation, track down a fugitive or magic artifact, bring a fugitive to justice, foil an enemy's plot, exact revenge in the name of their clan or employer, or to help other heroes and adventurers on a noble mission. Tattooed Defenders are multifaceted warriors who can be found in every Atlantean clan and city, as well as on journeys and missions across the universe.

In the cities, at dimensional hubs, and Atlantean trading posts, Defenders may function as personal security and enforcers for wealthy families, clan leaders, clan Alchemists and Atlantean businesses. This is likely to include work as bodyguards and armed escorts for merchant caravans, spacecraft and V.I.P.s, undercover operatives, investigators, counter-espionage agents, enforcers and fixers. Tattooed Defenders who are attached to a particular family (probably for generations), employed by a particular business or clan Alchemist, or powerful family clan, but are unable to protect their employer, leader, or family clan, may find themselves without a master or employment. And without a

secure place within the Atlantean society of that particular clan. Like the samurai of feudal Japan, there is great shame and stigma when a Tattooed Defender has failed his master and/or clan. This applies even when the Defender(s) was not present when the attack happened. The honor and code of the Tattooed Defenders is such that even the absent are responsible for the failure or lost. Their thinking is that if they had been more diligent and prepared, they would have been present (or learned of the treachery prior to it), and might have made a difference. They were not, thus they share the blame of failure that resulted in the loss of their leader, family or business they were suppose to serve and protect. Such is the culture of the Tattooed Defenders. When this happens, the Tattooed Defenders find themselves without a master or a purpose.

Ronin Tattooed Defenders

Like the ronin samurai of Japan, a masterless Tattooed Defender lives with the stigma and shame of having failed his charge. For the Defender, it means the first order of business is to avenge his master. Such Ronin Defenders often become obsessed with avenging the master/family/employer or clan they have failed and dedicate themselves to hunting down and terminating those responsible for the tragedy. However, the quest of the Ronin Defender does not end with finding the one who pulled the trigger. Ronin Defenders seek bigger answers. They want to know why their master was slain and who hired the killers behind the murder or the destruction of the business or family. Once that information is uncovered, the Ronin Defender's mission of vengeance continues with the hunting down of *every last person* who had any hand in the matter, even if it means destroying an entire company, an enemy army, or a fellow Atlantean family or small clan. If demons or the Sunaj were responsible, the Ronin Defender may vow to hunt and destroy as many as he can until his last dying breath. His master shall be avenged or the Ronin will die trying. This may lead to joining up with other Ronin Defenders, Atlanteans or adventurers and heroes.

Should the Ronin Defender accomplish his goal of avenging his master, only then is he able to make himself available to another Atlantean clan, family or employer as a Tattooed Defender. Some never go back to hold that official position again. Instead, becoming a wandering mercenary for hire or adventurer in search of work and noble deeds to perform. Doing good is a way to redeem his own family's name as well as promote the good name of the family, clan or employer he had failed.

Tattooed Defender O.C.C. Abilities:

These are abilities and areas of expertise in addition to those common to all True Atlanteans, like Sense Ley Lines, Sense Rifts, and Operate Dimensional Pyramids. See the True Atlantean R.C.C. earlier in this book, page 45.

1. Magic Tattoos Denote Heritage: Staked heart and flaming sword as discussed under the Atlantean R.C.C. and described under the various clans.

2. Increased P.P.E. from Magic Tattoos: Base P.P.E. is 1D4x10+40 for all Tattooed Defenders. Add 10 P.P.E. points for each additional level of experience and +6 P.P.E. for each additional tattoo. **Note:** The Tattooed Defender can also draw energy from ley lines and nexus points, up to 25 P.P.E. per each activation of a magic tattoo or 20 P.P.E. per melee round to power or use a magic device.

3. Increased P.P.E. Recovery: The Tattooed Defender's P.P.E. replenishes itself at the rate of 15 points for every hour of meditation, rest or sleep; 25 P.P.E. when meditation is performed on a ley line.

4. M.D.C.: Tattooed Defenders have a base M.D.C. of 1D6x10, +10 M.D.C. per each additional level of experience, and another 11 M.D.C. for males and 13 M.D.C. points for females for each additional tattoo after the initial six. (Counts as Hit Points in S.D.C. settings with a Natural A.R. of 13.) Due to the number of magic tattoos, they are considered supernatural beings with Supernatural P.S. and P.E., so their physical attacks inflict M.D. and hurt supernatural beings and Mega-Damage creatures.

5. O.C.C. Bonuses: +1 on all Perception Rolls, +2 on Perception Rolls pertaining to crime scene investigation, finding clues, and noticing suspicious behavior or something out of place, +1 to parry, +2 to disarm, +2 to pull punch, +2 to save vs Horror Factor, and +2 to save vs possession. Attribute bonuses from physical training and magic are +2 to M.A., +1D4 to P.S. (Supernatural), +1D4 to P.P. and P.B. Make sure you include the True Atlantean R.C.C. bonuses too.

6. Magic Tattoos: The Tattooed Defender starts with the following magic tattoos:

The two Marks of Heritage (standard).
One Flaming Weapon
One Flaming Shield
Eyes: Three (supernatural vision)
Knight in Full Body Armor
Guardian Power Tattoo (exclusive to the Defender)
Two Power tattoos of choice.
Two Simple Weapon tattoos of choice.
Two Animals tattoos of choice.
One Monster tattoo of choice.

Each new level of experience, the character's clan elder or a clan Alchemist can add two simple tattoos (animal or simple weapons) or one major tattoo (power, monster, or magic weapons). Tattooed Defenders tend to avoid (and are discouraged by clan alchemists to receive) Dimension Tattoos. **Note:** Receiving one or two new tattoos may require traveling to a different dimension, so the character may have to disappear for a few days from time to time. It is possible that circumstances do not allow the character to get the tattoos immediately after attaining the next level of experience. The most tattoos any T-Man can get at any time is two. There must be at least six months between the acquisition of another pair of tattoos.

Military Area of Specialty (MOS): Select one of the following areas of specialty or roll percentile dice to make a random determination. All MOS skills are in addition to O.C.C. and O.C.C. Related Skills.

01-10% Combat Mechanic:
Pick one: Automotive Mechanics or Aircraft Mechanics
Armor/Field Armorer (+10%)
Basic Mechanics (+20%)
Basic Electronics (+10%)
Computer Programming (+10%)
General Repair & Maintenance (+20%)
Jury-Rig or Locksmith (+20%)

11-20% Combat Medic:
Brewing: Medicinal (+10%)
Holistic Medicine (+10%)
Biology (+20%)
Field Surgery (+20%)
Paramedic (+15%)
Chemistry or Chemistry: Pharmaceutical (+10%)

21-30% Communication Expert:
Computer Operation (+10%)
Basic Electronics (+10%)
Electronic Countermeasures (+20%)
TV/Video or Optic Systems (+14%)
Cryptography or Computer Programming (+20%)
Sensory Equipment (+20%)

31-40% Espionage:
Demolitions (+20%)
Electronic Countermeasures (+15%)
Intelligence (+15%)
Interrogation (+10%)
Prowl (+15%)
Surveillance (+10%)
Hand to Hand: Martial Arts

41-50% Soldier/Grunt:
Forced March
Land Navigation (+5%)
Physical: One of choice.
Pilot: One of choice (+10%); excluding Power Armor, Robots, or Ships.
W.P.: One Ancient Weapon of choice.
W.P.: One Modern Weapon of choice.

51-60% Point Man/Scout:
Note: Requires an I.Q. 9 or higher, a high P.P. & Spd are helpful.
Detect Ambush (+15%)
Detect Concealment or Camouflage (+15%)
Optic Systems (+20%)
Land Navigation (+14%)
Prowl or Tracking (people) (+10%)
Tailing (+10%)
Wilderness Survival or Intelligence (+10%)

61-70% Pigman/Heavy Weapons:
Note: Requires a P.S. of 15 and a P.E. of 12 or higher.
Recognize Weapon Quality (+20%)
Weapon Systems (+20%)
W.P. Rifles
W.P. Heavy Military Weapons
W.P. Heavy M.D. Weapons (including rail guns).
W.P.: One of choice (any, Ancient or Modern) or two Demolition skills (+10%).

71-80% Power Armor/Robot Commando:
Mathematics: Advanced (+15%)
Navigation (+10%)
Pilot: Robots & Power Armor (basic; +10%)
Pilot: Robot & Power Armor Combat: Basic
Pilot: Robot Combat Elite: One of choice.
Sensory Equipment (+10%)
Weapon Systems (+10%)
Automatically gets a power armor suit, probably something common to the Three Galaxies, but can be any.

81-90% Transportation Specialist:

Basic Mechanics (+10%) or Combat Driving (+5%)

Navigation (+20%)

Pilot: Automobile or Motorcycle (+20%)

Pilot: Hover Craft (ground) or Hovercycle (+15%)

Pilot: Tanks & APCs (+10%)

Pilot: Jet Fighter, Combat Helicopter or Small Space Fighter (+10%, select one).

91-100% Investigator/Detective/Security/Military Police:

Crime Scene Investigation (preserving evidence; +10%)

I.D. Undercover Ops or T.V./Video (+15%)

Intelligence (+15%)

Pick Locks (+20%)

Streetwise or Find Contraband (+20%)

Surveillance (+20%; includes Tailing)

Undercover Ops (+15%)

And gets a Crystal Stun Mace

Atlantean Tattooed Defender O.C.C. Stats

Alignment Restrictions: Any, but most Atlanteans tend to be of good alignment with a few exceptions.

Attribute Requirements: P.S. and P.P. of 12 or higher.

O.C.C. Skills: These are in addition to MOS skills and reflect basic training.

Language and Literacy Dragonese/Elf, American, and Greek at 98%.

Language: Other: One of choice (+15%).

Climbing (+10%)

General Athletics

Mathematics: Basic (+15%)

Military Etiquette (+20%)

Radio: Basic (+20%)

Running

Sign Language (+10%)

W.P. Knife or Sword

W.P. Energy Pistol

W.P. Energy Rifle

Hand to Hand: Expert, which can be changed to Martial Arts at the cost of one O.C.C. Related skill or Commando for the cost of two skill selections.

O.C.C. Related Skills: Select three other skills at level one, plus select one additional skill at levels 3, 6, 9, 12 and 15. All new skills start at level one proficiency.

Communications: Languages and Literacy only.

Cowboy: None.

Domestic: Any.

Electrical: Basic only.

Espionage: None, other than possible MOS skills.

Horsemanship: General or Exotic only (+5%).

Mechanical: Automotive and Basic Mechanics only.

Medical: None, other than possible MOS skills.

Military: Any (+10%).

Physical: Any, except Acrobatics.

Pilot: Any (+5%).

Pilot Related: None, other than possible MOS skills.

Rogue: Any.

Science: Advanced Math (+5%) and Astronomy only.

Technical: Any (+10%).

W.P.: Any.

Wilderness: Land Navigation and Wilderness Survival only.

Secondary Skills: The character also gets to select two Secondary Skills from the Secondary Skill list at levels 1, 4, 8, and 12. These are additional areas of knowledge that do not get any bonus, other than possible bonuses from a high I.Q. All Secondary Skills start at the base skill level.

Standard Equipment: Suit of environmental body armor or Naruni equivalent force field (150 M.D.C.), a high-powered energy rifle and energy pistol of choice, a weapon for each W.P. and 1D4+2 E-Clips for each, 1D4 silver-plated knives or sword, a silver cross (may be worn as jewelry), a wooden cross, a dozen wooden stakes and mallet, pocket mirror, portable computer the size of a cell phone, portable language translator, and a first-aid kit. Additional equipment is issued depending upon the Tattooed Defender's assignment.

Crystal Guardian Armor (special): The Tattooed Defender are able to use something known as Guardian Armor, a type of magical power armor, and Super-Guardian, a sort of giant robot. Both are more like Crystal Golems piloted by the Defender. See description in the section about Crystal Magic and Artifacts. Use of these special magic armors are made possible via the *Guardian Power Tattoo* exclusive to the Tattooed Defender O.C.C.

Money: 4D6x1,000 in precious gems or artifacts. Tattooed Defenders have all their needs provided for them by their clan. They receive the equivalent of 2,000 credits a month when on active duty. Retired Tattooed Defenders, Ronin and independent agents/mercs get paid by the job.

Cybernetics: None, if it can be avoided. Due to their magic tattoos and sense of heritage, all True Atlanteans strive to get to a Healing Pyramid where they can be made whole. If not, Atlanteans will settle for cybernetic Bio-Systems. All Atlanteans are attracted to "natural" things, and mechanical systems are not natural. Moreover, cybernetics reduce the potency of magic. Only True Atlanteans who do not use magic, other than a few basic tattoos, may consider cybernetic implants.

Tattooed Monster Hunter, Revisited

If there is anyone who understands monsters, how they think, how to infiltrate them and how best to fight them, it is Clan Skellian's Monster Hunters. Undead Slayers and Tattooed Defenders have existed for thousands of years, the Atlantean Monster Hunter of *Clan Skellian*, however, is something new and exclusive to that clan, at least for the time being.

Clan Skellian is one of the few Atlantean groups to return to Earth to make their home. They reside in South America on Rifts Earth where strange monsters, mutants and aliens abound. Like all Atlanteans, the Skellian clansmen are well versed in fighting vampires, demons and other enemies of mortals. To advance the methods and means of destroying supernatural evil and other enemies of humanity, the members of Clan Skellian have managed to create a new type of tattoo. One that creates a sort of disguise around the Tattooed Man. This is not metamorphosis. Rather, the magic creates a physical manifestation that is worn by the Atlantean Monster Hunter like a costume or suit of power armor. It completely encloses the Monster Hunter and mimics all the particular features, scent, voice and language of a specific monster.

This enables the Clan Skellian Monster Hunters to walk among their enemies without being recognized as a dangerous invader. This has enabled them to infiltrate and spy upon societies of monsters, mutants and D-Bees, and even demons and Deevils, to gather intelligence, and perform all manner of espionage and targeted strikes. The society of many monsters is tribal, so killing a couple of their main leaders, witches or wise men often sends the tribe into disarray, making them more vulnerable to larger attacks or simply undermining their plans. When a new leader rises to power it is likely to be weeks, often months later, and he or she may have a different agenda that is less threatening to Atlanteans or humans.

The Monster Hunter has been very successful in the role of espionage, as well as rescue missions to free captives imprisoned by the monsters, sabotage, theft, and surgical strikes. As word spreads about the effectiveness of Clan Skellian Monster Hunters (but not how they manage to do what they do), some other clans have taken notice. However, the magic tattoo that makes this all possible is a well-kept secret, even from other Atlantean clans, the Aerihman clan in particular. Clan Skellian is not yet ready to share their secrets. It should be noted that if another Atlantean clan does come across a Monster Hunter, the warrior does not deny he is using a new type of magic, but does not go into details about it. When it is necessary to don the magical disguise, the Monster Hunter tries to go off someplace secluded to make the change.

Rumors abound about the Skellian Monster Hunters. One is that the members of the clan have uncovered a new type of crystal magic used to create an amulet or stone that makes them invisible to supernatural beings and evil monsters. Another is that the clan has uncovered a treasure trove of ancient Nazca or Mayan magical artifacts that either enables them to metamorph, a feat that is supposed to be impossible for True Atlanteans, or create some sort of convincing illusion that enable the Monster Hunter to walk among monsters undetected. Other rumors include a crystal, artifact or new type of magic that gives the Monster Hunter the ability to control demons and monsters like puppets, or to possess the bodies of such monsters for the purpose of espionage. Many of these rumors originate from the various cover stories Atlantean Monster Hunters have told heroic allies and teammates in the field; mostly non-Atlanteans. As a result, nobody suspects it is a new type of magic tattoo, not even other Atlanteans. It seems likely that Clan Skellian will eventually share their knowledge with other Atlanteans, but for now it is their secret and exclusive to members of the Skellian clan.

Tattooed Monster Hunter Abilities:

These are abilities and areas of expertise are in addition to those common to all True Atlanteans, like Sense Ley Lines, Sense Rifts, and Operate Dimensional Pyramids. See True Atlantean R.C.C. earlier in this book, page 45.

1. Magic Tattoos Denote Heritage: Staked heart and flaming sword as discussed under the Atlantean R.C.C.

2. Increased P.P.E. from Magic Tattoos: Base P.P.E. is 1D4x10+50 for all Monster Hunters. Add 10 P.P.E. points for each additional level of experience and +6 P.P.E. for each additional tattoo. **Note:** The Monster Hunter can also draw energy from ley lines and nexus points, up to 20 P.P.E. per each activation of a tattoo or 15 P.P.E. per melee round to power or use a magic device.

3. Increased P.P.E. Recovery: The Monster Hunter's P.P.E. replenishes itself at the rate of 20 points for every hour of meditation, rest or sleep; 25 P.P.E. when meditation is performed on a ley line.

4. M.D.C.: Tattooed Monster Hunters have a base M.D.C. of 2D4x10, +10 per each additional level of experience, and another 11 M.D.C. for males and 13 M.D.C. points for females for each additional tattoo after the initial six. (Counts as Hit Points in S.D.C. settings with a Natural A.R. of 12.) Due to the number of magic tattoos, they are considered supernatural beings with Supernatural P.S. and P.E., so their physical attacks inflict M.D. and hurt supernatural beings and Mega-Damage creatures.

5. Advanced Knowledge of Atlantean Pyramids: Monster Hunters are seasoned dimensional travelers and have a full understanding of Dimensional Pyramids. They can operate Dimensional Pyramids at 40% +5% per level of experience.

6. O.C.C. Bonuses: +2 on Perception Rolls involving monsters, the supernatural and disguise, +1 on initiative, +2 to save vs magic (in addition to P.E. bonuses), and +6 to save vs Horror Factor. Attribute bonuses from physical training and magic: +1 to M.E., +2 to P.S. (Supernatural Strength), +2 to P.E., and +4 to Spd. Make sure you include the True Atlantean R.C.C. bonuses too.

7. Magic Tattoos: The Monster Hunter starts with the following magic tattoos.

The Marks of Heritage
One Simple Weapon
Two Magic Weapons
Two Animals
Two Monsters
Six Monster-Shaping Tattoos
Two Power Tattoos

One additional tattoo from any category of choice, including Dimension Tattoos.

Each new level of experience, the character's clan elder or a clan Alchemist can add two simple tattoos (animal or simple weapons) or one major tattoo (power, monster, magic weapons, or monster-shaping tattoo). Monster Hunters are discouraged by clan Alchemists from receiving more than one Dimension Tattoo. **Note:** Receiving one or two new tattoos may require traveling to a different dimension, so the character may have to disappear for a few days from time to time. It is possible that circumstances do not allow the character to get the tattoos immediately after attaining the next level of experience. The most tattoos any T-Man, even a Monster Hunter, can get at any time is two. There must be at least six months between the acquisition of another pair of tattoos.

Atlantean Monster Hunter Stats

Attribute Requirements: I.Q. 10 or higher and M.E. 20 or higher. A high P.S. and/or P.P. is helpful but not required. Note that attributes may be temporarily altered by magic tattoos. The effects, bonuses and penalties are cumulative.

Alignment: Any, most Atlanteans tend to be good with a few exceptions.

O.C.C. Skills:
Concealment (+15%)
Disguise (+15%)
Intelligence (+10%)
Language and Literacy Dragonese/Elf, American, and Greek at 98%.
Language: Other: Two of choice (+15%).
Lore: Demons and Monsters (+25%)
Lore: Magic (+15%)
Performance (+15%)
Radio: Basic (+10%)
Tracking (+15%)
Wilderness Survival (+15%)
W.P. Sword
W.P. Energy Pistol
W.P. Energy Rifle
W.P.: One of choice.
Hand to Hand: Martial Arts

O.C.C. Related Skills: Select four other skills at level one, plus one additional skill at levels 3, 6, 9, 12 and 15. All new skills start at level one proficiency.
Communications: Any (+5%).
Cowboy: None.
Domestic: Any (+5%).
Electrical: Basic only.
Espionage: Any (+15%).
Horsemanship: General or Exotic only (+10%).
Mechanical: Basic only.
Medical: Animal Husbandry, Brewing: Medicinal, First Aid, Holistic Medicine, and Paramedic only (+10%).
Military: Any (+10%).
Physical: Any.
Pilot: Any, except robot and power armor skills (+10%).
Pilot Related: Any (+10%).
Rogue: Any (+4%).
Science: Any (+5%).
Technical: Any (+5%).
W.P.: Any.
Wilderness: Any (+5%).

Secondary Skills: The character also gets to select two Secondary Skills from the Secondary Skill list at levels 4, 8 and 12.

These are additional areas of knowledge that do not get any bonus, other than possible bonuses from a high I.Q. All Secondary Skills start at the base skill level.

Standard Equipment: A weapon for each W.P. or Techno-Wizard equivalents with 1D4 E-Clips for each, 1D4 silver-plated knives or one knife and a silver plated sword, a wooden cross, a dozen wooden stakes and mallet. When masquerading as a monster, the character will have suitable clothing and equipment to augment his disguise.

Money: 4D6x1,000 in precious gems or artifacts, plus 1D6x1,000 in exotic monster trophies such as claws, teeth, bones, etc., that may have uses in alchemy or herbology. Monster Hunters are not motivated by wealth. They are truly dedicated to infiltrating, routing and destroying supernatural menaces. They are experts at spying on and exterminating monsters.

Cybernetics: None, if it can be avoided. Due to their magic tattoos and sense of heritage, all True Atlanteans strive to get to a Healing Pyramid where they can be made whole. If not, Atlanteans settle for cybernetic Bio-Systems. All Atlanteans are attracted to "natural" things, and mechanical systems are not natural. Moreover, cybernetics reduces the potency of magic. Only True Atlanteans who do not use magic, other than a few basic tattoos, may consider cybernetic implants.

Atlantean Nomad, Revisited

By Carl Gleba and Kevin Siembieda

The Atlantean Nomad is not what is commonly known as a "Tattooed Man" – dimension spanning, Atlantean warriors with Mega-Damage bodies and a dozen-plus tattoos that come to life. Nomads possess only 5-6 magic tattoos including the Marks of Heritage, which, in some ways, makes them the boldest of Atlantean adventurers and dimensional travelers. For protection, they use conventional M.D.C. light to medium environmental body armor, and/or Atlantean force field generators (on par with anything *Naruni Enterprises* has to offer), or TW armor, and M.D. tech-based weapons, Techno-Wizard weapons and other magical and alien weapons and gear. Driven by wanderlust to visit alien worlds and dimensions to learn and experience all that the Megaverse has to offer them, they know there is much to see, and accept most people on face value until they prove otherwise. For these Atlanteans, life is a journey. There is too much to see and experience to chain themselves to a desk and a routine nine-to-five existence, or any conventional life. Nomads seek knowledge and enlightenment through travel and by experiencing the lives and cultures of countless other beings.

These are the Atlanteans who see themselves as citizens of the Megaverse. Though their clan may have a city or world they have adopted as their own, the Nomads feel at home anywhere in the universe and regard all sentient life forms as their brethren. Their level of empathy toward others is very high. They try not to be judgmental and try to accept people for who and what they are. Nomads seek to find common ground between themselves and others, focusing on the things they share, not the things that make them different. When people meet an Atlantean who is not a specialized combat class with many magic tattoos like the Defender,

C WALTON 2016!

Undead Slayer, Monster Hunter or Voyager, odds are they have encountered a Nomad. In fact, for most outsiders, the Nomad is their image of True Atlanteans.

This life of dimensional travel and visiting worlds makes Nomads something of a Jack-of-all-trades, with a focus on the skills and abilities that help them survive in a wide range of environments and cultures. Most Nomads are sincerely fascinated by other people and their cultures, so most are semi-professional anthropologists who know how to quickly recognize key behaviors, customs and taboos, to best fit in and avoid offending the people they walk among. Nomads are seldom rude or offensive, having learned how to blend in with sentient alien species and skirt the line of acceptable protocols. After all, saying, doing and even eating the wrong thing can get you imprisoned, tortured or killed. Nobody knows this, and how to blend in, better than the Atlantean Nomad. For this reason, many Atlantean Nomads become diplomats for their clans later in life. To be good dimensional travelers, Atlantean Nomads learn to be tolerant and accepting of alien beings and their cultures.

Some outsiders compare Atlantean Nomads to Wilderness Scouts, but the analogy only works to the extent that they like to travel and explore new worlds and dimensions. Many Atlantean Nomads have few to no wilderness, tracking or hunting skills whatsoever. They travel to learn about other people, cultures, worlds and dimensions, not tromp through forests and jungles, though they are not opposed to such things, and have probably visited many desolate locations and wildlands in their many sojourns across dimensions.

They also tend to be natural problem solvers who like to help communities and individuals in distress. The humanitarian efforts and good deeds of Atlantean Nomads have helped earn True Atlanteans the reputation of being noble heroes who defend and protect all life forms. The more flamboyant and powerful Atlantean warrior O.C.C.s adding the exclamation point to such statements by their heroics and slaying of monsters. There are so many Nomads that they are considered to be the "typical Atlantean" by many outsiders.

Atlantean Nomad O.C.C. Abilities:

These are abilities and areas of expertise in addition to those common to all True Atlanteans. See the True Atlantean R.C.C. earlier in this book, page 45.

1. Magic Tattoos Denote Heritage: Staked heart and flaming sword as discussed under the Atlantean R.C.C., both are fully functioning magic tattoos.

2. Increased P.P.E. from Magic Tattoos: Base P.P.E. for Nomads is 5D6+20 points. Add 10 P.P.E. points for each additional level of experience and +6 P.P.E. for each additional tattoo (+10 P.P.E. for Dimension Tattoos). **Note:** The Nomad can also draw energy from ley lines and nexus points, up to 25 P.P.E. per each activation of a tattoo or 20 P.P.E. per melee round to power or use a magic device.

3. Increased P.P.E. Recovery: The Nomad's P.P.E. replenishes itself at the rate of 10 points for every hour of meditation, rest or sleep; 20 P.P.E. when meditation is performed on a ley line.

4. M.D.C.: None. Atlantean Nomads are NOT Mega-Damage beings nor are they considered to be supernatural in any way. Their P.S. is equal to Augmented (not Supernatural) and they must use body armor, power armor, force fields, magic or other means to protect themselves just like any other human.

5. O.C.C. Bonuses: +2 on Perception Rolls, +1 on initiative, +1 to dodge, +2 to pull punch and roll with impact, and +2 to save vs Horror Factor. Nomad attribute bonuses: +1D4 to M.A. and P.P., +1 to P.S. (Augmented Strength), as well as +2D6 to Hit Points and +3D6+3 to S.D.C. Make sure you include the True Atlantean R.C.C. bonuses too.

6. Magic Tattoos: The Atlantean Nomad starts with five tattoos.

Two Marks of Heritage (discussed under the Atlantean R.C.C.).

The Eye of Knowledge.

Two of choice. Any magic tattoo may be selected, but Nomads usually select two Dimension Tattoos as it is the only time they can get them, or one Dimension Tattoo and one Magic Weapon.

The Nomad can select one additional tattoo upon reaching 5th level experience. The new tattoo selection is limited to animal or simple weapon.

7. Advanced Knowledge of Atlantean Pyramids: Nomads are seasoned dimensional travelers and have a full understanding of Dimensional Pyramids and how to operate them at 40% +5% per level of experience.

8. Clan Lore (special): In their travels, Nomads meet many other Atlanteans and are very curious about other clans, large and small. Nomads tend to know more about Atlantean history and key points about other clans, even the small, obscure ones, than others. This includes their general alignment, outlook on life, feelings about Atlantis, notable allegiances, notable triumphs and failures, and similar fundamentals. **Base Skill:** 40% +5% per level of experience.

9. Specialized Area of Study: The following are common additional areas of study Atlantean Nomads often learn before they go out exploring the universe. Roll percentile dice for random determination on the table below, or select one of choice when first creating the character and again at level six. Any skills gained through a special ability start at level one proficiency.

01-10% Advanced Knowledge of Pyramids: Add +15% to operate Dimensional Pyramids, +10% to operate Healing Pyramids, and +5% on all other types. This Nomad has intimate knowledge on how all stone pyramids are built and how they work, and knows where to look to find secret passages and chambers inside stone pyramids (01-75% chance).

11-20% Advanced Knowledge of Dimensions: The Atlantean Nomad has either studied or spent time in several other dimensions and knows them well. The Nomad is an expert in six other worlds or dimensions. Add +20% to Dimension Lore skill when dealing specifically with those dimensions. Just like the skill, the Nomad will know where all the hot spots are like Center on Phase World, the Splynn D-Market on Rifts Earth and so on. The Lore: Dimensions skill is found under the Shifter O.C.C. on page 126 of **Rifts Ultimate Edition**.

21-30% Dimension Sense Ability: Just like a Shifter O.C.C., this Nomad is able to meditate upon arriving at a dimension and get a sense of the dimensional makeup. The base percentage is 35% +5% per level of experience. Dimension Sense is described under the Shifter O.C.C. in the **Rifts Ultimate Edition** on page 121.

31-40% Ley Line Expert: After years of study, the Nomad understands Ley Lines almost as well as a Ley Line Walker. This is because they constantly use Ley Lines in their journeys. The sensing abilities of a Nomad are doubled, so they can sense a Ley Line up to 10 miles (16 km) away and a nexus up to 20 miles (32 km) away. They can also sense Rifts up to 40 miles (64 km) away, but are unable to pinpoint their exact location. They only know that it is close or far and the general direction.

41-50% Spaceship Pilot: The Nomad has learned to enjoy piloting spacecraft (probably in the Three Galaxies), and has the following skills: Pilot Space Fighter (50% +3% per level), Pilot Small Spacecraft (60% +3% per level), Navigation: Space (40% +5% per level) and Lore: Galactic/Alien (25% +5% per level of experience). All enjoy a +15% skill bonus. See **Dimension Book 2: Phase World®**, page 150, for skill descriptions.

Don't want spacecraft skills? In the alternative, select four piloting skills of choice, any, excluding Military and Robots (+15%).

51-55% Nomad Sneak: This Atlantean Nomad is a bit of a rogue and a sneak. He is attracted to rumors, innuendo and intrigue, likes to unravel mysteries, and finds the dark world of espionage and crime more exciting than he would like to admit. His skills reflect his predilection: Escape Artist, Pick Locks, Prowl, Research and Tailing, all of which get a +15% skill bonus.

56-60% Nomad Scholar: The Nomad Scholar spends time reading, researching and studying various philosophies, firsthand. The Nomad Scholar strives to find new people and D-Bees to expand his knowledge. Add four skills selected from the Technical skill category, each with a +15% bonus.

The scholar has also made scholarly friends among 1D4+1 groups of non-Atlantean people at different locations/worlds/ space stations, or dimensions. These scholarly friends will go out of their way to help the Nomad Scholar with information, rumors, gossip and scholastic studies. They are not as quick to engage in combat and risk their lives in battle, but they may do so to help their friend in times of need.

61-65% Nomad Scientist: The Nomad considers himself a scientist and has a solid scientific background. Select four Science skills of choice with a +15% bonus for each. The Nomad Scientist also has a small, hidden or mobile lab/research facility to conduct his studies and experiments.

66-70% Nomad Explorer: The Nomad loves to explore and travel. The following skills help: Astronomy and Navigation, Archeology, Climbing, Horsemanship: Exotic, and Wilderness Survival, all of which get a +10% skill bonus.

71-75% Nomad Diplomat: Nomad Diplomats spend most of their time seeking friendships and alliances for their clan. They are away from home a lot more often, working on strengthening existing ties and making new ones. The Nomad Diplomat speaks two additional languages, has Public Speaking, Law: General, and Lore: D-Bees at +10%. The Nomad Diplomat will be on good terms with 1D6 notable Atlantean clans where they can seek shelter and in general, have a place to go where additional allies can be found. The Nomad Diplomat will also have good relations or contacts with 1D4 other settlements or races. For example, the Nomad Diplomat will know someone of a decent rank in Lazlo and can expect to find friends and allies in that city.

76-80% The Great Communicator: This Nomad has a gift for gab and likes to meet and learn about different people. His additional skills include, Barter, Begging, Dance, Public Speaking, Sing or Play Musical Instrument (professional quality), and Radio: Basic, all of which get a +15% skill bonus.

81-85% Nomad Wheeler and Dealer: This Nomad knows a bargain when he sees it, and knows how to negotiate. He has the following skills: Appraise Goods, Barter, Performance, and Recognize Weapon Quality, all of which get a +20% skill bonus.

86-90% Nomad Rescuer: This Nomad cares about helping people and has skills suitable for a first responder, as follows: Excavation, Firefighting, Paramedic, and Field Surgery or Holistic Medicine, all of which get a +20% skill bonus.

91-95% Nomad Fixer: This Nomad is skilled at fixing and maintaining machines, and has the following skills: Computer Operation, Computer Programming, Basic Electronics, and General Repair & Maintenance, all of which get a +15% skill bonus.

96-100% Nomad Paladin: This individual started out on the path of becoming a Tattooed Defender or an Undead Slayer, but before training and tattoos were completed, the individual dropped out (or washed out) and became a wandering Nomad. The character has received combat training and uses it to protect the innocent and fight injustice wherever it is found. These self-styled nomadic paladins have the following skills: Three W.P. skills of choice (any, Ancient or Modern) and start with Hand to Hand: Expert which can be changed to Martial Arts (or Assassin if an evil alignment) at the cost of one O.C.C. Related Skill.

Instead of the usual Nomad or Defender tattoos, the *Nomad Paladin* starts with the following nine:

Marks of Heritage (standard two tattoos for their clan).
One Flaming Weapon
One Flaming Shield
Eyes: Three (supernatural vision).
Knight in Full Body Armor
One Simple Weapon tattoo of choice.
Two Dimension Tattoos of choice.

Note: This makes him a minor Mega-Damage being with Supernatural P.S. and P.E. Combine all S.D.C. and Hit Points and make them M.D.C. +10. +11 M.D.C. for males (13 for females) per each additional tattoo after the initial six, and +1D6 M.D.C. per level of experience.

Base P.P.E. is 1D4x10+10 plus six P.P.E. per each magic tattoo (10 P.P.E. for each Dimension Tattoo), and +1D6 P.P.E. per level of experience.

Atlantean Nomad O.C.C. Stats

Attribute Requirements: None, though a good I.Q. and high M.A. are very helpful.

Alignment: Any, but most are Principled (30%), Scrupulous (35%), and Unprincipled (15%).

O.C.C. Skills:

Anthropology (+20%)
Basic Math (+20%)
Dimensional Lore (see Voyager O.C.C.)
First Aid (+10%)
Land Navigation (+15%)
Language & Literacy: Dragonese/Elf, American, and Greek at 98%.
Languages: Speaks two additional languages of choice (+15%).
Lore: Demons & Monsters (+15%)
Lore: Faeries & Creatures of Magic (+10%)
Wilderness Survival or Intelligence (+10%)
Swimming (+5%)
W.P. Blunt

W.P. Sword

W.P. Energy Rifle

Hand to Hand: Basic which can be changed to Expert at the cost of one O.C.C. Related Skill, or to Martial Arts (or Assassin if an evil alignment) for the cost of two O.C.C. Related Skills.

O.C.C. Related Skills: In addition to *Specialized Area of Study, #9* above, select five other skills. Plus select one additional skill at levels 3, 7, 11, and 15. All new skills start at level one proficiency.

Communications: Any (+5%).

Cowboy: None.

Domestic: Any (+10%).

Electrical: Any.

Espionage: None.

Horsemanship: General or Exotic only.

Mechanical: Any.

Medical: Any, except Cybernetic Medicine, Entomological Medicine, Pathology, and Medical Doctor.

Military: None.

Physical: Any.

Pilot: Any (+5%).

Pilot Related: Any (+10%).

Rogue: Any (+5%).

Science: Any.

Technical: Any (+10%).

W.P.: Any.

Wilderness: Any (+10%).

Secondary Skills: The character also gets to select five Secondary Skills from the Secondary Skill list plus one additional Secondary Skill at levels two, six and ten. These are additional areas of knowledge that do not get any bonus, other than possible bonuses from a high I.Q. All Secondary Skills start at the base skill level.

Standard Equipment: Energy rifle, and one other weapon related to his W.P. skills, 1D6 E-Clips for each weapon, pocket knife, one silver-plated blade weapon, silver cross (may be worn as jewelry), pocket mirror, a survival knife, Vibro-Saber, a cross of some kind, backpack, oversized satchel, 1D4 sacks/bags, utility belt, sleeping bag or tent, first aid kit, 1D6 flares, two rocket flares, 1D4+1 smoke grenades, portable computer the size of a cell phone, language translator, sunglasses and goggles, air filter, gas mask, 100 feet (30.5 m) of rope, pocket tool kit, flashlight, and Mega-Damage body armor. Nomads love magic items and weapons, and will acquire at least a few over the years.

Money: 1D4x10,000 in credits and 4D6x1,000 in precious gems or artifacts, and may have valuable secrets, information or services that can be sold or used for trade. Nomads have a much greater need for money to buy equipment and continue adventuring and exploring. They often accumulate small fortunes, but these fortunes are typically in the form of ready cash, credits, magic items, or possessions that can be easily liquidated to finance the individual's travels. That said, Nomads are always on the move, adventuring and exploring, so they do not carry a lot of valuables on them, only what they think they will need for that excursion. As a result, they are frequently selling items they collect to finance more ventures or to put cash into the bank. Nomads always have access to their finances via a wide variety of options, including intergalactic banks on Phase World and/or elsewhere in the Three Galaxies, and even with the Naruni and Splugorth.

Cybernetics: None, if it can be avoided. Due to their magic tattoos and sense of heritage, all True Atlanteans strive to get to a Healing Pyramid where they can be made whole. If not, Atlanteans will settle for cybernetic Bio-Systems. All Atlanteans are attracted to "natural" things, and mechanical systems are not natural. Moreover, cybernetics reduces the potency of magic. Only True Atlanteans who do not use magic, other than a few basic tattoos, may consider cybernetic implants.

Tattooed Undead Slayer, Revisited

By Carl Gleba and Kevin Siembieda

Atlantean Undead Slayers are an elite force of supernatural monster hunters. They travel from dimension to dimension protecting innocents and freeing those enslaved and fighting against supernatural horrors whenever they are found. They might be thought of as transdimensional knights errant, except their true goal is to eradicate supernatural evil, with an emphasis on vampires and Vampire Intelligences. Yes, Undead Slayers are brave and help people when they can, but their mission is to destroy the undead and supernatural evil. A job they are unapologetically ruthless and methodical at accomplishing. Hesitation or mercy can cost lives, so neither can be allowed. Not when fighting supernatural evil. Many who have witnessed Undead Slayers in action report being horrified by the level of brutality and mercilessness exhibited by the warriors in battle – barely able to tell which is the hero and which is the monster. Undead Slayers ask for no quarter and expect none in return. Their work is not for the faint of heart and they seldom apologize for doing what needs to be done. As you might expect, many Undead Slayers are battle hardened. They are so focused on their task of extermination that they do not find the time to comfort the people they have come to save from monsters, or help them deal with the trauma or rebuild their lives or community. For most Undead Slayers, that is not part of their job description. That's someone else's job. Theirs is to destroy monsters and move on to the next infestation.

One Undead Slayer put it rather indelicately, like this:

"You don't ask a rat catcher for advice on how to rebuild your life or deal with loss. You ask him to exterminate the vermin. When he does his job right, the problem is gone and he leaves for his next job.

"We Undead Slayers are not much different. We are glad to help. Pleased to destroy every last vampire, demon or monster so they never hurt anyone ever again. It's a noble cause, but it is dirty work. An ugly, dangerous job. We do it because it needs doing. So don't ask us to hold your hand and try to soothe your sorrows after we've been awash in the blood and gore of our enemies. We don't have time to help you mourn your losses. We understand your grief. We've lost people to the vermin too. A lot of them. We are hunted by the very monsters we seek to destroy, and by the wretched souls who revere and serve them. When our work is done, don't ask us to give you more. We have

nothing to give you. We need to move on. There are more monsters to slay, and not enough of us to do it. Be thankful that we came and put an end to the nightmare. You'll find a way through this. People always do. You're stronger than you think."

So it is that Undead Slayers are dedicated and relentless in their crusade to destroy all vampires and wicked monsters. They wander the dimensions and visit worlds seeking out supernatural evil with the express purpose of destroying it and the creature's willing henchmen. As warriors, Undead Slayers try to avoid becoming entangled in regional politics or the affairs of people, especially the rich and powerful. They are there to destroy supernatural menaces, the undead in particular, nothing more. That said, the heroes do not easily tolerate inhumanity to man, social injustice such as slavery, or public displays of abject cruelty or terror. If the opportunity avails itself, most Undead Slayers will take a stand against evil, regardless of whether it comes in the guise of fellow humans or the supernatural. They also know that a monstrous appearance does not automatically equate to being a monster, and judge people by their actions, not by their looks or rumors about them.

Some clans are more active than others in trying to eradicate supernatural evil. Larger clans tend to dedicate more Undead Slayers to the cause, as well as include them among their fighting forces to defend their clan, cities and holdings. In larger military conflicts, Undead Slayers are usually deployed as special forces to lead surgical strikes and commando raids, but are sent wherever they are needed, including the front line and in defense of their adopted worlds.

When out hunting supernatural evil across the Megaverse, it is common for a group of 2-8 Undead Slayers to travel with one or two Tattooed Voyagers, a couple of Nomads, a Defender or two, a mage and one or two other Atlantean O.C.C.s. Undead Slayers are also known to join mixed groups of adventurers, Cosmo-Knights, Cyber-Knights and other bands of heroes. Such allegiances are for a short while or to champion a particular mission or cause, and sometimes last for years or a lifetime. When an Undead Slayer forges a friendship, the bond is unbreakable unless he is betrayed. Those who betray an Undead Slayer had better kill him or face his undying wrath.

Undead Slayers enjoy the company of people who possess a good, noble and heroic spirit. As is true of most Atlanteans, these warriors are attracted to goodness and helping underdogs, and protecting the innocent who have nobody else to stand up for them. Dedicated heroes, Undead Slayers cannot seem to help themselves from championing good causes that oppose the forces of evil.

With the outbreak of the **Minion War** and incursions into the realms of mortals by the demons of Hades and Dyval, it seems Atlantean heroes, and Undead Slayers in particular, are needed more than ever. While some have joined other combat forces across the Three Galaxies, Rifts Earth and elsewhere, other Undead Slayers, Monster Hunters, Voyagers and Atlantean heroes are held back to fight smaller battles on the fringes where they are needed just as badly. These champions fight these smaller battles, often in the most unexpected of places.

Like all Atlantean dimensional travelers, Undead Slayers always keep an eye out for fellow True Atlanteans, and always try to have their backs, regardless of their clan affiliation. Atlanteans are a rare breed with plenty of enemies, so it is important for them to watch out for one another. And now with the Minion War and a mysterious group of assassins hunting Atlanteans, that is more important than ever. If there is a down side to such a strong sense of allegiance to one another, it is that they tend to trust other Atlanteans more than anyone else.

Atlantean Undead Slayer O.C.C. Abilities:

These are abilities and areas of expertise in addition to those common to all True Atlanteans. See the True Atlantean R.C.C. earlier in this book, page 45.

1. Magic Tattoos Denote Heritage: Staked heart and flaming sword as discussed under the Atlantean R.C.C., both are fully functioning magic tattoos.

2. Increased P.P.E. from Magic Tattoos: Base P.P.E. is 1D4x10+50 for all Undead Slayers. Add 10 P.P.E. points for each additional level of experience and six P.P.E. for each tattoo. **Note:** The character can also draw energy from ley lines and nexus points, up to 20 P.P.E. per each activation of a tattoo or 15 P.P.E. per melee round to power or use a magic device.

3. Increased P.P.E. Recovery: The Undead Slayer's P.P.E. replenishes itself at the rate of 20 points for every hour of meditation, rest or sleep; 25 P.P.E. when meditation is performed on a ley line.

4. M.D.C.: Undead Slayers have a base M.D.C. of 2D4x10 plus 10 P.P.E. per each level of experience (starting at level one), plus each additional tattoo beyond the first six of them, instills the male Undead Slayer with 11 M.D.C. and the females with 13 M.D.C. points. Due to the number of magic tattoos, they are considered to be minor supernatural beings with Supernatural P.S. and P.E., so their physical attacks inflict M.D. and damage the undead, supernatural beings and Mega-Damage creatures.

5. Advanced Knowledge of Atlantean Pyramids: Undead Slayers are seasoned dimensional travelers and have a full understanding of Dimensional Pyramids. Add +10% to their Operate Dimensional Pyramid skill.

6. Vampire Hunting Abilities (special):

Bonuses Applicable Only when Fighting Vampires: +3 on Perception Rolls involving all aspects of the undead, +2 on initiative, +1 to strike, parry, and dodge, +2 to strike when going to impale/stake the heart, +2 to save vs insanity, +3 to save vs the Horror Factor of vampires, their protectors and summoned animals, and +1 to save vs possession (any).

Gut Feelings, Hunches and Realizations Involving Vampires: By third level, the Undead Slayer develops a sort of sixth sense about vampires and the dangers they represent. These "feelings" only apply to vampires and their minions.

- Bad feeling that something is not right. The Undead Slayer gets a bad feeling when he's walking into a vampire's trap. It helps to recognize a potential ambush site up ahead, decide to take a different route back to camp, and similar. Success Ratio: 35% +5% per level of experience and +1 to Perception Rolls and +1 to initiative when a hero has a "bad feeling."
- Feeling that vampires are around or exerting control and influence over a community even though he is told otherwise. "I don't care what the Sheriff said. There are vampires here. I can feel them." Success Ratio: 60% +3% per level of experience.
- Finding and recognizing evidence of the undead's presence or involvement, attacks on people, evidence of the Slow Kill bite, and/or of vampire influence and visitations. Success Ratio: 60% +3% per level of experience.

- Hunch that someone is a vampire servant, henchman or assassin. Success Ratio: 40% +5% per level of experience.
- Recognize a Vampire Mind Slave when he sees one: 60% +3% per level of experience.
- Recognize a Wild Vampire when he sees one: 84% +3% per level of experience.
- Recognize a Secondary Vampire when he sees one: 60% +3% per level of experience.
- Recognize a Master Vampire when he sees one: 50% +3% per level of experience.
- Guess where the vampire's lair is located based on his knowledge of the undead and reports of the vampire's activities and other evidence and survey of the area. Success Ratio: 20% +3% per level of experience; +25% to find the lair or coffin, locate a secret panel that leads to it, etc., when he is at the actual suspected location. "Nope, this isn't it. Wait. What about over there? Yeah, this is more like it."

Lore: Vampires: This is a comprehensive study of vampires, specifically, and all other types of undead, in general. The focus on vampires includes separating truth from fantasy, their true powers, abilities, strengths, weaknesses, ways to destroy them, proper disposal of vampire bodies, and their use of henchmen and servants. It also includes methods and strategies for fighting and slaying vampires as well as stories about their origins, the Vampire Kingdoms, vampire society, their behavior, hideouts and lairs. **Base Skill:** 70% +3% per level of experience.

Vampire Combat: Knows all vampire weaknesses and vulnerabilities, common tactics, methods of attack, defenses against such attacks and tactics, training in the types of weapons and materials that can damage and slay vampires, and so on.

Resistance Against Vampire Seduction: +1 to save vs Vampire pheromone-based trance at levels 1, 3, 5, 7, 11 and 15.

Resistance Against Vampire Mind Control: +1 to save vs Mind Control and +2 to save vs Hypnotic Suggestion.

Sense Vampires: Undead Slayers have a more refined sense for vampires. They can sense the presence of vampires and Vampire Intelligences within a 600 foot radius (183 m), but cannot pinpoint the exact source/person responsible for the sensation.

7. Command Trust and Leadership: Undead Slayers are trained to be team players and work with others, be they fellow warriors, slayers, or civilians. As a result, most Undead Slayers carry themselves with such an air of confidence and certainty that people are quick to trust and follow them. The reputation of Undead Slayers is so powerful that just announcing you are an Atlantean Undead Slayer captures people's attention. Training and that fabled commanding confidence enables a single Undead Slayer to calm down, quiet and lead, or direct large groups of civilians (50 people per level of experience). He can also settle the nerves of a small squad fighting force (10 +1D6 per level of experience), and keep them, calm, working as a team, and focused on the objective at hand; 55% chance +2% per level of experience they will follow his lead or accept him as their field leader in a crisis situation against vampires. On a successful roll, all non-Undead Slayers receive a morale bonus of +1 to initiative and +1 to save vs Horror Factor, but only when the Undead Slayer is within 250 feet (76.2 m).

8. O.C.C. Bonuses: +1 on all Perception Rolls, +3 on Perception Rolls involving vampires and other undead (this is in addition to the Vampire Perception bonus, above, for a Gut Feeling), +1 one attack per melee round when fighting vampires or any undead and demons/supernatural evil, +1 to strike and parry, +1 to save vs magic of all kinds (in addition to P.E. bonuses), +4 to save vs Horror Factor, half for other Horror Factor rolls. Attribute bonuses: +2 to M.E., +1D6 to P.S. (Supernatural), +1D6 to P.P., and +2 to P.E. and Spd. Undead Slayers are considered minor supernatural beings and have Supernatural Strength and Endurance. Make sure you include the True Atlantean R.C.C. bonuses too.

9. Advanced Tattoo Training: Undead Slayers rely heavily on their tattoos. In fact, for many, they are the only weapons and means of protection that they employ. This gives them the edge as undisputed masters of Tattoo Magic. At level four, the Undead Slayers are so in tune with their tattoos that they no longer have to touch a tattoo to activate it. With a mere thought (it still counts as one melee action), the warrior can activate any one of his tattoos. Moreover, in the course of a lifetime, Undead Slayers can receive as many as 36 magic tattoos, but no more than two per level of experience. All magic tattoos are available, except Dimension Tattoos. Keep in mind that the Undead Slayer must have the necessary P.P.E. to activate the tattoos in question.

10. Magic Tattoos: The Undead Slayer starts with the following magic tattoos:

The two Marks of Heritage (standard)

One Flaming Weapon (an M.D. weapon that will hurt vampires)

Bow and arrow or crossbow. The four arrows are in flames (M.D.) and have wings (triple range and magically return).

Power: Protection from Vampires (heart impaled by stake).
Power: Turn Dead (the cross).
Power: Invulnerability (heart in chains).
Power: Control the Forces of Air (cloud in chains).
Power: Healing Basic (rose).
Power: Healing Super (Phoenix).
Power: Knowledge & Reading (eye).
And make the following selections:
Two additional Power tattoos of choice.
Two Simple Weapons of choice.
Two Magic Weapons of choice.
Two Animals of choice.
One Monster of choice.

Each new level of experience, the character's clan elder or a clan Alchemist can add two simple tattoos (animal or simple weapons) or one major tattoo (power, monster, or magic weapons), but are not required to do so, player's choice. Undead Slayers avoid Dimension Tattoos.

Getting one or two new tattoos may require traveling to a different dimension, so the character may have to disappear for a few days from time to time. It is possible that circumstances will not allow the character to get the tattoos immediately after attaining the next level of experience.

Atlantean Undead Slayer Stats

Attribute Requirements: I.Q. 10 or higher and M.E. 20 or higher. A high P.S. and/or P.P. is helpful but not required. Note that attributes may be temporarily altered by magic tattoos. The effects, bonuses and penalties are cumulative.

Alignment: Any, most Atlanteans tend to be good with a few exceptions.

O.C.C. Skills:
Basic Math (+20%)

Boxing
Gymnastics
Intelligence (+10%)
Language and Literacy: Dragonese/Elf, American, and Greek at 98%.
Language: Other: Three of choice (+15%).
Lore: Demons and Monsters (+25%)
Lore: One of choice (+10%).
Tracking (+15%)
Radio: Basic (+10%)
Swimming (+5%)
Wilderness Survival (+15%)
W.P. Archery
W.P. Knife
W.P. Sword
W.P. Energy Pistol
W.P. Energy Rifle
Hand to Hand: Martial Arts

O.C.C. Related Skills: Select two other skills at level one, plus select one additional skill at levels 3, 6, 9, 11 and 14. All new skills start at level one proficiency.

Communications: Any (+5%).
Cowboy: None.
Domestic: Any.
Electrical: Basic only.
Espionage: Any (+10%).
Horsemanship: General or Exotic only (+10%).
Mechanical: Basic only.
Medical: Animal Husbandry, Brewing: Medicinal, First Aid, Holistic Medicine, and Paramedic only (+10%).
Military: Any (+10%).
Physical: Any.
Pilot: Any, except robot and power armor skills (+10%).
Pilot Related: Any (+10%).
Rogue: Any (+5%).
Science: Any (+5%).
Technical: Any (+5%).
W.P.: Any.
Wilderness: Any (+5%).

Secondary Skills: The Undead Slayer also selects four Secondary Skills from the Secondary Skill list. These are additional areas of knowledge that do not get any bonus, other than possible bonuses from a high I.Q. All Secondary Skills start at the base skill level.

Standard Equipment: Typically has a high-powered energy rifle and energy pistol, 1D6 E-Clips for every weapon, 1D4 silver-plated knives, a silver-plated sword, a wood cross, a silver cross (may be worn as jewelry), a dozen wooden stakes and mallet, pocket mirror, large satchel, backpack, portable computer the size of a cell phone, language translator, sketch book, 1D6 pencils and pens, goggles, and is likely to have 1D4 types of Techno-Wizard anti-vampire weapons (favorite include storm flare, Globe of Daylight flares and a TW water shotgun) and/or other magic items.

Money: 2D6x1,000 in credits and 4D6x1,000 in precious gems or artifacts. However, Undead Slayers are not motivated by wealth. They are dedicated to destroying vampires and supernatural evil. They can accumulate small fortunes from time to time, but eventually spend that wealth on more monster slay-ing weapons and equipment or on helping and protecting others.

Cybernetics: None, if it can be avoided. Due to their magic tattoos and sense of heritage, all True Atlanteans strive to get to a Healing Pyramid where they can be made whole. If not, Atlanteans will settle for cybernetic Bio-Systems. All Atlanteans are attracted to "natural" things, and mechanical systems are not natural. Moreover, cybernetics reduces the potency of magic. Only True Atlanteans who do not use magic, other than a few basic tattoos, may consider cybernetic implants.

Tattooed Voyager

It is the job of the *Atlantean Tattooed Voyager* to be the vanguard into new dimensions and alien worlds. These individuals are part commando, part dimensional explorer, and part walking Rift generator. A sort of living doorway to the Megaverse. They specialize in magic tattoos known as *Dimension Tattoos* which enable them to cross the dimensional threshold with ease.

Not everyone can handle the use of Dimension Tattoos. In principle, they work like any other magic tattoo, but many Atlanteans find them too powerful and unnerving to use, or the responsibility too much to bear. Other Tattooed Men might have one or two Dimension Tattoos, but Voyagers have 6-11 and love dimensional travel, exploration into the unknown and world-hopping even more than other Atlanteans. Some believe that Dimension Tattoos somehow link the tattoo user to the fabric of the Megaverse, compelling them to want to seek adventure by traveling across the dimensional divide, and instilling them with an unparalleled wanderlust even among Atlanteans. Tattooed Voyagers scoff at the notion, saying that like ancient mariners of Earth, they are born with a desire to travel, seek adventure and see the universe. This is probably true enough, but Tattooed Voyagers seem to be cut from a different cloth.

Voyagers have a reputation for being fearless. All Atlanteans enjoy visiting new worlds, uncovering new knowledge and secrets, but none more than Tattooed Voyagers. If anyone can dive through a random Rift and find a way back home with stories of new wonders, it is the Atlantean Tattooed Voyager. However, unlike many of their kin, Voyagers are not academics, scientists nor even true explorers. For them it is all about the journey to discovery. The hunt to find and return with their objective or a particular resource, secret or goal. Once the objective has been found, Voyagers are happy to let others carry on from there, and anxiously await their next challenging mission. These are the guys who discover a new world, secrets, or resources, hand it over to their clan leaders and move on.

Bold and adventurous, these risk takers are driven by their inquisitive and thrill-seeking natures. Compelled to find new challenges and travel, most Voyagers don't think twice about stepping into a random Rift to see what's on the other side. They love the thrill of being the first (or one of the first) to experience something new. Making first contact with new life forms is nice, but for the Tattooed Voyager, it is the thrill of discovery, or outsmarting an enemy and making a quick escape, that gives them the biggest kick.

Atlantean Voyagers are thrill-junkies. They love stepping into the unknown and living to tell the tale. They also love challenges, figuring out puzzles, secrets and mysteries. The more "impos-

sible" the mission, the more they like it. All of this makes them assets for espionage missions and commando operations. The Tattooed Voyager loves to be the first one sent in to scout ahead, find and circumvent ambushes and traps, figure out where a fugitive or enemy is hiding, and gather intelligence for a greater cause. They enjoy the danger of scouting missions in hostile or unknown territory as well as rescue missions, espionage and commando raids against enemies and monsters.

In their capacity as Atlantean warriors/soldiers/protectors, Voyagers are the guys who get Tattooed Defenders, Undead Slayers, sorcerers and teammates to alien realms, or an enemy encampment for raids or rescue operations, and bring them back home. They are the ones who provide the all important means and method of insertion and extraction to and from a particular war zone, world, or dimension. When entering an unknown or hostile environment, the Voyager may be the group's only way in and out, so they are often the most protected members of the team, which can be difficult as Voyagers are quite adventurous and willing to take risks.

Despite their daring nature, Tattooed Voyagers are keenly aware of their responsibility to get their teammates back home alive, and take it very seriously. While they may risk their own life, especially to save another, they never risk the lives of the troops or teammates counting on them. Getting them home is always their top priority. Which tempers their impetuous risk taking on missions. Knowing they may be the only way home for the rest of their team is part of the adrenaline rush they thrive upon. They love being the hero everyone is counting upon, and strive to live up to the challenge and responsibility. This attitude makes many Tattooed Voyagers wild men in the face of combat. Willing to brave the unknown, face impossible odds and defy death to rescue their teammates, fellow Atlanteans or any innocent people in need. That said, they are not suicidal kamikaze warriors. They assess a situation and are happy to whisk away those they can rescue now, and come back soon to rescue those left behind. These guys love popping in under the cover of darkness or using the element of surprise to make fast rescues or launch commando-style raids, or engage in espionage missions to get the job done, whatever it is. That makes them part commando, part spy, and part getaway drivers who use the Rifts and Dimensional Tattoos for the getaway.

Tattooed Voyagers use their magic tattoos to reopen dimensional Rifts, open new Rifts and manipulate Rifts and stone pyramids to communicate with support teams or home base across the dimensional divide, as well as to travel from one world or dimension to another. It is the Tattooed Voyager who opens the dimensional portal and goes in with a strike team of tattooed warriors on a commando raid, surprise attack, jailbreak, etc., right under the noses of the enemy, as well as on scouting missions and espionage operations. While there are Atlantean Shifters, Nomads and mages who can do these things, nobody does it better, or with such panache, than the Tattooed Voyager.

A True Atlantean from any clan may become a Tattooed Voyager, and every clan from Aerihman (and Sunaj) to Tsitas has them. When not in the service of their clan, Tattooed Voyagers are off traveling, exploring or working with non-Atlantean heroes, mercs or adventurers. These individuals cannot sit still for long and are always off on some new quest or crusade.

Tattooed Voyager O.C.C. Abilities:

1. Magic Tattoos Denote Heritage: As discussed under the Atlantean R.C.C. and varies with each clan.

2. Increased P.P.E. from Magic Tattoos: Base P.P.E. is 1D6x10+60 for all Atlantean Voyagers. Add 10 P.P.E. points for each additional level of experience and six P.P.E. points for each magic tattoo, except *Dimension Tattoos* which provide the Voyager with 10 P.P.E. each. **Note:** The character can also draw energy from ley lines and nexus points, up to 30 P.P.E. per each activation of a tattoo or 25 P.P.E. per melee round to power or use a magic device.

3. Increased P.P.E. Recovery: The Atlantean Voyager's P.P.E. replenishes itself at the rate of 10 points for every hour of meditation, rest or sleep; 20 P.P.E. when meditation is performed on a ley line or at a Stone Pyramid.

4. M.D.C.: Atlantean Voyagers have a base M.D.C. of 1D6x10 plus each additional magic tattoo beyond six instills the male Voyager with 11 M.D.C. and the females with 13 M.D.C. points. In addition to M.D.C. from tattoos, the Voyager gains 1D6 M.D.C. per each additional level of experience. Due to the number of magic tattoos, they are considered supernatural beings with Supernatural P.S. and P.E., so their physical attacks inflict M.D. and hurt supernatural beings and Mega-Damage creatures.

5. Sense Ley Lines: Range of 10 miles (16 km) plus 5 miles (8 km) per additional level of experience.

6. Sense Ley Line Nexus: A range of 15 miles (24 m) plus 5 miles (8 km) per additional level of experience.

7. Sense Rifts: 40 miles (64 km) +20 miles (32 km) per each additional level of experience. Like a Shifter, whenever a Voyager is on a ley line, he can sense a Rift on any of the connecting ley lines regardless of the distance and knows the direction and whether the Rift is large or small. While on a ley line, the Voyager can also sense other dimensional disturbances such as teleports or dimensional anomalies at 10 miles (16 km) per level of experience.

8. Lore: Dimensions: All Voyagers study various dimensions. Those knowledgeable in this skill have studied several different dimensions and will know things like Hades is the home to demons and what demons live there, Wormwood is referred to as the Living Planet, and Phase World resides in the Three Galaxies where the Naruni and Splugorth are known to trade, among other odd tidbits as they relate to various dimensions. Extremely alien dimensions may impose anywhere from a -15% to -50% skill penalty, while places the character has personally visited on three or more occasions provide a +10% skill bonus. **Base Skill (for Voyagers):** 35% +5% per level of experience.

9. Operate Dimensional Pyramids: Voyagers are well versed in how Dimensional Stone Pyramids work and how to operate them better than most. Base Skill is 78% +2% per level of experience.

10. Bonuses: +2 on Perception Rolls dealing with dimensional anomalies, Rifts and dimensional travel, +2 to dodge, +1 to roll with impact, +1 to save vs magic of all kinds (in addition to P.E. bonuses), +2 to save vs Horror Factor. Attribute bonuses: +1 to I.Q. and M.E., +1D6 to M.A. and +1D4 to P.P. and P.E. Atlantean Voyagers are considered minor supernatural beings and have Supernatural Strength and Endurance. Make sure you include the True Atlantean R.C.C. bonuses too.

11. Magic Tattoos: A first level Atlantean Voyager starts with 13 magic tattoos:

Two Marks of Heritage (discussed under the Atlantean R.C.C.).

Two Simple Weapons of choice.

One Magic Weapons of choice.

One Animal or Monster tattoo of choice.

Two Power tattoos of choice.

Five Dimension Tattoos of choice.

12. Additional Tattoos: Each new level of experience, the character's clan elder or a clan Alchemist adds either two new simple tattoos (animal or simple weapon) or one Dimension, Power, or Magic Weapon tattoo. Of course, Voyagers lean towards the *Dimension Tattoos* and are one of the few Atlantean O.C.C.s allowed to get more than one or two of them. To receive a new tattoo may require traveling to a different dimension, which means the character may have to disappear for a few days from time to time. It is possible that circumstances will not allow the character to get the tattoos immediately after attaining the next level of experience. The most tattoos any Atlantean can get at any time is two, and there must be six months between the acquisition of another pair of tattoos.

Atlantean Tattooed Voyager Stats

Alignment: Any, most Atlanteans tend to be good with a few exceptions.

Attribute Requirements: Voyagers, like Undead Slayers are the elite of the elite, and there are very strict standards to become a Voyager. I.Q. of 11 or higher, an M.E. of 14 or higher. P.S. and P.E. are Supernatural.

O.C.C. Skills:

Astronomy & Navigation (+20%)

Land Navigation (+10%)

Language and Literacy: Dragonese/Elf, American, and Greek at 98%.

Language: Other: One of choice (+15%).

Literacy: Other: One of choice (+20%).

Lore: D-Bees (+20%)

Lore: Demons & Monsters (+20%)

Lore: Dimensions (See the description under #8, above.)

Lore: Magic (+15%)

Mathematics: Basic (+30%)

Xenology (+10%)

W.P. Ancient: Two of choice.

W.P. Modern: One of choice.

Hand to Hand: Expert; can be changed to Hand to Hand: Martial Arts (or Assassin if evil) at the cost of one O.C.C. Related Skill.

O.C.C. Related Skills: Select five other skills, plus one additional skill at levels 3, 6, 9 and 12. All new skills start at level one proficiency.

Communications: Any (+10%).

Cowboy: None.

Domestic: Any.

Electrical: Basic only.

Espionage: Any (+10%).

Mechanical: Basic only.

Medical: First Aid or Paramedic only (+5%).

Military: Any (+10%).

Physical: Any.

Pilot: Any, except robot and power armor skills (+5%).

Pilot Related: Any (+10%).

Rogue: Any.

Science: Any.

Technical: Any (+10%).

W.P.: Any.

Wilderness: Any (+5%).

Secondary Skills: Select three Secondary Skills from the Secondary Skill list. These are additional areas of knowledge that do not get any bonus, other than possible bonuses from a high I.Q. All Secondary Skills start at the base skill level.

Standard Equipment: One weapon for each W.P. (blade weapons will be silver-plated), 1D4 E-Clips for each weapon (as applicable), a Vibro-Knife (1D6 M.D.), 1D4 flares, 1D4 smoke grenades, two silver-plated knives, a silver cross (may be worn as jewelry), a wood cross, a dozen wooden stakes and mallet, a pocket mirror, a portable computer the size of a cell phone, a language translator, goggles, air filter, digital camera, notebook, 1D6 pens and markers, backpack, 1D4 medium-sized sacks, clothing, bar of soap, comb or brush, and other personal items. Starts with one Techno-Wizard weapon (G.M. discretion). They love magic and are certain to acquire more magic weapons and items in the future.

Money: 3D6x1,000 in credits, 4D6x1,000 in precious gems or artifacts, and may have valuable information or services that can be used for trade. Though Voyagers are not motivated by wealth, they may accumulate small fortunes from time to time, but will eventually spend much of it on magic items and helping and protecting others.

Cybernetics: None, if it can be avoided. Due to their magic tattoos and sense of heritage, all True Atlanteans strive to get to a Healing Pyramid where they can be made whole. If not, Atlanteans will settle for cybernetic Bio-Systems. All Atlanteans are attracted to "natural" things, and mechanical systems are not natural. Moreover, cybernetics reduces the potency of magic. Only True Atlanteans who do not use magic, other than a few basic tattoos, may consider cybernetic implants.

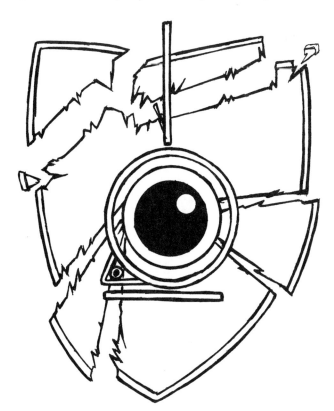

The Sunaj

A secret society within the Aerihman Clan

No one, not even most Aerihman, knows that the infamous and enigmatic Sunaj assassins are actually members of an Illuminati-like secret society within their own Aerihman clan. Most clan members are not privy to this secret, and the tiny percentage who suspect the truth, keep their suspicions to themselves out of misguided loyalty to the Aerihman clan.

Most Atlanteans and outsiders believe the Sunaj are a mixed organization of D-Bees, humans and aliens who serve as the enforcers and assassins for the Splugorth, demons, and evil beings across the Three Galaxies and beyond. Their origin unknown. Their purpose seems obvious, the accumulation of wealth and the power that comes with serving tyrants and monsters.

When you need to kill someone who is too powerful or too well protected, or too well connected to be touched by ordinary means, you hire the Sunaj. If the mission is heartless and masses of people will suffer for it, or the job is too dangerous for anyone else to consider, you hire the Sunaj – specialists in black ops, murder and wholesale slaughter.

Service to the Splugorth and other powerful enemies of Atlanteans by the Sunaj is a deliberate ploy, and one that has worked very well for the Aerihman behind the secret organization. It keeps everyone from ever suspecting the famous and heroic monster-slaying Aerihman clan could have anything to do with the Sunaj. It is impossible to imagine any Atlantean, let alone the

Aerihman, would serve the Splugorth or demons, and certainly not become involved in a campaign to assassinate fellow True Atlanteans. Except that is exactly what is going on.

This unlikely and strategic alliance with the Splugorth gives the Sunaj organization and its agents access to dimensional portals across the Megaverse that are not commonly known or available to Atlanteans. It also keeps their hated enemies, like the Splugorth, close, and enables them to gather intelligence and learn secrets and weaknesses about the very beings they pretend to serve so dutifully. These "unholy allegiances" also gives the Sunaj the opportunity to meet and make more unlikely allies and connections with heroes and villains alike. All of whom they manipulate to the benefit of their secret society and to further the destiny of the Aerihman clan as they see it.

The Aerihman leaders who run the Sunaj are very selective and secretive about recruiting new members into the Sunaj Illuminati. Candidates for the Sunaj must display a zealous commitment to the cause and the philosophies of the militant Sunaj order to be considered. That includes being willing and able to kill other True Atlanteans or anyone who threatens their organization, even if it is a loved one. Remember, Aerihman, in general, see the other Atlantean clans as weak and misguided. The Sunaj take these sentiments much further, and are firmly committed to wiping out as many members of the other clansmen as necessary to achieve their vision for the Aerihman clan, and in a way, all Atlanteans. Sunaj show unwavering loyalty to the Aerihman clan and most important of all, to the Sunaj secret society. They are tested repeatedly throughout their training and systematically conditioned (some would say brainwashed) into being the agents the Sunaj Illuminati needs to further its twisted agenda. The resulting recruits are the cream of the crop and proud of their place and purpose in the Sunaj organization. Each and every one of them fanatically loyal to the secret society and willing to do anything to protect it and its secrets. All members of the Sunaj Illuminati, be they hardened killer, mage or average citizen, are willing to fight to the death or take their own life to prevent capture and revealing damaging information under duress.

Those who become Sunaj keep it a secret from friends and family, and even their spouses. On the other hand, there are cases where several members of a family – parents, sons, daughters, husbands, wives, and select kin – are all Sunaj.

Game Master Note: A player character who is a member of *Clan Aerihman* can elect to be any of the **Sunaj O.C.C.s**. Non-player characters may be one of these or any of the more common O.C.C.s available to Atlanteans, but remember, all Aerihman are NOT the Sunaj. Quite the opposite. And all members of the Sunaj secret society are not Sunaj Assassins, Sunaj Shadow Assassins or Sunaj Shadow Mages. There are plenty of psychics, practitioners of magic, Nomads, Undead Slayers, mercenaries, and ordinary citizens (though usually in high places) who are card carrying members of the secret society that never go off on missions of murder or espionage.

Sunaj Tactics and Plans

Lord Aerihza, head of the Aerihman clan/nation, is also the secret leader of the Sunaj. He sees himself as a visionary chosen by the hand of fate to lead his clansmen to their rightful destiny as leaders of all Atlanteans and lords of Atlantis. After years of political maneuvering, scheming and the creation of the Sunaj organization, he is finally seeing many of his plans beginning to come to fruition. And with the other Atlantean clans being none the wiser.

Closest to his heart is being the leader of the Sunaj. The secret special forces deployed to manipulate and bring the Aerihman clan closer to their destiny.

The Sunaj have existed in one form or another for at least a century, but until 50 years ago, had been a tiny, shadowy cult of unorganized elitists and extremists. It has been under Lord Aerihza's steady hand that it has grown to become the increasingly deadly and influential Illuminati that is subversively changing the political landscape and working toward leading the Aerihman clan to dominate all Atlanteans.

The tactics utilized by the Sunaj are the same as many secret organizations that rely on fanaticism and secrecy. The Sunaj have two tiers of operatives: **the hidden** among Aerihman society who usually hold positions of influence and authority to help and shield the activities of their secret society, and **the soldiers of destiny**, Sunaj Assassins, mages, spies, and saboteurs scattered across the Megaverse who get blood on their hands for the cause. They may operate as a lone agent, in pairs or in small groups. Whether one individual or a group of Sunaj, the agents are considered a terrorist **cell**.

Each cell is independent and specializes in one or two areas of operation. Each cell is insulated from the others and knows nothing about the other cells' personnel, agenda, activities or existence. This works out well, because if one Sunaj cell is discovered, they know nothing that can hurt others and cannot compromise additional secret operations. Most members of the Sunaj do not have any idea how many Sunaj exist, though they believe they are part of a large and growing movement that is becoming more powerful every day. Should a captured cell implicate the Aerihman clan (unlikely), the clan denies it, condemns the villains as rogues who acted under their own volition, and is happy to publicly execute them.

A typical Sunaj cell may be given specific short-term objectives and assignments, such as infiltrate organization X, kill so and so, destroy or steal this or that, or get information about X, Y, or Z. Or a cell may be given a long-standing mission like hunt and terminate all non-Aerihman Atlanteans, or get in the good graces of the Splugorth to learn everything about their operations, etc. Long-term operatives, sleeper agents, spies and saboteurs are then left on their own to accomplish the task over a period of time. For instance, a cell may be solely dedicated to *scouting and gathering intelligence* on other Atlantean clans. Since Atlanteans are scattered across the Megaverse, the home cities of most clans are unknown to the others, a deliberate secret intended to keep each clan safe. Thus, if Lord Aerihza and his Sunaj are to launch any large-scale attacks against the other clans, he needs to uncover the location of their strongholds, colonies and home city-states wherever they may be. As a result, he has Sunaj spies travel to locations where other Atlanteans are believed to exist, or join up with adventurer groups and heroes who have one or more Atlanteans as members or who might encounter and befriend Atlanteans.

Sunaj scouts and spies often disguise themselves, whether it is as a friendly *Atlantean Nomad* or helpful human sorcerer, or other benign disguise such as a hero or mercenary to win the trust of their Atlantean brethren and learn all they can. With this cover, the deadly Sunaj spy does not require Sunaj armor, and can come

and go from worlds and Atlantean outposts without suspicion, especially when local authorities and heroes think they know the person and vouch for them. Disguised Sunaj reconnaissance operatives are able to interact with the very Atlanteans they plan to sabotage or destroy. This is made all the easier by the fact that most Atlanteans consider the members of other clans as brothers and sisters, and generally, welcome fellow Atlantean visitors with open arms, even the prickly Aerihman. This closeness and feigned camaraderie enables the Sunaj spies to hear rumors, learn names, and get clues to people and places that can point them to the intelligence they are assigned to uncover.

Many Sunaj scout teams use the Splugorth-controlled Atlantis and Phase World as a base of operations. Both are interdimensional hubs that see a lot of traffic and all sorts of adventurers, and locales where dimensional travelers gather without suspicion. Since fellow Atlanteans and their associates often visit or pass through both hubs, the locations provide another means to find, meet, observe and tail Atlantean clansmen and other targets to alien worlds and perhaps back to one of their strongholds or secret city-states. The many dimensional gateways to alien realms found on Phase World as well as Atlantis via the Splugorth's many Stone Pyramids, makes them two of the best locations for a Sunaj base of operations, especially when traveling the Megaverse. Phase World is trickier, because travel through the dimensional gates is closely watched and regulated, but still offers plenty of opportunities and leads. Center itself is like a lawful and policed dimensional market, but there is plenty of corruption, with eyes that can be bought and shadows to lurk within.

Lawless Atlantis on Rifts Earth is ideal for those spies and assassins who desire to travel the Megaverse unnoticed by the authorities or heroes. Atlantis is a hotbed of villainy and a place of countless shadows and secrets, making it attractive to criminals, mercenaries and anyone who wants to keep a low profile. Furthermore, any skullduggery that may take place in Atlantis can be blamed on the Minions of Splugorth and/or other dangerous forces that visit the continent and its fabled Splynn Dimensional Market. Atlantis, after all, is a dangerous place for anyone, and especially so for Atlanteans, who are the enemies of the Splugorth and the vast number of monsters and villains who visit. It is perfect for adventurers, spies and outlaws looking to make connections or to gather intel.

Sunaj Raider Cells are another common operation that may be used to sabotage, kill and rob rich targets, opposition forces and other Atlanteans. Sunaj raider cells are always searching for magic artifacts, weapons, new technologies and new contacts to assist them in their quest for power and domination. Sunaj raiders follow rumors and clues about the whereabouts of other Atlanteans, magic, secrets, and treasure to acquire said resources through murder and treachery.

When not trying to expand their clan's power base with more powerful magic and artifacts, they conduct raids against Atlantean clans to probe their defenses or to weaken them by stealing valuable assets. Sunaj raider cells may be given a specific target such as a clan elder or any person of importance, some kind of resource, or left to choose their own course of action. Like Atlantean Nomads who wander the Megaverse looking for adventure and new experiences, Sunaj raider cells sometimes roam the dimensional travel lanes and hot zones to take advantage of whatever opportunities come their way. This may range from assassination of enemy targets while disguised as pirates or raiders, to the "acquisition" of rare and unique magic relics, weapons, technology, and even personnel. Sunaj assigned to raider operations often join or come to lead bands of pirates and other criminals. They may also serve a crime lord or tyrant as his hit men or protectors. In all cases, the raiders establish friendships, contacts and potential pawns within the organizations they appear to serve.

Though the super-secret Sunaj are best known as assassins, they engage in all sorts of **black ops**, including kidnaping. The targets of these focused attacks may be members of a specific Atlantean family or group for blackmail, or to acquire information or to leverage someone to do something for them. Victims of a kidnaping may be ransomed if it suits the purpose of the cell, or nabbed for interrogation and released (or allowed to escape) without ransom. Other times, the kidnap victim may be slain or just vanish after interrogation or receipt of the ransom. A kidnaping may also be used as a diversion, or as a way to gather more intelligence or draw out the real target.

Kidnaping the right person yields far more useful information than simple financial reward or killing them. Interrogations are usually very thorough with the interrogator asking a wide range of questions. Some questions are meant to cover their true intent via misdirection because there are times when it is useful to release a kidnap victim and follow him to where more intelligence can be gained, or mislead him into taking action that reveals more information, like pinpointing rival Atlantean resources, leaders, strongholds, cities and operations on other worlds and dimensions.

Sunaj Execution cells are either small with 4-12 members or very large, the size of a platoon or company. The typical small execution cell is composed of Sunaj Assassins and other "specialists." Sunaj are, as a rule, sent out to find and kill people who are causing problems for the secret society or the Aerihman clan, and to further some clan leaders' agenda. This includes declared enemies and supernatural threats commonly known to all, but also extends to notable leaders of hostile Atlantean clans, Atlantean heroes and non-Atlantean heroes associated with them. Anyone who may get in the way of their schemes or threatens the Sunaj or the Aerihman clan are targets for extermination. Such targets may include Aerihman clan elders, clan Alchemists, and notable clan leaders who represent a threat to the current Sunaj secretly in power (or who want to be in power), not just those of the rival Atlanteans who oppose them.

Large Execution cells are typically composed of a mixed group and are likely to include Tattooed Defenders and other Atlantean O.C.C.s that are members of the Sunaj. In addition, each large execution cell has smaller scout, raider and execution cells working within it. The number of troops within the large combat cell is 1D4x100 strong. This large, dangerous group is likely to pose as a mercenary company, space pirates, dimensional raiders, or outlaws. As such, they can be mustered and brought to bear against an enemy target of roughly comparable power and numbers. When the target is larger or more powerful, this is when the large execution cell needs to use its influence and connections to bring in additional, or more powerful, combat forces. This simply requires stirring up the right people to instigate an attack. If the group of heroes or villains being manipulated are profit-oriented thieves and cutthroats, all that needs to be done is to show evidence that a successful attack will yield huge profits. If the combat force is an enemy of the target, all they may need to be motivated to attack is the right intelligence and some assis-

tance to knock out defenses and communications, which the Sunaj are happy to provide. If the combat force being manipulated are demons or other army of monsters, they may be motivated by revenge, bloodlust, or any of the above.

Execution cells are used when an enemy or rival Atlantean enterprise or settlement is to be wiped out. As a rule, the Sunaj first assign a **scout cell** to gather all the necessary intelligence and identify key targets (people, places and resources). A **raider cell** causes a distraction and/or sabotages or steals key resources like disabling a Dimensional Pyramid, Power Pyramid, communications, weapons depot, defensive position, weapon caches, powerful practitioners of magic, notable leaders, diplomats, prisoners, etc.; and a **execution cell** teleports in to wipe out a specific segment of the enemy forces – the key role of Sunaj Assassins, Sunaj Shadow Assassins and Sunaj Shadow Mages. Execution missions may be carefully planned assassinations performed by the Sunaj before the enemy even realizes they are under siege, or via commando-style raids or focused military assaults, all done with precision and speed. Targets are identified and taken or destroyed.

Against rival Atlanteans, the Dimensional Pyramid is likely to be the first target captured or destroyed in large-scale battles to prevent escape or the arrival of reinforcements. Its command center seized and all pyramid abilities disabled. Second is the systematic neutralization of magic users. Assassins take down as many of them as possible just prior to, or at the onset of, the attack. If the assault is intended to kill everyone, which is often the case, a larger force of mixed troops follow the initial wave of raiders and assassins to engage in wholesale slaughter. To cover their tracks, the Sunaj cell is likely to make it look as if the deed was done by non-Aerihman forces such as pirates, dimensional raiders, alien invaders, demons, Minions of Splugorth and other forces who can be made to take the blame for the attack. As noted above, odds are that Sunaj operatives have instigated and manipulated other forces to launch the devastating attack in the first place, making additional subterfuge unnecessary. The manipulated combat force is completely unaware of the involvement of the Sunaj and would be insulted by the suggestion of their involvement. Sunaj leaders love it when their operatives and assassins can arrange to incite others to do their murderous dirty work for them.

Sabotage is the way. Aerihman leaders of all Sunaj cells are skilled in the art of duplicity and sabotage. They have learned it can be just as effective to engage in subtle and covert acts of treachery to destroy their enemies as it is to destroy them outright. This makes sabotage a favorite and common tactic of the Sunaj, particularly among Shadow Assassins and Shadow Mages. For instance, a Sunaj cell is much more likely to try to disable an enemy's defenses and let another enemy of theirs know about it so that enemy launches a devastating attack. No one is the wiser that the Sunaj manipulated the incursion, and the Minions of Splugorth or other enemy are blamed for the attack. In fact, Sunaj cells and ruthless Aerihman clansmen have gotten very good at orchestrating disaster and murder without ever getting their hands dirty, or anyone suspecting their involvement. This has proven effective time and time again. Of late, the Sunaj have taken advantage of the **Minion War**. All they need to do is whisper the right thing into the ear of the right demon or Deevil commander, drop the right clue, or cause the right confrontation (sometimes disguised as the Atlantean clansmen they want targeted), and boom, demonic beings are tearing through a Rift, causing all kinds of havoc in an Atlantean city, outpost or colony world, or wherever the Sunaj want the attack directed. Likewise, picking off enemies under the cover of battlefield chaos is another Sunaj tactic.

Some Sunaj cell leaders have gone so far as to put themselves in a position of leadership or an advisory position among the Minions of Hell, so they can best direct the hell-spawn against the enemies and rivals of the Aerihman clan or to draw them out. In this regard, the Minion War has turned into a boon for Lord Aerihza in more ways than just using the demons or Deevils as fodder. Sunaj agents, and the people they dupe, tip off groups of Atlantean Undead Slayers. The tip is something like, "We've heard rumors of vampires preying upon the population of X," or "Overheard some demons (or mercs, or outlaws, etc.) say that they had (one or more) Atlanteans (or other heroes) held captive. They plan to torture them slowly. The location? Yes, I can provide that." And similar ploys to lay traps for Atlanteans and their heroic allies. Such statements are often true, although the exact strength of the minions or monsters is probably misrepresented or the Sunaj plan to lead them into a trap or pick them off one by one. When the Atlantean hero(es) arrive to save lives and destroy monsters, a Sunaj execution squad is waiting in the shadows in case he survives the trap. The Sunaj Assassins usually hang back to let the heroes waste their strength and ammo fighting the evil they have come to destroy, then strike without warning when the heroes are weakened, distracted or at their most vulnerable. Such subterfuge and treachery has been used with great success. The ultimate plan is to whittle down the Atlantean Champions of Light and undermine their defenses, leaving rival clans unable to fend off the inevitable Aerihman onslaught that is coming one day.

Another dirty tactic to wipe out enemies and rival Atlanteans is making it look like an accident or natural disaster. Destruction and deaths caused during events like earthquakes, tsunamis, or hurricanes are seldom questioned, and such natural disasters can be arranged via the use of magic or Elemental beings. For example, if Sunaj agents discover a fault line weakness on the ocean floor not far from an Atlantean or enemy coastal or island outpost, they may use magical or technological means to cause one or more earthquakes. Which in turn, create a tsunami elsewhere. Earthquakes, tidal waves and storms are all capable of widespread damage to rival Atlantean colonies, and incredibly difficult to prove they were an intentional attack. For one thing, the cause of the earthquake or tsunami could have occurred hundreds or thousands of miles away. The use of natural phenomena to hurt an enemy varies with the situation and from environment to environment, but can be very effective. At one place, the disaster might be an avalanche or mudslide caused by an earthquake, at another, an erupting volcano, or tidal wave, or a storm (magically intensified), and so on. **The Aeries Sunaj cell** has already pulled off several such "invisible attacks," as they like to call them, and have in plans for more.

The evil rogue Aerihman and their Sunaj Assassins also take advantage of genuine disasters to make the death toll climb higher. This is done by sabotaging rescue efforts to escalate the number of casualties and creating "incidents" and "accidents" that create more problems for survivors and their rescuers. This can include instigating local warlords and bandits to steal medical supplies, food, water and other precious necessities, accidents that cause more destruction or undermine relief and rescue efforts, and outright murder disguised as accidents and bad luck.

Chaos reigns at any disaster site. Nobody is likely to pay close attention to who comes and goes. During a time of crisis, medicine, supplies and people go missing. Others are accidentally killed by falling debris or fire, or in a vehicular crash, or other mishap. Likewise, communications goes down or roads and bridges may be destroyed, and any number of possible "complications" occur during disasters. Nobody is likely to investigate the cause, especially if there appears to be a reasonable explanation, like the foundation must have been weakened by the earthquake or flood waters, someone must have knocked over the lamp that started the fire, and so on. With so many people injured, dying and in need of help, there is no time to worry about mistakes and unfortunate accidents. It is all about damage control and making the best of a bad situation to save lives.

The chaos is also perfect for people to go missing. Depending on the level of disaster and corresponding chaos, many bodies may never be recovered, and inevitably, people get hurt or go missing, including some of the heroes who come to help. The perfect cover for Sunaj Assassins and saboteurs who can target and make individuals "vanish" with little or no suspicion. And since bodies are likely to be dumped into mass graves, or incinerated, evidence of foul play goes unnoticed.

The Sunaj are also skilled at disguising themselves and making people believe another party is responsible for theft, raids and sabotage that cause medicine, food, water, vehicles, etc. to go missing/stolen or be destroyed. That disguise might be a local group of bandits or insurgents, to dimensional raiders, slavers, mercs, space pirates, or aliens. And again, nobody is likely to have the time to investigate to prove otherwise or to retrieve the stolen goods or people who have gone missing. Instead, relief workers take action to preserve the resource and protect the people they still have.

In the end, nobody is the wiser, and a sabotaged vehicle or collapsed building is not likely to be investigated thoroughly enough, if at all, for sabotage, arson or murder to be identified. Certainly not in the middle of the crisis. Likewise, it is difficult to prove sabotage when a ship is at the bottom of the ocean or buried under tons of debris, or the evacuation spacecraft goes missing, lost in space or hijacked by miserable pirates. While foul play may be suspected, there is no time to gather evidence of it. It is a chaotic environment with other lives at stake. All efforts must be spent on saving the living.

Man-made "accidents" and violence require much less work and are more easily arranged, but they can be tricky when the true organization behind it needs to remain in the shadows. As noted earlier, acts of sabotage and murder are secretly handled by Sunaj cells who often make their efforts look like an accident or the handiwork of some other evil force. Sometimes the Sunaj take credit for the incident, other times they pin it on another group or individual, or leave it a mystery. The most insidious schemes involve the Sunaj arranging or instigating non-Atlantean forces to do their dirty work for them. This is done by planting ideas and information in the right ears, secretly provoking the right people with the right info (outright lies) to stir up violence and trouble. Sometimes the most important thing a Sunaj can do is to secretly help a group of warring rivals, bandits, or madmen to take deadly action against their enemies for them. This way, the Sunaj secret order of assassins, and the

Aerihman clan masterminds behind it all, escape any implications of involvement or blame whatsoever.

Always the political showman, Lord Aerihza and other Aerihman leaders who are secret members of the Sunaj, make angry speeches condemning such horrible attacks and send out Aerihman authorities to investigate or try to track down the villains responsible and destroy them in the name of justice. Of course, this is just another ploy to pin the incident on someone else. By having non-Sunaj Aerihman obliterate those responsible, it ties up any loose ends and eliminates any possible witnesses who might be able to implicate Sunaj involvement.

Patient and maniacal, the Sunaj and their leaders are willing to spend months, sometimes years, to stage such disasters and arrange such incidents and accidents from behind the scenes. Their pawns never realizing they have been played. Or if they do realize it, they do not know who was pulling their strings.

Plagues and biological warfare are not used unless there is a viable cure available to the agents in the field, though some are so dedicated, they don't care if they die in the name of their cause. Besides, biological warfare is not very effective against True Atlanteans due to their high resistance to disease, heightened healing abilities, and their vast medical and magical knowledge. However, disease and natural disaster can be very effective in creating problems for other life forms, tying up resources and causing related deaths, especially if you can successfully undermine relief efforts.

Independent Sunaj operatives. Sunaj leaders also like to send out independent assassins and agents who are not part of a particular Sunaj cell or operation. These *independent operatives* report to a high-ranking Sunaj who gives them their orders or acts as their handler and relays information to them, and then back to the master he serves.

Independent operatives, like the Sunaj cells, know nothing or little about any of the other cells or individuals in the secret society, so if they are captured and interrogated, they can do no damage to other agents and operations in the field. Many Sunaj individuals and pairs operate in this manner. Their identities unknown. Their mythology tying them to the Splugorth or other evildoers known to use the mysterious Sunaj as hired mercenaries, assassins and willing minions.

The Aerihman masterminds behind this campaign have been remarkably successful at preventing the outside world from discovering who pulls the strings of the Sunaj, and that they are actually True Atlanteans with a terrible agenda. If the Splugorth know or suspect the identity of the Sunaj, they are playing along, perhaps to use the deadly assassins for their own purposes for as long as possible. As such, the Sunaj have earned a valued place among the Splugorth's minions in just a few decades.

One notable independent operative, **Ren the Hunter**, has managed to obtain a position as head of a *D-Squad Pursuit unit*. His primary task for the Sunaj is to perform loyal service to the Splugorth, stay alive, and report back on Splugorth activity and any pertinent information to help the clan. Ren is playing both sides to profit for himself. If his superiors ever learned of his treachery, there could be deadly consequences. Or not. As long as he provides his clan with what they want and he never does anything to hurt the Sunaj, the clan, or their plans, they may not care that he has built his own little empire and swims in wealth and opulence. The credo of the Sunaj is the end justifies the means.

Notable Sunaj Cells

The Sunaj Aeries Cell

The Aeries are located in **Center** on **Phase World**. The organization is secretly led by a Sunaj who goes by the name **Lord Maximus Aeries**. The Aeries Cell started out as a small execution squad, however as Lord Aeries has grown in power and prestige, he has been given several additional small cells under his command with the secret blessing of Lord Aerihza.

These days, Lord Aeries himself is assigned only the most important and choice missions, but most of the time he is content sending his small Sunaj cells and other handpicked minions outside the Sunaj on missions while he remains safe back at his base of operations. What Lord Aerihza does not yet know, is that Lord Aeries is using more and more non-Atlanteans in his operations. Something that is frowned upon among the Sunaj unless it has been sanctioned by the leadership first. It is widely held by the Aerihman clan and other Atlanteans that only those of the "True Bloodline" can be trusted in important and sensitive matters. To use outsiders and inferiors is to court danger, not just for the Sunaj cell, but for the entire secret organization, and perhaps the Aerihman clan.

Lord Aeries, for the most part, considers the non-Atlanteans expendable cannon fodder. Lackeys who unwittingly do his bidding for money or out of fear of him, so if any of them are killed, there is no real damage done to his Sunaj cell. So far, he has been cunning enough to keep all his underlings content, loyal and out of trouble. Information is tightly controlled and most of the non-Sunaj under his command have no idea that they are contributing to plans of the Sunaj or in the genocide of True Atlanteans. All they know is that they work for the clever criminal kingpin and dimensional raider, *Lord Aeries*. Most believe they are space pirates and dimensional raiders whose job is to infiltrate and steal from targets of opportunity. They also don't suspect that Lord Aeries is, himself, an Atlantean, as whenever they meet him he is wearing his traditional Sunaj armor which covers his entire body.

Each Aeries cell has a Sunaj squad leader who is responsible for all the members in the cell as well as the proper execution of missions. Other Sunaj may be members of the team, but they answer to the team leader and he or she answers directly to Lord Aeries. The team leader only tells the cell operatives what they need to know, which is very little. That's fine by the raiders and pirates, whose attitude is, tell us what to do and who to do it to, when and where, and they are good to go. As long as the raid goes well, injury and losses are minimal and their cut of the profits are good, these bushwhackers and cutthroats don't care who is calling the shots or why.

Lord Aeries had been very successful with his use of non-Atlantean henchmen. All was going very well until he made the mistake of assembling a group of Megaversals. He thought by putting them under the control of his daughter, a high-ranking *Sunaj Undead Slayer*, that the group would learn their place quickly. He was wrong. This group of Megaversals has earned the name **Lords of Chaos** due to their wild antics and attracting attention to themselves yet somehow pulling off the mission by unconventional means, cunning and luck.

After numerous missions, the Lords of Chaos put together the clues that Aeries was targeting Atlanteans for extermination. While the members of the Lords of Chaos are opportunists, they have no quarrel with Atlanteans, who are generally regarded as heroes. They have no interest in becoming hero-slayers. Being raiders and crooks is one thing, destroyers of heroes, especially True Atlanteans, is quite another. Under the nose of their handler, they orchestrated their escape, taking a space cruiser and a small fortune with them, and leaving the Undead Slayer to face her father and explain how this could happen.

To date, Lord Aeries has refused to let this insult go and is personally leading one of his Sunaj cells to find the Lords of Chaos and make them pay. His wife, who is second in command, has taken charge of the other cells while Lord Aeries and his daughter Athena deal with the Lords of Chaos. His obsession with finding the group and making them pay for their defiance may lead to Lord Aeries' undoing.

The Splynn Sunaj Cell

As the name suggests, the Splynn Sunaj cell operates out of the Splynn Dimensional Market on Atlantis. They are led by an *Aerihman Voyager* named *Augustus*. This is a small scout cell that is composed of two Sunaj Assassins, one Shadow Assassin, one Shadow Mage, two Voyagers, one Tattooed Defender (with the Scout MOS), and one Atlantean Ley Line Walker. All are members of the Sunaj and wear some variation of Sunaj armor and wield a variety of weapons and equipment purchased from the Splynn Dimensional Market. The Splynn cell also has a dozen *Ogre Tattooed Men* it uses as shock troops and enforcers.

Augustus has been spreading rumors to rival Atlantean clans that on Atlantis, ruins exist from **Atlantia**, the fabled city that was the first to disappear in ancient times. According to the lies he tells, the ruins of Atlantia contain ancient Atlantean artifacts and magic items. This has attracted numerous True Atlanteans to visit Splynn. Members of the Splynn Sunaj cell, in disguise, often manage to present themselves to serve as native guides who can take lone individuals and small groups to an isolated location on Atlantis that is said to lead to the underground ruins of Atlantia. Lying in wait along the way are the Sunaj Assassins and/or mages to dispatch the unsuspecting Atlanteans. Those they murder are stripped of all their belongings, which are sold in the dimensional market – nothing is to be kept because it could be identified and used to implicate the members of the cell. The bodies of their victims are fed to a monster or otherwise disposed of. Interrogation of Atlanteans before killing them is uncommon, as the goal is to kill unsuspecting True Atlanteans, not anything else. Keeping prisoners for any length of time is dangerous and asking for trouble, especially if the prisoners escape. Any information that may be gleaned through conversation is passed up the chain of command within the Sunaj.

For the most part, the Splynn cell is autonomous and allowed to act on their own. In addition to waylaying True Atlanteans and spreading rumors and disinformation, they are sometimes called in to train a new Sunaj Scout or to orchestrate scouting missions elsewhere on Rifts Earth. Recently, a member of the Splynn cell has successfully befriended and infiltrated a group of adventurers that include a **Clan Skellian Monster Hunter.** The Sunaj is a female Sunaj Assassin calling herself Sonja and pretending to be a mercenary soldier who lost her teammates in a battle with Minions of Splugorth. The information about the monster transforming magic tattoos is something that the Aerihman clan is very interested in learning about. The problem is Clan Skellian keeps those secrets carefully guarded and even after two years of trying, the Splynn cell has been unable to pinpoint a Skellian Alchemist who knows all the secrets. The Splynn cell hopes that Sonja's joining this group will eventually get her (and them) into Clan Skellian's home base, and when the secrets can be taken, the Sunaj of Splynn cell will strike.

The Splynn cell does their best to avoid *Ren the Hunter* (see **Rifts® World Book 21: Splynn Dimensional Market** for details on this ruthless NPC). Ren is not known to be a Sunaj by any of the other Sunaj cells operating in Atlantis or South America. So far, interaction between Ren and the Splynn cell has been non-existent, though each knows of the other as their cover identity via their reputation. Given the opportunity, Ren will use the Splynn cell to further his own goals.

Sunaj Lords of Hell Cell

The Lords of Hell is a large Sunaj extermination cell operating out of Hades under the command of a Sunaj Assassin who calls himself *Caesar*. He has 300 seasoned Sunaj operatives (150 Sunaj Assassins, 100 Shadow Assassins and 50 Shadow Mages) at his disposal, but his real strength is in the number of demons he commands. He has managed to take over a tribe of *Gurgoyles* (wingless Gargoyles) and Gargoylites (impish tricksters), giving him 2,000 of the sub-demons at his disposal. He operates out of the *Stone Forest* in the northern continent of Hades.

Caesar secretly reports directly to Lord Aerihza and both seem to be cut from the same cloth. The Lords of Hell have been dispatched on a half dozen missions where the Atlantean death toll has numbered into the thousands. Caesar keeps his Gurgoyle legion on a tight leash, but despite that, most of them like how they are allowed to commit wholesale slaughter against innocents. You can be sure to expect a bloodbath whenever the Lords of Hell are involved.

The group is in league with an up and coming Demon Warlord who has aspirations of becoming a Demon Lord. So far, they have not been drawn into the Minion War, though they have run a few black ops for their demon patron that had peripheral war connotations.

The Black Hand Cell

The Black Hand is a devious group of Aerihman Undead Slayers who operate out of *World Gate* on **Wormwood**. The group is officially labeled a raider cell, but they act more in the capacity as an execution cell. The group of six Undead Slayers, two Voyagers, two Shadow Assassins and one Shadow Mage (the latter three disguised as Atlantean Nomads) are a force to be reckoned with, especially when they hook up with other Atlantean groups.

The Black Hand do *not* use the Sunaj armor and do not try to hide that they are Aerihman Atlanteans. Instead, they present themselves as heroic monster slayers traveling the dimensions, hunting the undead and protecting the innocent from unspeakable evil. And from time to time, they do. However, it is all a ruse to win the confidence of other heroes, particularly fellow True Atlanteans. The members of the Black Hand purposely try to join up with other groups of heroes to gather intelligence about other Atlanteans and their whereabouts. When they get the opportunity to join with other True Atlanteans or their allies, the Sunaj do so and work to gain their trust. Once the members of the Black Hand believe they have obtained a substantial amount of information on the whereabouts of other Atlantean groups, outposts or treasures that they can seek out, they turn on their "comrades" and slay them.

The Mauian Order (Revised)

Lemurian pawns of the Sunaj

To escape the destruction of Atlantis, many Atlanteans fled across the Megaverse via magic and Rifts. Many, many more perished in the cataclysm. As for Atlantis itself, the island continent was torn from its reality on Earth and sent someplace unknown. Presumably a dimensional limbo or time hole perhaps, where it remained lost to everyone who searched for it.

Atlantis being warped to another plane of existence also drained the Earth of its precious, natural P.P.E. reserves. Drying up ley lines to the tiniest trickle of energy and causing ripples of destruction and trouble around the globe. This came in the form of earthquakes, tidal waves, and storms that ravaged other lands and killed tens of thousands of non-Atlantean people. Among those to fare the worst were the Atlanteans' longtime allies, the *Lemurians*.

Lemurian civilization depended upon magic energy even more than the Atlanteans. The mystic energy kept their cities afloat, enabled Lemurian Biomancers to create their war steeds, living armor, living weapons, and even food and clothing. When Atlantis vanished, taking magic energy with it, the Lemurians had to make a choice, settle among the people of Earth without magic, or try and escape to a dimension where magic could sustain them and preserve their way of life. Tens of thousands of Lemurians died because of the Atlanteans' folly. Among the survivors, most Lemurians chose to leave Earth, and in so doing would become trapped in a pocket dimension until the Rifts returned them many millennia later.

The Rifts and the return of magic brought the Lemurians back to Rifts Earth. Most saw the entire affair to be a tragic accident and are happy to be home. In the aftermath of what happened, many Lemurians remain wary of True Atlanteans, but they remain their allies.

Not all Lemurians are quite so forgiving. There is a small percentage of them who lost too much in the Atlanteans' devastating "accident" to be forgiving. Their anger and hatred for the arrogant and irresponsible Atlanteans has been passed down through generations. These Lemurians hate True Atlanteans more than the Sunaj and have formed their own secret sect. The group calls itself the **Mauian Order** and has vowed to destroy Atlanteans and their dragon allies, the *Chiang-Ku*.

Led by a charismatic leader, *Maui-Tikitiki,* the Mauian Order has successfully hunted and destroyed hundreds of True Atlanteans and Chiang-Ku dragons, as well as caused trouble for At-

lantean clans by sabotaging their plans, undermining their operations, and helping other enemies of Atlanteans. As the Mauian Order grows in size and confidence, so does their aggression and the extremes they are willing to consider to exact their murderous revenge. To this end, members of the Mauian Order have resorted to working with the likes of the Sunaj, the Minions of Splugorth, vampires, demons and Deevils.

Except for the Sunaj, Atlanteans have no idea who or what the Mauian Order is, or why they hate them so. Any Atlantean to survive an attack by the Mauian Order knows only that his attackers seemed to be some sort of bloodthirsty dimensional raiders without any clear or obvious allegiance to any specific group. Only the Sunaj assassins have started to put the pieces of this puzzle together. Since the Sunaj are becoming known as enemies of Atlanteans, the Mauian Order has employed the assassins on several occasions to scout out, infiltrate and destroy small bands of Atlanteans. They do so, of course, without revealing that the Sunaj are themselves True Atlanteans. As a result, it has become clear to the Sunaj exactly who and what the Mauian Order is, and they are happy to use these maniacs to their own advantage.

Lord Aerihza, the leader of the Aerihman clan (and also the leader of the Sunaj secret society), has yet to decide how far they can manipulate the Mauian Order. For the time being, they continue to observe the group and learn as much as possible about the Order, while using them to gather additional intelligence on Atlanteans as well as feeding the Mauians information they can use against Atlantean clansmen. This growing relationship with the insidious Sunaj makes the Mauian Order unsuspecting pawns the assassins are using to destroy Atlanteans and rivals. Lord Aerihza is delighted to let the Mauian order do some of the Sunaj's handiwork and let them take the blame. It gives the Aerihman clan and the Sunaj a scapegoat to cover their own tracks. ("Who could have done this?" The answer: "The Mauian Order," even if it was actually the Sunaj.)

The Mauian Order is completely in the dark about being used as a weapon to destroy Atlanteans by the Aerihman clan. The Mauians do not question how the Sunaj get such useful intelligence to use against the hated Atlanteans. All that matters is that the info is reliable. As for the Sunaj, like everyone else, the Mauians have no idea they are secretly True Atlanteans. They believe they are just another group with good reason to hate Atlanteans, and that makes them valuable allies. An ally who has consistently proven to be trustworthy and reliable, just the way the Sunaj want it.

The twisted machinations of Lord Aerihza and his Sunaj do not stop here. He is orchestrating a major conflict between the Mauian Order and Atlanteans by leaking the location of **Alexandria** to the Order. Just as he had hoped, the Mauian Order has hatched a plan to launch a major terrorist strike at the next Atlantean clan meeting to be held there in six months. This plays right into the hand of Lord Aerihza, who intends to use the heinous and cowardly attack as a reason to go to war against all Lemurians (not just the radical Mauian Order). His hope is that other Atlantean clans will join in the war on Lemuria. A war the Aerihman clan is happy to spearhead. Then, he hopes he can sit back and watch the other Atlantean clans and Lemurians destroy each other. While both parties are locked in combat, he intends to steal as many of the Lemurian secrets of Biomancy gene magic as he can to use against his fellow Atlanteans and other enemies in the future.

Sunaj Exclusive O.C.C.s

The following O.C.C.s are exclusive to **the Sunaj**. An Illuminati-like secret society within the Aerihman clan. The selection process to become any of the elite Sunaj O.C.C.s within the order is so rigid and secret, that only the most dedicated and loyal to the extreme Aerihman cause are ever approached for recruitment. Anyone who becomes one of these Sunaj O.C.C.s – **Sunaj Assassin, Sunaj Shadow Mage** and **Sunaj Shadow Assassin** – is expected to forever serve the needs of *the Sunaj* over their own needs or the needs of their family! Those who are not fully committed and leave or betray the Sunaj secret society, are considered dangerous rogues to be hunted down and killed. There are no second chances within the Sunaj.

Note: The overwhelming majority the Aerihman people are NOT members of the Sunaj. It is true that most members of the Aerihman clan are warlike, believe they and all True Atlanteans are superior to humans and most races, and that their brethren need to accept this "truth" and take their rightful place as rulers of these lesser beings. However, most stop short of the notion of taking military action against Atlanteans who do not agree with their view. Many presently feel disenfranchised and isolated from the other clans, but they remain loyal to their kinsmen, overall.

Indeed, members of the Aerihman clan are counted among some of the greatest and noblest heroes throughout Atlantean history. The famed Undead Slayers originate with the Aerihman and the clan still boasts the greatest numbers of the heroic and selfless Undead Slayers and Tattooed Defenders of any. If they ever learned the truth about the Sunaj and their horrifying campaign of murder and genocide leveled against fellow Atlanteans, there are many Aerihman warriors who would lead the charge to destroy the Sunaj, down to every last member.

Still, if the secret society ever went public, there is a frightening percentage of Aerihman who would side with the Sunaj. This could have wide-reaching consequences if the leader of the Aerihman, Lord Aerihza, revealed himself to also be the head of the Sunaj and he called for the Aerihman people to rise up and join him in embracing their true destiny. How large a portion would side with him is hard to say. Ten percent? Twenty percent? A third? Whatever the number, it would create chaos within the clan and blemish the reputation of the Aerihman to such a degree they might never recover from it.

O.C.C.s common to the Sunaj Order of Assassins

The Sunaj specific O.C.C.s described in this section are among the most common within the secret society. However, a Sunaj killer or operative can be any of the O.C.C.s available to True Atlanteans, including the Tattooed Defender, Undead Slayer, Nomad, Voyager, Stone Master, or any practitioner of magic, among others.

Common division of O.C.C.s within the Sunaj Secret Society:
38% Sunaj Assassins
10% Shadow Assassins (new O.C.C.)
9% Shadow Mages (new O.C.C.)
4% Tattooed Defenders (new O.C.C.)
10% Undead Slayers
4% Tattooed Men, other.
4% Nomads
6% Tattooed Voyagers (new O.C.C.)
1% Temporal Wizards
4% Ley Line Walkers
2% Shifters
3% Practitioners of magic, other.
1% Psychics, other.
4% Other non-magic O.C.C.s; just about any.

Sunaj Assassin

A Secret Tattooed Man

The Sunaj Assassins are members of a secret, Illuminati-like society within the Aerihman clan. The Sunaj organization recruits militant zealots from within the Aerihman who believe they and their leaders know a better way for the Atlantean people and are willing to do something about it. Secret members of the Sunaj include influential clan leaders, assassins, psychics, practitioners of magic and seemingly ordinary Aerihman active within the clan and scattered across the Megaverse.

The initial selection process to become a Sunaj has not changed, and only the most dedicated to their beliefs are selected for this secret service to their people. Aerihman clansmen who are vocal about their clan's superiority, believe the Atlanteans have a duty to take Atlantis from the Splugorth, and that it is the destiny or right of the Aerihman to build a new Atlantean Empire, are scrutinized as potential recruits into the order of the Sunaj. They are secretly put through a battery of psychological and physical tests to see if they possess the mettle to become a Sunaj and are capable of killing their fellow Atlanteans in order to further the agendas of the Aerihman through secret and alternative means. Of course, potential new members cannot be just willing to kill rival Atlantean clansmen. Sunaj assassins need to be able to deceive, steal, and annihilate anyone who stands in their way without regret or hesitation. And must be able to do all this in secrecy, without any recognition for their service and sacrifice. They must also be prepared to die to preserve their secrets and the order of the Sunaj.

These fanatics believe what they do is for the greater good of all Atlanteans, regardless of the cost to others. They share the mentality that the ends justify the means, and there should be no loose ends which could jeopardize the Order or their grand agenda. All of this contributes to the Sunaj reputation for brutality and utter ruthlessness.

The Sunaj is so secret, and their selection process so stringent, that most Aerihman Atlanteans do not know the Illuminati-like organization even exists. Over the years, the Sunaj secret society has grown in numbers and influence with Sunaj leaders, members and friends in high places. Powerful men and women who help protect, fund and conceal the activities and identity of its membership. It is the foot soldiers — the Sunaj Assassins, Shadow Mages, and Shadow Assassins — who are, in effect, the mysterious and murderous face of the Sunaj, but it is the more powerful and influential members hiding in plain sight who pull their strings and develop the Order's master plan. Like the fabled

Illuminati of ancient Earth, the Sunaj secret society has its members and spies everywhere.

It is their sense of righteousness and superiority in the service of a greater purpose that motivates all members of the Sunaj secret society. It also serves as the intangible, deeply personal reward for their silent service and sacrifice. There is nothing greater than to serve a noble and important cause to benefit the Aerihman clan. The need for secrecy only raises the bar and makes it all feel so much more grand and important — something much greater than themselves. So it is that every Sunaj is a zealot willing to take his secrets to the grave rather than risk them being revealed or damage the Order. A captured Sunaj remains calm and defiant because he knows his brethren will find him and either rescue him (often in a bloodbath in which everyone who might know too much is slaughtered or slain as an act of retribution), or silence him before he can be forced to hurt the Order in any way.

Sunaj front-line troops in the field disguise their Atlantean heritage with the trademark Sunaj black armor and customized monstrous helmets and face-plates that mask their human nature and give them the appearance of D-Bees or demons. Nobody knows who or what is under the mask. Among their secret weapons is *Tattoo Magic*, and more recently, *Shadow Magic*.

On Rifts Earth, the Sunaj can be found anywhere, but are most common in Atlantis, at the *Splynn Dimensional Market* or in the service of Lord Splynncryth and other Splugorth. Though considered the lapdogs of the Splugorth, Sunaj are known to sell their services as assassins, spies, kidnapers, enforcers and mercenaries to anyone who can afford them. When a potential client has a "job" the Sunaj finds appealing or which offers them or the Aerihman clan some advantage, but the client does not have the funds

to pay the Sunaj what is customary, the villain may take the job for a fraction of his usual fee, or for a percentage of the loot, and sometimes pro-bono. Sunaj always have two ulterior motives in mind. One, undermining or destroying Atlantean clansmen who do not agree with the Aerihman clan's position, which are most, and two, uncovering the weaknesses of the Splugorth so they may one day take Atlantis back from them. The Sunaj Aerihman believe in keeping their enemies close and enjoy the game of winning their trust so they may strike them down when least expected. A third contributing motive can be revenge.

Whether on a job for hire or on their own time, the Sunaj are always gathering intelligence on people and groups they see as enemies, rivals or potential assets. Hunting and killing True Atlanteans and acquiring secrets and magic artifacts, or just making a name for the Sunaj are also at the top of their "to do list." Those who sell their services as freelance operatives and guns for hire are often under the command of a Sunaj cell leader who is careful to calculate what can be gained by their service to the right clients. Gains that are about more than cold, hard credits to support the Sunaj cause.

Since the creation of the Sunaj just 50 years ago, the organization has proven to be a stellar success for Lord Aerihza and the Aerihman clan (though they do not know it).

Sunaj Assassin Special O.C.C. Abilities:

1. Magic Tattoos Denote Heritage: Standard staked heart and flaming sword tattoos, as discussed under the Atlantean R.C.C.

2. Increased P.P.E. from Magic Tattoos: Base P.P.E. is 1D4x10+30 plus P.E. attribute number to start for all Sunaj Assassins. Add 10 P.P.E. points for each additional level of experience and six P.P.E. for each additional tattoo. **Note:** The Sunaj Assassin can also draw energy from ley lines and nexus points, up to 20 P.P.E. per each activation of a magic tattoo or 15 P.P.E. per melee round to power or use a magic device.

3. Increased P.P.E. Recovery: P.P.E. replenishes itself at the rate of 20 points for every hour of meditation, rest or sleep.

4. M.D.C.: Base M.D.C. of 2D4x10 plus each additional tattoo beyond six instills the male assassin with 11 M.D.C. and the females with 13 M.D.C. points. The Sunaj Assassin also gains 2D6 M.D.C. per each additional level of experience. Sunaj Assassins are Mega-Damage beings with Supernatural P.S. and P.E., and whose physical attacks inflict M.D. to the undead, supernatural beings and other Mega-Damage creatures and opponents.

5. Advanced Tattoo Training: Sunaj Assassins are taught early on to be able to activate their tattoos without touching them. Starting at level one, the Sunaj can activate their tattoos through concentration and force of will, but it uses up two melee attacks. If they need the tattoo in a pinch they can still touch it, using only one melee attack to activate it. Starting at level four, the Sunaj can activate their tattoos with just a thought which counts as one melee attack.

This advanced training also enables the experienced Tattooed Assassin to activate additional tattoos above and beyond the six limit, as long as he has have sufficient P.P.E. available. A maximum of seven tattoos can be activated at level 4, eight at level 8, and nine at level 12.

6. Magic Tattoos: The Sunaj Assassin starts with nine tattoos. The Sunaj Assassin's focus is on *Power Tattoos* and *Magic Weapons*. Sunaj do not bother with Dimension Tattoos as they often use magic pyramids to travel or are accompanied by a *Tattooed Voyager*.

The two Marks of Heritage, stake through the heart and flaming sword.

Death Touch (skull & thorns) tattoo.

Explosion (self-destruction) tattoo.

One additional Magic Weapon tattoo of choice.

Five Power tattoos of choice.

Acquiring new Tattoos: At experience levels 3, 5, 7, 9, 11, 13, 15, 17, 19, etc., a Sunaj's clan elder or Alchemist presents the Sunaj Assassin with one new Power Tattoo. This may require traveling to a different dimension, so the Sunaj may have to disappear for a few days from time to time. The number of Power Tattoos that the Assassin can get at any one time is one and there must be at least *six months* before the acquisition of another tattoo. Note that the receipt of a new tattoo may be withheld indefinitely as punishment by a clan elder or Alchemist, usually under orders from a Sunaj cell leader or Lord Aerihza himself for acts of cowardice, stupidity or failure. Of course, what is taken away can be given back, so if the Sunaj redeems himself, he can be given back any magic tattoo that has been withheld from him. Similarly, from time to time a Weapon, Magic Weapon, Animal or Monster tattoo may be given to the Sunaj as a reward for courage or outstanding service.

7. Psionic Powers: All Sunaj Assassins are Major or Master Psychics with psionic abilities. Non-psychics and Minor psychics can both become members of the Sunaj, but as a different O.C.C., not the infamous Sunaj Assassin.

Major psychics select eight psionic abilities from one psionic category or a total of six abilities from two or more of the following categories: Physical, Sensitive and/or Healer. The Super-Psionics category is not available. I.S.P. is the number from the M.E. attribute plus 4D6. Add 1D6+1 I.S.P. for each level of experience.

A Master Psychic is typically a powerful psionic such as a Mind Mage, Burster, Zapper and others, with Super-Psionic powers available to them. They make the deadliest of Sunaj Assassins. **Important Note:** If this is the case, use the *psionic abilities* and *I.S.P.* of that Psychic O.C.C. (including psionic powers acquired with level advancement), but use the skills, bonuses, etc., from the Sunaj Assassin O.C.C. listed here, with the following adjustments:

● The Master Psychic starts with the following reduced O.C.C. Skills:

Boxing (provides an extra melee attack per round).

Disguise (+20%)

Intelligence (+15%)

Language & Literacy: Dragonese/Elf, American, & Greek at 98%.

Lore: Demons & Monsters (+10%)

Mathematics: Basic (+25%)

Prowl (+10%)

Tracking (people; +20%)

W.P. Blunt or Sword (pick one)

W.P. Energy Pistol or Energy Rifle

Hand to Hand: Assassin

● Reduce the number of Related Skills to 3 to start and gain half as many with level advancement.

● Reduce Secondary Skills to 2.

● Reduce O.C.C. bonuses by half (round up).

● Start with *two Power Tattoos* instead of five, and only receive a new Power tattoo at levels 3, 7, 11, 15, 19, etc.

A Master Psychic tends to rely upon his psionic powers and magic tattoos rather than skills and weapons.

8. O.C.C. Bonuses: +2 on all Perception Rolls, +1 on initiative, +2 to strike, +1 to disarm, +3 to pull punch, +2 to save vs mind control via psionics and drugs, +1 to save vs illusions and possession, and +4 to save vs Horror Factor. Attribute bonuses due to their physical training and magic includes: +2 to M.E., +1D6 to P.S. (Supernatural), +1D6 to P.P. and Spd. Their P.S. and P.E. are supernatural due to their magic tattoos. Make sure you include the True Atlantean R.C.C. bonuses too.

Sunaj Assassin O.C.C. Stats

Alignment: All Sunaj are selfish or evil, with many being Aberrant. Remember, there is a strict selection process and those who do not pass are weeded out.

Attribute Requirements: I.Q. 10 or higher, M.E. 12 or higher, P.E. 14 or higher.

Psionic Ability: Must possess Major psionics or Master psionics.

O.C.C. Skills:

Boxing (provides an extra melee attack per round).

Disguise (+20%)

Gymnastics

Intelligence (+15%)

Land Navigation (+15%)

Language & Literacy: Dragonese/Elf, American, and Greek at 98%.

Languages: Speaks three additional languages of choice (+10%).

Lore: Demons & Monsters (+10%)

Mathematics: Basic (+25%)

Prowl (+10%)

Swimming (+5%)

Tracking (people; +20%)

Wilderness Survival <u>or</u> Pick Locks (+20%)

W.P. Archery

W.P. Blunt

W.P. Sword

W.P. Energy Pistol

W.P. Energy Rifle

Hand to Hand: Assassin

O.C.C. Related Skills: Select six other skills, plus select two additional skills at levels 4, 8 and 12. All new skills start at level one proficiency.

Communications: Any (+10%).

Cowboy: None.

Domestic: Any.

Electrical: Basic Electronics only.

Espionage: Any (+10%).

Horsemanship: General or Exotic only.

Mechanical: None.

Medical: First Aid only (+5%).

Military: Any (+10%).

Physical: Any.

Pilot: Any (+10%).

Pilot Related: Any (+10%).

Rogue: Any (+5%).

Science: None.

Technical: Any (+10%).

W.P.: Any.

Wilderness: Any (+5%).

Secondary Skills: The Sunaj Assassin also gets to select four Secondary Skills from the Secondary Skill list. These are additional areas of knowledge that do not get any bonus, other than possible bonuses from a high I.Q. All Secondary Skills start at the base skill level.

Standard Equipment: One weapon per W.P. and 1D4+2 extra E-Clips for each. Weapon may include any common items (and depending on the G.M., not so common) sold in the Three Galaxies, among the Minions of Splugorth, and on Rifts Earth. Sunaj do not use Atlantean made weapons and gear so they cannot be traced to Atlanteans. The preference seems to be Kittani and Splugorth weapons, as well as magic weapons. Additional equipment includes a laser scalpel, two silver-plated throwing knives, a cross of some kind, 2D4 wooden stakes, and a mallet. Sunaj prefer magic weapons and armor when they can get their hands on them, but do not start out with any. See armor below.

<u>Sunaj Assassin Environmental Armor</u>: Described below.

<u>Vehicle</u>: A small lightweight means of transportation such as a horse, gryphon, or monstrous mount, a hovercycle or small hovercraft, a jet pack, etc. The animal or vehicle should be suitable for going over rough terrain.

<u>Other Common Equipment</u>: Disguise makeup kit with at least one complete disguise (wigs, prosthetics applications, makeup, glue, etc.), sunglasses and goggles, air filter, gas mask, 100 feet (30.5 m) of rope, pocket toolkit, flashlight, canteen, compass, pocket computer, and Mega-Damage Sunaj Assassin environmental armor (110 M.D.C., good mobility) or other medium armor like CS Dead Boy armor, Gladiator, Crusader, Bushman or Naruni. Additional equipment may also include lock picking tools, more makeup and disguises, clothes and props for disguises, surveillance equipment, and so on.

Money: 6D6x1,000 in universal credits and 1D6x1,000 in gold, precious gems or artifacts. Sunaj Assassins can accumulate vast fortunes, but they are not motivated by wealth. They are dedicated to destroying True Atlanteans and acquiring power. Most will donate 2D4x10% of their fortune to the building of the Sunaj and the Aerihman empire.

Cybernetics: None, if it can be avoided. Due to their magical nature and sense of heritage, the Sunaj, and all True Atlanteans, strive to get to a Healing Pyramid where they can be made whole. If not, Atlanteans will settle for cybernetic Bio-Systems. All Atlanteans are attracted to "natural" things, and mechanical systems are not natural. Moreover, cybernetics reduces the potency of magic. Only True Atlanteans who do not use magic, other than tattoos, may consider cybernetic implants.

Sunaj Environmental Body Armor

The Sunaj have created an iconic and sinister body armor that has become their signature look. All Sunaj wear a black environmental armor with a cape or cloak, and an ominous helmet and faceplate. The design of the armor varies only slightly from assassin to assassin; it is the demonic-looking helmet where individual Sunaj can make their armor unique. The only requirement is that the helmet looks monstrous, demonic and otherwise inhuman. This is to evoke fear and intimidation as much as it is to trick people into believing the Sunaj are inhuman monsters and perhaps even real demons.

To that end, Sunaj helmets seldom show human features. Instead, they have snouts and muzzles, horns and tusks, and shapes that seem likely to fit upon the brow of an inhuman predator. Many Sunaj assassins custom design their personal helmet, and may have 2-6 different helmets to further mislead people into believing there are more Sunaj than there really are, or because the assassin likes to wears a particular helmet and face mask for different assignments or against a particular enemy. (The illustration shows only a small range of the types of Sunaj helmets an assassin might consider.)

Despite the strikingly different Sunaj helmets and face plates, most helmets and body armor all have the same fundamental stats and parameters.

Sunaj Environmental Body Armor: A light, composite plate armor that offers excellent protection and minimal restriction of movement. The helmet is always designed to have the features of a monster.

Class: SA-14 Sunaj Assassin Combat Body Armor.

Size: Roughly human with many 7+ feet (2.1 m) tall.

Weight: 16 pounds (7.2 kg).

Mobility: Good; -5% to Climb and -10% to Prowl, Swim, perform acrobatics and similar physical skills/performance.

M.D.C. by Location:

Head/Helmet – 90

Arms – 60 each

Legs – 80 each
Main Body – 120

Special Weapon Systems or Features: None.

Sunaj EBA (Environmental Body Armor) Features:

- Complete environmental battle armor suitable for use in all hostile environments including space and underwater. Maximum depth tolerance is 600 feet (183 m).
- Computer controlled life support system with regulated internal cooling and temperature control, artificial air circulation systems, gas filtration, and humidifier. Computer controlled life support system that monitors and displays bio-data of the wearer as well as the capacity and failure of life support systems and damage to the armor. The wearer will know *approximately* how much M.D.C. is remaining and whether or not the armor has been breached.
- Computer controlled, independent oxygen supply and purge system that automatically engages in low oxygen or contaminated air environments. Eight hour oxygen supply. However, the air purification, recycling and circulation system can provide breathable air in outer space or a hostile environment for up to 10 days before it becomes too toxic.
- Internal, voice actuated *support* computer and database. This secondary computer provides mathematical computations and serves as a database of basic military data, protocol, rules, laws and procedure. It also includes a friend or foe feature to identify enemy troops, monsters, demons, D-Bees and common combat vehicles as part of a complex recognition/identification system. Data is based on an optical link or camera feed or verbal description (larger margin of error with verbal description). The computer can also "read" for the soldier in 22 different languages common to Earth and the Three Galaxies (85% level of accuracy). This is done via an optic link via a multi-optic system built into the helmet or via a built-in camera.
- Internal cooling and temperature control.
- Artificial air circulation systems, gas filtration, humidifier.
- Insulated, high-temperature resistant shielding for up to 300 degrees centigrade (572 Fahrenheit). Normal fires do no damage. Nuclear, plasma, magic fires and Mega Damage fire all do full damage.
- Radiation shielded.
- Modular connectors and clamps on the back of the Sunaj environmental body armor provide for the attachment of a jet pack or other types of backpacks, oxygen tanks, ammo drums and other gear.
- Ammo and supply waist belt, shoulder belts, and shoulder holsters are all standard issue. Pilots and officers have choice of shoulder or hip holster.

Sunaj Helmet Features: The entire helmet can be completely removed or just the faceplate.

- Tinted, polarized, eye panel that darkens in bright light and lightens in the dark.
- Directional, short-range radio built into the helmet. Effective range is 20 miles (32 km).
- External audio speaker to communicate without having to remove the faceplate or helmet.
- Built-in loudspeaker; 80 decibels.
- Built-in Language Translator. Includes all common languages of the people of the Three Galaxies, Kittani, Kydian, Dragonese/Elf, Demongogian, and many known languages of Rifts Earth.
- Multi-Optics system with passive nightvision, active infrared and ultraviolet optics, laser targeting, telescopic (one mile/1.6 km), and macro (20x magnification).
- HUD (Heads-Up Display) system with a full digital display that appears on the visor.
- Vital Signs Monitor and Display: An integral, miniature life signs monitor built into the suit monitors the wearer's heart rate, blood pressure, respiration, body temperature and other vital signs. It is tuned to the specific life signs of the armor's owner, so if these drop below registered norms it alerts the wearer of the situation and suggests action to be taken, such as medical care, etc.
- Concealed Helmet Camera (optional): A digital camera is built into the faceplate or top, or side of the helmet and is concealed so it is barely noticeable or looks like a bit of ornamentation. It can be turned on and off with a simple command and is used when a client wants visible proof of a kill, and for recording suspects, documents and information. The memory in the helmet can store up to 500 hours of video. The camera automatically stops recording when the helmet or faceplate is removed. **Note:** About 80% of the Sunaj have a camera in their helmet. The rest do not, preferring no documentation of their actions.
- The helmet is designed with connectors to hook snugly to the collar of the armor or a spacesuit and other modular systems, and seal airtight, automatically connecting with environmental features of the suit.

Sunaj Shadow Mage

Shadow Magic is something ancient. A mystic art Atlanteans of old once dabbled in, long before the island continent vanished from the face of the Earth. Surviving ancient Atlantean texts only speak of Shadow Magic in a few passages, and always in an unfavorable light. Based on these old writings, some believe Shadow Magic was regarded as a "dangerous, dark magic," even a "curse" by those who dared to use it. There are references to it leading to the "corruption of the soul," "self-destruction," and as being "useful only in matters most foul." Shadow Magic was never very popular in ancient Atlantis. In part, because it did not further the Atlanteans' goal of self-enlightenment, so the magic was eventually abandoned and forgotten by all but a few.

Today, only the tiniest handful of Atlantean historians have ever heard of Shadow Magic, and they know of it only in passing. While the use of Shadow Magic was forsaken by Atlantean society, it never completely vanished. The dark art was kept alive by a few, who used it to further their own gain. Perhaps, then, it is no surprise that the mystic art survived among a few obscure cults and individuals within the Aerihman clan. Its magic used with the utmost discretion and secretly passed down from generation to generation among only the most gifted, elite and discreet family members. At one point, probably fewer than two dozen individuals held onto the secrets of Shadow Magic. In the last century that has changed within the Aerihman clan. Most notably, the "Shadow Arts," as they are known among the Sunaj, have quietly reemerged within the secret society of assassins.

Lord Aerihza's own wife is a secret practitioner. So when several of his most trusted Sunaj leaders suggested they give the

eldritch magic a larger role within the Sunaj, and his wife agreed, he gave them his blessing. The irony is not lost on Lord Aerihza that the Sunaj themselves exist in the shadows and are unknown to Atlantean society. In a way, it seemed appropriate – even fateful – that Shadow Magic would become a force within the Sunaj. It had already existed among a few Sunaj leaders, but now, the magic discipline would be given a more active role within the Order. The end result, the creation of new agents to further the cause: the *Sunaj Shadow Mage* and *Sunaj Shadow Assassin.* Both of which bolster and diversify the ranks of the infamous Order of Sunaj Assassins.

The use of this ancient, dark magic is one more secret weapon to further the Sunaj agenda. It also breaks the mold of the tattoo wielding Sunaj Assassin and adds an additional layer of mystery as well as further distances the Sunaj from any connection to Atlanteans.

The Shadow Mage is not a traditional Ley Line Walker or Wizard. They are more like agents of chaos who function among the Sunaj as magic-wielding spies, saboteurs and support personnel. They use their magic in subtle ways to harm or work against their enemies from behind the scenes, and to support other Sunaj in the field from the shadows. Shadow Mages are excellent for intelligence gathering, quiet insertions and extractions of Sunaj operatives, rescue operations, jailbreaks, hiding and concealing operatives, acts of intimidation and all manner of covert operations. Sunaj Shadow Mages are quickly becoming spy-masters who lurk in the shadows and use their magic to cover the trail of Sunaj Assassins who wait, hidden, until ready to strike down their enemies or any fool who may threaten their agenda. Shadow Magic is ideal for ambushes and other acts of treachery for which the members of the Sunaj secret society are famous.

Darkness is Power (special): In theory, Shadow Magic spell invocations can be learned by any practitioner of magic. However, Shadow Mages rarely share their secrets with other magic users, which is why Shadow Magic is largely a forgotten and lost art. When it does surface, its sinister reputation and connection to the Shadow Realm keep most sorcerers from learning Shadow Magic. Some practitioners of magic insist they can sense a darkness and danger even when learning just a few Shadow spells. It is enough to prevent them from learning more. These sorcerers report they feel a sinister influence or supernatural presence within the magic itself. Most demons and demon worshipers also avoid Shadow Magic, giving credence to the belief held by some that the *Shadow Lords* and denizens of the *Shadow Dimension* may be ancient Chaos Demons no longer in favor with mortals and said to be dangerous and unpredictable agents of entropy. Archaic Chaos Demons are rivals to modern demonkind, so their magic is discouraged among their worshipers.

A dark influence, some claim the pursuit of Shadow Magic casts a smoldering darkness over the hearts of those who use it. Making its practitioners cold, ruthless masters of lies and treachery. Perhaps this is why Shadow Magic has forever been relegated to death cults and assassins, and those who work in secret from the shadows. Indeed, Shadow Mages are so attuned and devoted to the Shadow Arts, they learn few spells that are not Shadow Magic. Among the ones they do learn outside their discipline are spells used to torture, dominate and kill, such as Agony, Blind, Forcebonds and Desiccate the Supernatural. They never select spells that cast light or electricity, and even tend to avoid healing magicks.

Over time, it is said that the darkness of their magic becomes a part of the spell caster's essence and the way he thinks. It erodes their sense of right and wrong, and makes it difficult for them to trust anyone other than their Sunaj brethren. Most Sunaj Shadow Mages believe the end justifies the means and that one must fight fire with fire. All keep their cards close to their vest, guard secrets carefully, lie and cheat without hesitation, are suspicious and distrusting of everyone, and are ruthless in dealing with enemies and rivals. It also means the best possible alignment for these spell casters is Unprincipled, with the majority being *Anarchist* and *Aberrant evil.*

Shadow Mage O.C.C. Special Abilities:

1. Magic Tattoos Denote Heritage: Staked heart and flaming sword as described under the Aerihman clan, and the Explosion (self-Destruction tattoo); three total. At present, all Sunaj are of the Aerihman clan. The Shadow Mage's ability to cast Shadow Magic means he cannot get more than a total of four magic tattoos. To get more would negate his abilities to cast magic. The Shadow Mage's discipline is casting Shadow Magic, not magic tattoos.

2. Base P.P.E. of the Shadow Mage: 2D4x10+45 +P.E. attribute number. Add 2D6 P.P.E. points for each level of experience starting at level one. **Note:** The Sunaj Shadow Mage can also draw energy from ley lines and nexus points, up to 20 P.P.E. per each activation of a magic tattoo or to cast a spell or to power or use a magic device.

3. Increased P.P.E. Recovery: The Shadow Mage replenishes P.P.E. at the rate of 20 points for every hour of meditation, rest or sleep, but only when recovery is done within a shadow larger than the mage or in a completely dark area. If there is bright artificial light, overcast sunlight or bright sunlight and no suitable shadow in which to sit and meditate, the Shadow Mage only recovers 5 P.P.E. per hour. Darkness is always a welcomed friend.

4. M.D.C.: None. Shadow Mages are NOT Mega-Damage beings nor are they considered to be supernatural in any way. Their P.S. is equal to Augmented and they must use body armor, power armor, force fields, magic or other means to protect themselves just like any other human.

5. Mastery of Shadow Magic (Spell Casting Bonuses): Shadow Magic is the overriding specialty of this practitioner of magic. No body knows it better, except for the demonic Shadow Lords. The Shadow Mage's affinity for the shadows and darkness means they can cast the 18 spells below and ALL Shadow spells they may learn later at *half* the usual P.P.E. cost listed (round up), plus when they cast the spell the normal duration is doubled!

Note: The number in parenthesis is the normal P.P.E. needed for other spell casters. *Reduce that number by half (round up) when cast by a Shadow Mage (or a Shadow Lord).*

Animate Shadows (6)
Cloud Shadow (100)
Ethereal in Shadows (25)
Shadow Clone (30)
Shadow Mask (4)
Shadow Meld (10)
Shadow Puppet (24)
Shadow Senses (16)
Shadow Shift (16)
Shadow Stalker (40)
Shadow Tentacles (8 or 16)

Shadow Walk (6)

Summon Denizens of the Shadow Plane (70 or 140)

+5 additional Shadow Magic spells of choice. The five spells can be selected from Shadow Magic levels 1-4.

6. Learning New Spells: The Shadow Mage starts out with the 13 spells above +5 of choice. All cast with superior ability. For each new level of experience, the Shadow Mage may learn TWO additional Shadow Magic spells selected from levels 1-6, or ONE spell invocation chosen from a level equivalent to his own level of experience or lower. When the Shadow Mage reaches 7th level experience, he can select two Shadow Magic spells from ANY level 1-15, or one non-Shadow invocation from any level equal to or less than his own level of experience.

From time to time, the Sunaj Shadow Mage may be taught one additional Shadow Magic spell or a non-Shadow invocation as a reward for outstanding service to the Sunaj, the Aerihman clan or one of its leaders. Game Master discretion. These reward spells should not be handed out like candy, they are a rare privilege.

7. Spell Strength: +1 to Spell Strength (the number opponents must save against when a spell is cast at them) at levels 3, 7, 11 and 15. **Note**: -2 to Spell Strength in daylight or bright artificial light. This penalty does not apply when the spell is cast while standing in shadow.

When under the influence of a ley line, spell range and duration are increased by an additional 50%, double at a ley line nexus.

8. O.C.C. Bonuses: +1 on Perception Rolls pertaining to hiding, escape, Shadow Magic, and Shadow beings, +1 to dodge, +3 to save vs Horror Factor (H.F.), and +1 to save vs all types of magic at levels 5, 10 and 15. Attribute bonuses from training and magic are +1D4 to M.A., +1D4 to M.E. or I.Q. (pick one; player's choice), and +3D6 to S.D.C. in addition to possible skill bonuses.

Friend of Shadows (special): Unafraid of the denizens of the Shadow Realm because they see the Shadow Mage as one of them, and the creatures will not attack unless directly commanded to do so by a Shadow Wraith or Shadow Lord, or unless the Mage attacks it first.

Shadow Bonuses (applicable only in shadow/darkness): +2 to Perception Rolls while in shadow or darkness, but -2 in daylight or in bright artificial light; +1 to strike, parry and dodge when in shadow or darkness, +3 to save vs Shadow Magic spells leveled against them, impervious to insanities that involve darkness, shadows or the denizens of the Shadow Dimension and is never afraid of the dark (feels at home and safe in darkness).

When in shadow or darkness, the character recovers/heals from physical injury/Hit Points/S.D.C. or M.D.C. at a rate of 1D6 points per hour of rest or meditation.

9. Vulnerability and Penalties: The Shadow Mage's strong bond to shadows and the darkness they represent imposes a number of penalties upon them.

When exposed to sunlight with no shadows for the Shadow Mage to find comfort in, all spell effects, range, damage, duration, penalties, etc., of Shadow Magic are *reduced by half*. No penalty if cast from a shadow or dark location.

-2 on Spell Strength in daylight or bright artificial light; as noted above.

-2 on Perception Rolls and initiative, and -5% on skill performance in daylight, even when overcast (no shadows) or when exposed to bright artificial light.

Vulnerable to silver! Any kind of silver blade or bullet does double damage. If the Shadow Mage is a Mega-Damage being, then an S.D.C. silver weapon does its usual damage x2 as Mega-Damage, so a silver-plated sword that normally inflicts 2D6 S.D.C. either does 4D6 S.D.C. or 4D6 M.D. to the Shadow Mage if he is an M.D.C. creature.

Over time, some Shadow Mages (01-05% chance per level) become allergic to sunlight and suffer from headaches and nausea when exposed to it for more than one hour. -15% to skill performance, reduce speed 20%, -1 melee attack and -1 on all combat bonuses.

Psionics: None.

Sunaj Shadow Mage Stats

Alignment: Selfish or evil; 36% Aberrant, 30% Miscreant, 12% Diabolic, 16% Anarchist and 6% other. Though it is said that Shadow Magic is not an inherently evil form of magic like Soulmancy, there is anecdotal evidence to the contrary and the magic is rarely used for good. Could there be a good Shadow Mage? Yes, it's possible. However, the Sunaj are not. Thus, alignment is restricted to Anarchist and Evil. It may be possible for there to be Shadow Mages elsewhere in the Megaverse or a renegade Sunaj/Aerihman Atlantean, but such a character is likely to be considered a traitor to his clan and a liability that needs to be eliminated. **Note:** Shadow Magic should be exceedingly rare. Game Masters have the final say in their games as to whether or not they will allow a Shadow Mage character *outside* the Sunaj for any human, D-Bee or other species. Just remember that beings who are not Atlanteans do NOT possess the Atlantean racial skills or magic tattoos.

Attribute Requirements: I.Q. 13 or higher and an M.E. 12 or higher; applicable to all races.

O.C.C. Skills:

Concealment (+5%)

Land Navigation (+10%)

Language & Literacy: Dragonese/Elf, American, Greek at 98%.

Language: Whisper (the language of Shadow Beast and the Shadow lords) 78% +2% per level of experience.

Languages: Speaks two additional languages of choice (+15%).

Literacy: One of choice (+20%).

Lore: Demons and Monsters (+15%)

Lore: Magic (+15%)

Lore: One of choice (+10%).

Mathematics: Basic (+40%)

Pilot: Hovercraft <u>or</u> Horsemanship Exotic (select one; +10%).

W.P. Ancient: Select one of choice.

W.P. Modern: Select one of choice.

Hand to Hand: Basic, but it can be changed to Hand to Hand: Expert at the cost of two O.C.C. Related Skills.

O.C.C. Related Skills: Select four other skills at level one, and one additional skill at levels 3, 6, 9, 12 and 15. All new skills start at level one proficiency.

Communications: Any (+10% to Language and Literacy skills).

Cowboy: None.

Domestic: Any (+10%).

Electrical: Basic only.

Espionage: Escape, Impersonation, Intelligence and Prowl only (+10%).

Horsemanship: General only (+10%).

Mechanical: Basic only.

Medical: Any.

Military: None.

Physical: Any except Acrobatics, Boxing, Gymnastics, Kick Boxing or Wrestling.

Pilot: Any except robots and power armors, and military.

Pilot Related: None.

Rogue: Any.

Science: Any (+5%).

Technical: Any (+10%).

W.P.: Any.

Wilderness: Any.

Secondary Skills: The character also gets to select two Secondary Skills from the Secondary Skill list. These are additional areas of knowledge that do not get any bonus, other than possible bonuses from a high I.Q. All Secondary Skills start at the base skill level.

Standard Equipment: Black or dark, lightweight M.D.C. body armor (1D4x10+45 M.D.C. or a Naruni force field), dark clothes or robes, hooded cloak or hooded cape, black leather gloves. Their look very much resembles the Sunaj Assassin and some even wear a similar helmet or mask, while others where no headgear or something lightweight.

One weapon for each W.P. skills and 1D4 E-Clips for each, a pocket knife (1D4 S.D.C.), a silver-plated knife (1D6), survival knife (1D6 S.D.C.), Vibro-Knife (1D6 M.D.), some like to use a spear or staff as a weapon, a gold cross (may be worn as jewelry), wooden cross, pocket mirror, two pens, notebook, digital pocket computer with camera, backpack, satchel, four small sacks, two medium sacks, handcuffs, communicator/radio, canteen, sunglasses, tinted goggles, air filter, 30 feet (9.1 m) of rope, utility belt, sleeping bag, flashlight, E-Clip powered lantern, and some personal items.

Money: 6D6x1,000 in universal credits and 2D6x1,000 in gold, precious gems or artifacts. Sunaj Shadow Mages are not motivated by wealth. Most are dedicated to serving the Sunaj Illuminati (and the Aerihman clan in general). They also like to acquire power and use it. Most donate 1D6x10% of their fortune to the secret society.

Cybernetics: None, if it can be avoided. Due to their magical nature and sense of heritage, the Sunaj, and all True Atlanteans, strive to get to a Healing Pyramid where they can be made whole. If not, Atlanteans will settle for cybernetic Bio-Systems. All Atlanteans are attracted to "natural" things, and mechanical systems are not natural. Moreover, cybernetics reduces the potency of magic. Only True Atlanteans who do not use magic, other than tattoos, may consider cybernetic implants.

Sunaj Shadow Assassin

With the Aerihman's plan to quietly subjugate their fellow Atlanteans starting to take shape over the last couple of decades, the number of suitable recruits for *Sunaj Assassins* is always limited.

To be recruited, the Aerihman clansman must exhibit rabid loyalty to the clan and fanatical belief in the Aerihman's superiority to lead the other clans. Moreover, the potential assassin must be willing to hunt and kill fellow True Atlanteans from other clans. Most people do not have the stomach for the genocide and treachery required to be a *Sunaj*. Moreover, all Sunaj Assassins must possess Major or Master psychic abilities. Not as difficult as that may sound since the Aerihman have bred themselves to have a greater range of psychics among their people, but it is still a prerequisite that limits available candidates. Of course, possessing psychic abilities provides great advantages to spies and assassins, so it does make sense for the Sunaj Assassin. Having psychic abilities helps the Sunaj Assassin to fend off psychic assaults and mind probes. Add in magic tattoos, M.D.C. bodies, and Supernatural strength, and you can see why the infamous Sunaj is such a deadly adversary.

The Sunaj Assassin is a finely honed, living weapon, and the pinnacle of Atlantean training, but like any weapon or resource, it can be overused. And if overused, the Sunaj organization could become predictable and countered. Better to keep the enemy guessing. So it is that a branch of the Sunaj without psychic abilities or magic tattoos have been trained in both the art of the assassin and Shadow Magic. This new, deadly operative is the **Sunaj Shadow Assassin.** While the Shadow Assassin lacks tattoos, save for the Marks of Heritage, they make up for it with their use of Shadow Magic for the purpose of espionage and murder. Such a mage-assassin broadens the capabilities and versatility of the Sunaj combat force and helps to grow the Sunaj army of assassins, spies and saboteurs. The unexpected element of magic, especially in a mixed group (say a few Sunaj Assassins, a couple Shadow Assassins and one Shadow Mage), can give the lethal Sunaj an even sharper edge and broader capabilities when it comes to slipping through enemy defenses unseen.

Being able to hide in shadows and darkness makes the Sunaj Shadow Assassin nearly invisible. Add a Shadow Mage into the mix, who can manipulate the shadows with much greater range and skill to provide cover for the traditional Sunaj Assassins and other agents, and the team is silent like ghosts and as deadly as vipers in the dark. The Shadow Assassin is the perfect agent to scout to check ahead, plant evidence, spy from the shadows, cut communications and alarms, engage in theft or sabotage, pave the way for other operatives, keep exits clear and support the more powerful and experienced Sunaj Assassin. Under the cover of darkness, they can leap out of the shadows to surprise and ambush unsuspecting guards or provide support for the lead Sunaj Assassin, and make exceptional lookouts who melt in and out of the shadows.

The Shadow Assassin may be part of hit squad, reconnaissance team or brought in for specific missions. If the *Sunaj Assassin* is a "sword" sent to kill enemies, then the *Shadow Assassin* is a "scalpel" – a precision device for the surgical removal of problems. These assassins working from the shadows are meticulous, planning their jobs down to the last detail. They make their surgical strike and leave before anyone knows they were ever

present. This leaves the enemy guessing about who might have been responsible and how they pulled it off. Whereas the Sunaj Assassins have built a deliberate reputation to strike fear in their enemies and like to leave a calling card and collateral damage in their wake, the very existence of Shadow Assassins is unverified and unconfirmed. They are the stuff of rumors and unsubstantiated suspicions. Shadow Assassins are *ghosts* who prefer to remain unseen and unrecognized. They are patient and use subterfuge and Shadow Magic to attack from the shadows. Shadow Assas-

sins seldom announce their presence, and strike from without warning and then fade away. Nor do they take credit for their handiwork. They like being the unknown and unstoppable force. The bogey-man in the dark, unseen until it is too late. Sure they may not have the notoriety of the bold and infamous Sunaj Assassins, but their cell leaders know they get the job done and this filters up to Lord Aerihza, and that is all that matters. In fact, Sunaj Shadow Assassins have been so successful in the last eight years that it is only recently that their suspected existence has come to light, and then only because of the meddling Splugorth who have quietly, but publicly speculated on their existence and pointed to the Sunaj.

A friendly rivalry has developed between the two types of Sunaj assassins, which often leads to demonstrations of one-upmanship and derring-do. However, they remain brothers-in-arms on the same team and with one mission: bring down the other clans and by doing so, raise up the Aerihman clan.

When standing side by side, in black cloaks and armor, it is very difficult telling the difference between a Tattooed Sunaj Assassin and a Sunaj Shadow Assassin, until they strike. Both wear the dark, trademark Sunaj armor, similar helmets and hooded capes or cloaks. If there is a difference, it is that the Shadow Assassins wear even less splashes of color, and the way they move. *The Sunaj Assassin* is bold and moves with the power and grace of a jungle cat on the prowl. When he turns his gaze upon you, you know you are the prey and in serious trouble. The *Shadow Assassin,* by comparison, always seems to be lurking in the background quietly slipping from one shadow to the next. Look away for a moment and he is gone from sight. Until you realize he has somehow snuck up on you and is about to strike.

Sunaj Shadow Assassin O.C.C. Special Abilities:

1. Magic Tattoos Denote Heritage: Staked heart and flaming sword as described under the Aerihman clan, and Explosion (self-destruction) tattoo. At present, all Sunaj are of the Aerihman clan. The Shadow Assassin's limited ability to cast Shadow Magic means he cannot get more than a total of four magic tattoos. To get more would negate his abilities to cast magic.

2. Base P.P.E.: 1D6x10+20 plus P.E. attribute number to start. The Shadow Assassin gains 2D4+2 P.P.E. for each level of experience starting at level one. **Note:** The Sunaj Shadow Assassin can also draw energy from ley lines and nexus points, up to 20 P.P.E. per each activation of a magic tattoo or 15 P.P.E. per melee round to cast as spell, or to power or use a magic device.

3. Increased P.P.E. Recovery: The Shadow Assassin replenishes P.P.E. at the rate of 10 points for every hour of meditation, rest or sleep, but only when recovery is done in a shadow larger than the mage or in darkness. If there is bright artificial light, overcast sunlight or sunlight and no suitable shadow, the Shadow Assassin only recovers 5 P.P.E. points per hour. Most Shadow Assassins find a dark, secluded area to meditate and rest in.

4. M.D.C.: None. Shadow Assassins are NOT Mega-Damage beings nor are they considered to be supernatural in any way. Their P.S. is equal to Augmented and they must use body armor, power armor, force fields, magic or other means to protect themselves just like any other human.

5. Shadow Magic: The Shadow Assassin knows just enough Shadow Magic to be dangerous. That includes only the most rudimentary principles of magic and a handful of spells to help him in his work as an assassin. Shadow Assassins cannot learn other types of spells, and seldom learn more than two dozen Shadow Magic spells in their lifetime.

Animate Shadows (6)
Ethereal in Shadows (25)
Shadow Defense (10)
Shadow Mask (4)
Shadow Meld (10)
Shadow Puppet (24)
Shadow Stalker (40)

Shadow Strike (6)
Shadow Walk (6)
+3 Shadow Magic spells of choice. The four spells can be selected from Shadow Magic levels 1-4.

6. Additional Shadow Spells: The Shadow Assassin is able to acquire one additional Shadow spell per each new level of experience starting at level two. One additional Shadow Magic spell *may* be taught to the assassin on by a Shadow Mage as a boon or rewards for exceptional service and loyalty, but such a reward is limited to one maximum per level of experience and does not happen on a regular basis nor every level. Reward spells must be earned.

7. Spell Strength: The Shadow Assassin is +1 to Spell Strength at levels 4, 8 and 12, but must be standing in a shadow or darkness when casting the spell to get the bonus. In daylight, even when overcast, or under bright artificial lights, the Shadow Assassin gets no Spell Strength bonus.

8. O.C.C. Bonuses: +1 on Perception Rolls pertaining to backstabbing, ambush, escape, and Shadow Magic, +1 on initiative, +2 to strike, parry, dodge and entangle, +2 to pull punch, +1 to roll with impact, +3 to save vs Horror Factor (H.F.), and +1 to save vs mind control via psionics and drugs. Attribute bonuses from training and magic are +1 to M.A. and M.E., +1D4+2 to P.P. and +4D6 to S.D.C., in addition to possible skill bonuses. Make sure you also include the True Atlantean R.C.C. bonuses.

Shadow Bonuses (applicable only in shadow/darkness): +3 to Perception Rolls while in shadow or darkness, but -3 in daylight or in bright artificial light; +1 attack per melee when in shadow or darkness, +2 to strike, parry and dodge when in shadow or darkness, +1 to save vs Shadow Magic spells leveled against them, impervious to insanities that involve darkness, shadows or the denizens of the Shadow Dimension, and is never afraid of the dark (feels at home and safe in darkness).

When in shadow or darkness, the character heals from physical injury/Hit Points/S.D.C. (or M.D.C.) at a rate of 1D6 points per hour of rest or meditation.

9. Weakness/Vulnerability: Because the Shadow Assassin is practicing a long lost and forbidden magic, the full consequences of its use are not known. One such vulnerability is silver. Weapons made of or coated in silver, be it blade, arrow or bullet, do double damage. Another is the Sunaj Shadow Assassin becomes a nocturnal hunter, who prefers to prowl and hunt at night and sleep during the day. By fourth level experience, their eyes become sensitive to light (-1 to all combat maneuvers like initiative, strike, parry, dodge, etc.) in sunlight and bright lights, which is why they always wear sunglasses or tinted goggles or a helmet with a tinted or light sensitive transition visor that darkens in bright light.

Psionics: None, or perhaps is a Minor Psychic with a couple psychic abilities.

Sunaj Shadow Assassin Stats

Alignment: All Sunaj are selfish or evil. Remember there is a strict selection process and those who do not pass are weeded out.

Attribute Requirements: I.Q. and M.E. 12 or higher, P.P. of 15 or higher.

O.C.C. Skills:
Disguise (+10%)
Electronics: Basic (+5%)

Intelligence (+15%)

Land Navigation (+10%)

Language & Literacy: Dragonese/Elf, American, Greek at 98%.

Languages: Speaks three additional languages of choice (+10%).

Locksmith (+30%)

Lore: Demons & Monsters (+15%)

Lore: Magic (+10%)

Mathematics: Basic (+25%)

Prowl (+15%)

Surveillance (+10%)

Tracking (+10%)

W.P. Ancient: One of choice.

W.P. Blunt or Staff (pick one).

W.P. Sword

W.P. Energy Pistol

W.P. Energy Rifle

Hand to Hand: Assassin

O.C.C. Related Skills: Select four other skills at level and one additional skill at levels 3, 5, 8, 11 and 14. All new skills start at level one proficiency.

Communications: Any (+10%).

Cowboy: None.

Domestic: Any.

Electrical: None.

Espionage: Any (+15%).

Horsemanship: General or Exotic only.

Mechanical: None.

Medical: First Aid only (+5%).

Military: Any (+5%).

Physical: Any.

Pilot: Any (+5%).

Pilot Related: Any (+5%).

Rogue: Any (+10%).

Science: None.

Technical: Any (+10%).

W.P.: Any.

Wilderness: Any.

Secondary Skills: The character also gets to select four Secondary Skills from the Secondary Skill list. These are additional areas of knowledge that do not get any bonus, other than possible bonuses from a high I.Q. All Secondary Skills start at the base skill level.

Standard Equipment: Standard Sunaj Assassin M.D.C. body armor, but with a simpler helmet that usually lack large horns, dark clothes, hooded cloak or hooded cape, black leather gloves. They look very much like a Sunaj Assassin.

One weapon for each W.P. skill and 1D4 E-Clips for each. They tend to prefer weapons that cannot be traced to Atlanteans or the Aerihman. The preference seems to be Kittani and Splugorth weapons. The Shadow Assassin does not start out with a personal vehicle, but one can be provided if the assignment calls for one.

Other equipment will often include disguise makeup, at least one complete disguise (wigs, prosthetics applications, makeup etc.), 100 feet (30.5 m) of rope, two pairs of handcuffs, pocket toolkit, compass, a large silver-plated knife (1D6 S.D.C.), survival knife (1D6 S.D.C.), Vibro-Knife (1D6 M.D.), some like to use a spear or staff as a weapon, wooden

cross, pocket mirror, two pens, notebook, digital pocket computer with camera, backpack, satchel, two small sacks, communicator/radio, canteen, sunglasses, tinted goggles, air filter, utility belt, sleeping bag, flashlight, E-Clip powered lantern, and some personal items.

Additional equipment may also include lock picking tools, more makeup and disguises, clothes and props for disguises, surveillance equipment and so on.

Money: 5D6x1,000 in universal credits and 1D6x1,000 in gold, precious gems or artifacts. Shadow Assassins can accumulate vast fortunes, but they are not motivated by wealth. They are dedicated to destroying True Atlanteans and acquiring power. Most donate 2D4x10% of their fortune to the building of the empire.

Cybernetics: None, if it can be avoided. Due to their magic tattoos and sense of heritage, all True Atlanteans strive to get to a Healing Pyramid where they can be made whole. If not, Atlanteans will settle for cybernetic Bio-Systems. All Atlanteans are attracted to "natural" things, and mechanical systems are not natural. Moreover, cybernetics reduces the potency of magic. Only True Atlanteans who do not use magic, other than a few basic tattoos, may consider cybernetic implants.

Shadow Magic

Shadow Magic is an arcane form of spell casting that originated in the Shadow Dimension. The undisputed power of most shadow realms are *Shadow Lords*, which some believe are the originators of this magic. Others point to ancient Alien Intelligences from another time and place.

Many insist Shadow Magic is inherently evil and that you can feel the darkness as you learn the magic and every time you cast a spell. According to some legends and rumors, Shadow Magic slowly corrupts the soul of its user, turning it black and his heart cold. Other tales claim the use of this dark magic leads to destruction, especially for those who call upon the creatures of the Shadow Dimension. A place rumored by some to be a type of Hell and its inhabitants demonic creatures of darkness and chaos.

Whether any of this is true or not, Shadow Magic does seem to be crafted for nefarious purposes, such as frightening and intimidating others, spying, stealing, ambush and murder. The magic certainly has a long history of such use and for confounding and slaying enemies, unseen. As a result, it has been the magic of death cultists, thieves and assassins. Even among societies where Shadow Magic is not forgotten, it is usually outlawed, and practiced by the most dangerous and wicked of sorcerers. For these reasons and others, most civilized people consider Shadow Magic to be one of the *dark arts* like Soulmancy, Necromancy and Bio-Wizardry, and it is shunned by most practitioners of magic. It was banned from Ancient Atlantis long before the continent vanished. The Sunaj making use of this rare arcane form of magic can only add to Shadow Magic's unsavory reputation.

Note: Also see the **Sunaj Shadow Mage O.C.C.** for more details about Shadow Magic and its reputation and use.

Duration of Shadow Magic spells is double for Shadow Mages and quadruple for Shadow Lords!

Light Weakens Shadow Magic

Reduce the effects of Shadow Magic by half when exposed to light. Unlike most spells, Shadow Magic is strongest when used at night and when cast from shadows during the daytime. If cast when exposed to sunlight even when overcast, or bright artificial light, without a shadow large enough to step into and be completely covered in shade, Shadow Magic is weak.

Penalties from Light: Range, damage, duration, penalties, bonuses, etc., are all reduced by HALF when the user/spell caster of Shadow Magic (Sunaj Shadow Mage, Shadow Assassin or any mage, and even the Shadow Lords themselves) does not have a dark place from which to cast the spell.

Magic that creates bright light can either help (creates shadows) or hinder (dispels shadows and exposes the Shadow Magic user to light, reducing the potency of the spells he casts while he is illuminated, by half). A selection of light spells and conditions that have an influence on Shadow Magic and Shadow beings are listed below. For any spell not listed, or with the addition of new spells in later books, Game Masters are going to have to use their best judgment based on the information presented here.

Blinding Flash: There is not much of a discernible impact since the spell is a quick flash of light and has the usual effect of blinding the individual. Increase the duration by 50% when used on the denizens of the Shadow Dimension (Shadow Beasts, Shadow Lords, etc.).

Call Lightning and all types of Electrical Attacks: Lightning and electricity inflict full damage to Shadow Mages, Shadow Assassins and creatures of the Shadow Dimension, even when they are Ethereal in shadow or darkness!

Charismatic Aura: This spell does not function on mages or assassins trying to hide in shadow because the person with Charismatic Aura needs to be seen in order for this spell to have any effect on those who see him. Of course, it works fine when the Shadow Mage steps out of the darkness to show himself in order to make threats or deliver an appeal or speech.

Chromatic Protection: A character using Shadow Magic will not want to use this spell because it envelops the individual in a faint blue light that is visible in the darkness and thus would negate any attempts to hided in darkness. If a Shadow creature or Shadow Mage attacks someone or something imbued with Chromatic Protection on them, the effects are the same as *Blinding Flash* at double the duration (2D4 melee rounds).

Electric Arc: Same as Call Lightning, above.

Globe of Daylight: Light is trouble for Shadow Magic. If there is a powerful enough light source (it can be sunlight, a magical Globe of Daylight or strong artificial light), there may be no place for the Ethereal Shadow Mage to hide. He or she is revealed for all to see, and without a large enough shadow to step into, the individual is revealed, no longer Ethereal, and effectively out in the open where he is vulnerable until the light is turned off or until he can find a shadow to hide in. Without a large enough shadow to step into, the Mage or Shadow being cannot disappear or turn Ethereal in Shadow and may suffer other consequences from the light.

Note: All of the above is relevant in wide open spaces. HOWEVER, the environment will dictate the effective outcome for the use of a Globe of Daylight spell or any bright light source. If there are large objects like furniture, boulders, debris, trees, etc., and even people, the light source creates strong light AND shadows. That means a Globe of Daylight could create plenty of shadows for a Shadow Mage, Shadow Assassin or Shadow creature to hide in, escape through or from which to launch attacks. The fact that the spell caster can move and reposition a Globe of Daylight may help him to eradicate shadows or to slowly pursue an opponent using Shadow Magic (or abilities), but its use is not an automatic win or necessarily a good thing. If the Shadow being can move with the shadows being cast, it can remain at full power and hidden.

Lantern Light: Creates a small orb of light, but it is not as powerful or effective as the Globe of Daylight and has no effect on Shadow Beasts or Shadow Mages unless the lantern light is turned up to its maximum intensity (equal to a 300 watt bulb) and the Shadow beings are within 10 feet (3 m) of it. There are no shadows in that 10 foot (3 m) radius, so any Shadow beings (or Shadow spell caster) would be revealed in its light and function at half its usual strength while in the lit area; unless there are objects that cast shadow (see the Note for Globe of Daylight, above).

Lasers and Light Blasts: Lasers inflict half damage to Shadow Mages and Shadow beings even when they are *Ethereal in Shadow or Darkness!* Lasers and light attacks do full damage to those exposed and weakened by sunlight or bright artificial light.

Lightblade: This spell does not give off enough light to impact the environment or cast shadows, but does full damage to the Shadow Mage, Shadow Assassin and Shadow beings even when they are in shadows or darkness, or otherwise protected by the Ethereal spell. The Ethereal in Shadow spell will not protect them from magic Lightblade. Moreover, the Lightblade striking any shadow weapons, such as Shadow Blade and Night Stick, negates the shadow weapon but is, itself, destroyed in the process. The two weapons cancel each other out and both magic weapons are negated and disappear. The Lightblade can also be used to parry *Shadow Barrage* and *Shadow Tendril Bolts*. The target to parry is equal to the saving throw of each spell. Finally, Lightblade does 50% more damage to Shadow Skin and Shade Armor.

Light Target: This spell surrounds its victim in an aura of bright light. If cast around one of the denizens of the Shadow Dimension, it makes it impossible to hide in shadows or darkness and has the effect of bathing them in strong, artificial light which reduces their shadow abilities and stats by half! This spell is incredibly effective against Shadow Lords and their Shadow being minions. Against a Shadow Mage or Shadow Assassin, the light aura around them prevents them from hiding in shadow or from becoming Ethereal, and may interfere with other Shadow Magic spell, but they are otherwise unaffected and can still fight and cast Shadow spells.

Lightning Arc: Same as Call Lightning, above.

See in Magic Darkness: This spell is crafted to penetrate shadows and darkness. Those enchanted with See in Magic Darkness can see clearly into ordinary shadows and see whatever Shadow

Assassins or Shadow beings may be lurking inside. The spell also makes it possible to see in most magical darknesses, but not all.

Shadow Vision: This Shadow Magic is the ultimate spell to see what lurks in the shadows and Shadow Magic created darkness and enchantments like the Shadow Mask, Shadow Pools and Shadow Pits.

Shadow Magic Spells

By Kevin Siembieda, Carl Gleba and Bill Coffin

Notes: Some Shadow Magic spell effects can be combined and used simultaneously, such as Shadow Defense and Shadow Strike, or Animate Shadows and Give Shadows Sound.

The P.P.E. cost for Shadow Mages and Shadow Lords is half (round up). Applicable only to Shadow Magic. If a Shadow Magic spell costs 10 P.P.E., the Shadow Mage (and Shadow Lord) only requires 5 P.P.E. to cast it, plus the spell duration is double for the Mage.

The Duration of Shadow Magic spells is double for Shadow Mages (not Shadow Assassins and other spell casters) and quadruple for Shadow Lords!

Level One

Animate Shadow (6)
Lengthen Shadows (4)
Moonlight (4)
Shadowcast (6)
Shadow Mask (4)
Shadow Reach (4)

Level Two

Aura of Darkness (6)
Darklight (6)
Ominous Shadow (6)
Shadow Vision (8)
Shadow Walk (6)
Slip Shadow (5)
Whispered Voice (6)

Level Three

Give Shadows Sound (8)
Shadow Bolt (6)
Shadow Defense (10)
Shadow Displacement (8)
Shadow Globe (10)
Shadow Skin (8)
Shadow Strike (6)
Shadow Writing (8)

Level Four

Field of Shadow Tendrils (10)
Ride the Night Wind (12)
Shade Armor (10)
Shadeshield (12)
Shadow Meld (10)
Shadowsight (15)
Wall of Darkness (15)
Whispering Shadows (8)

Level Five

Conceal Objects in Shadow (14)
Eyes in the Dark (14)
Night Stick (18 or 26)
Shadow Senses (16)
Shadow Shift (16)
Wall of Shades (20)

Level Six

Circle of Shadows (20)
Manipulate Shadows (20)
Shadow Boxer (20)
Shadowfire (20)

Level Seven

Ethereal in Shadow (25)
Shadow Pocket (30)
Shadow Pool (30)
Shadow Puppet (24)
Shadow Tendril Bolts (30)

Level Eight

Shadesword (22)
Shades of Death (25)
Shadow Clone (30)
Shadow Tentacles (10 or 18)
Shadow Trap (30)

Level Nine

Banish Shadows (66)
Shadow Hold (40)
Shadow Stalker (40)

Level Ten

Cloak of Darkness (80)
Cloud Shadow (100)
Curse of Darkness (120)
Shadow Hole (95)
Summon Shadow Beast (140)

Level Eleven

Shadow Door (240)
Shadow Envelope (45 or 290)

Level Twelve

Shadow Fog (250)
Shadowgate (300)

Level Thirteen

Shadow Wall (400)

Level Fourteen

Shadow Essence (480)
Summon Denizens of the Shadow Dimension (480)

Level Fifteen

Shadow Self (1,000)

Level One

Animate Shadow

Range: 100 feet (30.5 m) +10 feet (3 m) per level of experience.
Duration: Five minutes per level of the spell caster. (Double for Shadow Mages. Quadruple for Shadow Lords.)
Limitation: The spell caster can animate one specific shadow per spell casting, with the shadow repeating its animated sequence (opening and closing, pointing, dancing, shaking its fist, waving its arms, reaching for someone, etc.) over and over for the full duration. If the spell caster remains within 100 feet of the Animated Shadow, he can change the animation to make the shadow move and perform in other ways. Before he leaves, the mage will set it to repeat one particular animated sequence up to two minute long per level of experience.
Saving Throw: Standard.
P.P.E.: Six

The spell caster is able to make any shadow come to life like a two-dimensional animated silhouette on wall, the ground, or other surface. The shadow must already be present and the magic simply alters and animates it. He can make the shadow on the side of a building open to reveal a gaping silhouette maw lined with jagged teeth that snaps at all who pass or walk up to the door; the shadow of a pole may bend and wave or dance in place; shadows of vines or wires might writhe like snakes; a shadow from a tree branch may form into a hand with long, bony fingers that points the way or waves people off, or becomes a shaking fist. Shadows that move or mouth words, etc., are scary and bizarre.

Roll to save vs magic: Ordinary people who witness such strange occurrences and fail to save vs magic are likely to pause and turn and walk away or flee for their lives. The average person is not likely to enter a door that is covered by a scary animated shadow that resembles a giant barking dog, an angry skeleton or monster, or that turns into a giant mouth or angry pair of eyes, or is covered by one or more ghostly silhouettes.

Heroes and adventurers are a different story. In their case, a failed roll to save vs magic has the same effect as *failing to save vs Horror Factor.* The character is momentarily frozen with fear by the Animated Shadow. He loses one melee attack, loses initiative for that melee round, and cannot defend against the first attack leveled at him. Fortunately, he snaps out of this stupor quickly and is able to engage in combat that same melee round. By the second melee round, the character is himself again; roll combat as usual. **Note:** See the **Give Shadows Sound** spell for increased penalties when combined with Animate Shadow.

Roll to save vs magic for each new Animated Shadow encountered.

Lengthen Shadows

Range: Self or object that casts a long shadow, or lengthens an existing shadow, 10 feet (3 m) per level of experience.
Duration: Four minutes per level of experience.
Saving Throw: None.
P.P.E.: Four

The spell caster can cause any person or object, including himself, to cast a long, dark shadow in any direction he desires, regardless of other existing light sources. This unnatural shadow can be used for dramatic effect to intimidate or startle others, but is more often created to assist Sunaj operatives. The creation of a long shadow can create a bridge from one shadow to another or give assassins and Shadow Mages a path to travel unseen, or a dark place within which to hide, vanish or become Ethereal, and similar uses.

Moonlight

Range: Near self or up to 30 feet (9.1 m) away.
Duration: Three minutes (12 melee rounds) per level of experience.
Saving Throw: None.
P.P.E.: Four

A small globe of true moonlight is magically created. The light is bright enough to dimly light up a 10 foot (3 m) area per each level of its creator's experience. Because it is moonlight it does not trigger light or heat sensors and does not look out of place. It creates enough light that close work like picking a lock, operating a machine, reading a book, seeing down a corridor or seeing dimly in a room, can all be done. Moonlight does not adversely affect Shadow creatures. The spell caster can mentally move the globe of moonlight along with himself (at a maximum speed of 12), and he can also send it up to 30 feet (9.1 m) away.

Shadowcast

Range: Two objects per level of experience.
Duration: Two minutes per level of the spell caster's experience.
Saving Throw: None.
P.P.E.: Six

This simple spell creates a temporary shadow over a small area about the size of an 8 foot (2.4 m) table. Any item or person remaining motionless is concealed by the shadow cast over them. The shadow seems natural and is dark enough that unless someone comes within five feet (1.5 m) of the item or unmoving person cast in shadow, they go unnoticed. This is used to conceal and protect. The shadow is stationary, and any living creature covered by it must remain still to remain concealed.

Shadow Mask

Range: Self only or one other by touch.
Duration: Ten minutes per level of experience. (Double for Shadow Mages and Shadow Lords.)
Saving Throw: Standard.
P.P.E.: Four

This magic creates a shadowy haze that covers and conceals the person's head and facial features. Even in light, the face appears as if a dark nylon stocking is pulled over the head. In shadow or darkness, the face appears to be completely covered by a dark shadow, revealing no features at all, just a black silhouette.

Shadow Reach

Range: Self only, up to 10 feet (3 m) per level of experience.
Duration: Instant.
Saving Throw: None.
P.P.E.: Four

The spell caster is able to make his own shadow grow and move in any direction he desires, regardless of the light source. In this case, the spell caster can motion to make his shadow reach up and grab a railing, balcony, ledge, window sill, the edge of a roof, tree limb, rope, etc., and then make his shadow contract to pull him up to that location with it! This spell cannot be used to grab and hold another person or object. It is a simple method of short movement and climbing.

Level Two

Aura of Darkness

Range: Self or one other by touch. Creates an aura of darkness that radiates 2 feet (0.6 m) around the enchanted individual.
Duration: Five minutes per level of experience.
Saving Throw: None.
P.P.E.: Six

This cloaking spell is ideal in darkness for hiding, escape and setting up an ambush (+10% to the Prowl skill in darkness). This magic cloaks the spell caster in a form-fitting aura or field of darkness that follows him everywhere, making him a hazy black silhouette. The mage can see perfectly from within the haze of darkness, but those outside the radius of magic cannot see into the darkness. At night, it renders the cloaked individual virtually invisible, although he can still be detected by infrared and heat sensors, thermo-imaging optics, motion detectors and similar sensor systems. Furthermore, the Aura of Darkness may noticeably obscure a particular part of the background/area around him, making it obvious to visual detection, especially in well lit areas or when bathed in light – the magic darkness cannot be dispelled by ordinary light, but it stands out like a sore thumb in the light.

In combat, opponents who attack a character cloaked in darkness from any distance are -2 to strike due to the fact that they cannot see exactly where his head, face, heart, etc., is located unless guided by thermo-optics or similar heat-based optic system, and even then they are -1 to strike. Likewise, skills like Pick Pockets and Palming (trying to plant something on the obscured character) are performed against the black blur at half proficiency because their target is obscured in the equivalent of a black cloud.

Darklight

Range: Near self or up to 30 feet (9.1 m) away.
Duration: 10 melee rounds per level of experience.
Saving Throw: None.
P.P.E.: Six

The spell caster creates a small globe of ultraviolet light that illuminates a 10 foot (3 m) area per level of experience. This light will not keep any supernatural creatures at bay, but it will, for some strange reason, reveal the invisible to the spell caster, only he sees the invisible. The spell caster can mentally move the globe of Darklight along with himself (at a maximum speed of 12), and he can also send it up to 30 feet (9.1 m) away.

Ominous Shadow

Range: 10 feet (3 m) long, three feet (0.9 m) wide per level of the spell caster; line of sight.
Duration: One melee round (15 seconds) per level of experience. (Double for Shadow Mages and Shadow Lords.)
Saving Throw: Standard.
P.P.E.: Six

The spell caster is able to make his own shadow grow in any direction he desires, regardless of the light source, and look distorted and monstrous. This is done for dramatic effect and to inflict fear. Anyone caught in his oversized, ominous shadow must roll to save vs magic. Failure to save means they are temporarily frozen with fear for one melee round (15 seconds). Transfixed on the spell caster, watching and waiting for him to attack them and listening closely to anything he has to say (+20% for the mage to intimidate or impress).

After the first melee round (or if attacked during that first melee round), the victims are able to attack or take action. However, while still inside the Ominous Shadow, attacks leveled at the *spell caster* are done *without* benefit of the victims' usual combat bonuses. Fighting anyone else while in the Ominous Shadow has a penalty of only -1 on all combat maneuvers to strike, parry, dodge, etc. The sense of fear and dread goes away immediately after the spell ends, or after a victim manages to step out, or is pulled outside of the Ominous Shadow. In most cases, the spell caster takes no action against his victims in favor of holding them in dread and a diminished state.

Shadow Vision

Range: Self; line of sight up to 100 feet (30.5 m).
Duration: Two minutes per level of the spell caster.
Saving Throw: None.
P.P.E.: Eight

This spell enables the spell caster to see in shadows and darkness as well as through Shadow Magic darkness, including Aura of Darkness, Shadow Mask, Shadow Meld, Shadow Pool and other types of Shadow spells. This enchantment also enables the spell caster to see the Shadow Melded, the entrance to Shadow Holes, Shadow Pools, Shadow Traps are outlined and visible, and the combat penalties of Shade Armor are negated.

Shadow Walk

Range: Self, or self and one other by touch.
Duration: Four minutes per level of experience.
Saving Throw: None.
P.P.E.: Six

This spell enables the spell caster to cast a long shadow in front of himself. When walking in his own shadow, as well as other, natural shadows around him, the spell caster makes no sound and leaves no footprints, even when walking on dry leaves, gravel, sand, mud or snow. Nor do his footsteps leave a heat signature. All traces of his passage are swallowed up by the shadows.

Moreover, if the spell caster directs his shadow to go up the side of a wall or building, the mage can walk "up" the shadow covered surface. Defying gravity and the laws of physics. Thus, Shadow Walk can be used to reach windows, ledges and rooftops. **Note:** Shadow Walk requires a walking pace up to a slow jog, never a full run (maximum Spd 10).

Slip Shadow

Range: Self or others by touch.
Duration: Five minutes per level of experience.
Saving Throw: None.
P.P.E.: Five

While this spell is in effect, the mage has no shadow whatsoever, making it easier for him to sneak around unnoticed. This spell adds a +10% bonus to any Prowl rolls made under its duration; those who do not have the Prowl skill can, under this spell, effectively Prowl at 20%.

Whispered Voice (Communication)

Range: Self and teammates. Range of transmission is 500 feet (152 m), plus 100 feet (30 m) per additional level of experience. For the magic to work, ALL those with whom the Whispered Voice is to be applied (10 maximum per spell casting) MUST be clustered together and touching when the spell is first cast. Anyone left out is NOT part of the communication circle.
Duration: 10 minutes per level of the spell caster.
Saving Throw: None.
P.P.E.: Six

This enchantment has two effects. One, it enables those affected to understand the language of the Shadow Lord and the denizens of the Shadow Dimension.

Two, it also connects them through shadows. It enables the spell caster and his teammates to communicate by whispering into a shadow or dark area and have their words heard by that individual as if the person was standing and speaking right next to him. To deliver the message, the recipient's name must be spoken first, followed by the message. "Tom, I'm at the north corner. All is clear." "Rob, we have trouble at the main entrance." As long as the person speaking and the individual meant to receive the message are both in shadow or darkness, they can communicate back and forth like a two-way radio transmission. They just need to always say the person's name first. Words spoken in the heat of the moment without the name said first are NOT transmitted through the shadows and remain unheard.

Limitations and Potential Problem: 1. Though a group of people may be part of the magical communication, only one, named person can receive the message at a time. 2. Among mortals, only the person whose name is spoken hears the message meant for him. However, any Shadow Lords, Shadow Beasts or other shadow creatures within the radius of transmission ALSO HEAR THE MESSAGE. All of them! This could be bad. Very bad.

Level Three

Give Shadows Sound

Range: Touch or 100 feet (30.5 m); line of sight.
Duration: Five minutes per level of the spell caster. (Double for Shadow Mages. Quadruple for Shadow Lords.)
Limitation: Simple sounds only, played in a loop and activated by sound and motion.
Saving Throw: Standard.
P.P.E.: Eight

The spell caster is able to enchant a shadow to make one simple sounds like a low growl, barking, heavy breathing, howling, snorting (like an angry bull), hissing, gurgling, a bone chilling scream or wailing, scratching, indistinguishable whispering, giggling, laughter, crying, coughing, the rattle of leaves, the sound of howling wind and similar. *No words are possible.*

The sound can be made to repeat at intervals as if on an audio loop, or to occur as a response to motion and/or sound that comes within 5 or 10 feet (1.5 to 3 m) of the shadow.

This spell is often combined with *Animate Shadow* for the following results: Victims who fail to roll to save vs magic suffer from Horror Factor, momentarily freeze in their tracks, and lose two melee attacks/actions as well as initiative for that first melee round, and are -2 on Perception Rolls and -2 on initiative for the next two melee rounds.

Shadow Bolt

Range: 50 feet (15.2 m) per level of experience.
Duration: Instant.
Damage: 2D4 M.D. plus an additional 1D4 per level of experience. This spell inflicts M.D. in Mega-Damage environments and S.D.C. damage in S.D.C. environments.
Saving Throw: The victim may dodge if he sees the bolt coming and rolls, but is -5 to do so when it is cast in darkness.
P.P.E.: Six

The spell caster fires an inky black ray of dark energy from any part of his body he chooses – fingers, eyes, mouth, etc. This spell does not require specific gesturing of any kind. Add +2D4 M.D. when cast at a ley line, and add +4D4 M.D. when cast at a ley line nexus.

Shadow Defense

Range: Self. The mage must be casting a shadow to use this magic.
Duration: Two melee rounds (30 seconds) per level of experience.
Saving Throw: Standard.
P.P.E.: Ten

The spell caster's own shadow momentarily comes to life for a second to parry incoming attacks from directions the spell caster is not directly facing or engaging. The shadow looks completely ordinary, except that when the spell is cast the shadow is behind the spell caster regardless of the light source and is at least as long as he is tall, longer if conditions permit. While the spell caster is engaging one opponent, if another enemy throws a knife or fires a gun at his back from behind, his Shadow suddenly leaps into action to try to parry the incoming attack and then turns back into a normal-looking shadow. If another opponent rushes in from the side, the shadow springs to life again to parry his attack and goes back to normal as soon as he steps back or moves off. The shadow looks completely ordinary, except that when the spell is in effect the shadow is behind the spell caster regardless of the light source and is at least as long as he is tall, longer if conditions permit. It comes to life only for the moment or two needed to parry the incoming attack.

In combat, the shadow has the same abilities and bonuses as the spell caster to parry, and it will try to parry all incoming attacks from the back and sides. As always, high roll wins, defender wins ties, and a successful parry means the attack was blocked or knocked away. In the case of projectiles, the arrow or bullet is safely deflected to the ground on either side of the spell caster. A failed parry means the attack strikes and does damage. **Note:** Energy blasts/bolts, laser fire, and psionic attacks cannot be parried or defended against by this magic. Nor can it parry or block anything heavier than 300 pounds (135 kg), so it cannot block a boulder or automobile thrown by a demon. Shadow Defense may be used simultaneously with Shadow Strike.

Shadow Displacement

Range: Corresponding shadow must be no more than 100 feet (30.5 m) and within line of sight. Unless they are using Shadowsight, then range is equal to the Shadowsight spell.
Duration: One melee round.
Saving Throw: None.
P.P.E.: Eight

The spell caster is able to reach into a shadow at his location and have his arm come out of a shadow as far as 100 feet (30.5 m) away; farther with Shadowsight. This can be useful for startling or scaring someone near or in a different shadow by tapping him on his shoulder or punching him (standard punch damage; power punch is not possible), or grabbing something or flicking a switch from across a room or across the street. Attacking this way is awkward so all attacks are -2 to strike. This spell only enables the spell caster to reach through a shadow. He cannot completely step through it. See *Shadow Shift* for that.

Shadow Globe

Range: Up to 30 feet (9.1 m) away, plus 10 feet (3 m) per level of experience.
Duration: Three minutes (12 melee rounds) per level of the spell caster.
Saving Throw: None.
P.P.E.: Ten

Shadow Globe has two effects. The first is to create a globe of pale light. Not daylight/sunlight, but moonlight. Black tendrils appear to wrap around and cover parts of the globe. The tendrils do not smother the light, but cover it enough to create up to 2D6 shadows in a 12 foot (3.7 m) area per level of its creator. This spell is ideal when additional shadows are needed in a given area or to counter the effects of a Globe of Daylight or other illumination.

The second use is to snuff out the light from an existing Globe of Daylight. In this case, the Shadow Globe flies over to the Globe of Daylight and seems to crash into it, spreading an inky darkness over the entire Globe of Daylight and covering its light. There is no saving throw because the Globe of Daylight is not being attacked per se, but simply being covered in darkness. The net result is losing a preexisting Globe of Daylight and effectively putting its light under a barrel. The spell caster of the Globe of Daylight can cancel his spell which also makes the Shadow Globe vanish with it. Either way, the magical daylight is effectively eliminated.

Shadow Skin

Range: Self or self and one other by touch.
Duration: 10 minutes per level of experience or until destroyed.
Saving Throw: Standard.
P.P.E.: Eight

This spell creates a skin-tight, soft suit of flexible, black armor that feel like thin rubber. The primary purpose for the skin is stealth and concealment. Consequently, the Shadow Skin covers the wearer from head to toe like a body suit with a pull over mask that completely covers the head and face. If he is wearing clothing or other armor, they are covered in the inky darkness of the Shadow Skin as if it were an outer covering. The face, hands, everything is covered by the rubbery shadow which means the wearer leaves no finger or palm prints nor footprints with any discernable features. The recipient of the enchantment can breathe and see through the Shadow Skin as if it were not there. Movement is unimpaired.

Shadow Skin only provides minimal M.D.C. protection: 6 M.D.C. per level of experience. (Six S.D.C. per level with an A.R. of 12 on S.D.C. worlds.)

Bonuses: The Shadow Skin adds a +10% bonus to the Prowl skill or provides a base Prowl of 33%, and a +10% bonus to the Chameleon spell if it is cast after the Shadow Skin in put into place. Shadow Skin also keeps the wearer cool and comfortable up to 150 degrees Fahrenheit (65.5 C) and prevents leaving behind forensic evidence (hair, fibers, DNA, finger or palm prints, etc.).

Shadow Strike

Range: Self. The mage must be casting a shadow to use this magic.
Duration: Two melee rounds (30 seconds) per level of experience.
Saving Throw: Standard.
P.P.E.: Six

Once per melee round, the spell caster's own shadow suddenly comes to life for a second to punch, push or kick an oopponent who is within range of it – i.e. within range of the shadow – before turning back into an ordinary shadow. This could mean striking an opponent off to the sides or behind the spell caster. And if his shadow is long, that attack could be leveled at someone 10-20 feet (3-6.1 m) away!

The shadow hits with the same P.S. and power (include P.S. bonuses) as the spell caster, himself, and inflicts whatever damage he would inflict with one of his own punches or kicks. A shove/push does one point of damage and pushes the victim 1D4 feet (0.3 to 1.2 m) away. **Note:** The shadow's attack counts as *one extra attack per melee round*. A power punch is possible but it uses up two of the shadow's attacks, which means it will go a melee round without an action after a power punch. The shadow only attacks. It does not parry, nor push its spell caster out of harm's way. It cannot use a weapon of any kind, it's a shadow. It can be combined and used simultaneously with Shadow Defense.

Shadow Writing

Range: Touch or 100 feet (30.5 m) away with an existing shadow; line of sight.
Duration: Five minutes per level of experience (double for Shadow Mages, quadruple for Shadow Lords).
Saving Throw: Not applicable.
Limitation: The spell caster usually creates the words or symbol, leaves it, and goes on his way. It remains in place for the duration of the spell. If the spell caster remains within 100 feet (30.5 m) of the Shadow Writing, he can change the writing on the wall (or other surface) once every melee round (15 seconds). Before he leaves, the mage may leave one particular symbol or set of words in place until the spell duration ends, or have the Shadow Writing dissipate.

Size of the Shadow Writing is up to six inches (0.15 m) tall per level of experience. A symbol can be twice as large. The words or symbol can be larger if the pre-existing shadow was large to begin with. Shadow Writing can be written whether it is light or dark out.
P.P.E.: Eight

The spell caster can touch a surface (a wall, fence, the ground, a boulder, the hood of a vehicle, etc.) and cause shadowy wisps to flow from his fingers to create words or simple symbols written in shadow and left there for any passerby to see. Or he may cause an existing shadow to unspool and form into words or symbols. Sometimes forming right before people's their eyes.

Words written in shadow are simple, short statements or phrases such as: "Turn Back." "Danger, do not enter." "Beware." "Stop." "Entrance." "Exit." "This way." "No trespassing." "You are being watched." "Demons behind this door." Six words like, "Death awaits those who go further," is as long as the written message can be. Symbols may also be drawn in shadows to offer warnings, clues and direction, such as a skull and crossbones, an arrow to point the way, a hand held palm up to indicate "stop" or a hand pointing the way, an X to mark the spot, a spiral circle to indicate magic, or the face of a demon, a heart impaled by a stake, snakes, a flower, stick people, a fist, claw, or claw marks, and so on. Of course, the symbol or words may not always be recognized or interpreted correctly, but they have their uses.

As noted under limitations, if the spell caster remains within 100 feet (30.5 m) of the Shadow Writing, he can change the writing on the wall once every melee round (15 seconds) to engage in a sort of silent conversation without revealing himself. This can be a means of silent communication with allies, a mechanism to warn the innocent, or to trick or confound enemies.

Level Four

Field of Shadow Tendrils

Range: Area effect, up to 160 feet (48.8 m) away but requires a shadow or area of darkness to rise out of. Each tendril has a reach of 6 feet (1.8 m).
Duration: Two melee rounds per experience level of the spell caster.
Saving Throw: As per dodge requiring 14 or higher.
P.P.E.: Ten

4D6+10 narrow, shadowy tendrils rise up and out of the shadows within a 20 foot (6.1 m) diameter. They may rise up from the floor, or angle down for the ceiling or protrude from the sides of walls to block a passage, hallway or stairwell. Each moves around as if sensing movement nearby. It is a simple enough matter to run through the shadow dodging and weaving through the field of tendrils as they reach for every person who comes within their grasp. As shadows, weapons do not harm the tendrils, slicing right through them without harm. Yet somehow the tendrils are able to momentarily ensnare a passerby, grabbing and pulling at the individual, slowing him down as if he were trying to push through a tangle of vines or move through water. Each tendril that successfully strikes and entangles its victim reduces the character's speed by 10% and inflicts a penalty of -1 on initiative and the ability to strike, parry and dodge. The tendrils have a limited reach of 6 feet (1.8 m) so it is unlikely for the character to be entangled by more than three or four of them at a time.

Directed sunlight such as from a Globe of Daylight causes the tendrils to recoil and not grab at people. Laser beams that inflict as little as 1 S.D.C. point of damage, destroy any tendril they strike; attackers need a 13 or higher to hit. Silver weapons also destroy Shadow Tendrils with a single point of damage. However, destroyed tendrils reform in one melee round (15 seconds).

Ride the Night Wind

Range: Self only, or self and one other by touch.
Duration: 15 minutes per level of experience.
Saving Throw: None.
P.P.E.: Twelve

This Shadow Magic enables the spell caster to levitate, hover and fly in the darkness of the night and when in shadow; never in sunlight or areas illuminated by artificial light. Hover speed is the same as walking speed, flying speed is a maximum of 30 mph (48 km). Maximum height/altitude is 1,000 feet (305 m).

Shade Armor

Range: Self, or two others by touch, or cast upon one other up to 100 feet (30.5 m) away; line of sight required.
Duration: One minute per level of experience.
Saving Throw: None.

P.P.E.: Ten

A dark grey mist forms over the recipient of this enchantment and seems to settle over him like a shadowy outer covering. Wisps of darkness move across the body as if shadows are moving over him from an unidentified source. Like the *Armor of Ithan* spell, Shade Armor is weightless, noiseless and offers magical protection: 12 M.D.C. per level of the spell caster. (12 S.D.C. per level and an A.R. of 16 in S.D.C. environments.) It also offers a +5% bonus to Prowl in shadows/darkness. Magical Lightblades and weapons made of silver or coated in the metal do double damage to Shade Armor! Lasers, magic and other weapons do their normal damage.

Shadeshield

Range: Self.
Duration: Five minutes per level of experience.
Damage: 2D6 if used as a bludgeon.
Saving Throw: None.
P.P.E.: Twelve

This spell conjures a large shield of pure darkness to be used by the spell caster. The shield offers standard resistance to physical attacks, and can be used as a bashing weapon as well as to parry physical attacks, and even certain incoming magical attacks. This is a little tricky, however, when trying to parry energy blasts, electricity, lasers, lightning, etc., and suffers a -5 penalty to parry. Spells which may be parried by a Shadeshield include: Call Lightning, Ball Lightning, Electric Arc, Energy Bolt, Fire Ball, Fire Bolt, Mini-Fireballs, Lightning Arc, Plasma Bolt, Power Bolt, Shadow Bolt, Spectral Hand and Sword, Shadesword, Hail, Ice Ball, Ice Bolt, Shards of Ice and similar.

Shadow Meld

Range: Self.
Duration: Two minutes (8 melees) per level of experience.
Saving Throw: None.
P.P.E.: Ten

This unique magic enables the spell caster to step into shadows, becoming totally invisible, even to a "See the Invisible" spell. The shadow must be at least five feet (1.5 m) tall or long to become an effective hiding place. The shadow serves as a superior means of hiding or moving unseen. The mage can move, walk, or run through the length of the shadow or from shadow to shadow. While in shadow/darkness, the character Prowls at a 60% proficiency (or at +15% to normal skill, whichever is higher).

Intense light will dispel the shadow, leaving the mage revealed. Of course, sanctuary can be found by fleeing into another shadow. Feeble light, less than 10 torches or 300 watts, will only create more shadows.

While hidden in shadow, the character is still susceptible to magic, psionic and physical attacks, although attackers are -5 to strike him (because they cannot see him). Area effect magic does not suffer any penalty. Infrared/thermo-optics are the only means that can be used to see the character in a shadow.

Shadowsight

Range: Self; 100 foot (30.5 m) radius.
Duration: Two melee rounds per level of experience.
Saving Throw: None.

P.P.E.: Fifteen

When under the effect of this spell, every shadow within range becomes the spell caster's eyes and ears. Wherever there is a shadow within range, the mage can spy effortlessly and without any chance of detection, as if he were actually standing, concealed, in the shadow itself. Indoors and underground, this spell gives the mage virtually complete surveillance capabilities over a large area. As the spell caster moves, so does the area of effect. However, the mage must direct his attention to a particular shadow and the sights and sounds around it, not all shadows at once. Shadowsight cannot see through walls, but if there is a shadow around the corner or on the other side of a wall, and within range of the spell, then the spell caster can still view and hear what is happening.

Wall of Darkness

Range: Covers a 20 foot (6 m) area plus 10 feet (3 m) per level of experience.
Duration: 10 minutes per level of experience.
Damage: Special.
Saving Throw: Standard.
P.P.E.: Fifteen

This magic creates a towering wall of pure, magical darkness. No light can pass through it, nor can one see what is on the other side of it. Anyone who comes into contact with the wall must save vs magic or be magically paralyzed for one melee round. The effects of this paralysis are identical to those of the spell *Paralysis: Lesser*. Should a hand or arm be paralyzed, that person cannot pick up objects, write, or use that hand or arm in any way for 15 seconds. Likewise, a paralyzed leg makes standing difficult, walking a real challenge, and running flat-out impossible. Those with a paralyzed leg have their Speed reduced by 80%, and they are at -2 to parry and dodge. If one's entire body is paralyzed, he falls down and lies perfectly still. He can still breathe, and the heart will not stop, but other than that, the person is largely helpless. Those who fall into the Wall of Darkness will need a friend to fish them out somehow, otherwise they remain paralyzed for the full duration of the spell, recovering only when the wall disappears.

Whispering Shadows

Range: 500 foot (152 m) radius, plus 100 feet (30 m) per additional level of experience.
Duration: One minute per level of the caster.
Saving Throw: None.
P.P.E.: Eight

Using a nearby shadow, the spell caster need only speak into it to send his voice as a whisper to all shadows within range of effect. This is usually done to deliver a message to many people within the radius of effect or earshot of a nearby shadow. The spell caster's voice cannot be followed as it seems to be nowhere and everywhere at once. It is used not so much for communication, but rather to get out an important warning, message or information to a wide area at once, or to intimidate, taunt or harass the enemy. To hear a disembodied voice speaking from the shadows or across the darkness is frightening and unnerving. Horror Factor 10. Worse, it cannot be turned off. The only way to avoid the message is to get out of range or turn on the lights. Even then, the whispering voice might be heard from the darkness or shadows nearby.

Level Five

Conceal Objects in Shadow

Range: Two objects per level of experience.
Duration: 30 minutes per level of experience or as long as the shadow exists.
Saving Throw: None.
P.P.E.: Fourteen

The spell caster can place objects in a shadow or dark area/room and make the item seemingly disappear. It becomes one with the shadow just like Shadow Meld. The item(s) are visible only to the spell caster and those with Shadow Vision activated. The spell is used for hiding weapons, gear, loot, an extra set of clothes/disguise, etc., or concealing stolen items and coming back for it/them later, and similar uses. As long as the shadow or darkness is present, the items are invisible and undetectable. This could be a dark corner in an alley, under the stairs, under a shady tree, behind the shed in someone's backyard, or right out on the street corner provided passing traffic does not illuminate the area with the concealed items.

The object(s) must be portable and comparatively small, like a spear, sword, battle axe, empty backpack or sack, silver cross, energy rifle loaded with an E-Clip, computer, book, video camera, a pair of pants, a suit coat, a bar of gold, a gem, a sandwich, etc. It cannot be a backpack, purse or sack filled with many smaller items (unless those items correspond with the number the spell caster can conceal), or large like an entire safe, suit of power armor or vehicle. It can also be used to hide a bomb, though if it has a motor or ticks, someone might hear it and find it.

The items remain hidden in the shadow or darkness until there is strong light shown upon them or the spell duration elapses, or the shadow they are hidden in shrinks or moves; shadows outdoors shrink and grow throughout the day depending on the position of the sun. For example, a weapon hidden inside a dark closet is invisible, melded with the darkness or the shadow that exists when the closet door is opened. However, if the closet has a light and it is turned on, or someone shines a flashlight in the dark corner of the closet where the weapon is stashed, it is revealed.

Eyes in the Dark

Range: All shadows in a 50 foot (15.2 m) radius, plus 10 foot (3 m) radius per level of experience.
Duration: Two minutes per level of experience.
Saving Throw: Save vs Horror Factor of 16 or higher.
P.P.E.: Fourteen

All shadows within the radius of the caster suddenly have 1D4+2 pairs of eyes peering out at the spell caster's opponents. The eyes move and blink, and give the illusion that numerous creatures like the Shadow Beast are peering out and ready to attack. This is distracting for all around. Those who fail to save vs H.F. 16 or higher are –2 on initiative, -1 to strike, parry, and dodge, plus they are –10% on all skills performed while the spell is in effect. They also roll to save vs Horror Factor (16) again the next melee round. A consecutive failed H.F. roll means the penalties are added together. Keep rolling every melee round until the character finally saves; penalties accumulating with every failed save.

Those who make their first saving throw are unaffected and in addition, do not need to make the saving throw vs Horror Factor again until one minute (4 melee round) has passed. Combining this spell if combined with Whispered Voice adds +2 to the Horror Factor!

Night Stick

Range: Self only.
Duration: Two minutes per level of experience.
Damage: Blunt Club/Nightstick: 2D6 M.D. +1 M.D. per level of experience. Staff (6-7 feet/1.8 to 2.1 m long): 3D6 M.D. +1 M.D. per level of experience. And applicable penalties. Half damage in sunlight.
Saving Throw: -2 to save vs magic.
P.P.E.: Eighteen (club) or Twenty-Six (staff).

The spell caster is able to conjure forth a magical weapon out of thin air – actually from a shadow or darkness (cannot be conjured in sunlight). The black weapon appears to be a nightstick/club or a larger staff composed of darkness. Like its counterpart spell, *Shadesword*, anyone struck by the weapon takes damage and must save vs magic or suffer a penalty of –2 to strike, parry, disarm and dodge for one melee round (15 seconds). The duration of the penalties is cumulative with multiple strikes, but the penalty number does not increase.

Shadow Senses

Range: Self or one other by touch.
Duration: Four minutes per level of the spell caster (double for Shadow Mages and quadruple for Shadow Lords).
Saving Throw: None.
P.P.E.: Sixteen

This enchantment works only in darkness and shadow, imparting the spell caster with special senses.

1. Shadow Vision: The mage is able to see in total darkness as if he had the See in Magic Darkness spell or Nightvision; range: 1,000 feet (305 m). And, in fact, he can see in magic darkness.

2. Hear Night Sounds: Applicable only when in a dark environment or a connecting shadow. Hearing is enhanced and amplified, enabling the mage to hear and locate sounds at three times the normal level of hearing. He can hear and follow footsteps or the sound of the wind, or rushing water, or a running motor, voices, a muffed gunshot, etc., to help him navigate in darkness or to eavesdrop on people in the dead of night or from the shadows. Ambushing a character using Shadow Senses is difficult because he can hear sounds as low as a whisper up to 300 feet (91.4 m) away. Anyone trying to sneak up on somebody using Shadow Senses while he is in darkness is -20% to Prowl and does NOT get a Critical strike from an attack from behind. The Shadow Senses alert him to the incoming attack and enable him to move just enough to avoid the Critical Strike (does normal damage).

3. Perception Bonus: +2 on Perception Rolls related to detecting likely ambush locations, noticing a person hiding in shadow, all things Shadow Magic, finding shadows/darkness, making shadows, and noticing the presence of Shadow Beasts and other denizens of the Shadow Realm.

4. Sense Shadows: This magic helps the character sense and locate the presence of shadows and dark places within a 200 foot (61 m) radius. It also enables the enchanted individual to sense the presence of Shadow creatures such as Shadow Beasts and Shadow Lords within that radius. He cannot tell what the creature is nor its exact location, but knows if there is one, a few, or many, and if it/they are near or farther away within the sensing radius. Shadow Assassins and Shadow Mages and ordinary beings hiding in the shadows do NOT register (see Perception Bonus).

Penalty: With Shadow Senses activated, the mage is vulnerable to bright lights and is -3 to save vs light spells such as Blinding Flash and Globe of Daylight, both of which are painful, causing temporary blindness (-10 to strike, parry, dodge). Moreover, daylight vision and artificial light brighter than 60 watts reduces the character to seeing through squinted eyes with a range of a mere 15 feet (4.6 m). The duration of blindness caused by Blinding Flash, flash grenades or any sudden exposure to bright light is double. Retreating back into comforting darkness or a shadow reduces the duration of light blindness by half.

Shadow Shift

Range: Self, or self and as many as one other by touch. The "shift" can be made up to 50 feet (15.2 m) away per level of the spell caster. Line of sight and shadows required.
Duration: Instant and counts as one melee attack/action.
Saving Throw: None.
P.P.E.: Sixteen
Note: Each "relocation" counts as one spell and one melee attack.

This spell is great for a fast escape or instant, nearby relocation as it enables the spell caster to enter one shadow and appear at another one up to 50 feet (15.2 m) away (per level of experience). The shadows do not need to be connected, but do have to be large enough to cover a man and the distant shadow must be visible from where the spell caster is standing. The spell has less to do with teleportation than it does a form of dimensional shifting from one shadow location to another one within the same reality. The shadow must be no smaller than five feet (1.5 m) tall, long or in diameter.

Whenever the spell caster enters a massive shadow that is 20 feet (6.1 m) to hundreds of feet, he may disappear and reappear anywhere within that same shadow, provided the "relocation" does not exceed the 50 foot (15.2 m) range per level. If the shadow reaches a rooftop, bridge or ledge, then its location is accessible via Shadow Shift. Trying to shift onto a moving vehicle that passes under or through a shadowy location is possible, but risky. Roll 1D20. 1-10 is a failure, 11-20 is a success. Staying on top of a fast-moving vehicle is likely to require additional effort and skill or combat rolls. Also remember that each Shadow Shift requires casting of the spell and uses up one melee attack/action.

Wall of Shades

Range: Varies, can be cast up to 50 feet (15.2 m) away, but is typically used around the mage.
Duration: One minute per level of experience.
Saving Throw: None, but a spell like Dispel Magic Barriers will instantly negate the spell. Also each shade can be individually dispelled if pierced by silver.
P.P.E.: Twenty

Unlike Shadow Wall, this spell offers no physical barrier. Rather it creates several shades that block light and create shadows. The shades hover in the air or can be in any position that creates an optimal shadow. Up to two shades are created per level of the spell caster. Since the light source varies, so too will the size of the shadows. Each shade produces a shadow that is 1D4x6 feet (1.8 to 7.2 m) in size. The spell caster can elect to combine the shades, making larger shadows if desired. Also there has to be some kind of light source in order for this spell to be effective. In the absence of direct light, a Globe of Daylight will work.

Level Six

Circle of Shadows

Range: Self for a 6 foot (1.8 m) radius per level of experience (double the length and duration for Shadow Lords).
Duration: Four minutes per level of experience.
Saving Throw: Standard.
P.P.E.: Twenty

The spell caster magically sends his own shadow in all directions, like the spokes of a wheel with him in the center. The unusual cluster of shadows is instantly disturbing to all who see it, giving people pause before entering the circle of shadows.

Stepping into the shadows all around the mage requires a save vs Horror Factor (14 or higher to save). Those who fail to save suffer the temporary effects of H.F. and will not enter the ring of shadows for one melee round (15 seconds).

Those who save and dare to enter the circle can press forward and take action, but do so with penalties. Characters who enter the Circle of Shadows are jumpy and unnerved by movement within the shadows. Movement caught out of the corner of their eye, but when they turn around there is nothing there. All of this reduces Perception Rolls and all combat bonuses by half (round down). Likewise, performance of skills while in the Circle of Shadows is reduced by half, and -1 attack per melee round. The spell caster and his allies or minions are not affected.

A Circle of Shadows also creates a haven in which other Sunaj Assassins, Shadow Assassins and Shadow Mages can lurk unseen until they attack. If the shadows in the circle touch other, natural shadows, it creates a bridge with which their shadowy brethren can reach them to escape, hide or wait in ambush to attack.

Heroes would be wise to remember that like a spider's web made of shadows, they never know what lurks and waits for them inside the circle. A favorite ploy of the Sunaj Shadow Mage is to create a web of shadows that conceal several Shadow Assassins or Shadow Beasts within it. These fiends do not attack until some foolish hero(es) steps into the web, at which point they spring their trap and strike.

Manipulate Shadows

Range: 100 feet (30.5 m) plus 10 feet (3 m) per level of experience.
Duration: Three minutes per level of experience.
Saving Throw: None.
P.P.E.: Twenty

The spell caster is able to manipulate four shadows plus 2 per level of experience. With this spell the mage is able to bend them, connect them, make them appear twice as wide, elongate them, move them around and hold them in place, etc. This spell is used to complement other shadow spells.

Shadow Boxer

Range: Self only, with a reach of 10 feet (3 m) +1 foot (0.3 m) per each additional level of experience. The mage must be casting a shadow to use this magic.
Duration: One minute (four melees) per level of experience.
Damage: Special.
Saving Throw: None.
P.P.E.: Twenty

This spell animates the spell caster's shadow so that it may participate in combat! When the mage's shadow comes to animated life it adds one extra attack per every three levels of the spell caster's experience. The shadow itself has no Hit Points and cannot be harmed by anything other than a Dispel Magic spell.

To attack, the Shadow Boxer can only use its fists, grapple or inflict the blunt equivalent of whatever weapon the spell caster might have been holding. If a rifle or blade, it can only use it as a blunt weapon. Punch and blunt weapon damage is equal to the P.S. of the spell caster (Atlanteans without augmentation from magic tattoos have Augmented P.S.). A power punch is possible, but counts as two of the Shadow Boxer's attacks.

The Shadow Boxer strikes at the end of the melee round after the spell caster has used up all of his attacks for the round, UNLESS the spell caster is not fighting. If the spell caster spends the entire melee round (15 seconds) using his combat actions to perform a skill(s) or do something else rather than fight, or if he is engaged in a purely defensive response (parrying and dodging only, no fisticuffs, spell casting or psionic attacks), the *Shadow Boxer becomes his proxy* and steps in to do the fighting. Under those circumstances, the Shadow Boxer gets *three extra attacks* (in addition to those it usually has) and intercepts and attacks any foe(s) trying to harm the spell caster. This includes parrying any incoming attacks from ranged weapons and energy blasts. The speedy boxer is -3 to parry incoming attacks and energy blasts from ranged weapons.

The Shadow Boxer has all the same attributes (P.S., P.P., Spd, etc.) and bonuses as the spell caster, but it cannot speak, perform skills or cast spells, nor use any physical objects, weapons or equipment. Although animated and moving as if it has a life of its own, the shadow must remain attached to its maker. As a result, the shadow can stretch out to attack opponents as far as 10 feet (3 m) away, but nothing beyond that. The only exception to this is if the spell caster has a bow or other missile weapon in hand. When that is the case, the Shadow Boxer may draw and fire a shadow arrow out to the weapon's normal range, but inflicts only 1D6 S.D.C. damage.

Note: The spell caster's shadow is not intelligent nor does it have its own free will. It automatically responds to close combat attack(s) directed at the shadow's owner. Otherwise, it behaves like an ordinary shadow. Magic-using assassins have used this to their advantage more than once by casting the spell and springing their shadow into action when their intended victim(s) least suspect it. The Shadow Boxer cannot be created in total darkness. The mage must be casting a shadow to use this magic.

Shadowfire

Range: Can be cast up to 100 feet (30.5 m) away. Affects a 100 foot (30.5 m) radius, +10 feet (3 m) per level of experience.
Duration: One melee round (15 seconds) per level of experience.
Damage: 3D6 M.D.
Saving Throw: None.
P.P.E.: Twenty

This spell causes all shadows within range to transform into patches of burning darkness, a weird kind of black magical flame. Whoever comes into contact with Shadowfire sustains 3D6 M.D. Although this is technically burn damage, the spell Heal Burns will have no effect on wounds of this type. The flame only harms the living, which means that inanimate corpses and skeletons and the undead are unharmed. The only way to spread this fire is to somehow create more shadows in the area.

The only way to extinguish Shadowfire is by exposing it to strong artificial light, sunlight or a Globe of Daylight. Dispel Magic can also be used to extinguish one burning area of shadow at a time. However, as long as the Shadowfire spell remains in effect, as soon as such sources of light are removed and the shadows return, so do the dark flames.

Level Seven

Ethereal in Shadow

Range: Self only.
Duration: One minute per level of experience. (Double for Shadow Mages. Indefinite for Shadow Lords.)
Saving Throw: None.
P.P.E.: Twenty-Five

One of the most powerful spells in any mage's arsenal is the ability to become as insubstantial as a shadow. This includes clothing and any items carried on his person, including those inside a backpack as well as items in pockets, pouches and holsters or held in the spell caster's hands when the invocation is cast. All turn into a shadow along with the mage himself. **Note:** This also means if the character was handcuffed or bound before becoming Ethereal, he remains bound as an Ethereal shadow. The handcuffs or rope do not fall away, they become part of the shadow.

When Ethereal, the spell caster appears as a featureless, dark shadow without an apparent owner. The transition from physical to insubstantial shadow requires first stepping into a shadow large enough to cover his entire body. The transition takes three seconds and uses up one melee attack.

As an Ethereal shadow, the spell caster is immune to most physical attacks. Bullets, rail gun rounds, arrows, blades, explosive force, cold, heat, fire, and most energy blasts pass right through him without harm. Only lasers (made of light) hurt, but inflict half their usual damage to an Ethereal shadow, while lightning and electrical blasts inflict their full damage. The character does not register on most sensor systems either, including infrared and heat sensors. Motion detectors have a 50/50 chance of registering a fast-moving Ethereal Shadow Mage, but not a slow one (Spd of 7 or less), or a character who is using the Prowl skill while ethereal. As a "shadow," the character moves in silence. (Base Prowl of 45% or +15% if the Shadow Mage has the Prowl skill, which most do. The bonus applies even in a lighted area.) When he steps into a shadow large enough to conceal him, the Ethereal shadow seems to vanish and is unlikely to be seen at all. (+20% to Prowl in shadows and darkness; +30% when standing motionless or trying to hide while inside darkness.) Only when someone is looking hard for the motionless interloper and comes within three feet (one yard/meter) of him is the Ethereal shadow noticeable. When running down a street lit by lampposts, the Ethereal mage will seem to appear as an animated shadow under the light only to vanish every time he steps back into darkness.

The mage also has a Horror Factor of 11 while Ethereal.

Though Ethereal, it is in a very particular way, so the mage cannot pass through solid walls, doors, sealed windows, or people, but can squeeze through the bars of a jail cell and similar types of fencing, including chicken wire, cyclone fencing, and barbed wire.

To pick up an object, operate machinery, or to touch someone, the Ethereal Shadow Mage must cancel the magic and become his normal, physical self. Once canceled, that transformation is used up, even if the spell caster had several minutes of the spell left. To become Ethereal again, the Mage must step into a shadow and cast a new Ethereal spell upon himself.

<u>Limitations</u>: **1.** An area of darkness large enough for the spell caster to step into and be completely covered by the shadow/darkness, is required to cast this spell. Without it, the spell cannot be cast. The spell can be canceled anywhere at any point.

2. While Ethereal, the Shadow Mage can still run, Prowl, and dodge as usual. He also has the same bonuses and number of attacks per melee round, except being Ethereal he cannot actually strike another person, nor pick up objects, open doors, or even flip a light switch or operate a keyboard or touch screen. He is a walking shadow without weight or physicality. Likewise, he can perform skills that require the mind, like reading and tracking, but not physical skills that require touch or weight. This makes the mage a wonderful spy who can hide in shadows or darkness and listen to what is going on around him, unseen and nearly undetectable.

3. Cannot speak. The living shadow can see, hear, and smell, but cannot touch or speak while Ethereal. Characters with psionic abilities may use their psychic powers while an Ethereal shadow, but at double the usual I.S.P. cost and the psi-ability functions at half power, duration, range, damage, etc. Spell casting and verbal communication are not possible while Ethereal.

4. Light is trouble for Shadow Magic. If there is a powerful enough light source (it can be sunlight, a magical Globe of Daylight or strong artificial light), there may be no place for the Ethereal spell caster to hide. He or she is revealed for all to see. Without a large enough shadow to step into, the spell caster is no longer Ethereal, and out in the open where he can be attacked. He must either dive into a nearby shadow or someplace dark to regain being Ethereal. Without a large enough shadow to step into, the spell caster cannot turn Ethereal again, but he can cast other magic, including creating a magical area of darkness.

The Ethereal spell caster remains vulnerable to light-based spells, lasers, electricity and psionics while Ethereal. Even though fire emits light, heat and flames, it has no effect on the Ethereal spell caster while in darkness. Neither do cold and toxic gases. Water offers an unusual peril, as the Ethereal individual sinks when dropped into deep water. As a shadow he cannot swim, so he must resume physical form to swim, or sink and drown unless he has an air supply.

Shadow Pocket

Range: No more than 3 feet (0.9 m) from the spell caster.
Duration: One week per level of the spell caster.
Saving Throw: Not applicable.
P.P.E.: Thirty

This is a shadowy version of the D-Pocket spell, but without the need for a physical container as items are stored in an extra, dimensional space similar to the Shadow Dimension. Any small shadow will do. Upon casting the spell, as much as 30 pounds (13.5 kg) of items can be stored in the Shadow Pocket. For the duration of the spell only the spell caster or whoever he designates can reach into the shadow and pull out the item(s).

The item(s) is tucked away safely in that particular shadow, and cannot be accessed until the shadow reappears. That means the spell caster cannot access the shadow until it is a suitable size. That's typically 6+ hours every day (more in summer). He needs to remember the general location, but can sense his Shadow Pocket when he is close to it (within 1,000 feet/305 m), and most actually remember the exact shadow.

Five P.P.E. must be spent to reopen the Shadow Pocket. The weight limit for the item or items placed inside is 30 pounds (13.5 kg) and the object(s) cannot be bigger than the shadow it is placed into. The Shadow Pocket is attuned to the mage who cast it, so only he can retrieve items left inside. Should the spell caster die or not come back for the item(s), the Shadow Pocket automatically opens up and expels the contents when the spell duration comes to an end.

Shadow Pool (Trap)

Range: By touch or up to 20 feet (6.1 m) plus 10 feet (3 m) per level of experience; line of sight required.
Duration: One minute per level of experience.
Saving Throw: Dodge, but needs a Natural 18, 19, or 20.
P.P.E.: Thirty

The spell caster is able to change one shadow per spell casting into a black, murky pool of water. This applies to shadows on the ground and on the sides of walls. The shadow looks like normal until someone steps or leans on it and falls in. The Shadow Pool is 10 feet (3 m) deep per level of the spell caster.

Those who fall in are lost in black water, engulfed in pitch-black darkness. They cannot see where the shadow starts or ends, making it difficult to find the edge and climb out. The more people struggle and swim, the farther they get from the edge, as there is no sense of direction. Worse, those who fall into a Shadow Pool can be heard by their comrades, but not seen. There is a 01-15% random chance of a victim accidentally feeling a hard edge and being able to pull himself out of the pool. (+5% if he is fol-

lowing the sound of people on the surface who are calling out to him.) Each attempt to escape counts as two melee attacks. Those wearing heavy armor may be encumbered and tire more quickly, sink and drown. Game Masters should take this into consideration, but be merciful.

A daring rescuer can tie a rope or cord around himself and dive in after a lost teammate, but unless he has *Shadow Vision*, he too swims around blind. (Nightvision doesn't work, but with Shadow Vision he can see the edge of the pool as clear as can be.) His only guide, the voice of his teammate in the pool. If they can find each other, they can follow the rope to the edge and climb out. Until then, all he/they can do is tread water in the pitch-black darkness of the Shadow Pool until the spell duration ends. The size of the Shadow Pool depends on the size of the shadow it was cast upon.

A note about Shadow Pools. A Shadow Pool "mostly" appears to be an ordinary shadow until someone falls into one. Mostly is the key word. First, those with Shadow Vision active can clearly recognize shadows that have been turned into Shadow Pools, provided they are looking around and not just running into action. Second, even without Shadow Vision, people who are careful and looking hard at the shadows may notice a shadow that seems to ripple. Shadow Pools exhibit small, subtle ripples just like those created when a bug lands on the surface of water, or a rock is tossed into it or a strong wind creates a subtle wave. It's difficult to notice, but it is there if you look for it.

Shadow Puppet (Twin)

Range: Self only.
Duration: Two melee rounds (30 seconds) per level of the spell caster (double for Shadow Mages and Shadow Lords).
Saving Throw: None.
P.P.E.: Twenty-Four

The spell caster becomes enveloped by a dark haze as if he were in a shadowy cocoon. At the same time, a second, identical shadowy figure appears that looks exactly the same, also cloaked in hazy darkness. Unlike the Multiple Image spell, the twin is not an illusion, but an actual, solid, shadow manifestation.

The duplicate follows every move of the spell caster. In combat, the two fight as one, both battling the same opponent or two separate foes in close proximity, making the exact same moves. The Shadow Puppet automatically strikes out at any opponent who comes within range. Ideal for close-quarters combat or to create confusion as to which is the real Shadow Mage and which is the fake because the features of both are blurred and look the same.

When the spell caster speaks, so does the Shadow Puppet in the exact same words, tone and volume, as if the two are reciting or singing in a duet. If another spell is cast, it is impossible to tell which one cast it. (Only the real mage can cast the spell, as the puppet is a shadow – a copy of the original, miming his actions and words.) The Shadow puppet attacks with the same strength, abilities and bonuses as the mage it mimics.

This odd double-threat gives the Shadow Mage an edge in close combat that provides him and the puppet with the following bonuses: +1 on initiative, and +1 to strike, parry and disarm.

The Shadow Puppet has 10 M.D.C. per level of the spell caster and takes half damage from normal weapons, full damage from magic weapons and light attacks; double damage from silver weapons. (In an S.D.C. environment, the Shadow Puppet has 10 S.D.C.)

Shadow Tendril Bolts

Range: 50 feet (15.2 m) per level of experience; line of sight.
Duration: One melee round.
Damage: 2D6 M.D. per each of the four Tendril Bolts. The four bolts can all be directed at one, two or four targets simultaneously.
Saving Throw: Dodge at –4 as the bolts come flying out of numerous shadows, which can be scattered all around a given area.
P.P.E.: Thirty

The spell caster fires a bolt of darkness into a nearby shadow (it cannot be fired directly at a target), and instantly up to four bolts come flying out of four nearby shadows from numerous directions either all at the same target from four different directions, or four blasts at four different targets at once. Counts as one attack for the spell caster. The bolts are difficult to dodge and come from odd angles, making avoiding them that much more difficult. Once the spell is cast, the mage can fire four Shadow Tendril Bolts up to four times in a single melee round. Each counts as one of his melee attacks.

Level Eight

Shadesword

Range: Self.
Duration: Two minutes per level of experience.
Damage: 1D6 M.D. per level of experience. This magic weapon does M.D. in Mega-Damage settings and S.D.C. in S.D.C. settings.
Saving Throw: Standard.
P.P.E.: Twenty-Two

This spell conjures a bladed weapon of pure darkness. The shape of the weapon is up to the spell caster, but most prefer to make this item a one-handed sword so they may use it with a Shadeshield in the other hand. In addition to the damage it inflicts, anyone struck with a Shadesword must save vs magic. Those who fail not only take damage, but fight at -2 to strike and parry for the next melee round. Anyone receiving multiple hits from a Shadesword must save vs magic for each, or suffer a cumulative negative bonus for an extended duration (one melee per each strike by the sword).

While the spell is in effect, its maker can not sheath or throw the Shadesword, or the spell will break and the weapon vanishes. Likewise, if it is knocked from its creator's hand the magic ends.

Shades of Death

Range: By touch or up to six feet (1.8 m) away.
Duration: One day per level of experience.
Saving Throw: None.
P.P.E.: Twenty-Five

This spell can place a comatose or mortally wounded character into a life maintaining coma that lasts one day per level of the spell caster. This spell is useful for buying time to get a severely hurt and stricken comrade to a healer, medical facility, or Healing Pyramid that can save his life. Shades of Death has no recuperative powers. It is simply a type of life support that keeps the severely injured person in a coma until he can be taken to a medical facility. If by the end of the spell's duration no means of healing is found, the stricken person will die 2D6 minutes after the spell stops working.

Shadow Clone

Range: Self only.
Duration: 10 minutes per level of the spell caster (double for a Shadow Mage; until the Clone is destroyed or the spell canceled for Shadow Lords).
Saving Throw: None.
P.P.E.: Thirty

The spell caster is able to transform his own shadow and use it like a puppet or robot. The shadow seemingly detaches from the spell caster, turns into a 3D shadow and temporarily becomes solid – an exact replica of the spell caster – in order to interact with the physical world. Well, not quite an exact duplicate. The Shadow Clone looks just like the spell caster, but his skin seems a bit ashen (something most people do not recognize) and his body, while solid, is not alive and is not made of flesh and blood. For those who may check for such things, the Shadow Clone has no heat signature.

For the duration the spell and the clone's existence, the real Shadow Mage falls into a trance, so he should be hidden someplace safe and/or protected. The spell caster sees through the eyes of his Shadow Clone and controls it as if it were his own body. The solid shadow can hide in, and Prowl through shadows at 88%. Its physical attributes are equal to those of the spell caster, and all combat bonuses are the same, but the Shadow Clone is limited to 100 M.D.C., +10 M.D.C. per level of the spell caster.

The physical shadow is vulnerable to all weapons, but takes only 10% the normal damage. Lasers and magic inflict full damage. Silver S.D.C. weapons do equivalent damage as M.D., while M.D. silver weapons do double M.D. to the Shadow Clone.

The spell caster cannot cast spells through the Clone because it is not a living body. Nor can the Clone channel and use ley line energy to cast spells. The Shadow Mage can, however, speak through it and use it to spy, fight, etc., without fear of being killed or captured himself. If the Shadow Clone is captured, the mage cancels the magic and his Clone melts into a two-dimensional shadow and fades way. If the Shadow Clone is destroyed, the mage suffers a shock to his system, temporarily loses 1D6+2 Hit Points (or M.D.C. as the case may be) and 20 P.P.E., but is otherwise fine. His consciousness back in his own flesh and blood body, the lost Hit Points/M.D.C. and P.P.E. returns at the normal rate. It should be noted that the spell caster can return to his own body by cancelling the spell at any time.

Shadow Tentacles

Range: Up to 160 feet (183 m) away but requires a shadow or area of darkness to rise out of. The tentacles' reach is 10 feet (3 m) +1 foot (0.3 m) per level of experience.
Duration: One melee round per experience level of the spell caster.
Saving Throw: As per parry or dodge at -2.

P.P.E.: Ten for Shadow Tentacles with 12 S.D.C. each per level of the spell caster's experience. Eighteen P.P.E. for tentacles with 10 M.D.C. each per level of experience.

The spell caster can create one large tentacle for each level of experience. A shadow is required for the tentacle to form. One tentacle can rise out of a shadow as small as two feet (0.6 m) in diameter. In large areas of darkness or shadow, the mage can create one tentacle for each level of his experience. The tentacles are solid manifestations that can be clustered close together or spread out across the large shadow from which they are grown. The tentacles rises up out of the darkness and begin to flail about, looking for victims. Depending on where the shadow is located, tentacles may rise up from the ground, hang down from the ceiling or protrude from the side of a wall, vehicle or tree.

The tentacles are quick but not intelligent. They are not controlled by the spell caster, not even a Shadow Mage, but seem to somehow sense when a target is near, and lash out at it. Each tentacle is +1 on initiative and +3 to strike or entangle. Each has three attacks per melee, +1 at level 5, 10, and 15 of the spell caster. They do not dodge and vanish when a tentacle's S.D.C. or M.D.C. is reduced to zero.

Methods of Tentacle Attack: The spell caster can pick one of three types of attack by the tentacles. Once the spell is cast, he can leave the area to let the Shadow Tentacles do their work.

1. Striking Shadow Tentacles: The tentacles flail about, striking anything – people, animals, vehicles – that comes within reach. Damage: S.D.C. tentacles do 2D6 Hit Point/S.D.C. damage. M.D.C. tentacles 2D6 M.D. per strike.

2. Entangling Shadow Tentacles: Rather than attack to hurt or kill, these tentacles grab and hold onto its victims. It may lash around an arm, leg or ankle, and snake around its victim(s) to hold him tight to prevent movement or pursuit. Entangling tentacles pull their victims to them and cocoon around them to pin legs and arms to the side for the duration. The tentacle does not let go even after its victim has stopped moving. Only when the spell duration ends or the spell caster cancels the magic, does the tentacle release its victim and disappear back into the shadow it came from. Of course, the tentacle releases its victim when it is destroyed.

3. Crushing Shadow Tentacles: In this case, one or more tentacles lash around an arm, leg or ankle, and each snakes around its victim(s) with the purpose of crushing and killing him like a boa constrictor. Damage: S.D.C. tentacles inflict 2D6 Hit Point damage per constriction, with each constriction considered one of its attacks. M.D.C. tentacles inflict 2D6 M.D. per attack.

Tentacle strength is the equivalent of a Supernatural P.S. 20 +2 per level of experience! To forcibly pull a Shadow Tentacle off a victim requires a combined Supernatural P.S. that is 50% greater than the tentacle's own P.S., triple that number if the people working at it possess ordinary P.S. Exposing the Shadow Tentacle to sunlight (Globe of Daylight is one way), turns its Supernatural P.S. into ordinary P.S. and makes the Shadow Tentacle vulnerable to ordinary S.D.C. or M.D.C. weapons, as the case may be, allowing them to inflict half their full damage. The Shadow Tentacle can be destroyed to release its victim, but in darkness they are impervious to most ordinary and M.D. weapons. Only lasers, magical light weapons and magic weapons do full damage; silver weapons do double damage.

The spell caster can, of course, cancel the magic at any time.

Shadow Trap

Range: 10 feet (3 m) away per level of experience. The width of the pit varies depending on the size of the shadow and must be larger than the intended target. The maximum width can be no bigger than 50 feet (15.2 m) in size.

Duration: Two minutes per level of the caster.

Saving Throw: Victims can try and dodge, but need a modified roll of 20 or higher. Add the character's dodge bonus.

P.P.E.: Thirty

Shadow Trap manipulates an existing shadow and temporarily turns it into a pit trap. The shadow looks perfectly ordinary until somebody steps into the shadow and falls in. There is a sensation of vertigo for a moment, and then he finds himself at the bottom of a pit (no damage). The sides of the pit are smooth and provide no surface to climb. Victims need to fly out, jump out, or wait out the duration of the spell. The pit is 10 feet (3 m) deep per level of the spell casters.

What the people in the pit do not realize is that when they fall into a Shadow Trap, they seem to vanish. No one can see or hear the victims unless they have *Shadow Sight*. The Shadow Trap and anyone inside the pit are clearly visible to a character with Shadow Sight.

Spell casters often use this trap to capture enemies as well as a delaying tactic, or as an ambush. A wicked spell caster may place their minions or a Shadow beings in the trap, ready to pounce upon anyone who drops in.

Level Nine

Banish Shadows

Range: 100 feet (30.5 m).

Duration: Immediate result. Creatures banished to the Shadow Dimension remain there until summoned again, or the creature has an opportunity to reenter the mortal realm via a magic summoning, Shadowgate or Rift.

Saving Throw: -4 for Shadow Realm animals to save (they are easy to banish). Shadow Beasts: Standard save vs magic. Shadow Wraiths: +5 to save. Shadow Lords are not affected by this spell.

P.P.E.: Sixty-Six

A useful spell for forcing lesser Denizens of the Shadow Dimension, such as Shade Hunters, Shadow Behemoths and Shadow Beasts back to the Shadow Dimension.

This spell can also shut an existing Shadow Door and, in effect, lock it shut for 1D4x10 minutes per level of experience.

In the alternative, it can be used to negate Animated Shadows, Ominous Shadow and Shadow Tendrils.

For double the P.P.E. cost, the spell caster can magically make ALL shadows retreat and move away from him in a radius of 15 feet (4.6 m) per level of experience, so that no shadows are near him. If night or in a dark area, the lighting within the area of banishment becomes equal to *overcast,* which reduces the abilities of Shadow Beasts and other Denizens of Shadow by half, but does not keep them out.

Shadow Hold

Range: Ten feet (3 m) per level of the spell caster.

Duration: Two melee rounds (30 seconds), per level of experience.

Saving Throw: Standard.

P.P.E.: Forty.

This spell is intended to capture an opponent without harming him by using his own shadow against him. The intended victim's shadow can be no smaller than half his size/length. When the spell is cast, the target's shadow comes to life, grows to the size of his intended victim, and grabs him in a bear hug. The shadow's purpose is to pin and hold/incapacitate its target. Nothing else. It does no damage. Such an attack usually comes as a complete surprise and is almost impossible to avoid as the attacking shadow is attached to its intended victim and goes wherever he goes. Until the spell duration elapses or is cancelled, the shadow holds onto its victim and prevents movement, or grapples with its victim until it can grab hold, which has the same effect as tying him up and preventing the victim from taking other action.

The shadow come to life temporarily takes on a pseudo-physical form with the exact same P.S., P.P., combat bonuses, attacks per melee, and Hit Points/M.D.C. as its owner, so it is like wrestling with yourself. Victims can parry and dodge but need to beat an 18 or higher. The victim may try to parry and dodge (with bonuses) but the shadow has all the same abilities. Roll as if the shadow was an opponent, high rolls win, as usual. Physically hitting or shooting the shadow does not harm it and it has no mind so psionics and mind control do not work against it.

Once it has grabbed hold it cannot be pulled off its victim (after all, it is a part of him, sort of), even by superior numbers and much greater strength. Its victim is bound and held tight by his own shadow, unable to move. **Note:** The shadow resists and fights against all physical actions, pinning the arms and hands of its victim, and fighting against any attempt to move or walk. However, the victim can still speak and call out warnings, issue commands, talk and cast spells. Likewise, psionic abilities can be used against other opponents as they come into range and line of sight.

One possible way to escape: Characters with the Escape Artist skill have an advantage. The Shadow imposes a skill penalty of -20%, but if the pinned character rolls under the skill (with penalty) he can slip his shadow's hold, and his shadow returns to normal.

Shadow Stalker

Range: Self only.
Duration: Up to 15 minutes per level of experience.
Saving Throw: -1 to save.
P.P.E.: Forty

This powerful enchantment is ideal for tailing and spying on a specific foe or target, and for smuggling oneself into places with tight security. The invocation enables the spell caster to step into another person's shadow and disappear into it without a trace. Undetectable by sensors, magic or psionics, the person inside the shadow goes along for the ride inside the shadow of that individual, like an invisible hitchhiker. Conditions must be right, starting with an environment where the target being stalked is casting a decent sized shadow. One big enough for the mage to step into. Then, the target must remain in an environment where he continues to cast a shadow or walks through darkness. As soon as the person being stalked enters a brightly lit area where the shadows are tiny or directly under the person, the stowaway spell caster is instantly forced out of his target's shadow and is revealed. Appearing only a few inches away from the individual whose shadow he had been hiding inside of. Such a sudden reveal is likely to create instant alarm that quickly escalates into violent conflict. Mages who are smart and paying attention make sure they "jump off" and into sheltering darkness or another shadow BEFORE being forced out when their target enters a brightly lit environment. Likewise, exposure to a Globe of Daylight and other magical or conventional light may reveal the hitchhiker riding along in another person's shadow, provided it is cast overhead and close enough to eliminate or minimize that person's shadow.

Riding along inside another person's shadow is rather like riding along tucked down on the floor between the backseat and the front seats so the driver doesn't know you are there. From that vantage point, the person hidden on the floor of the car behind the front seats can clearly hear everything the driver and other front seat passengers are saying, as well as any other ambient sounds or people the driver stops to speak with. However, the concealed backseat passenger only gets slight glimpses of where they are going and the people the driver may talk to along the way. It is the same for the mage hidden inside another person's shadow. He hears everything the person he is hitched to has to say, and what is said to him. He may recognize voices and other sounds and smells, but only catches fleeting glimpses of the streets and locations they pass by on their travels. It may or may not be enough to inform him of where he is, where he has been and where they are going. Nor may he actually see the people "the driver" is speaking with, though their conversation may offer clues to their identity and the stowaway mage may recognize the voice if familiar with that person already, or recognize the voice when he meets and hears that person speak. So while not perfect, it is all still valuable reconnaissance and perfect concealment.

Making an exit. The mage concealed within another person's shadow can tell when they are in darkness, passing through shadows or about to enter bright light. Likewise, he'll know if there are people around or not. This helps him to make a calculated and unnoticed exit. He can step out of the shadow at any point. The most ideal moment is to exit in darkness when nobody else is around or when in a crowd, where nobody is likely to notice another person suddenly appear in the crowd. Only someone looking directly at the person whose shadow he is hitching a ride in or someone directly behind that person is likely to notice the mage stepping out of the person's shadow.

Sunaj Shadow Mages and Shadow Assassins often use this spell to launch a surprise attack. In so doing, they appear to jump right out of the person's shadow or appear out thin air to either attack that individual or someone he is meeting with.

Being discovered in the shadow: Every five miles (8 km) traveled, or 10 minutes of time that elapses, whichever comes first, there is a chance the person being stalked realizes something is wrong. Roll to save vs magic with a -2 penalty for the victim to save. If the victim/target makes a successful saving throw, he cannot shake the feeling that something is wrong and that he is being watched or followed. As a result, most people get paranoid and err on the side of caution, keeping their mouths shut, eyes open, stay away from contacts and partners, cancel or avoid any pre-arranged meetings or criminal activity, and engage in nothing illegal or suspicious to draw attention to themself or their plans. Victims familiar with Shadow Magic, such as Shadow Mages or any Sunaj, may actually suspect they are a victim of this Shadow Magic spell and go to a brightly lit environment and be ready for the appropriate response, 1) reveal the hitchhiker with light, and 2) be prepared to capture or kill him!

Level Ten

Cloak of Darkness

Range: Self, up to 10 feet (3 m) away.
Duration: One minute per level of experience.
Damage: Special.
Saving Throw: First save vs Horror Factor 12, then dodge to avoid the capture by the cloak. Then save vs magic (standard 12 or higher) to escape in one melee round.
P.P.E.: Eighty

A potentially devastating spell, this magic is generally shunned by those of good alignment because of its inherent cruelty.

Upon casting this spell, a huge, rippling jet-black cloak billows out from the spell caster's back, moving as if it were alive. (Or, if the caster is already wearing a cloak, then it is transformed into this likeness.) The mere sight of the Cloak gives the spell caster a Horror Factor of 12, but those who run away are the lucky ones. For those who successfully save vs Horror Factor, the mage uses the Cloak as a sinister weapon against them, commanding it to drape over any one opponent (up to Giant-size) and swallow them whole!

To perform this, the spell caster must first roll to strike, adding in only the Cloak's natural bonus of +3. To defend against the Cloak, one may only dodge out of the way, as the Cloak cannot be parried.

Those struck by the Cloak are swallowed up by it. Victims feel as if they are endlessly falling into a pit of pure, icy darkness. The dark magicks of the Cloak of Darkness instantly sap the victim of half of their Hit Points (or M.D.C. as the case may be), although it leaves their S.D.C. intact. At this point, victims must save vs magic. Those who succeed are lost inside the Cloak for only one melee round (15 seconds), after which they are spit out, shaking and hurt but otherwise okay.

A failed save vs magic causes the victim to remain inside the darkness of the Cloak for three minutes or the duration of the spell, whichever is shorter. Once the victim is finally spit out, the terrifying experience leaves him shaken and he fights with all combat bonuses at half and skill performance is also half for the next 1D4 minutes.

Thankfully, the spell caster can only keep one person swallowed up at a time, so the current victim must be disgorged before the next one can be swallowed. The same opponent may be swallowed and disgorged repeatedly, each time the victim losing half his current Hit Points or M.D.C. Each attempt to strike and swallow (roll to strike as usual) counts as one melee attack.

Cloud Shadow

Range: Area effect, 100 foot (30.5 m) diameter per level of experience.
Duration: One minute per level of experience (double for Shadow Mages, quadruple for Shadow Lords).
Saving Throw: -2 to save. The penalty does not apply to Shadow Mages. Shadow Lords are impervious to the fear penalties associated with the spell.
P.P.E.: One Hundred

Think of this as a giant, Ominous Shadow. A large, dark shadow spreads across an area as if cast by a dense storm cloud overhead, only there is no cloud in the sky. Inside the Cloud Shadow, the darkness seems unnatural. The light is very low, like shortly after the sun goes below the horizon line, but enough to see. However, fine details cannot be made out unless close (within two feet/0.6 m), and artificial light seems filtered and functions at half strength/intensity. *Nightvision* is also reduced by half, and the temperature inside the shadow is 30% cooler than outside of it.

There are sounds of unintelligible whispers, low rumbling and deep guttural growls inside the large shadow. From the corner of your eye there is movement – something rising up in the darkness, preparing to lunge, but when you turn around to get a better look, there is likely to be nothing there. All of this makes everyone within the area of the Cloud Shadow nervous and jumpy. The sights and sounds are distracting and wear on the nerves of those inside the darkness, except for the spell caster and his allies who may be lurking in the darkness.

Everyone inside the massive shadow must roll to save vs magic. A failed roll means fear takes hold. Civilians are likely to panic and run away to find shelter behind locked doors and shuttered windows. Most hide and cover their faces, too afraid to look out at what might be coming. Heroes, warriors, adventurers, and those experienced in magic and/or the supernatural hold their ground and are able to push down the fear creeping up their spine. However, trapped inside the giant, ominous Cloud Shadow, those who fail to save lose initiative and all combat bonuses — unmodified die rolls only – and skill performance is done with a -20% penalty. These penalties remain in place as long as the character(s) remains inside the Cloud Shadow. The penalties are immediately gone when a character steps outside the shadow, but instantly return upon reentering it.

Since the Cloud Shadow is an area effect invocation, once it has been cast, the spell caster is free to move about unaffected by it, to take action, including casting other combat spells.

Shadow spells and enchantments that require darkness all work inside this magical shadow, and beings who are Ethereal or become invisible in darkness reap all the benefits of such powers or magic. Likewise, any Shadow Beings, Shadow Assassins and Shadow Mages are at full strength while in the Cloud Shadow, even if the unnatural shadow is created during daylight hours. This is where the real danger lays, because a Cloud Shadow can serves as the battlefield or playground for Shadow Mages and Sunaj Shadow Assassins as well as the denizens of the Shadow Realm.

The size and shape of the Cloud Shadow can vary. A Shadow Mage can stretch the Cloud Shadow to run down the length of a street or highway or make it more circular or oblong like the shadow from a real cloud, only darker. This spell is ideal whenever a large shadow is needed to cover an entire block, a building, stadium or part of a neighborhood!

Curse of Darkness

Range: Touch or ten feet (3 m) per level of experience.
Duration: 24 hours per level of experience, or permanent for a cost of 240 P.P.E.
Damage: Special.
Saving Throw: Standard.
P.P.E.: One Hundred and Twenty, double to make permanent.

The victim of this curse is temporarily turned into a creature of the dark, unable to withstand any exposure to sunlight. Like a vampire, the cursed individual burns, taking 3D6 points of damage *per melee round* of exposure to true sunlight. Damage is M.D. for Mega-Damage beings and Hit Points/S.D.C. for others. Exposure to a Globe of Daylight inflicts a mere 2D6 points of damage per melee round. Likewise, the cursed individual is blinded by sunlight (-10 to strike, parry, dodge, etc.), but not artificial light.

Living with the curse requires the victim to either become entirely nocturnal, stay indoors except at night, or to cover himself from head to toe with some kind of protective clothing or armor to keep the sun off; full plate armor works so long as the visor is kept down. Otherwise, the only remedy to this is a *Remove Curse* spell or convincing the spell caster responsible to remove it (not likely). Most deities and Alien Intelligences also have the power to remove the curse, but what are the odds of meeting a god and having him do it?

Shadow Hole

Range: Self and up to one person per level of experience.
Duration: One hour per level of experience.
Saving Throw: Standard for unwilling victims.
P.P.E.: Ninety-Five

Similar in effect to a Time Hole spell, the spell caster is able to create a shadowy extradimensional hole in which to hide. Like the mouth of a cave, those inside can see out, but from the outside, all that is perceived is a shadow. The hole is invisible to normal detection, even Nightvision, but those with *Shadow Vision* will see it, and *Sense* and *See Dimensional Anomaly* will also reveal the opening. Shadow Dimension beings can also see the entrance and enter if they so choose.

The hole is big enough to accommodate the spell caster, plus one additional person per experience level of the spell caster. There is no time displacement when in a Shadow hole, and for each hour spent inside the Shadow Hole, one hour passes outside. The advantage is the people inside are hidden (to most beings) and safe inside, the shadow is stable and does not move or change shape or size should the light source change, and those inside can see what's happening outside as if they were standing in a doorway. While it is best to cast this spell in an area where the shadow will not be seen as unusual, only the most observant or those looking for something suspicious will notice if the shadow does not match the others around it. Even then, those inside are safe unless the individual manages to see the entrance. No one else can enter unless they can see the entrance.

Summon Shadow Beast

Range: Immediate.
Duration: For straight-out combat situations: Two minutes (8 melee rounds) per level of experience. Three hours per level of experience to do labor, or stays until it has finished its mission or been destroyed (see below for details).
Saving Throw: None.
P.P.E.: One Hundred Forty

This inter-dimensional spell summons a creature not of this world to do the bidding of the spell caster. Shadow Beasts are large, vicious predators from a strange, little known world called the Shadow Realm, Shadow Dimension or Realm of Shadows, and other names. They stand 9-12 feet (2.7-3.7 m) tall, and possess sharp claws and wicked fangs. The are powered by night and

darkness, but deadliest of all is their ability to completely merge into the smallest shadow, becoming completely invisible. While hidden in shadows they are undetectable, even by a See the Invisible or Nightvision spell, since they are not truly invisible, but one with the shadow. The creature is a natural born predator that loves to hunt and kill, so it gladly follows orders to do so.

See complete stats in the Shadow Dimension section toward the back of the book.

Abilities in Darkness or Shadows (M.D. Environments):

- Invisible and undetectable even to tech sensors and optics.
- I.Q. 7, M.E. 7, M.A. 7, P.S. 30 (Supernatural), P.P. 24, P.E. 30, P.B. 3, Spd 24; Supernatural P.S. and P.E.
- 75 M.D.C. (On S.D.C. worlds, Hit Points: 90, S.D.C.: 20, A.R. 10.)
- Damage: 5D6 S.D.C. for a restrained punch, 3D6 M.D. full strength punch, 4D6+2 M.D. for a slashing or stabbing "claw strike," 6D6 on a power punch (counts as two attacks) and 3D6+3 from a bite attack.
- Combat: Six attacks per melee round, +2 on initiative, +3 to strike, +4 to parry, dodge and disarm. +8 to save Horror Factor.
- Impervious to cold, heat, disease, drugs and poison. Regenerates damage at a rate of 2D6 M.D. per melee round.
- Skills of Note: Prowl 90%, Climb 80/75%, Land Navigation 60%, Wilderness Survival 80%, Track 40%, and understands Dragonese and the language of the mage who summoned it.

Abilities in Light (M.D. Environments):

- Completely visible and detectable by sight and sensors!
- I.Q. 7, M.E. 7, M.A. 7, P.S. 18 (normal strength, not Supernatural), P.P. 16, P.E. 15, Spd 8.
- 35 M.D.C. (On S.D.C. worlds, Hit Points: 45, S.D.C.: 10, A.R. 5.)
- Combat: Two attacks per melee round, +1 initiative, +1 to strike, +2 to parry, dodge and disarm. +4 to save vs Horror Factor.
- Damage: 1D6 M.D. for punch, 1D6+3 from claw attacks. (On S.D.C. worlds, 3D6 damage for any attack.)
- Impervious to cold, heat, disease, drugs and poison. Regenerates damage at rate of 2D6 M.D. per melee round in shadow or darkness, but can NOT regenerate in bright light or sunlight, even overcast sunlight.
- Skills of Note: Prowl 45%, Climb 40/38%, Land Navigation 30%, Wilderness Survival 40%, Track 20%, and understands Dragonese and the language of the mage who summoned it.

Controlling the Shadow Beast. In a combat situation, the spell caster can command and control the Shadow Beast for two minutes (8 melee rounds) per level of experience. After that, the exhilaration of combat enables the creature to break free of the mage's control and either return to its home dimension or stay in ours (if it is having fun, it may even continue to fight).

In non-combat situations, the mage can send the Beast on a simple mission such as "Bring me so and so," or "Slay so and so," and the creature will remain in this dimension until the mission is completed or it is slain. Or the mage can command it to stand guard or perform labor for him for three hours per level of experience. **Note:** There is a 01-15% chance that the Shadow Beast will not return to its own dimension. Under this circumstance it is a free agent beyond the control of the spell caster who summoned it. If this happens, it will remain in the world wreaking havoc and killing innocent people for food and pleasure. Likewise, it will kill any who try to send it back.

Level Eleven

Shadow Door

Range: Ten feet (3 m) tall.
Duration: One minute per level of experience to locate a Shadow Door in the area, or to open one. The Shadow Door remains opened for only one melee round (15 seconds).
Saving Throw: None.
P.P.E.: Two Hundred Forty

This spell enables the spell caster to sense the location of an existing Shadow Door within 1,000 feet (305 m), find it, see it, and open it to go through it. If there is no Shadow Door around to open, this spell will create a temporary one that remains open for one melee round (15 seconds).

Entering the Realm of Shadows is almost certain death, as it is a hellish domain of night and monsters where mortals are seen as prey and playthings. Odds are, visitors will not survive 12 hours in the place.

This spell is usually used for one of two reasons. One, to locate an existing Shadow Door and guard it to make sure nothing ever goes in or out of it. Or, in service of a Shadow Wraith or Shadow Lord who may summon his underling to come to the Shadow Dimension to make a report or otherwise serve him.

Shadow Envelope

Range: Self only.
Duration: One hour per level of the spell caster for a temporary envelope or 5 years per level if long term.
Saving Throw: Not applicable.
P.P.E.: Forty-Five for a temporary. Two Hundred Ninety for long term.

Shadow Envelopes are often used as a safe haven to sleep, rest, meditate, heal, hide out for a while, and to temporarily store a small getaway vehicle, loot, gear, dead bodies, teammates, minions or prisoner(s). Just like the Dimensional Envelope spell, the mage is able to create a small extradimensional pocket somewhere in the Shadow Dimension that is opened via a Shadow Door. The size of the space is a 10 foot (3 m) x 10 foot (3 m) x 10 foot (3 m) area, about the size of a small bedroom.

Once the envelope is created it will last for the duration of the spell. The entrance must be a shadow and as big as a door or larger to enter. Normal time passes within the envelope, and people can survive inside, but it is pitch-black within. Any light spells are cast at half their usual intensity and duration, and cost twice the P.P.E. There is enough air for the duration of the spell.

The Shadow Envelope can only be accessed by its creator, via any shadow large enough to act as a door. Unlike Shadow Pockets, this spell is keyed to the spell caster, so when he closes the "door" to the Shadow Envelope, no one else can see in, and those inside cannot see out or get out on their own. When the spell duration ends, anything or anyone inside simply appears where the Shadow Envelope was first created/opened. Of course, the one who created it can open the door at any time – to access the Shadow Envelope the mage must spend 10 P.P.E. – or cancel the magic at any time. If cancelled, the Envelope's contents appear where the mage is standing at the moment of cancellation.

Level Twelve

Shadow Fog

Range: 1,000 foot (305 m) area per level of the caster.
Duration: 30 minutes per level of experience at night, dawn or dusk. Half that time in bright sunlight.
Damage: None.
Saving Throw: None.
P.P.E.: Two Hundred Fifty

Most fog is white, but not the Shadow Fog. It is a dense gray mist with even darker areas of grey. Moreover, it rises 20 feet (6.1 m) overhead where the Shadow Fog seems to be at its most dense, creating a thick canopy that blocks the sun. Light does filter through, but the darkness in the fog resembles night and allows the Denizens of Shadow and even vampires to function in the fog as if it were nighttime, regardless of the time of day. The thick, dense fog cloud covers a very large area (1,000 feet/305 m per level of the caster and up to 30 feet/9.1 m tall from the ground). It is as thick as pea soup and reduces visibility to a mere five feet (1.5 m). Any magical light source doubles the range of visibility, but creates glare and discomfort in the swirling fog. Only the spell caster can see clear as normal in the Shadow Fog. However, the Denizens of Shadow, vampires, and characters with nightvision (magical or natural) can see up to 10 feet (3 m), and characters with Shadow Vision can see 15 feet (4.6 m). Remember, this is not just about darkness, but also the dense, swirling mist of the fog. **Note:** Only the spell caster sees perfectly and does not suffer the penalties below. For those who can see 10 feet (3 m) or farther in the fog, the penalties are half (round up).

Penalties: Everyone in the Shadow Fog, with the exceptions noted above, is jumpy and -6 on Perception Rolls, -5 to strike, parry, disarm and dodge, and -20% on the performance of all skills. Line of sight spells and attacks are extremely limited. Running faster than a Spd of 8 imposes a 01-75% likelihood of running into something or tripping and falling down. Both use up two melee attacks, cause the victim to lose initiative for that melee round and make a noise that can be heard 120 feet (36.6 m) away. A noise that may attract an enemy.

Penalties for long-range attacks beyond the distance one can see in the fog apply to everyone but the spell caster. Firing long-range weapons into the fog (guns, arrows, thrown weapons) is shooting blind (-10 to strike).

Those outside the fog peering in can see nothing and even sound is muffled from within the fog (half usual volume and distance carried). Optic systems, even passive nightvision, are rendered useless. Modern sensors work only to a small degree (-50%) due to some sort of interference, with spotty reception at best. Reduce penalties by one half if using modern sensors like infrared or thermal imaging. Those who use sonar or superior sense of hearing, see range reduced by half, and properly reading tech devices is done at -20%. Blind characters, like Altara Blind Warrior Women, are not impaired at all by this spell (but reduce radar range by half), and those who hunt and track by smell are at a decided advantage.

Shadowgate

Range: Ten feet (3 m) per level of experience.
Duration: One melee round per level of experience.
Saving Throw: None.
P.P.E.: Three Hundred

This spell opens a portal between this world and the Realm of Shadows, that dark and mysterious world from which all Shadow Beasts come. As long as the portal remains open, one Shadow Beast, Shade Hunter or Shadow Behemoth may be called forth and bound to the spell caster's service every melee round. In this fashion, a sorcerer may assemble a pack of Shadow Beasts or other Shadow monsters with which to wreak havoc.

This power does not come without a price, however. For every single Shadow Beast or other Shadow monster summoned through the Shadowgate, the spell caster must perform a *Battle of Wills*, just as a Shifter would. If the spell caster succeeds, the Shadow creature does as he commands for 1D6x10 minutes (double for Shifters/Summoners and Shadow Mages), after which the creature must either be sent back to the Shadow Dimension (automatic, all that is needed is a large shadow), or left to its own devices in the world it was summoned to. Letting any Denizens of the Shadow Realm loose in the world is to unleash a bloodthirsty monster. However, the creature will not slay the one who summoned and released it into the world as a thank you for the opportunity. However, should they meet again, all bets are off and it is likely to slay the spell caster for having dared to summon it in the first place. These indiscriminate killing machines are a nightmare, but unleashed by wicked sorcerers to cause havoc and slaughter enemies and rivals. **Note:** Shadow Beasts drawn through the Shadowgate behave exactly as if they would under the Summon Shadow Beast spell.

The battle of wills: Roll percentile to see what creature responds to the summons of the Shadowgate. The spell caster must roll higher than the number listed below to win the battle.

01-70% Shadow Beast (intelligent) – 11
71-84% Shadow Behemoth (animal) – 7
85-94% Shade Hunter (animal) – 9
95-99% Shadow Wraith (intelligent) – 14, but it is very rare that a Shadow Wraith responds to a Shadowgate summons.

100% Shadow Lord (intelligent) – This deific being cannot be summoned or controlled via this spell. There is, however, a chance a Shadow Lord notices a Shadowgate and investigates out of curiosity. If he or she should step through the Shadowgate, the creature is likely to expect the mortal responsible for opening the gate to bow before him and become a willing servant for as long as the monster stays in the realm of mortals. Those who balk and defy the Shadow Lord's will are likely to be struck down. Any Shadow monsters already brought through the Shadowgate immediately defer to the Shadow Lord as their master. See *Summon Denizens of the Shadow Dimension* for more details about likely responses by a Shadow Lord.

Level Thirteen

Shadow Wall

Range: Can be cast up to 100 feet (30.5 m) away per level of experience.
Duration: Five minutes per level of experience.
Saving Throw: None.
P.P.E.: Four Hundred

This spell creates a huge, pitch-black wall. The wall's maximum dimensions are 30 feet (9 m) long, by 10 feet (3 m) high, by 3 feet (0.9 m) thick, per level of experience.

As a wall, it must be touching the ground or a floor, and is relatively straight; i.e. a long wall, say 120x40x12 feet (36x12x3.7 m), may curve a bit, but is fundamentally straight. It cannot be cast as a slab in the air or made into a circle, square or "V" shape. However, a square, rectangle or "V" could be made by creating several such walls butted within inches of each other (this applies to all magic walls unless stated otherwise).

The Shadow Wall is immaterial, existing only as dark energy, like a shadow given form and dimension. Nonetheless, it is highly effective at stopping things from passing through it. Any living being who attempts to pass through the wall can do so, but at a snail's pace of only one foot (0.3 m) per melee round (15 seconds). The sensation is rather like trying to push through a fierce wind. Since the Shadow Wall is magical, nightvision or optic systems that normally enable them to see in the dark don't work and they are completely blind (-10 to strike, parry, and dodge) and while moving through the Shadow Wall they cannot even see their hand in front of their face.

Each melee round, those moving through the Shadow Wall find themselves dropping in magic and psionic energy. The Shadow Wall siphons 10% of their P.P.E., I.S.P., and even technological energy (E-Clips) every melee round! Living creatures passing through the wall also suffer an "energy drain" that amounts to physical exhaustion, also at a rate of 10% per melee round (15 seconds). Armor, power armor or being inside a robot or vehicle, is no protection against this effect to the person(s) inside. Trying to plow through the wall in a vehicle causes it to also practically stop and move at the same snail's pace as people. Flying over the wall is an option for those who have it available to them.

Rail gun rounds, bullets, missiles, arrows, and other fast-moving kinetic weapons can pass through the wall, but see their speed, range and damage reduced by 80%! The same is true of explosive devices. Furthermore, no sensors or optics can penetrate the Shadow Wall, so any shooting is done blind (-10 to strike).

Level Fourteen

Shadow Essence

Range: Limited to the current dimension of the caster.
Duration: Two hours per level of experience.
Saving Throw: None or standard.
P.P.E.: Four Hundred Eighty

The spell caster is able to split his own life essence to take possession of a Shadow Beast to, in effect, split himself in two: Himself at a diminished capacity and the Shadow Beast at full capacity, only it is he who sees and experiences whatever it does, and he controls its every action. The possessing spell caster is able to control the Shadow Beast as if it was his own body. If the spell caster was already the Beast's master when he casts the spell, the creature gets no saving throw. Otherwise, it gets a standard save vs magic.

A possessed Shadow Beast can travel hundreds or thousands of miles away in the same dimension, and the spell caster still remains in possession of it and controls it as if it were him inside of the Beast. The spell caster's own body also remains functioning, but at a diminished capacity. The spell caster's attacks/ actions per melee are reduced to just two per melee round, the performance of skills is reduced by half and takes twice as long to do, speed and combat bonuses are reduced by half, and the mage has no initiative (attacks last). However, the Shadow Beast he controls functions at its full capability. This makes the mage a double threat.

Summon Denizens of the Shadow Dimension

Range: Immediate area up to 20 feet (6.1 m) away, but requires a shadow or area of darkness large enough for the monster to climb forth.

Duration: For straight-up combat, five minutes per experience level of the spell caster. Five hours per level of experience to do labor, or it may stay until it has finished its mission or is destroyed.

Saving Throw: The Shadow Creatures summoned by Ritual can only save with a roll of a Natural 19 or 20. A Shadow Lord (just one) can also be summoned by this means, but he cannot be controlled.

A successful save means the Shadow monster is not under the control of the mage, and does not need to obey him. It can instantly vanish back to the Shadow Dimension or it may elect to stay in the world of mortals to reap mayhem. A duplicitous and wicked creatures such as a Shadow Beasts or Shadow Wraith may pretend to be under the spell caster's control or it may choose to follow his commands if it finds the one who summoned it amusing or rewarding, such as slaughtering heroes or innocent people.

P.P.E.: Four Hundred Eighty

The advantage of this spell is that the sorcerer can summon the exact shadow creature he desires and does not open a Shadow Door or Rift; the creature magically appears. There must be a large shadow that is bigger than the creature that is to be summoned. The spell caster has two options when summoning: he can perform a ritual, in which case the summoned being is almost certain to be instantly under his control (unless it rolls a Natural 19 or 20 to save), or he may use an instant spell summoning, in which case the creature gets a much reduced saving throw (needs 12 or greater to save). If the beast saves, the spell caster has no command over it and he can only hope it listens and will hear him out and attack people other than himself. A Shadow Lord cannot be summoned when this magic is used as an instant spell, only in a ritual.

The ritual takes 1D4x10 minutes to perform during daylight hours, but only 3D6 minutes when performed at night. In all cases, regardless of the time of day or whether this invocation is done as a spell (instant results) or ritual (more likely to have command over the creature), a shadow is required and it must be larger than the creature being summoned.

The Sunaj Shadow Mage can summon and command one *Shadow Behemoth* or *Shade Hunter* for every level of experience, or one *Shadow Beast* for every two levels of experience, or one *Shadow Wraith* for every four levels of experience. When trying to summon a *Shadow Lord*, only he, and no other Denizens of Shadow, can be summoned. Chance of success in summoning a Shadow Lord is 15% per level of experience. Thus, a 7th level Shadow Mage is guaranteed to get one to appear. How that may work out for him could be good or bad. The mage had better have a compelling speech ready and be willing to serve the Shadow Lord in some important way to get the creature's cooperation. Anger the creature and he is likely to destroy you.

The summoning of a Shadow Lord is always to make a deal and either beg for his help or barter for his services or knowledge. A creature of Chaos and Darkness, a Shadow Lord is most likely to strike a deal and help an evil or conniving Shadow Mage who appeals to the monster's dark nature. As it is with most Demon Lords, Shadow Lords enjoy helping mortals cause other mortals suffering and destruction. They understand emotions like hate and revenge, envy and lust for power, and know how to use them to create greater chaos and pain. A Shadow Lord may remain after being summoned for as long as the creature desires, and can return to the Shadow Realm any time he chooses. It should be noted that a Shadow Lord cannot usually enter the world of mortals unless summoned and allowed into that world.

Shadow Lords are unpredictable. Game Masters may roll on the following or pick the desired result, or a reaction of their own.

01-10% If angered, the creature may destroy the mage then and there or carry him back to the Shadow Dimension.

11-20% Or if angry, destroy all of the summoner's henchmen, beat or torture him and terrorize and humble the actual mage, before leaving him trembling and injured, but alive.

21-40% If annoyed, the Shadow Lord may simply vanish from whence he came, or ...

41-80% Agrees to help, perhaps even stay, to cause death and destruction, especially if it involves conquest, winning worshipers and minions, or crushing an old enemy or rival, or Champions of Light. However, the Shadow Lord serves no man. He has agreed to "help," not serve the mage who summoned him, because it amuses or appeals to the monster's dark nature to do so. The mage should never treat the Shadow Lord as a henchman nor as a partner, but as a benevolent god who has granted him favor. For now. Beware.

81-90% The Shadow Lord stays in the mortal realm to do as he desires, but he forces the summoning sorcerer (and the spell caster's henchmen/teammates) to serve him or die. Using the mage as an advisor/native guide and minion. The Shadow Mage's only release from this forced servitude is to trick the Shadow Lord into going back to the Shadow Dimension (and without taking him with him), destroy the monster, or kill himself.

91-00% Ignores the summoning sorcerer entirely, and goes off to do as he pleases. One more Demon Lord unleashed into an already troubled world.

Level Fifteen

Shadow Self

Range: Self only.
Duration: Permanent.
Saving Throw: None.
P.P.E.: One Thousand

This spell transforms the spell caster from a flesh-and-blood character into a creature of the Shadow Dimension! Those so transformed become a kind of monster able to merge with shadows (as per the Shadow Meld spell) at will and function very like a Shadow Beast. The mage retains his human shape, skills, knowledge and mental attributes, but will lose all other body features. His face becomes a distorted, monstrous, more primordial version of its once human appearance, musculature becomes chiseled and hard, arms and legs are hairy, skin color is a dark grey, and the eyes and mouth, when opened, glow red.

This monstrous appearance confers a *Horror Factor of 12*, and the reaction of most people who see the character is to shun or attack the character in fear. After all, he or she appears to be some kind of demon or monster (which is true). If a Mega-Damage creature before the transformation, the M.D.C. is unchanged. If a Hit Point/S.D.C. being, add the Hit Points and S.D.C. together and turn them into M.D.C. in Mega-Damage environments and Hit Points/S.D.C. with a Natural A.R. of 14 in S.D.C. environments. REDUCE BY HALF in sunlight or bright artificial light, along with the monster's physical attributes and skills percentage. The Denizens of the Shadow Realm, which the Shadow Self is now, are reduced in power by half in bright light.

The transformed individual is now a nocturnal creature of the night with nightvision (2,000 feet/610 m) and Supernatural P.S. and P.E. in shadows and darkness. Food and drink no longer appeal to the newly minted monster. Now he craves to feed upon the raw flesh and blood of other living beings, preferably sentient ones, but also drinks in their fear and P.P.E. at the moment of death, just like the *Shadow Beast*. Speaking of which, other Shadow monsters regard the character as one of them now. The equivalent starting rank of a Shadow Beast until the individual can prove himself more deadly. Which should be easy as the transformed mage retains all of his spell casting knowledge, spells, P.P.E., skills and abilities. He remembers being human, but that is all in the past. The Shadow Mage reborn as his wicked Shadow Self is something immortal and terrible.

The transformed Shadow Self should be easily ranked on par with a Shadow Wraith, and if capable and ruthless, perhaps a few steps beyond. Of course, this could make Shadow Lords see such individuals as potential rivals. Indeed, if the Shadow Self sorcerer manages to slay a Shadow Lord in single combat, he becomes a Shadow Lord with all the powers and spell knowledge possessed by such a monster.

The Shadow Self may still associate with mortals and wear clothing and use weapons and magic items if he chooses, or he can forego the trappings of civilization and behave in a more demonic manner. The choice is his. Of course, the creature sees himself as superior to all mortal beings, and will probably seek to rule over them and be worshiped as a living god.

<u>Vulnerabilities and Weaknesses of the Shadow Self</u>: Identical to all Denizens of the Shadow Dimension. See *Shadow Wraith* Vulnerabilities for complete details. The Shadow Self is considered to be a demon, regardless of alignment. The dramatic change also inflicts one random insanity that surfaces within 1D4 weeks. This too is permanent. Roll on the **Random Insanity Table** in the **Rifts**® main rule book.

Other Magic O.C.C.s

Atlantean Crystal Mage

The Crystal Mage combines some of the abilities and skills of a Stone Master, with those of a jeweler and a spell caster. The magic comes from centuries of experimentation and was only just beginning its ascension in the public eye when the *Janus Experiment* devastated the Atlantean people and made Atlantis vanish.

Stone Magic was the solid foundation for energy, transportation, medicine and society in Atlantis. It was also the underlying tool for building and construction in everyday life. As a result, Crystal Magic took a second seat and was used to supplement and illuminate the Atlantean cities. The use of crystals and Crystal Magic helped to provide light in homes and pyramids, light street lamps, and added to the cities' defenses. Since Stone Masters were the chief architects and top mages in the land, Crystal Mages always worked under them and their craft was never quite recognized or appreciated for everything it could do. Still, its practitioners were content with their position and in serving Atlantean society.

When the continent of Atlantis disappeared, the art of Crystal Magic also faded. It has only been in the last several centuries that True Atlanteans have begun to give Crystal Magic much greater attention and recognize it as a distinct and worthy classification of magic. Those who hold the secrets of Crystal Magic are likely to be members of clans that focus on Stone Magic and/or practice Alchemy.

In ancient times, Crystal Mages started out as artisans who also created beautiful works of art, statues, archways, jewelry and other works of art with stones, crystals and jewelry. Over time, they began to develop and apply their magic to more dramatic use such as lighting entire cities, light shows, communication, weapons and armor.

Today, most Crystal Mages retain the eyes and souls of the artist, so many still use their magic to make beautiful jewelry, statues and works of art. When it comes to Crystal Weapons they are often tasked with working with a Stone Master or an Atlantean Alchemist to create magical crystal artifacts used by Atlanteans. Some notable crystal weapons and artifacts are described after the *Crystal Magic Spells* section elsewhere in this book.

Crystal Mage Special O.C.C. Abilities:

1. Magic Tattoos Denote Heritage: The standard two common to all Atlanteans, see the Atlantean R.C.C.

2. Base P.P.E. of the Crystal Mage: 1D6x10+70 + P.E. attribute to start. Add 10 P.P.E. points for each additional level of experience. **Note:** The Crystal Mage can also draw energy from ley lines and nexus points, up to 20 P.P.E. per melee round to use magic abilities, cast a spell or power a magic device. 30 P.P.E. at a ley line nexus or at a stone pyramid.

3. Increased P.P.E. Recovery: The Crystal Mage replenishes P.P.E. at the rate of 10 points for every hour of rest or sleep; 15 P.P.E. per hour of Meditation, 20 P.P.E. when on a ley line or nexus point, and 30 P.P.E. when meditation is done inside a Crystal Pyramid.

4. M.D.C.: None. Atlantean Stone Masters are NOT Mega-Damage beings nor are they considered to be supernatural in any way. Their P.S. is equal to Augmented (not Supernatural) and they must use magic, body armor, force fields, or other means to protect themselves just like any other human. HOWEVER, they use ley lines and stone pyramids to increase their rate of healing.

5. Advanced Knowledge of Atlantean Pyramids: Crystal Mages are seasoned dimensional travelers and have a full understanding of all stone pyramids and how to operate them at 40% +5% per level of experience.

6. Sense the Location of Crystals: The Crystal Mage has the ability to locate crystals simply by sensing them. This is vital when trying to locate underground deposits of crystals and gems for components in casting their spells and creating certain crystal artifacts. Range varies. Passively, the range is only 10 feet (3 m) per level of experience. When actively searching, the range is 100 feet (30.5 m) per level of experience.

7. Extract Crystals and Gems from Stone: By spending 5 P.P.E. per minute, and with some concentration, the Crystal Mage can extract crystal from the stone without damaging the crystal or the stone. The mage can mystically move crystals and gems from stone like pulling them from putty, so they can free the crystal held within it. Extracting 1-4 crystals typically takes 1D4 melees for small crystals, 2D4 melees for medium-sized crystals and 3D4+3 minutes for large crystals.

8. Shape and Polish Crystal with Hands: Crystal Mages are skilled artisans and often design beautiful pieces of jewelry from crystals and polished stone. They are able to do this with their bare hands by concentrating and spending some of their P.P.E. in the process. At the cost of 10 P.P.E. per hour, the Crystal Mage can shape or carve crystal in various shapes at 60% +3% per additional level of experience.

9. Channel P.P.E. and Light Through Crystals: This enables the Crystal Mage to grab and direct his own P.P.E. into Techno-Wizard weapons, magic talismans, magic amulets and other types of P.P.E. batteries to recharge them, as well as imbue magic into crystals and manipulate light through crystals. When on a ley line or nexus point, the mage does not have to use his own P.P.E., instead channeling as much as 20 P.P.E. points from the ambient energy per melee round (15 seconds) to activate a magic tattoo, cast a spell, power a magic artifact or to channel some of it into a crystal.

Imbue Crystals with P.P.E.: The Crystal Mage can channel some of his own P.P.E. and place it inside a gemstone or crystal; up to 10 P.P.E. points per level of experience or 10 P.P.E. per melee round from the ambient energy at a ley line. Maximum that can be placed in a single gem is equal to his channeling ability of 10 P.P.E. per level of experience.

Unless used for magic, the P.P.E. placed into a crystal slowly drains away at a rate of two points per hour. Any practitioner of magic can use the P.P.E. trapped in the crystal to bolster his own spell casting abilities. This is a way to help himself at a later time as well as other spell casters. P.P.E. can also be placed inside talismans and amulets or used to charge and power Techno-Wizard device.

Can NOT be used to activate Magic Tattoos.

Direct Light through Crystals: For the cost of one P.P.E., the Crystal Mage can make a crystal capture light and release it to create the effect of a lantern or 100 watt light bulb to illuminate a 10 foot (3 m) radius. The farther from the gem, the dimmer the light. Within a five foot (1.5 m) radius of the gem, the light is strong enough to clearly read a book. Damage: None. This is not sunlight and does not harm vampires or Shadow creatures nor hold them at bay. Duration: 10 minutes per level of experience.

Light Beam: For the cost of 1 P.P.E., a crystal can be used to capture and release a focused beam of light that can be used like a flashlight or searchlight. Damage: None. This is not sunlight and the beam does not harm vampires or Shadow creatures. Range: 20 feet (6.1 m) per level of experience. Duration: Five minutes per level of experience.

Laser Beam: Cost varies. See Damage. A crystal or gem is used to channel P.P.E. and capture and release a focused beam of light capable of inflicting damage. P.P.E. Cost is based on Damage: One P.P.E. for a laser beam that does 3D6 S.D.C. damage. 3 P.P.E.: 1D6x10 S.D.C. 6 P.P.E.: 1D4 M.D. 9 P.P.E. 1D6 M.D. 12 P.P.E. 2D6 M.D. This is not sunlight and the beam does not

harm vampires, but will hurt Shadow beings and ordinary people and structures. Range: 12 feet (3.6 m) per level of experience. Duration: Instant. Bonus: No special bonus to strike, W.P.s do not apply. **Note:** Needs a crystal or gemstone through which to channel, focus and fire the laser beam.

Create Crystal Pyramid: The mage can create a pyramid made of forming crystal that collects and channels P.P.E. to let a Cyrstal Mage recover spent P.P.E. at a rate of 30 P.P.E. per hour.

The crystal pyramid must be large enough for the mage to comfortably enter and sit inside of it, as if it were a tent or small temple of some kind. Yoga mats or blankets and pillows to sit on are common. To build it, the Crystal Mage needs three struts that go up and three on the bottom for the base. These rods can be made of any material, but Atlanteans prefer wood or stone to build the skeletal structure of the pyramid. Then the mage works his magic to create and grow clear crystal along the three skeletal bones of this small pyramid. Once they have grown the entire length, the crystal spreads out to cover the bottom three as well and double in size until the struts are the size and thickness of two-by-fours and there is a small, fully formed crystal cap located at the peak. It takes 1D6+6 minutes to completely form a small, four foot (1.2 m) tall pyramid, double for one twice that size; seldom makes one that is larger than that.

The pyramid and its crystal construction lasts for two hours per level of its maker's experience, after which the crystals become dull and smokey and crumble into dust that falls off the six connecting rods. Like all magic, the mage who made the crystal pyramid can cancel the magic at any time.

Crystal Pyramids are also used as shelters. It masks the scent of the person inside as well as food, insects do not go inside the structure, it magically prevents rain and wind from entering, and it is always 10 degrees Fahrenheit (12 C) cooler inside when the temperature is hot, and never drops below freezing in cold weather.

10. Spell Magic Knowledge: Starts with the abilities described here, the spells *Create Crystal Golem, Create Guardian* and *Create Super-Guardian* and can make all three at half the usual P.P.E. cost, plus a total of nine Crystal magic spells that can be selected from levels 1-5.

This Sorcerer's primary focus is Crystal Magic, but they learn a handful of conventional spell invocations. Select a total of four invocations at level one. Spells can be selected from levels 1-3 invocations.

At each additional level of experience, starting with level two, the Crystal Magic can select two Crystal Magic spells or two spell invocations. Spells can be selected from levels as high as three levels above the mage's own current level of experience.

11. Spell Strength. The Crystal Mage is +1 to spell strength at levels 5, 10 and 15.

12. O.C.C. Bonuses: +3 to Perception Rolls involving locating, identifying and working with gems, as well as level of quality, +1 to strike using Crystal Magic and Crystal weapons, and +1 to save vs Earth Elemental/Warlock magic.

Note: Strangely enough, Crystal Mages do not have Gem Shaping or the ability to draw Power from Stones in this same way. They are reserved by the Stone Master.

Crystal Mage Stats

Attribute Requirements: I.Q. 12 or higher, M.E 14 or higher, P.E. 14 or higher; applicable to all races.

Alignment: Any, most Atlanteans tend to be good with a few exceptions.

O.C.C. Skills:

Art (+30%)

Barter (+10%)

Excavation (+10%)

Mining (+30%)

Geology (+15%)

Language & Literacy: Dragonese/Elf, American, Greek at 98%.

Languages: Speaks two additional languages of choice (+15%).

Literacy: One of choice (+10%).

Lore: One of choice (+10%).

Mathematics: Basic (+40%)

Mathematics: Advanced (+20%)

Spelunking (+10%)

Whittling & Sculpting (+10%, but only when used on crystals and stone)

W.P.: Select one of choice, often Blunt or Staff.

Hand to Hand: Basic, but it can be changed to Hand to Hand: Expert at the cost of two O.C.C. Related Skills, or Martial Arts for the cost of four skills.

O.C.C. Related Skills: Select four other skills. Plus select one additional skill at levels 3, 6, 9, 12, 16 and 20. All new skills start at level one proficiency.

Communications: Any.

Cowboy: None.

Domestic: Any (+10%).

Electrical: Basic only.

Espionage: None.

Horsemanship: General and Exotic only.

Mechanical: Basic only.

Medical: First Aid, Holistic, or Psychology only.

Military: None.

Physical: Any except Acrobatics, Boxing, Gymnastics, Kick Boxing or Wrestling.

Pilot: Any (+5%).

Pilot Related: Any (+5%).

Rogue: None.

Science: Any (+10%).

Technical: Any (+5%).

W.P.: Any.

Wilderness: Any.

Secondary Skills: The character also gets to select three Secondary Skills from the Secondary Skill list. These are additional areas of knowledge that do not get any bonus, other than possible bonuses from a high I.Q. All Secondary Skills start at the base skill level.

Standard Equipment: 2D4 crystals, two weapons related to his or her W.P. skills, pocket knife, survival knife, spelunking gear, backpack, sunglasses, goggles, air filter, 100 feet (30.5 m) of rope, crystal carving tools with carrying case, magnifying glass, gem cutter's glass and tools, pocket mirror, utility belt, sleeping bag, flashlight, and light Mega-Damage armor.

Money: 1D4x10,000 in precious gems and crystals and 2D4x1,000 in credits. Like Stone Masters, Crystal Mages often accumulate large fortunes. They make a good living as artisans and crafters of magic crystals for the Atlantean people, so they are not as prone to go off adventuring. Of course, plenty do.

Cybernetics: None, if it can be avoided. Due to their magic tattoos and sense of heritage, all True Atlanteans strive to get to a Healing Pyramid where they can be made whole. If not, Atlanteans will settle for cybernetic Bio-Systems. All Atlanteans are attracted to "natural" things, and mechanical systems are not natural. Moreover, cybernetics reduces the potency of magic.

Atlantean Stone Master, Revisited

Stone Masters are practitioners of magic with a special gift, the talent to mend, shape, sculpt, transport, and commune with stone, rock and gems. It is as if the rock were a living substance psionically linked to the Stone Master and made to bend to his will and imagination. It is said that these sorcerers can move rocks as if by Levitation or Telekinesis. In addition to being able to blend and mold the rocks with their bare hands, Stone Masters are also able to draw magic from gemstones, detect the presence of water and supernatural beings under the earth and even command the earth itself to attack and defend against their enemies.

Stone Masters are responsible for the creation and construction of the Atlanteans' fabled stone pyramids which are created with incredible precision and without the benefit of machines. In fact, any construct built by a Stone Master is structurally sound whether it is a tunnel through a mountain, an aqueduct bringing life-giving water, or a 300 foot (91 m) pyramid which is often built in a matter of months. Stone Masters have a reputation throughout the Megaverse with respect to their work. They are linked to the earth itself and not to an Elemental being in another dimension. In fact, Stone Masters are not able to communicate with Elementals nor manipulate them or elemental forces. Their spiritual and mystical connection to the earth is so innate and strong they do not need it. They can command the earth by calling forth stone pillars and splitting the ground and raising walls on command. Moreover, that connection to the planet links them to the "earth energy" of ley lines and a deep understanding of how they work and how to tap the lines of energy just as engineers tap the flow of mighty rivers. This enables the Stone Masters to control ley lines through the creation of stone pyramids and use them in spectacular fashion for healing, building and dimensional travel.

Stone Masters see the earth as a giant, natural rock garden, filled with sculptures and crowned with rolling hills and magnificent mountains. They also see themselves as privileged sculptors who are allowed to reshape its contours, adding to the sculptures and work in the garden of life. They see the beauty in a boulder and the curves in a hill. They have no greater loyalty other than to protect the beauty of the land and to live in harmony with their environment. To a Stone Master, a sculpture of a Splugorth is as breathtaking as the sculpture of a woman. It is the craftsmanship and love put into creating the work that they see, not just the image itself. For them, the same applies to the buildings they erect and the cities and highways they create. As long as the building blends into or complements the natural surroundings of an area, the Stone Master is satisfied and content.

Atlantean Stone Master O.C.C. Abilities:

1. Magic Tattoos Denote Heritage: The standard two common to all Atlanteans, see the Atlantean R.C.C.

2. Base P.P.E. of the Stone Master: 2D6x10+60 + P.E. attribute to start. Add 10 P.P.E. points for each additional level of experience. **Note:** The Stone Master can also draw energy from ley lines and nexus points, up to 25 P.P.E. per melee round, to use magic abilities, cast a spell or power a magic device. Double at a ley line nexus or at a stone pyramid.

3. Increased P.P.E. Recovery: The mage replenishes P.P.E. at the rate of 10 points for every hour of rest or sleep; 15 P.P.E. per hour of Meditation, 20 P.P.E. when on a ley line or nexus point, and 30 P.P.E. when meditation is done inside a stone or crystal pyramid.

4. M.D.C.: None. Atlantean Stone Masters are NOT Mega-Damage beings nor are they considered to be supernatural in any way. Their P.S. is equal to Augmented (not Supernatural) and they must use body armor, power armor, force fields, magic or other means to protect themselves just like any other human. HOWEVER, they use ley lines and stone pyramids to increase their rate of healing.

5. O.C.C. Bonuses: +2 to save vs magic in addition to P.E. and racial bonuses, and +6 to save vs Horror Factor, but these bonuses are only in effect while the Stone Master is standing on earth. If for some reason he is in a dimension with no earth element, is hovering in the air, in an aircraft, or is in outer space, these bonuses are not applicable. The earth is the source of his strength and power.

6. Impervious to Earth/Mineral Toxins: The Stone Master is impervious to the many toxic minerals and components of stone and minerals such as lead poison, arsenic (a natural mineral), sulfur, oil, natural gas, and many others. This means he can handle and be with toxic minerals and breathe gases trapped underground without fear of being poisoned and killed by them. <u>P.P.E Cost</u>: None.

7. Advanced Knowledge of Stone Pyramids. These mages are, indeed, the Masters of stone pyramids. Nobody knows them and their secrets better. They can operate every facet of all stone pyramids: Dimensional, Healing, and Power Systems. Base skill is 80% +2% per additional level of experience. It should be noted that while Stone Masters know everything structurally about how the stone pyramids are built and how they work. Certain nuances might not be known to them (-15% penalty). For example, they know how the bio-beds in the Healing Pyramid work, but unless the Stone Master has medical training, say at least the Paramedic skill, he may not know the best application of the unit and could use them incorrectly or take much longer to get the desired results.

8. Sense Ley Lines: Range of 15 miles (24 km) plus 5 miles (8 km) per additional level of experience.

9. Sense Ley Line Nexus: A range of 20 miles (32 m) plus 5 miles (8 km) per additional level of experience.

10. Sense Rifts: 40 miles (64 km) +10 miles (16 km) per each additional level of experience. Like the Voyager, he can sense a Rift on any of the connecting ley lines regardless of the distance and knows the whether the Rift is large or small, near or far, but cannot sense dimensional anomalies.

All Stone Masters possess the following abilities.

Stone Master Utilitarian Magic Powers

Mold Stone: A Stone Master can mold solid granite or any type of stone and rock with his bare hands as if it were clay. This power does not transform the rock to clay! Anybody touching a work in progress finds the substance to be rock hard, even though the sorcerer molds it like soft clay! This enables the Stone Master to sculpt weapons like stone clubs, and make fabulous statues without any apparent seams or tool marks. It also enables him to magically create uniform bricks and blocks of stone not just from boulders and quarries, but by squashing together stones, pebbles, sand and clay, as well as repair and revitalize existing stone, bricks and concrete, smoothing out chips, sealing cracks, adding to an existing stone structure, and so on.

<u>Base Sculpting Skill</u>: 40% +5% per each additional level of experience (+10% for repair work). Also add a +10% bonus if the character has the Art skill too.

<u>P.P.E. Cost</u>: 20 per hour. Molding concrete or plaster (artificial stone) costs twice as much P.P.E. per hour. Asphalt and processed metals are not considered to be a stone.

● **Push Stone.** The character can dig through any form of rock. In an inexplicable way, he can push, scoop, and remove areas of stone with his bare hands as if it were soft clay to create indentations, troughs, lines, holes, ridges, etc., including holes that go right through a stone structure. By pushing rock out of the way, there is no debris or evidence of cutting or construction. Any extra stone can be pulled off and added to a different piece. The character can simply push and handle the rock like clay. This process can be used to create a peephole, portal, doorway, or other opening through a stone wall, boulder or a tunnel through a mountain! Much like molding stone, the process requires physical exertion and activity by the Stone Master (or a team of them), because the opening does not magically appear nor does the stone magically disappear. Working quickly, the sorcerer can push or dig through 500 pounds (225 kg) of rock per minute.

The Stone Master can use this power to pull and push stone up from a stone wall or floor to create a solid rock mound or appendage to block or shut a door behind him. Small appendages that jut out from the floor or wall are easy to break by using force (4D6 S.D.C.). Pushing a mound or ridge of rock from a stone floor is a much stronger impediment that requires the door to be removed from its hinges or destroyed to get through, but working quickly takes one or two melee rounds (15-30 seconds). Creating a simple mound from a stone floor takes one full melee (15 seconds), a simple, small appendage, two melee actions (6 seconds).

<u>P.P.E. Cost</u>: One P.P.E. per minute. Pushing, digging or pulling concrete or plaster – artificial stone – costs double the P.P.E. per minute. It is not possible to dig through asphalt, metal, plastic or rubber.

● **Pick Up and Carry Incredible Weights of Stone Without Exhaustion:** The character can pick up and carry massive amounts of weight when it comes to carrying stone, bricks, gravel, sand, clay, dirt, shale, crystals, gems and raw minerals (gold, silver, nickel, copper, lead, iron, uranium, etc.). Weight is equal to 1,000 times his P.S. attribute. So a character with a strength of 9 could pick up and carry 9,000 pounds (4,050 kg) or four and a half tons of rock. A character with a P.S. of 24 could carry 24,000 pounds (10,800 kg) or 12 tons, but only of rock and earth as noted above. Other substances, like wood, processed steel, plastic, cloths/textiles, people, grain, organic material, or anything other than stone and earth have the normal weight, encumbrance and fatigue effects.

P.P.E. Cost: One P.P.E. per minute.

- **Move Stone Mentally:** This power is used for transporting rocks and building with them. The Stone Master can pull rocks out of the ground and/or cause stones to roll along the ground toward him within 1,000 feet (305 m), and along with him to a particular area. He can move the stones, bricks and related earthen materials to create an image on the ground or to erect standing stones like Stonehenge, to make a pile of stone, build a wall, build or pyramid, and so on. The uses are many. **Note:** Using rolling rocks as an attack is not very efficient. The slow speed means that a living target can easily move or dodge out of harm's way. Furthermore, the target of a rolling rock attack will see and hear the boulder or pile of rocks rolling toward him well in advance of the rocks reaching him. Rolling rock attacks are always -4 to strike and living targets get to dodge or run out of the way.

However, under the right conditions, this method of moving rocks can be used to cause a landslide. Better yet, a floor or area can be covered with pebbles or small rocks and then magically made to roll/move around, making the surface of that area difficult to walk on, like a floor of rolling marbles. Victims of this trick lose two melee attacks, are -2 to strike, parry and dodge, and their speed is reduced by half.

Limitations of Move Stone Mentally: Earth-bound, it rolls along the ground at a maximum speed of 11 (seven and a half mph/12 km). The Stone Master can move up to 500 pounds (225 kg) per level of experience per minute; double at ley lines, quadruple at a nexus point.

Range and Area of Effect: 1,000 feet (305 m); double at a ley line or nexus point.

P.P.E. Cost: Two P.P.E. per minute.

- **Levitation and Telekinesis of Stone:** The ability to mentally levitate rock straight up or down and slowly move them through the air side by side as if by Telekinesis. Levitation and Telekinesis of rock is usually used for building and stacking and moving bricks, blocks and materials. The stone mage can levitate or move a rock platform through the air with somebody riding on top of it, but the passenger's weight counts as part of the rock's total weight and the rock must be big enough and strong enough to support that weight.

Limitation: Up to 500 pounds (225 kg) per level of experience per minute can be moved in this manner; double on ley lines, quadruple at nexus points. The range of the movement up, down, or sideways, is limited to 30 feet (9 m) per level of experience, double at ley lines and nexus points. **Note:** The rock moves at a ponderous speed of five, about three and a half miles per hour (5.6 km). So they do not make very good vehicles or weapons. However, dropping rocks on people can be an effective attack if they do not notice a boulder or pile of bricks floating in the air above their heads. Such attacks also require excellent timing.

P.P.E. Cost: Four P.P.E. per minute.

Rock Drop Attacks: Always -3 to strike no matter what. Damage: 1D6 S.D.C. damage for under 15 lbs (6.7 kg), 2D6+2 S.D.C. damage for 16 to 50 lbs (7 kg to 22.5 kg), 4D6+6 S.D.C. damage for 51 to 100 lbs (23 to 45 kg) and 1D6x10+10

S.D.C. per each additional 100 lbs (45 kg). A rock weighing 200 pounds (90 kg) will inflict the equivalent of one M.D. point. Add one M.D. point of damage for each additional 350 lbs (157.5 kg).

- **Locate Secret Passages (Skill).** The Stone Master can sense the location of secret compartments built into any *stone or underground structure*, including pyramids. Base skill is 20% +5% per level of experience (+50% inside a stone pyramid of any kind). Not applicable to wood or other types of material. Range is 5 feet (1.5 m) per level of experience.

P.P.E Cost: None.

- **Sense Water:** The Stone Master can sense the location of water above and below ground, including lakes and ponds, underground streams, spring water, pockets of water, sewers, and pipelines. The level of accuracy is 35% +5% per level of experience.

Limitations: Sensing range is one mile (1.6 km) per level of experience. The mage can sense water underground as deep as 200 feet (61 m) per level of experience. Double these ranges when on a ley line and quadruple at a nexus.

P.P.E. Cost: Four P.P.E. per ten minutes.

- **Sense Supernatural Beings Under the Earth.** Similar to sensing water, except the mage can sense the presence of supernatural beings such as ghouls, nymphs, and elementals within the earth, but not above the ground. The level of accuracy is 30% +5% per level of experience. Limitations: Sensing range is a half mile (0.8 km) per level of experience. The mage can sense underground beings as deep as 200 feet (61 m) per level of experience.

P.P.E. Cost: Four per ten minutes.

Stone Master Offensive Stone Magic Powers

Most Stone Masters rarely adventure, except perhaps, in their youth. By nature they are the type of person who sets down roots and builds communities. Others do their adventuring at a young age, but for the long-lived Atlanteans, that could be 50 or 100 years before they come home to settle down and build a practice.

- **Seismic Wave:** By stomping or pounding a stone staff onto the ground, the Stone Master is able to send a seismic wave out in a 30 degree arc. All within this cone are affected and need to make a saving throw of 15 or higher using only their Physical Prowess bonus to save. On a successful save, the defenders only lose one melee attack as they quickly regain their balance. Those who fail to save are knocked to the ground, lose two melee attacks and are shaken for the next 2 melees during which they are -2 on initiative and -1 to strike, parry, and dodge.

Range: 25 feet (7.6 m) per level of experience to a 30 degree arc in front of the Stone Master.

Duration: Instant.

Saving Throw: 15 or higher using only the P.P. bonus.

P.P.E. Cost: 10

- **Pillar of Stone.** The Stone Master causes a large stone pillar 10 feet (3 m) in diameter to violently thrust upward, out of the ground, and rise up to 20 feet (6.1 m) above the ground. Those who do not make their saving throw find themselves teetering atop of the stone pillar or the vehicle is knocked on its side (01-40% chance) when it was struck by the pillar as it rose up from the ground. Hover vehicle pilots can make a control roll at -20% if they fail to dodge. On a successful skill roll, they only lose one melee attack. A vehicles stuck on top of the pillar that is than 12 or 15 feet (3.6 to 4.6 m) long is probably safe from falling off, provided it is not jostled or its weight shift too much to any one side. Anything larger is much more precariously perched and there is a 01-33% chance of falling off the pillar of stone every melee round. The fall has a 60% chance of the vehicle landing on its side. Damage is 4D6 M.D. Any vehicle that is tipped over on its side cannot move until it is returned back to its normal orientation.

Those who make a successful save are struck and knocked to the ground in a rough fashion when the stone pillar rose, but manage to avoid being carried off by it. Due to the violent concussion, those in M.D. armor take 1D6 S.D.C. while Mega-Damage creatures or vehicles take 1D6 M.D.

The Stone Master can create one additional pillar for every two levels of experience, so he can make two pillars at level 3, three at level 5, four at level 7, and so on. The pillars can be spread out in an area anywhere within range of the sorcerer or clustered together. Game Masters should also consult crash damage for vehicles that crash into the pillars. Each pillar has 10 M.D.C. per level of the Stone Master so it is possible to destroy them.

Range: Can be cast 100 feet (30.5 m) away +50 feet (15.2 per each additional level of experience. Each pillar is 10 feet (3.5 m) in diameter.

Duration: One melee per level of the caster.

Saving Throw: Dodge, 15 or higher.

P.P.E.: 25

- **Wall of Stone.** This ability is similar to the Warlock spell of the same name. At the command of the Stone Master, a wall of stone rises out of the ground. The wall has 30 M.D.C. per level of the Stone Master. The wall is seamless and perfectly smooth, making climbing difficult, -10% to the Climbing skill.

Range: The Wall of Stone can be cast up to 50 feet (15.2 m) away per level of the Stone Master. The dimensions of the wall are 10 feet (3 m) long, by 10 feet (3 m) high by 5 feet (1.5 m) wide per level of the Stone Master.

Duration: Five minutes per level of the Stone Master or until destroyed.

Saving Throw: None. The Wall of Stone is used defensively only and cannot be toppled over or forced to rise under a foe.

P.P.E.: 20

- **Stone Barricade.** The Stone Master creates a low stone barrier three feet (0.9 m) high by 3 feet (0.9 m) long. It is used as cover by troops to hide behind and shoot from or placed on the battlefield to block and obstruct enemy vehicles. Each barricade has 30 M.D.C.

Range: The barricade can be cast up to 50 feet (15.2 m) away per level of the Stone Master; double on ley lines.

Duration: 30 minutes per level of the Stone Master or until destroyed. Double duration on ley lines.

Saving Throw: None.

P.P.E.: 8

- **Stone Spear Barricade.** The Stone Master is able to instantly create two dozen stone spikes/spears (per level of experience) pulled out of the ground in a line that it five feet (1.5 m) long or that fills a 25 square foot (2.3 m) area per level of experience. Each spear is 1-4 feet (0.3 to 1.2 m) long and tilted in the direction of the enemy. They are intended to stop vehicles and troops from advancing along that path. Each spike-like

stone spear inflicts 1D6 M.D. but may be closely spaced so that squeezing between them is impossible and running into a group of them means being impaled by 1D6+1 of them. Piloting land vehicles over the spears is impossible without taking considerable damage, except for hover vehicles that are able to fly over them. Each stone spear has 2 M.D.C. (or 200 S.D.C.) and can be damaged by S.D.C. weapons.

Range: Can be cast up to 50 feet (15.2 m) away per level of experience.

Duration: One melee round (15 seconds) per level of experience; double on ley lines.

Saving Throw: Dodge.

P.P.E.: 16

Stone Master Gem Powers

Another area of Stone Magic known to Stone Masters is Gem Magic, which enables the sorcerer to draw upon powers and abilities from gems, as well as cut, polish and reshape them. "Gems" include most semiprecious and precious gemstones, quartz, and crystals but not glass.

Gem Shaping

The Stone Master can shape a gemstone with his mind as well as his hands, and make it look as if it has been cut and polished by a professional, adding facets and accents as desired. The mage must be holding the gem and requires several minutes of concentration to "shape" it. Elegant and intricate designs can be accomplished and are especially desirable for earrings, rings and necklaces. This power enables the mage to cut rough stones into sparkling gems, or to recut and disguise stolen gems, changing their original appearance. These gems are usually of a superior quality and often sell at a higher percentage of the current market value (typically 50% to 75%). **Note:** All cuts and changes are permanent.

Base Skill at Stone-Cutting/Shaping with One's Mind: 8% for every level of experience. Spending P.P.E. or drawing P.P.E. boosts the skill percentage, +1% per each P.P.E. point up to a maximum bonus of 10%; double on a ley line or at a stone pyramid. Add another +10% bonus if the character has the Art skill. A failed roll means the stone is ruined — worthless.

Drawing Power from Stones

Stone Masters can channel P.P.E. into certain precious and semiprecious stones, particularly crystals, to cast equivalent magic and psionic powers. Powers said to be held within the stone and only need to be drawn out by the Stone Master. The powers listed are identical to the psionic or magic spell of the same name.

Requirements: All stones must be free of any serious flaw and must be cut and polished to have a faceted/crystal appearance. Chips and slivers cannot be used, only whole stones with a crystal cut. The cut and polished gems may be made into rings and other types of jewelry.

Limitations: 1. Only one type of power can be focused and released from a particular gem at a time.

2. The power can be drawn from small gems only three times, and large gems six times. After the third or sixth usage, the gem crumbles and turns to dust! Even after the first use, the gem becomes flawed or discolored (worth half normal value).

Range: Touch. The user must hold the gem in his hand or have the gem on his person in order to mentally concentrate on using the gem(s) and unleashing the power it holds. If the power gem is dropped or lost, that particular power instantly stops, but that usage is still used up.

Damage and Abilities: Varies with the gem; can activate one gem power per melee and can combine up to three different powers/gems.

Duration: One minute/four melee rounds per level of experience. All bonuses and powers are temporary. Attribute bonuses from super-abilities are NOT applicable.

P.P.E. Cost to Activate: 5 P.P.E. to activate stones considered to have little or no value like salt and sulfur. 10 P.P.E. to activate a semiprecious gem or crystal like quartz, agate, or amethyst. 20 P.P.E. to activate a precious gemstone like a zircon, aquamarine, diamond, ruby, sapphire or emerald.

Penalty: Remaining focused on the use of the power gem(s) means the user is -2 on Perception Rolls, initiative and dodging.

Note: Only the Stone Master can use the magic from the stones, it cannot be transferred or given to others, and The Crystal Mage does not possess this ability.

List of the Powers Available from Stones:

Bio-Manipulation – Star Sapphire
Cloud of Smoke – Sulfur Crystals
Cure Illness – Rose Quartz
Detect Concealment – Amber
Detect Psionics – Amethyst
Empathy – Garnet
Empathic Transfer – Most Sapphires
Energy Disruption – Ruby Quartz
Escape – Clear Zircon
Eyes of the Wolf – Alexandrite
Fire Ball – Red Ruby
Fire Bolt – Red Zircon
Float in Air – Clear Zircon or Diamond
Fool's Gold – Yellow or Brown Zircon
Fly as the Eagle – Diamond
Globe of Daylight – Clear Quartz
Heal Wounds – Agate or Emerald
Impervious to Fire – Smoky Quartz
Impervious to Energy – Red Zircon
Invisibility (Superior) – Emerald
Invulnerability – Diamond
Mask of Deceit – Yellow or Brown Zircon
Mind Block – Black Tourmaline
Negate Poison – Topaz
P.P.E. Battery – Diamonds and Emeralds
Protection From Faeries – Salt Crystals
Shadow Meld – Black Sapphire
Swim as a Fish – Aquamarine
Wisps of Confusion – Blue Ruby

The Powers of the Stones

Agate (red-orange): Heal Wounds (same as the spell). Average Cost: 3D4x10 credits per small stone, double for large stones.

Alexandrite: Eyes of the Wolf (same as the spell). Average Cost: 1D6x1,000 credits per small stone (triple for large stones).

Amber: Detect Concealment (same as the spell). Average Cost: 2D6x100 credits per small stone, triple for large stones.

Amethyst Crystal: Any of the following psionic powers can be drawn from this crystal: Detect Psionics, Hypnotic Suggestion, and meditation. Average cost: 2D4x100 credits per small stone (triple for large stones).

Aquamarine: Swim as the Fish: Superior (same as the spell). Average cost: 1D4x1,000 credits per small stone (triple for large stones).

Diamond: Invulnerability or Fly as the Eagle (same as the spells). Average cost for a small, nicely cut diamond: 1D6x1,000 credits. Large diamonds cost 15,000 credits per carat. The diamond must be at least one carat to use the power of Invulnerability (counts as a large gem).

P.P.E. Battery: Diamonds and emeralds can also be used to store P.P.E. energy. The gem must be at least one carat and can hold as much as 25 P.P.E. points per carat. A two carat diamond can hold 50 P.P.E., a five carat diamond, 125 P.P.E. To charge the gem with energy, the Stone Mage must meditate at a ley line nexus or stone pyramid and channel some of its energy into the gem. The entire process takes about 10 minutes per 25 P.P.E. Gems used as P.P.E. storage batteries can be used only as a battery, it cannot be drawn upon for magic powers. The energy can be drawn on at any time by the Stone Master as long as it is in his possession. The gem can be charged up to six times before it is used up and it crumbles.

Emerald (green): Invisibility: Superior or Heal Wounds (same as the spells). Average cost for a small, nicely cut emerald: 1D6x1,000 credits. Large emeralds cost 16,000 credits per carat!

Garnet: Empathy (same as the psionic power). Average cost for a small, nicely cut garnet: 4D4x100 credits. Large garnets cost 1,000 credits per carat.

Quartz (clear): Globe of Daylight (same as the spell). Average cost: 3D4x10 credits per small stone, triple for large stones.

Quartz (rose): Cure Illness (same as the spell). Average Cost: 5D6x10 credits per small stone (quadruple for large stones).

Quartz (ruby): Energy Disruption (same as the spell). Average Cost: 6D6x10 credits per small stone (quadruple for large stones).

Quartz (smoky): Impervious to Fire (same as the spell). Average cost: 5D6x10 credits per small stone (triple for large stones).

Ruby (deep red): Fire Ball (same as the spell). Average cost for a small, nicely cut ruby: 1D6x1,000 credits. Large rubies cost 19,000 credits per carat.

Ruby (blue): Wisps of Confusion (same as the spell). Average cost for a small, nicely cut ruby: 1D6x1,000 credits. Large rubies cost 18,000 credits per carat.

Sapphire (black): Shadow Meld (same as the spell). Average cost for a small, nicely cut sapphire: 2D4x1,000 credits. Large sapphires cost 20,000 credits per carat.

Star Sapphire: Bio-manipulation (same as the super psionic power). Average cost for a small, nicely cut star sapphire: 2D4x1,000 credits. Large star sapphires cost 20,000 credits per carat.

Sapphire (most other colors): Empathic Transfer (same as the super psionic power). Average cost for a small, nicely cut sapphire: 1D6x1,000 credits. Large sapphires cost 16,000 credits per carat.

Salt Crystals (off-white color): Protection from Faeries, +2 to save vs faerie magic and the faerie will not come closer than six feet (1.8 m) to the protected character.

Sulfur Crystals (yellow in color): Cloud of Smoke (same as the spell). Average cost for a small crystal: 2D4x10 credits (triple for large crystals).

Topaz (yellow or brown): Negate Poison (same as the spell). Average cost for a small crystal: 1D4x100 credits (triple for large crystals).

Tourmaline (black): Mind Block (same as the psionic power). Average cost: 2D6x10 credits per small stone (double for large stones).

Zircon (clear): Float in Air or Escape (same as the spells). Average cost for a small, nicely cut zircon: 4D6x100 credits. Large zircons cost 3,500 credits per carat.

Zircon (red): Impervious to Energy or shoot Fire Bolt (same as the spells). Average cost for a small, nicely cut zircon: 3D4x100 credits. Large zircons cost 2,000 credits per carat.

Zircon (yellow, brown or gold): Fool's Gold or Mask of Deceit (same as the spells). Average cost for a small, nicely cut zircon: 4D4x100 credits. Large zircons cost 300 credits per carat.

Note about Precious Gems: Precious gemstones tend to cost much more on Rifts Earth than in our modern Earth or in the Three Galaxies and other places, because they are far less accessible. Gems are typically found only in certain places in the world and may be very difficult to acquire. Rubies and sapphires of all kinds are especially rare in North and South America and Europe. They are found primarily in Burma, Thailand and Sri Lanka (they are typically 40% less expensive at those geographic locations). Emeralds are found mainly in Columbia (South America), Egypt, and South Africa. Aquamarine is found in Brazil, Columbia,

Siberia and the Urals (Russia). Diamonds are most abundant in South Africa, Brazil, and Venezuela, and found to a lesser degree in all of Africa and parts of Columbia, Mongolia, Siberia and the Urals (Russia). Synthetic diamonds and synthetic zircons (man-made) do not work for magic.

Stone Master O.C.C. Stats

Attribute Requirements: I.Q. 12 or higher, M.E. 14 or higher, P.E. 16 or higher, applicable to all races.

Alignment: Any, most Atlanteans tend to be good with a few exceptions.

O.C.C. Skills:
Astronomy & Navigation (20%)
Language & Literacy: Dragonese/Elf, American, Greek at 98%.
Languages: Speaks two additional languages of choice (+15%).
Mathematics: Basic (+40%)
Mathematics: Advanced (+20%)
Gemology (+10%)
Lore: One of choice (+10%).
Masonry (+15%)
Swimming (+5%)
Whittling and Sculpting (+20%)
W.P.: Two of choice.
Hand to Hand: Basic, which can be changed to Expert at the cost of one O.C.C. Related Skill and Martial Arts (or Assassin if an evil alignment) for the cost of two O.C.C. Related Skills.

O.C.C. Related Skills: Select five other skills. Plus select two additional skills at levels 3, 7, 11 and 15. All new skills start at level one proficiency.
Communications: Any (+5%).
Cowboy: None.
Domestic: Any (+10%).
Electrical: Any.
Espionage: None.
Horsemanship: General or Exotic only.
Mechanical: Any (+5%).
Medical: First Aid, Paramedic or Holistic Medicine only.
Military: Military Fortification only (+10%).
Physical: Any, expect Acrobatics, Gymnastics, and Wrestling.
Pilot: Any (+5%), except Military vehicles, Power Armor and Robots.
Pilot Related: Any (+5%).
Rogue: None.
Science: Any (+10%).
Technical: Any (+10%).
W.P.: Any.
Wilderness: Any.

Secondary Skills: The character also gets to select four Secondary Skills from the Secondary Skill list at level one, plus one additional Secondary Skill at levels 2, 6, 8, and 12. These are additional areas of knowledge that do not get any bonus, other than possible bonuses from a high I.Q. All Secondary Skills start at the base skill level.

Standard Equipment: One weapon per Weapon Proficiency skill, 1D4 E-Clips for each weapon, pocket knife (1D4 S.D.C.), survival knife (1D6 S.D.C.), a cross of some kind, 1D6 wooden stakes, backpack, sunglasses and goggles, air filter, 100 feet (30.5 m) of rope, pocket tool kit, sculpting tools in a carrying case, 1D4 large chisels, mallet, hammer, hand pick, shovel, putty knife, magnifying glass, gem cutter's glass and tools, pocket mirror, utility belt, sleeping bag, flashlight, and light M.D.C. body armor. As an important member of Atlantean society, the Stone Master is provided with a vehicle if needed, often a horse, hover vehicle or hovercycle.

Money: 1D6x10,000 in precious gems and 4D6x1,000 in credits. Stone Masters have a much greater aptitude for accumulating fortunes, prestige and power. They were also the most sedentary of the True Atlanteans, but that is changing with the latest generation. In the past, most would make a good living as an artisan, builder, prospector, water diviner, advisor to kings, court magician, and some even became the rulers of their own kingdoms.

Cybernetics: None, if it can be avoided. Due to their magic tattoos and sense of heritage, all True Atlanteans strive to get to a Healing Pyramid where they can be made whole. If not, Atlanteans will settle for cybernetic Bio-Systems. All Atlanteans are attracted to "natural" things, and mechanical systems are not natural. Moreover, cybernetics reduces the potency of magic.

Atlanteans and other O.C.C.s

No Combat Cyborgs, Headhunters, Juicers, Crazies and other modified men. Atlanteans avoid cybernetics and bionics at all cost. With their advanced healing centers, most opt to not receive a cybernetic or bionic limb. Consequently, Atlanteans find the thought of becoming a Full or Partial Conversion Borg, Crazy, Headhunter or Juicer appalling.

Champions of Light. This can be almost any Men-at-Arms or Adventurer O.C.C. True Atlanteans tend to be a noble people with ancient cultures that promote enlightenment and responsibility to others, including the preservation of goodness and propagation of peace. As a result, most Atlanteans share a sense of purpose in the universe, follow high ideals, and feel a duty to live well and use their knowledge and abilities for the betterment of all sentient life forms. That said, they, better than most, are familiar with vampires and other types of supernatural evil, and actively oppose them, as well as tyranny and wickedness wherever they can. This legacy of duty and heroics has earned True Atlanteans, in general, a reputation for being heroes and *Champions of Light*. Of course, there are exceptions, but most people who know of Atlanteans assume they are valiant "good guys." This orientation attracts many Atlanteans to the pursuit of knowledge, magic, healing and joining groups and organizations devoted to defending, policing, and protecting others. It is not surprising to find one or more True Atlanteans among groups of heroes and Champions of Light.

Atlanteans coming to Rifts Earth have discovered the noble Cyber-Knights and some have become entranced by what they represent. Some have even joined them. Atlanteans who become Cyber-Knights avoid the Cyber-Armor as it will impair their use of Marks of Heritage tattoos (costs 20% more P.P.E. to use their tattoos) and reduces their P.P.E. by half. Atlantean Cyber-Knights typically forsake the Cyber-Armor in favor of receiving additional magic tattoos and/or developing their psychic abilities. At the discretion of the clan leader (and the Game Master), an *Atlantean Cyber-Knight* may receive the two Marks of Heritage, a Flaming Sword, Flaming Shield and a total of four additional magic tattoos. Selections can be made from he categories of Simple Weapon, Magic Weapons, Animals and Monsters. This

makes the Atlantean Cyber-Knight a minor Mega-Damage being who possesses Supernatural P.S. and P.E.

Atlanteans may also join other bands of heroes like Cosmo-Knights, Reid's Rangers, Tundra Rangers, demon slayers, etc.

Explorers, Scientists and Scholars. Atlanteans study a variety of vocations including what might be broadly considered adventurers and explorers as well as warrior poets, scholars and educators. Due to the Atlanteans' aversion to cybernetics and bionics, there are very few Atlantean Cyber-Docs or scientists in the areas of cybernetics and robotics, or even conventional science and medicine. The use of magic, and stone pyramids compensates for what humans consider hard science. The average Atlantean adventurer or scholar will have the standard two Marks of Heritage tattoos plus 2-4 additional tattoos. The tattoos usually reflect their vocation and help them in its practice.

Practitioners of Magic. Atlanteans study a variety of magic disciplines. Magic practices that appeal to Atlanteans beyond those they developed themselves, like Stone Magic and Magic Tattoos, are *Ley Line Walker, Ley Line Rifter* and *Temporal Wizards. Mystics* are the next most common with the occasional Shifter. Atlanteans have only recently discovered Techno-Wizardry and the *Elemental Fusionist*. While there are not many Atlantean Warlocks, the Elemental Fusionist is appealing to some Atlanteans and some are joining the calling.

Atlantean magic users are fully aware of how receiving more than six tattoos will completely obliterate their ability to cast magic spells. As such, Atlantean practitioners of magic do not seek out additional tattoos and rarely receive more than one or two beyond the two Marks of Heritage.

Psychics. True Atlanteans are the descendants of Earth humans, and have the same percentage of psychics as humans. Each clan has a percentage of psychics among them, with most, if not all, the Psychic O.C.C.'s being represented. While magic tattoos have no impact on psychic abilities, most Atlantean psychics seldom have more than four or five tattoos total (includes the Marks of Heritage). The mysterious Sunaj Assassins being the exception. Like all psychics, Atlanteans with such abilities tend rely more on their psionic abilities than their magic tattoos.

Experience Tables

Atlantean Monster Hunter/ Undead Slayer	Atlantean Nomad/ Tattooed Defender
1 0,000 – 2,500	1 0,000 – 1,900
2 2,501 – 5,500	2 1,901 – 3,600
3 5,501 – 10,500	3 3,601 – 7,200
4 10,501 – 21,500	4 7,201 – 14,400
5 21,501 – 32,000	5 14,401 – 24,500
6 32,001 – 47,000	6 24,501 – 35,000
7 47,001 – 65,000	7 35,001 – 45,000
8 65,001 – 87,000	8 45,001 – 65,000
9 87,001 – 115,000	9 65,001 – 85,000
10 115,001 – 170,000	10 85,001 – 115,000
11 170,001 – 220,000	11 115,001 – 145,000
12 220,001 – 300,000	12 145,001 – 185,000
13 300,001 – 400,000	13 185,001 – 250,000
14 400,001 – 500,000	14 250,001 – 335,000
15 500,001 – 600,000	15 335,001 – 400,000

Atlantean Tattooed Voyager	Sunaj Assassin/ Sunaj Shadow Assassin	Atlantean Stone Master/ Atlantean Crystal Mage/ Sunaj Shadow Mage
1 0,000 – 2,500	1 0,000 – 2,600	1 0,000 – 2,400
2 2,501 – 5,500	2 2,601 – 5,200	2 2,401 – 4,800
3 5,501 – 10,500	3 5,201 – 10,500	3 4,801 – 9,600
4 10,501 – 21,500	4 10,501 – 21,200	4 9,601 – 19,200
5 21,501 – 31,500	5 21,201 – 32,300	5 19,201 – 28,400
6 31,501 – 46,500	6 32,301 – 47,400	6 28,401 – 38,600
7 46,501 – 64,000	7 47,401 – 62,500	7 38,601 – 52,200
8 64,001 – 85,000	8 62,501 – 88,000	8 52,201 – 72,400
9 85,001 – 110,000	9 88,001 – 112,000	9 72,401 – 98,600
10 110,001 – 160,000	10 112,001 – 163,000	10 98,601 – 140,200
11 160,001 – 210,000	11 163,001 – 222,000	11 140,201 – 200,400
12 210,001 – 285,000	12 222,001 – 295,000	12 200,401 – 260,600
13 285,001 – 360,000	13 295,001 – 395,000	13 260,601 – 310,200
14 360,001 – 440,000	14 395,001 – 495,000	14 310,201 – 410,400
15 440,001 – 520,000	15 495,001 – 595,000	15 410,401 – 510,000

Note: Each experience level beyond 15 requires 100,000 experience points. Atlanteans are long lived, so while it not common, it is possible for them to advance to Level 16 and beyond.

Crystal Magic Spells

By Kevin Siembieda and Carl Gleba

Level 1

Crystal (Blinding) Flash (1)
Lantern Crystal (1)
Blue Light Crystal (3)
Color Light (2)
Stone Knife (3)

Level 2

Crystal Beacon (4)
Crystal Knife (5)
Crystal Spotlight (5)
Detect Minerals & Crystals (6)

Level 3

Adhere Crystals and Gems (10)
Crystal Sword (10)
Crystal Throwing Star (5)
Dazzle (10)
Turn Rock into Crystal (10)
Warmth Stone (8)

Level 4

Carve and Shape Crystal (20)
Crystal Laser (10)
Message Stone (10)
Sun Crystal (8)

Level 5

Crystal or Stone Spikes (20)
Fire Stone (10)
Grow Crystal (20)
Image Projection Stone (20)
Summon Crystal (25)

Level 6

Crystal Armor, Simple (20)
Crystal Shield (20)
Exploding Crystal (25)
Encase Object in Crystal (20)

Level 7

Crystal Shards (15)
Crystal Spike Array (25)
Crystal Staff (30)
Enter Crystal (10/20)

Level 8

Crystal Solar Battery (50)
Crystal Wall (35)
Emerald Beam/Anti-Demon (20)
Negate Crystal Magic (40)

Level 9

Crystal Door (40)
Crystal Vault (50/300)
Entrap Entity in Gem (70/290)

Level 10

Create Guardian Armor (120)

Level 11

Create Super-Guardian (400)

Level 12

Create Crystal Golem (Ritual) (700)

Level 13

Crystal Arch (Ritual) (800/2,000)

Level 14

Crystal Cocoon Prison (Ritual) (900)

Level 15

Crystal Tower (Ritual) (2,000/10,000)

Spell of Legend

Crystal Palace (Ritual) (8,000/24,000)

Level One

Crystal (Blinding) Flash

Range: Area effect or a focused blinding flash. 10 foot (3 m) radius from the spell caster. Requires a crystal or light colored gemstone.
Duration: Instant.
Saving Throw: Standard, but the potential victim is -1 to save if an additional 3 P.P.E. are spent on the spell.
P.P.E.: One

This invocation enables the spell caster to cause a crystal or gem (or a mirror!) he is holding to unleash a sudden burst of intense, white light. This flash can be a wide burst of light, temporarily blinding everyone in its ten foot (3 m) radius, except for the spell caster. Or the mage can focus and direct the flash at ONE specific individual within 10 feet (3 m) of him.

Victims are blinded for 1D4 melee rounds, and are -10 to strike, parry and dodge. The chance of falling is 01-50% for every 10 feet (3 m) traveled. The magic has a limited range of 10 feet (3 m). Saving throw is standard; those who successfully save vs magic are not blinded. **Note:** Does not affect robotic, bionic or cybernetic eyes.

Lantern Crystal

Range: 10 feet (3 m); can light up a room.
Duration: 30 minutes per level of the spell caster, double for a Crystal Mage or when on a ley line.
Saving Throw: None.
P.P.E.: One

The Crystal Mage can make a physical crystal or cut gem radiate light like a lantern. It is less brilliant but longer lasting than the Globe of Daylight or the Lantern spells and anyone in possession of the gem can move it to a different location. This magic light crystal may be thought of as a magical lantern or portable light bulb. It is usually a simple crystal the size of walnut or a plum, but can be larger or as small as a pea. As long as it is a cut gemstone or faceted crystal, the magic works. The intensity of the light can be mentally adjusted by the spell caster to the equivalent of a 40 to 300 watt light bulb, whatever suits its creator/user. **Note:** This is *not* sunlight, so it will not damage vampires nor keep them at bay.

Blue Light Crystal

Range: Touch or 10 feet (3 m) but line of sight is required and the crystal must be faceted and clean/polished.
Duration: One hour per level of the spell caster.
Saving Throw: None.
P.P.E.: Three

The mage is able to instill a crystal (value must be more than 10 credits) with magic energy and make it glow with a pleasant, soft blue light. The magic crystal lights up a 10 foot (3 m) area per level of the spell caster. It is the equivalent of a 40 watt light bulb, but there is something soothing about the blue light and most people find they feel more relaxed and fall asleep more quickly and sleep more soundly. As a result one extra P.P.E. point or one extra S.D.C. (or M.D.C. point) is recovered per hour of sleep with the Blue Light on.

The light is not suitable for illumination, reading or detail work. Think of it as a soft nightlight that provides dim lighting to see and navigate in darkness without hurting the eyes or disrupting the vision of beings with Nightvision!

The crystal can be turned on and off at will by the spell caster, while others must place it under or in an opaque container, under a jacket or into a pocket to conceal its dim light. And in the latter case, the blue light may still radiate through openings or through thin fabric. **Note:** Many Crystal Mages have gem-studded staves, canes or bracelets/armlets so that they may use them to cast various spells such as this one. This is *not* sunlight, so it will not damage vampires or Shadow creatures, nor keep them at bay.

Color Light

Range: Touch the light source, or 10 feet (3 m) per level of experience for light generated by crystals.
Duration: Five minutes per level of the spell caster. Double the duration on ley lines.
Saving Throw: None.

P.P.E.: Two

This spell enables the spell caster to bend and alter the wavelengths of light radiation to alter the spectrum and change its color. To affect devices that project light, like a flashlight, the spell caster must hold or touch the device. If the light is generated by a crystal, he can alter the color of the light from a short distance. Changing the light spectrum to infrared makes the light invisible except to those who can see infrared. Likewise, ultraviolet light when cast on an area or object causes certain chemicals and bodily fluids to appear and glow a violet color, such as blood residue. Changing the color of light can also be done for fun and entertainment.

Stone Knife

Range: Touch.
Duration: One hour per level of the spell caster. At the end of the enchantment, the weapon reverts to its original form.
Damage: 1D4 M.D.
Saving Throw: None.
P.P.E.: Three

The spell turns a rock the size of an orange, or a 6-8 inch (15-20 cm) long sheet or shard of rock or sandstone into a stone blade with a blunt handle. **Note:** The magic stone weapon inflicts 1D4 S.D.C. in S.D.C. environments and does 1D4 M.D. in Mega-Damage settings. The weapon itself has 10 M.D.C. (or 100 S.D.C. depending on the environment).

Level Two

Crystal Beacon

Range: 100 feet (30.5 m) per level of experience; straight up.
Duration: Five minutes per level of the spell caster. Double the duration for double the P.P.E. cost
Saving Throw: None.
P.P.E.: Four

The Crystal Mage can make a physical crystal or cut gem of any size fire a beam of light straight up into the sky as a beacon. The narrow pillar of light spreads out and widens the higher it goes. The light can be a standard yellow light or a colored light; any color of the rainbow can be made. Used as a beacon for rescue or extraction from combat zones, as a signal to attack, hold off, retreat, come to that location, etc., Different colored light can me different things.

Crystal Knife

Range: Touch.
Duration: One hour per level of the spell caster. At the end of the enchantment, the weapon reverts to its original form.
Damage: 1D6 M.D.
Saving Throw: None.
P.P.E.: Five

The spell turns a crystal the size of an orange, or a 6-10 inch (15-25 cm) long sheet or spike of crystal or quartz, into a crystal blade with a blunt handle that is razor sharp and can be used for precision cutting and surgery. **Note:** The weapon inflicts 1D6 S.D.C. in S.D.C. environments and does 1D6 M.D. in Mega-

Damage settings. The weapon itself has 20 M.D.C. (or S.D.C. depending on the environment).

Crystal Spotlight

Range: 60 feet (18.3 m) +20 feet (6.1 m) per level of experience.
Duration: Three minutes per level of experience.
Saving Throw: Dodge, move out of the way or hide.
P.P.E.: Five

The spell causes a wide, bright beam of light to project from a crystal no smaller than a walnut. The light works like a high-powered spotlight. The beam widens to a circular spotlight 15-20 feet (4.6 to 6.1 m) in diameter. The crystal can be held in the hand, placed on the ground, put in a tree, or on a parked vehicle, etc., to stay focused on one particular location (a door, opening in the tree line or a fence, etc.), or the person in possession of the gem may use it very much like a searchlight with the beam pointing in whatever direction the gem is aimed. The spell caster may cancel the spell at anytime, turning the light off. Otherwise, it continues to beam light until the maximum duration ends.

Detect Minerals and Crystals

Range: 10 foot (3 m) area per level of the spell caster. For Crystal Mages, this spell doubles the range of their natural sensing abilities for the duration of the spell.
Duration: Five minutes per level of the caster.
Saving Throw: None.
P.P.E.: Six

This enchantment enables the spell caster to detect the presence and location of different kinds of minerals and crystals, including precious and semi-precious stones. It is very useful in locating hidden gems, crystals, silver, gold, etc. These stones and minerals may be natural in the earth or an item that has been dropped or hidden. The spell does not tell the mage the kind of minerals or crystal until he finds it, just that they are close and where to look.

Level Three

Adhere Crystals and Gems

Range: The spell caster has the ability to adhere crystals to each other or to another surface.
Duration: Spell ability lasts for 10 minutes per level of the caster. The results are immediate and permanent.
Saving Throw: None.
P.P.E.: Ten

The spell caster is able to magically "glue" or adhere crystals to crystals or crystals and gems to other materials such as stone, metal, wood and most any type of material. This is used to make jewelry, statues, staves, wands, ornamentation, and decorations.

Crystal Sword

Range: Touch.
Duration: 30 minutes hour per level of the spell caster. At the end of the enchantment, the weapon reverts to its original form.
Damage: 2D6 M.D.
Saving Throw: None.
P.P.E.: Ten

The spell turns a crystal or quartz no smaller than the size of a grapefruit, or a 2 foot (0.6 m) long sheet or spike of crystal or quartz, into a crystal sword with a blunt handle. **Note:** The weapon inflicts 2D6 S.D.C. in S.D.C. environments and does 2D6 M.D. in Mega-Damage settings. The weapon itself has 40 M.D.C. (or 400 S.D.C. depending on the environment).

Crystal Throwing Star

Range: 50 feet (15.2 m) +10 feet (3 m) per level of experience.
Duration: Turning a crystal or gem into a throwing star counts as one melee attack/action. Throwing it is another attack. Once created, the crystal remains a Throwing Star for one melee per level of the spell. When the duration ends, it turns back into the crystal or gem it was. If the crystal can be recovered, it can be used over and over again for various purposes.
Damage: Damage is 1D6 M.D., +1 M.D. for each level of experience (1D6+2 M.D. at level two, 1D6+3 M.D. at level three, and so on). **Note:** Damage is S.D.C. in S.D.C. environments and M.D. in Mega-Damage settings.
Saving Throw: Dodge. The spell caster is +1 to strike.
P.P.E.: Five

The spell caster is able to charge a small piece of crystal or gemstone with magic energy, press it flat between his hands to make it a small, flat disc or star with jagged edges like a throwing star and hurl it as a weapon with deadly accuracy. As it slices through the air, the crystal catches light and glitters like a star, day or night.

Dazzle

Range: Area effect. 10 foot (3 m) radius and can be cast up to 120 feet (36 m) away. Requires a crystal or gem that radiates the dazzling light display.
Duration: Two melee rounds (30 seconds) per level of the caster.
Saving Throw: -1 to save. Everyone in the area of effect must roll to save.
P.P.E.: Ten

Dazzle creates a sparkling, multi-colored light show in a given area. It is very distracting to those trying to perform complicated skills or locked in combat. Lights swirl and flash in different colors as well as shoot from various points like a laser show.

Penalties: Those who fail the saving throw are -4 on Perception Rolls, -2 on initiative, -2 attacks per melee, -2 to strike, parry, and dodge, and -30% to perform complicated skills. Speed is also reduced by 30% and the victim may feel a sense of vertigo/dizziness. The effects last for the duration of the spell whether or not the person leaves the area of effect.

On a successful save all penalties are half, round down, and if the victim of Dazzle leaves the area of effect and can no longer see the light show, the penalties end and he immediately returns to normal.

Turn Rock into Crystal

Range: Touch, must cover stone with both hands.
Duration: Permanent results.
Saving Throw: None.
P.P.E.: Ten

This spell enables the spell caster to turn coal or rock of any kind the size of a softball or grapefruit into a faceted crystal the size of a walnut or golf ball. A rock the size of a bowling ball can create a crystal the size of an orange but costs triple the P.P.E. This can be critical when no other source of crystal is around to use with Crystal Magic. The crystal only has a value of 1D6 credits, double if large.

Warmth Stone

Range: Touch a stone.
Duration: 30 minutes per level of the spell caster; double in sunlight or on a ley line.
Saving Throw: None.
P.P.E.: Eight

The spell caster can make a physical crystal or cut gem radiate warmth equal to a small campfire. This can come in especially handy on cold nights and in the winter. Though the crystal generates heat, enough to keep a room or the inside of a vehicle warm, the stone itself is not hot at all, nor does it generate light, smoke or noxious fumes. It is solar and magic based and simply glows with a soft red and orange color like a hot coal.

Level Four

Carve and Shape Crystal

Range: Touch.
Duration: One hour per level of the caster.
Saving Throw: None.
P.P.E.: Twenty

This spell endows the spell caster with the ability to carve and shape crystal at 82% by touch. This includes the knowledge and ability to make all types of jewelry cuts in addition to being able to use his hands to shape crystal and gemstones in various ways. At the end of the spell, all skills and knowledge are lost. This spell is nice to have when making something unusual or when time is of the essence. Most Atlantean Crystal Mages take great pride in their work and often become masters of carving stone and crystals without use of this spell.

Crystal Laser

Range: 100 feet (30.5 m) per level of experience.
Duration: Instant.
Damage: 1D4 M.D. per level of the spell caster's experience
Saving Throw: Dodge, -2 to dodge when target is 10 feet (3 m) or closer.
P.P.E.: Ten

Requires a clear, yellow or red crystal or gem of any size, but no smaller than a cherry. The spell channels P.P.E. through the gemstone to create a laser light blast to launch from the gem at an enemy; point and shoot.

Note: Damage is S.D.C. in S.D.C. environments and M.D. in Mega-Damage settings.

Message Stone

Range: Touch.
Duration: Immediate results, message lasts for one day per level of the spell caster
Saving Throw: None.

P.P.E.: Ten. Twenty to make the message last one week per level of the spell caster and sixty to make the message permanent (usually a message of love or a warning).

The spell caster is able to magically imprint his image and voice into a crystal or gem, and as record a spoken (60 words or less) message in the crystal. There are two ways to deliver the message. Anyone who touches the stone activates the message, or the message can get keyed to one specific person, but the spell caster must have a lock of hair or a recently worn (within the last 48 hours) article of clothing with which to place the crystal on to key it to that person's DNA. In that case, only that person can activate the message contained in the stone.

The image captured in the stone is usually that of the person imprinting the message, but it can also be the face of someone else, a photograph, video projection, drawing, map, diagram, etc. that is held up to the stone when the message recording is made.
Note: The crystal cannot be smaller than a golf ball but can be larger to gigantic, provided the crystal is one piece.

Sun Crystal

Range: 10 feet (3 m); can light up a room.
Duration: 80 minutes if fully charged.
Saving Throw: None.
P.P.E.: Eight

Captures and holds sunlight indefinitely until it releases it upon command (and 8 P.P.E.). For every hour a Sun Crystal is left out in the bright sunlight, it traps 10 minutes of sunlight and can hold up to 80 minutes of sunlight. It costs 8 P.P.E. to activate this solar light absorption process. Whether it is left in the sun for a full eight hours or a much shorter period, it costs 8 P.P.E. to make the crystal absorb sunlight. It takes two hours per 10 minutes in overcast conditions.

To release the sunlight, the spell caster must again spend 8 P.P.E. The Sun Crystal releases its captured sunlight, filling a 12 foot (3.6 m) area per each level of its creator's experience. Because it is *sunlight*, it wards off vampires, most other types of undead, and demons and monsters who fear or are hurt by sunlight, keeping them at bay just beyond the edge of the light. Shadow beings who dare to enter the light see their abilities reduced by half. A Sun Crystal may also have an impact on certain Shadow Magic spells.

The owner of the crystal can walk around with the lit crystal shining with sunlight and shut it off and on at will to preserve the light contained inside. A Sun Crystal can be recharged, as noted above.

Level Five

Crystal or Stone Spikes

Range: Up to 60 feet (18.3 m) away +10 feet (3 m) per level of experience.
Duration: Three minutes per level of experience. Double on ley lines.
Saving Throw: None other than avoiding the affected area.
P.P.E.: Twenty. Double the P.P.E. to double the duration.

The mage is able to make a stone or crystal spike form out of stone, concrete, sand, dirt, gravel or clay rise up from the surface of the ground, road, wall, mountain cliff, etc. It is conical like a stalagmite (growing up from the ground) or stalactite (growing down from the ceiling), only a bit narrower and has a very sharp point, like that of a javelin. The size of the spike can be controlled by the spell caster to be a few inches to several feet tall (depending on his level) – one foot (0.3 m) per level of the spell caster – and he can create two spikes per level of experience. These spikes are usually created as roadblocks, obstacles and fortifications.

Damage depends on the size of the spike(s) and whether the victim is impaled on the spike, runs into it or a vehicle or robot steps on it or crashes into it. **Note:** Damage is S.D.C. in S.D.C. environments and M.D. in Mega-Damage settings.

Impaled on spike 3-12 inches (7.6 to 30.5 mm) long: 1D6 S.D.C. or M.D.

Impaled on a spike 1-2 feet (0.3 to 0.6 mm) long: 3D6 S.D.C. or M.D.

Impaled on a spike 3 feet (0.6 m) long or larger: 4D6 S.D.C. or M.D.

Stepping a spike: 1D4 S.D.C. or M.D. per spike.

Riding over a spike with a tire: Punctures that one tire and inflicts 2D6 S.D.C. or M.D. If a conventional, air-filled S.D.C. tire, it goes flat in 1D4 melee rounds and imposes a -10% penalty to the piloting skill at 40 mph (64 km) or slower. -20% if going faster. Double penalties if half the tires are punctured and go flat, and reduce maximum driving speed by 40%. If more than half to all of the tires are punctured, the piloting penalty is -60% and speed is reduced by 80%, and the vehicle grinds to a halt if trying to drive over rugged, uneven terrain. **Note:** The same applies to hover vehicles if their hover jets are damaged by the spikes.

Running into the blunt side of a spike does 1D6 S.D.C. or 1D4 M.D. for speeds under 22 (15 mph/24 km).

Slamming into the blunt side of a spike does 2D6 S.D.C. or 2D4 M.D. for speeds of 23-68 (to 45 mph/72 km).

Slamming into the blunt side of a spike does 5D6 S.D.C. or 4D6 M.D. for speeds 70-132 (50-90 mph or 80 to 144 km).

Slamming into the blunt side of a spike does 1D6x10 S.D.C. or 1D4x10 M.D. for speeds over 140 (more than 100 mph/160 km). Double for every 100 mph (160 km) of speed.

Climbing Capability (special): The spell caster can control the size and placement of the spikes throughout the duration of the spell. More often than not, the spikes are created and left behind for the duration. However, the mage can control their placement/location, within range, and make them disappear, merging back into the surface like they were never there at all, and have them reappear at a new location within range. Sometimes this capability is used to help the spell caster climb up cliff facings and the sides of walls and concrete buildings, or stone pyramids, by making the spikes appear and disappear as needed to provide handholds and footholds as he goes up; +15% to Climb skill (or a base skill of 50%). Moreover, because he makes the spikes behind him disappear so that he can make them reappear as he climbs up, means they are not left behind for a pursuer to use.

Fire Stone

Range: 20 feet (6.1 m) per level of experience.
Damage: 3D6 M.D., +1 M.D. per level of experience.
Saving Throw: Dodge, -2 to dodge when the target is 10 feet (3 m) or closer.
P.P.E.: Ten

Requires a red ruby or sapphire of any size, but no smaller than a cherry. The spell channels P.P.E. through the gem to create a blast of fire, point and shoot. **Note:** Damage is S.D.C. in S.D.C. environments and M.D. in Mega-Damage settings.

Grow Crystal

Range: Self only.
Duration: The magically grown crystals last for one hour per level of experience, but can also be made permanent.
Saving Throw: None, appears to be a genuine crystal.
P.P.E.: Twenty for a temporary crystal or crystal formation, One Hundred P.P.E. to make permanent. Permanent crystals can be used to make armor, statues, decorations, etc.

The spell caster can take a few seed crystals or crystal dust, and use this spell to make them grow up to four times larger and spread out in a layer or sheet. These are common crystals with little value and is how the Crystal Mage can make Crystal Armor. The spell caster can focus to make the crystal formation to grow in a particular shape (long strips, strings, square, rectangular, circular, etc.). Not applicable to gemstones. The spell enable the mage to create two square feet (0.18 sq. m) per level of experience. Crystals spread and grow one foot (0.3 m) per melee round (15 seconds).

Image Projection Stone

Range: Touch.
Duration: Immediate results, and the message lasts for one day per level of the spell caster.
Saving Throw: None.
P.P.E.: Twenty. Forty to make the message last one week per level of the spell caster and One Hundred Twenty to make the message permanent (usually a message of love or a warning).

Similar to the Message Stone except the spell caster is able to magically imprint his image and voice into a clear or yellow crystal or gem with what is, in effect, a video recording that projects from the gem like a hologram!. The message lasts up to one minute per level of the spell caster. There are two ways to deliver the message. Anyone who touches the stone activates the message and the projection, or the message can get keyed to one specific person, but the spell caster must have a lock of hair or a recently worn (within the last 48 hours) article of clothing with which to place the crystal on to key it to that person's DNA. In that case, only that person can activate the message contained in the stone.

The image captured in the stone is usually that of the person imprinting the message, but it can also be the image of someone else speaking or forced to speak, or a group of people, or a series of photographs, drawings, map, diagram, etc., that are held up to the stone when the message is being recorded. **Note:** The crystal cannot be smaller than a golf ball but can be larger provided the crystal is one piece.

Summon Crystal

Range: Self only.
Duration: Permanent. One crystal per summoning. 1D4+1 crystals at double the P.P.E. cost
Saving Throw: None, appears to be a genuine crystal.
P.P.E.: Twenty-Five

This spell only works when the spell caster is at a location known to have crystals or semi-precious gemstones. Instead of digging or chiseling through rock, the spell caster is able to summon a walnut to golf ball-size piece of crystal. Such a stone is used in many of the crystal spells and constructs as a component. It is also useful in providing crystal for Techno-Wizards.

Level Six

Crystal Armor, Simple

Range: Self or two others by touch.
Duration: 20 minutes; double for Crystal Mages and Stone Masters, and at ley lines.
Saving Throw: None.
P.P.E.: Twenty

As the spell suggest, the recipient of this magic is covered in a semi-opaque crystalline body armor, from head to toe. The armor is faceted and sparkles in the light making it useless for stealth (-30 to Prowl), but provides some distinct advantages, such as 20 M.D.C. per level of the spell caster (30 S.D.C. per level of experience and an A.R. of 16 in S.D.C. worlds), weighs only 10 pounds (4.5 kg), is remarkably light (10 lbs/45 kg), bends freely at the joints and takes half damage from all light based attacks, such as lasers, as well as electrical attacks (the individual is grounded by the armor). **Note:** Sonic/vibration based attacks which do double damage. S.D.C. in S.D.C. environments and M.D.C. in Mega-Damage settings.

Crystal Shield

Range: Self only, but can be handed off.
Duration: 22 minutes, double for Crystal Mages and Stone Masters, and at ley lines.
Saving Throw: None.
P.P.E.: Twenty

Like the Crystal Armor, the mage is able to conjure a shield composed of magically lightweight crystal (6 lbs/2.7 kg). The shield takes half damage from all laser and light-based attacks. It is not indestructible and has 20 M.D. per level of the spell caster, but only takes damage when specifically targeted with the intent to destroy it. At the discretion of the spell caster, the shield is 3-5 feet (0.9 to 1.5 m) tall and 2-3 feet (0.6 to 0.9 m) or 3 feet (0.9 m) in diameter. It can be used to parry laser and light-based attacks (+1 bonus), otherwise the user's normal bonus applies. **Note:** Sonic/vibration-based attacks do double damage. S.D.C. in S.D.C. environments and M.D.C. in Mega-Damage settings. In S.D.C. worlds, the shield has 30 S.D.C. per level of the spell caster and an A.R. of 17.

Exploding Crystal (Hand Grenades)

Range: Created by touch. 100 feet (30.5 m) thrown.
Duration: Instant results, but the Exploding Crystal can be created and held for up to three melee rounds (45 seconds) before they explode. Otherwise, explodes on impact. One or two can be made per each spell casting. A crystal no smaller than a golf ball is required and it is destroyed upon impact.
Damage: 1D4 M.D. per level of the caster to a 4 foot (1.2 m) radius.

Saving Throw: Dodge at 15 or higher is needed to avoid the ensuing blast.
P.P.E.: Twenty-Five

The spell caster is able to charge as many as two crystals with magic energy that explodes in three melee rounds (45 seconds) or upon impact when thrown. The creation of each uses up two melee attacks. The crystal for each can be no smaller than a golf ball or plum, and no larger than an apple or orange. The best ones are relatively round, but any shape works, just reduce range by 25% if not round. The crystal is rolled, tossed or thrown at the desired target, exploding on impact. **Note:** Damage is S.D.C. in S.D.C. environments and M.D. in Mega-Damage settings.

Encase Object in Crystal

Range: By touch or up to 10 feet (3 m) away.
Duration: One month per level of the spell caster.
Saving Throw: None.
P.P.E.: Twenty

The mage is able to encase one or a few, small objects such as coins, gems, jewelry, portable data storage devices, pocket computer, small gun, artifact, and similar items in a solid crystal. This is usually done to preserve or protect the item. Only small items can be encased by this method with the maximum size of the item being 7 inches (17.8 mm) in diameter; usually much smaller. The item(s) is encased in a solid crystal sphere or square formed around it; the mage has a limited capacity to change the shape of the casing to either a small sphere, cube or rectangle. The crystal encasement has 10 M.D.C. per level of the spell caster (100 S.D.C. and an A.R. of 15 in S.D.C. environments). The item(s) cannot be seen inside unless the mage deliberately makes the casing semi-transparent. The spell caster may cancel the magic at any time to access the item(s) inside.

Level Seven

Crystal Shards

Range: 400 feet (122 m) plus 50 feet (15 m) per additional level of experience.
Duration: Instant or the mage can hold the spell for up to one melee before having to release the shards.
Damage: Varies with level of experience and the number hurled at an opponent. Four shards inflict 4D6 M.D., six do 6D6 M.D., eight do 1D4x10+3 M.D., ten do 1D6x10 M.D., twelve do 1D6x10+8 M.D., sixteen shards do 2D4x10+8 M.D., eighteen do 2D4x10+16 and twenty inflict 2D6x10. Note: Must be thrown in groups. Mage can make two shards per level of experience. They inflict Hit Point/S.D.C. damage to S.D.C. opponents and M.D. to Mega-Damage opponent.
Bonus: +2 to strike at 400 feet (122 m) or closer.
Saving Throw: -2 to dodge!
P.P.E.: Fifteen

This spell enables the mage to turn crystals or gems as small as the size of a pea or a cherry into small throwing spikes. He can transform two crystals per level of experience and hurl the crystal shards at near rail gun speed. When the spell is cast, the mage's hand (or hands) holding the crystals glows, the gems turn into shards and the mage can throw them all in one big burst at one target like a rail gun volley, or divide them into smaller groups of 4-10 in two or three different attacks. All must be thrown within the *melee round they were created*, and each burst thrown counts as one of the mage's melee attacks.

Crystal Spike Array

Range: Area effect covering a 10 foot (3 m) diameter per level of experience. Can be cast up to 200 feet (61 m) away +10 feet (3 m) per level of experience.
Duration: Three minutes per level of experience. Double on ley lines.
Saving Throw: None other than avoiding the affected area.
P.P.E.: Twenty-Five, or double the P.P.E. to double the duration.

The mage is able to make a stone or crystal spike form out of stone, concrete, sand, dirt, gravel or clay rise up from the surface of the ground, road, wall, mountain cliff, etc. Unlike the Crystal or Stone Spike spell, these spikes are only 4-6 inches tall (10-15 cm) but fill the entire area of effect with a spike roughly every six inches (15 cm) apart. This creates an a zone that may be impassable by ground vehicles and animals and must be gone around. Human-sized bipeds can try to tiptoe through the minefield of spikes, but it is dangerous and very time consuming. Maximum speed is 4. Falling on the bed of spikes inflicts 1D4x10 M.D. (or 1D4x10 S.D.C. in an S.D.C. environment), so it is best to avoid the area and go around. All the tires of wheeled vehicles are shredded in seconds, rendering it immobile and there is a 01-50% chance of crashing (-30% on piloting skill).

Crystal Staff

Range: Self or it can be handed off. The staff can be used a blunt weapon or can fire laser blasts with a range of 500 feet (152 m) +100 feet (30.5 m) per level of the spell caster.
Duration: Five minutes per level of experience, double for the Crystal Mage and Stone Master, and at ley lines. Each laser blast counts as one melee attack.
Damage: 2D6 M.D. +1 M.D. per level of experience as blunt weapon, same damage for each laser blast.
Saving Throw: Parry or dodge.
P.P.E.: Thirty

The mage is able to magically conjure a crystal staff that is 5-8 feet (1.5 to 2.4 m) long out of thin air. It is well balanced (+1 to strike and parry) and has good damage capabilities (above). Arguably, its two greatest benefits are that it can be used to parry lasers and other beam weapons, and *in sunlight or on a ley line* it can fire a 2D6 M.D. laser blast; each blast counts as one melee attack. The staff is not indestructible and has 100 M.D.C. (1,000 S.D.C. and an A.R. 15 in S.D.C. settings), but only suffers damage when it is specifically targeted with the intention of destroying the weapon. **Note:** As with the crystal armor and other crystal weapons, it takes double damage from sonic-based attacks, including Vibro-Weapons. Damage by the Crystal Staff is S.D.C. in S.D.C. environments and M.D. in Mega-Damage settings.

Enter Crystal

Range: Self.
Duration: Ten minutes per level of experience, double on a ley line.
Saving Throw: Not applicable.

P.P.E.: Ten or Twenty

The spell caster is able to physically step inside any human-sized or larger crystal formation at a cost of 8 P.P.E. or a crystal or gem no smaller than a cherry for 20 P.P.E. This is usually done to hide or to spy on others. While inside the crystal, the mage can see and hear everything within a 15 foot (4.6 m) radius, but he can do nothing else, not speak, not cast magic nor recover P.P.E. or Hit Points while inside the crystal.

The face of the spell caster can be seen in a small crystal, his entire body in a man-sized crystal or larger. In a small crystal his visage is almost certain to go unnoticed unless the gem is picked up and carefully examined. In the large crystal, he might go unnoticed or be mistaken as some sort of work of art, provided he remains still; +20% to remain hidden/unseen via Prowl skill if the large crystal is in the dark.

Level Eight

Crystal Solar Battery

Range: 10 feet (3 m); can light up a room.
Duration: A permanent creation! Two hours of energy per level of the spell caster. Double duration on a ley line and automatically recharges in sunlight.
Saving Throw: None.
P.P.E.: Fifty

The Crystal Mage can turn a crystal or gem into a solar battery. The gem must be no smaller than the size of a golf ball and generates energy equal to a small generator capable of providing enough to power a vehicle, devices or a small house. It runs/recharges indefinitely in sunlight. In dark or overcast skies it has enough just to run one hour per level of its maker at the time of its creation. Recharges at a rate of one hour's energy per every two hours of exposure to sunlight or one hour on a ley line. Often used to power homes, non-combat vehicles, weapons and devices.

The Crystal Solar Battery has one M.D.C. and, if handled with reasonable care, functions for 2D6+8 centuries. If manhandled in the field it lasts for 3D6x10 years, before it stops working.

Crystal Wall

Range: 50 feet (15.2 m) distance per level of the caster.
Duration: One minute per level of experience; triple on ley lines.
Saving Throw: None, although a dispel magic barrier will eliminate the wall.
P.P.E.: Thirty-Five

The spell creates a wall of solid crystal that is 10 feet (3 m) long, 10 feet (3 m) high, and 5 feet (1.5 m) thick per level of the caster. The wall also has 100 M.D.C. per level of experience and takes half damage from all light- and electrical-based attacks, however sonic attacks inflict double damage.

Emerald Beam (Anti-Demon)

Range: 100 feet (30.5 m) per level of experience.
Duration: Two beam attack a melee round (15 second). Each counts as one of the spell caster's melee attacks.
Damage: 1D6 M.D. to most mortal opponents, 1D4x10 M.D. to evil supernatural beings, including sub-demons, vampires, the undead, zombies, Chaos Demons, Lesser Demons, and similar

lesser evil supernatural being. 1D6x10 M.D. +1 M.D. per level of experience to Greater Demons, Demon Lords, dark gods, evil Alien Intelligences, and similar powerful, evil supernatural beings.

Saving Throw: Dodge only, a Natural 20 or a modified 24 is required to dodge it!

P.P.E.: Twenty.

An emerald is required to cast the spell upon and to fire the Emerald Beam from. No other green crystal can be substituted. Emeralds represent life, love, hope, growth, and spiritual awareness, thus the gem is used in certain healing magicks and against supernatural evil. The destructive power of the Emerald Beam against supernatural evil is legendary among Atlanteans.

Note: Damage is S.D.C. against S.D.C. opponents and M.D. against Mega-Damage beings. Dragons, the sphinx, faeries and other creatures of magic only suffer 1D6 M.D. like humans, as they are not supernatural.

Negate Crystal Magic

Range: Touch or 60 feet (18.3 m).
Duration: Instant.
Saving Throw: Special. 12, 13, 14, or 15 is needed for spell magic depending on the experience level of the mage the Negate Crystal Magic is trying to cancel. Usually 12 or 13 is needed, 16 or higher is always required to save vs ritual magic. A failed save means the negation attempt did not work. Try again if sufficient P.P.E. is available.
P.P.E.: Forty

This incantation will instantly cancel the effects or influence of most Crystal Magic spells, not artifacts and weapons. To determine whether the negation is successful or not, roll a saving throw. If the roll is a successful save against the magic in place, its influence is immediately destroyed/negated/canceled.

Negate Crystal Magic does NOT work against other types of magic, nor the Crystal Golem, Crystal Vault, Crystal Guardian Armors, or magical crystal artifacts and weapons, Stone Magic, Stone Pyramids, Techno-Wizard devices, Bio-Wizard constructs, Rune weapons, possession, enchanted objects, or magic symbols/circles.

Level 9

Crystal Door

Range: Touch or 10 feet (3 m) per level of the spell caster; line of sight required.
Duration: Five minutes per level of experience; double if on a ley line.
Saving Throw: None, see below.
P.P.E.: Forty. Three Hundred for the ritual version.

The spell caster is able to turn an existing "door" regardless of what it is made of into a Crystal Door that has 100 M.D.C. +10 per level of his experience. A Crystal Door can also be made out of thin air to fill a doorway or a window; maximum size is 8 feet wide x 10 feet tall (2.4 x 2m) or 80 square feet (square 7.4 sq. m), which means one or more spaces equal to a pair of double doors, or two normal doors or multiple windows if small and within line of sight, can be turned into solid crystal. If there is no actual door

or window, the open space immediately fills with crystal that appears out of thin air.

The purpose of the spell is to *seal the door(s) or windows, or equivalent openings,* shut so no one can get in or out as the case may be. Only the spell caster can easily open and close the Crystal door or window. To everyone else, the crystal will not budge one bit. The only way to get through the sealed opening is to destroy the crystal barrier (or use Negate Magic Barrier/Crystal Barrier). These crystal barriers each have 100 M.D.C. +10 per level of his experience.

Crystal Vault

Range: Touch by the spell caster.
Duration: One month per level of experience or one year per level of experience if the ritual version is used. Double if the Crystal Vault is inside a stone pyramid built on a ley line or nexus.
Saving Throw: None, see below.
P.P.E.: Fifty. Three Hundred for the ritual version.

The Crystal Mage is able to enchant a large crystal the size of a lunch box to that of a suitcase to as large as a walk-in safe or closet to become a vault to hold precious items. The large crystal is likely to weigh hundreds of pounds to one or several tons for the largest. The vault distorts the appearance of the contents so gold coins look like streaks of gold and other recognizable objects likes wands, jewelry, and weapons, become unrecognizable blurs and streaks that seem to be part of the stone. The enchanted crystal looks like a decorative geological specimen or piece of crystal art common in Atlantean homes. In fact, most Atlantean homes and businesses have several attractive geodes, minerals, crystals and fossils on display as decorative works, so it is impossible to tell whether such large stones are a natural stone or a Crystal Vault. Even if you could tell, the items inside are impossible to retrieve, because they become a part of the crystal. With the right pass code and the expenditure of 2 P.P.E., the items are irretrievable until the duration ends.

When the Crystal Vault is created, a pass code is encoded into the stone. By whispering the pass code to the crystal and infusing it with 2 P.P.E., the crystal changes to reveal every item inside as if they were frozen in a block of crystal clear ice. The owner of the vault simply reaches into the stone as if it were soft gelatin, and takes what he wants out. Spending another 2 P.P.E. closes the vault, turning it and its contents back into crystal.

The spell version can hold up to 50 pounds (22.5 kg) worth of items per level of the spell caster, and can range in size from a lunch box or briefcase to as large as a steamer trunk. To place an item inside, it must be small enough to fit inside the crystal. The ritual version can hold up to 500 pounds (225 kg) per level of the spell caster and the vault can be the size of a gun safe, walk-in closet or bank safe, provided a large enough crystal stone is available. All items inside the vault are completely enveloped by the crystal and magically become part of the stone, so living creatures cannot be put in the vault and are automatically ejected.

For those who don't know the pass code there is no way to retrieve the items held within the crystal vault. Negate Magic and Negate Crystal magic is ineffective on the vault as is not a magic barrier and even an Anti-Magic Cloud has no effect. It is really a large chunk of crystal with precious items held within. Small vaults have 10 M.D.C. per level of the caster, medium size vaults have 25 M.D.C. per level of the caster and large vaults have 100

M.D.C. per level. However, there is always a risk of damaging the contents. Blasting the crystal has a 60% chance plus 1% per each point beyond the maximum M.D.C. of the crystal of destroying the contents.

Rumors on Phase World suggest that the billionaire Thraxus has a whole room filled with hundreds of decorative crystals. Could there be Crystal Vaults holding magic items and precious gems and other valuables? Could they all be Crystal Vaults?

Entrap Entity in Gem

Range: Sensing range 100 feet (30.5 m). Activated by touch or when an entity comes within five feet (1.5 m) of the gem.
Duration: Seven days per level of experience.
Saving Throw: Varies. Haunting Entities need to roll an 18 or higher, Poltergeists 17, Tectonic 16, Syphons 15, or Possessing Entity 14.
P.P.E.: Seventy. Or Two Hundred Ninety P.P.E. to last one year per level of experience.

Entities are attracted to emotions, magic energy and gems, particularly Syphons and Possessing Entities. This spell enables the spell caster to place 70 P.P.E. into a gemstone (ruby, sapphire, emerald, diamond, etc.) that radiates of magic to attract Entities. When one comes within five feet of the gem, a magical beam of sunlight ensnares the Entity and pulls it in. One gemstone the size of an almond can hold four Haunting Entities, or three Poltergeists, or two Syphons, or one Tectonic or Possessing Entity. Once one particular type of Entity is trapped inside a gem, others of that type are attracted to it until the gem is full. The purpose of the magic is to capture and remove dangerous or troublesome Entities away from ley line nexus points, stone pyramids, and areas and homes inhabited by Atlanteans/mortals, and take them someplace away from population centers where they cannot cause too much trouble when released.

If the Entity fails to save vs magic, the creature is trapped inside the gem and is put into a stasis sleep. For it, each passing day seems like an hour and a year is but a day. Even Syphon Entities are trapped and rendered harmless by this magic. However, when the spell duration ends, all Entities awaken and happily flee the confines of the gem. Most moving away as fast as they can from the gem. Haunting Entities and Poltergeist probably do not stray far, and find a new place to haunt and pester mortals. Others take flight and don't stop for several miles. Only a Syphon may choose to remain inside the gem, making the gem its new home and hiding place from which to torment humans.

If the Entity makes a successfully save vs magic, it remains free, knows someone just tried to capture it, which may make it angry, and half the P.P.E. in the gem is used up in the process (all but 10 P.P.E. is used up if the trap is successful). It will need to be charged back up to full to be used as an Entity trap again.

Captured Entities may be released by the mage who caught the Entities at any time. However, the magic practitioner has no control of them and the evil beings may turn on the mage who successfully captured them, to exact vengeance or attack out of anger or spite. The more intelligent types may willingly agree to work with a mage, especially an evil one, or if such service will help the diabolical being in its own schemes or to inflict pain and suffering.

Level 10

Create Crystal Guardian Armor

Exclusively for Tattooed Defenders

Range: The suit must be made before it can be magically empowered. Once made, its full capabilities can only be activated by a Tattooed Defender.
Duration: Permanent and self-regenerates. Needs Guardian Power Tattoo to activate.
Saving Throw: None.
P.P.E.: One Hundred Twenty. Reduce cost by 30% when made inside a stone pyramid located at a ley line nexus.

The Crystal Mage creates a full suit of armor, complete with sealed helmet (clear glass visor), made entirely of crystals. He may be assisted in its creation by artisans, other Crystal Mages or Atlantean Alchemists. When the suit is finished and all other magicks are in place, he casts this spell to enchant the armor, making it an environmental body armor.

The basic armor has 125 M.D.C. (250 S.D.C. and Natural A.R. 15 in S.D.C. environments), weighs 60 pounds (27 kg; poor mobility, -30% to Prowl, Swimming, etc.), and has magical environmental features like Breathe Without Air, Impervious to Cold, Impervious to Fire, and lasers and light-based attacks do half damage, all of which are in effect for the wearer at all times. The suit can be restored at ley lines and stone pyramids at a rate of 10 M.D.C. per hour. All in all, a decent, heavy armor. This Guardian Armor, with its powers not fully realized, can be worn by a Crystal Mage or others in a pinch, but it does not have any of the bonuses described below.

When worn by a Tattooed Defender who as activated his Guardian Power Tattoo, however, the armor automatically integrates with the tattoo and its wearer to become something greater!

The Crystal Guardian Armor turns into a completely translucent, smooth suit of hard armor. It is practically a second skin for the Tattooed Defender and gives him the appearance of wearing glass armor. But this is no glass suit. M.D.C. regenerative capabilities and other features are ramped up to new levels.

M.D.C.: 225 (450 S.D.C. and Natural A.R. of 15 in S.D.C. environments), and the suit regenerates 1D6 M.D.C. per melee round, 2D6 M.D.C. per melee round at ley lines and stone pyramids. Should the armor be destroyed, it absorbs all the extra damage and disappears in a flash of light. No damage is carried over to the wearer.

Lightweight: 10 pounds (4.5 kg); excellent mobility, no movement penalties!

Magical Environmental Features: Breathe Without Air, Impervious to Cold, Impervious to Fire, and electricity, lasers and light-based attacks do *half damage,* all of which are in effect for the wearer at all times. And remember, the warrior can still access his tattoos and possesses other weapons and gear.

Note: *The Crystal Deflector Gauntlet* and sometimes the *Crystal Combat Gauntlet* (one, not both) can be worn and used as part of this armor. In the Three Galaxies, a Tattooed Defender wearing Crystal Guardian Armor could be confused for a Cosmo Knight.

WARNING: Wearing Crystal Guardian Armor can slowly kill its Tattooed Defender.

Life Essence Fuel (special): For this combination of magic to work, the Tattooed Defender must serve as a conduit between them. He activates his Guardian tattoo to activate and transform the Guardian Crystal Armor into a powerful second skin. But the crystal armor is powered by more than that spell, tattoo and the power crystals built into the suit. It is partially powered by the life essence of the Tattooed Defender. ONE M.D.C. (or Hit Point in S.D.C. settings) per 60 minutes is drained from the Tattooed Defender. When his personal M.D.C. is reduced to zero, the warrior lapses into a coma and may die. Tattooed Defenders are trained to keep track of their physical condition and to exit long before that happens (usually when down to half or one third their M.D.C.). But in a combat situation, that can be easier said than done, and some warriors may decide to sacrifice themselves to protect the innocent.

No regeneration of M.D.C. or P.P.E. for the wearer while clad in Guardian Armor. While inside the activated Crystal Guardian armor, the wearer cannot recover M.D.C. he has lost nor P.P.E. he may have spent on Tattoo Weapons or other magic tattoos. Nor can he channel ley line P.P.E. while inside Guardian armor. That's because it consumes the ambient P.P.E. all around it to maintain its power and to be constantly repairing damage. The wearer needs to exit the Crystal Guardian to meditate and heal or recover P.P.E. for himself. The Golem-like construct deactivates the moment the Defender leaves its body. There is no cost to re-enter and reactivate the construct if there was still duration time left. Duration stops ticking when he removes the Guardian armor, and it starts again when he puts it back on. HOWEVER, that energy/duration can only be placed on pause for 120 minutes. After that, it all drains away. To reactivate, the Defender must activate his Super-Guardian Power Tattoo (25 P.P.E.).

Vulnerabilities: Sonic based-attacks inflict double damage, including Vibro-Blades. Magic Crystal Weapons, whether artifacts or created via spell magic, inflict full damage.

Level 11

Create Crystal Super-Guardian

Exclusively for Tattooed Defenders (Pseudo-Golem).
Range: Touch, the construct must be made before it can be activated and empowered.
Duration: Permanent and self-regenerates. Needs Super-Guardian Power Tattoo to activate.
Saving Throw: None.
P.P.E.: Four Hundred and often performed as a ritual or with the assistance of other Crystal Mages, Chiang-Ku or Atlantean Alchemists. Reduce cost by 30% when made inside a stone pyramid located at a ley line nexus.

In some ways, the Super-Guardian defies precedent and description. It is created in a very similar way to a *Crystal Golem* right down to making a solid crystal humanoid form 11-14 feet (3.3 to 4.3 m) tall. But this "Golem-like" construct does not have intelligence or the ability to move or fight on its own. It needs a pilot. Like a giant combat robot, the thing is as lifeless as a statue until the Tattooed Defender activates his or her Super-Guardian Power Tattoo.

When the tattoo is activated, the Golem-like crystal construct glows as if lit by a light source from inside its body. The Tattooed Defender literally leaps up and into the Crystal Super-Guardian as if he were a ghost and ends up inside the torso. Flesh and blood Atlantean and crystal robot merged to become one! The Crystal Super-Guardian responding as if it were the Defender's own body. The Defender may be in inside there somewhere, but for all intents and purposes, he is temporarily one with the crystal body. It is now him, and he is now it. The crystal robot moves with the quickness of his own flesh and blood body (faster, really), and possesses all of his Atlantean attributes, Supernatural P.S., abilities, skills and bonuses. The Defender's own M.D.C. and P.P.E. remain his own, though his personal M.D.C. is slowly drained away and any P.P.E. spent on other tattoos (he can still activate them) cannot be recovered until he exits the crystalline construct.

All Crystal Super-Guardians look similar, but their exact appearance varies from one another because each is handmade by a Crystal Mage and his helpers – artisans and Atlantean Alchemists. For the average person, the Super-Guardian probably reminds them of a giant humanoid creature or Elemental made of ice. It does not become smooth and glassy like the Guardian Armor, instead, the Super-Guardian retains its crystalline appearance. It is typically clear, white or semi-transparent crystal with hints of pink, topaz or yellow. Crystalline spikes and protrusions cluster at the shoulders and upper arms, as well as on the head and forearms.

The Crystal Super-Guardian cannot be magically inhabited and controlled without a Super-Guardian Tattoo, just as the Crystal Guardian requires a specific Guardian tattoo. Both reserved for the Tattooed Defender.

A Defender is assigned one or the other for any given mission. Their respective magical crystal constructs waiting in a hangar until they are called to duty. For Defenders of Atlantean cities and outposts, these warriors function as law enforcement and peacekeepers. They do not don their Guardian or Super-Guardian armors until, like jet fighter pilots, they get the call to scramble and face an incoming threat that requires power and armor. That's when they jump into their combat power armor (Guardian) or Golem-like robot body (Super-Guardian) to face whatever threat has arrived. Guardian armor and Super-Guardians can function in many roles from front-line troops or troop support, to riot control and rescue operations, to missions off world.

WARNING: Piloting a Crystal Super-Guardian can kill its Tattooed Defender Pilot.

Life Essence Fuel (special): For this combination of magic to work, the Tattooed Defender must serve as a conduit between them. He activates his Super-Guardian tattoo to enter the Super-Guardian Pseudo-Golem and take control of its artificial body, but the crystal construct is powered by more than just the spell that created it, the power tattoo that activates its magic, and the power crystals built into it. The crystalline behemoth is partially powered by the life essence of its pilot. *Two M.D.C./Hit Points per 30 minutes* are drained from the Tattooed Defender. When his personal M.D.C. is reduced to zero, the warrior lapses into a coma and may die. These warriors are trained to keep track of their physical condition and to exit long before that happens (usually when down to half or one third their M.D.C.). But in a combat situation, that can be easier said than done, and some warriors may decide to sacrifice themselves to protect the innocent.

No regeneration of M.D.C. or P.P.E. for the pilot. Another condition of merging with this magical construct is that, while inside the Crystal Super-Guardian, the Defender cannot recover M.D.C. he has lost nor P.P.E. he may have spent on Tattoo Weapons or other magic tattoos. Nor can he channel ley line P.P.E. while inside the Crystal Super-Guardian, because it consumes the ambient P.P.E. all around it. He has to exit the Super-Guardian to meditate and heal or recover P.P.E. The Golem-like construct deactivates the moment the Defender leaves its body. There is no cost to reenter and reactivate the construct if there is still time left on duration. Duration stops ticking when he exits the Super-Guardian, and starts again when he comes back. HOWEVER, that energy/duration can only be paused for 90 minutes, after which it all drains away and to reenter, the Defender must activate his Super-Guardian Power Tattoo (40 P.P.E.).

Crystal Super-Guardian Stats

Height: 1D4+10 feet (3.3 to 4.3 m).
Weight: 1D4+8 tons.
Horror Factor: 15
M.D.C. by Location:
    Arms (2) – 160 each
    Hands (2) – 80 each
    Legs (2) – 230 each
    Feet (2) – 100 each
    Head – 150
    * Main Body – 600

* Depleting the M.D.C. of the Main Body to zero or below shuts down the magical Super-Guardian, forcing the Tattooed Defender to exit the construct. However, the pilot usually exit the body before that point, because as long as the Crystal Super-Guardian has ONE M.D.C. point, it will regenerate. Regeneration is automatic in sunlight (even overcast skies) and on ley lines and at stone pyramids. No regeneration in the dark. (**Note:** In S.D.C. environments, the S.D.C. equivalent is double the M.D.C. listed above, so Main Body is 1,200 S.D.C., head 300 S.D.C., etc., and it has a Natural A.R. of 15.)

Crystal Super-Guardian Regeneration (special): The magical automaton automatically regenerates *1D6 M.D.C. per melee round* (15 seconds) in sunlight, and *10 M.D.C. per melee round* on ley lines or at stone pyramids. No regeneration in darkness unless on a ley line or at a stone pyramid. Moreover, the Tattooed Defender can effect an immediate M.D.C. repair by feeding the Super-Guardian by willing a portion of his own life essence into it, something that drives and empowers the magical construct the entire time. Every M.D.C. point of the Tattooed Warrior regenerates four M.D.C. of the Super-Guardian. (In S.D.C. environments, 4 Hit Points gives the Super-Guardian eight S.D.C., or one S.D.C. regenerates two S.D.C. points for the armor.) **Note:** Also see *Life Essence Fuel,* above.

In sunlight, a completely destroyed limb of the Super-Guardian regenerates within one hour and the main body regenerates in 1D4 hours. On a ley line or stone pyramid, destroyed limbs are restored in 30 minutes and the main body within one hour. The Main Body M.D.C. is always restored first unless the Atlantean pilot deliberately directs regeneration to some other location on the body. If a complete regeneration from a scrap body part is required, it takes 24 hours.

The Crystal Super-Guardian is able to function at full capacity until the Main Body is reduced to 40 M.D.C. or less, at which point it functions in a diminished capacity with no bonuses and no lasers. **Note:** The only way to permanently destroy a Crystal Super-Guardian is to reduce the Main Body and all of its remaining body parts to zero (see M.D.C. by Location). When utterly destroyed, there is no way for it to regenerate, but leave a hand or foot intact, and the armored construct will completely regrow in a short matter of time. Leaving its remnants in darkness prevents regeneration until taken out into the light or onto a ley line.

Combat Capabilities (enhanced): Identical to the Tattooed Defender merged with the Crystal Super-Guardian, plus the following and bonuses.
Attacks per Melee: +2 in addition to those of the Defender.
Attribute Boost: +6 to Supernatural P.S. +4 to P.P., +24 to Spd, all in addition to the attributes of the Tattooed Defender. Man and magical construct become one, though the M.D.C. of the Defender remains his own except as drained from him to operate the Crystal Super-Guardian.
Bonuses (in addition to the Defender's own): +1 to strike, +2 to pull punch, +1 to roll with impact, +1 to save vs mind control and psionic attacks.
Damage (Melee Combat): As per Supernatural P.S. with the P.S. bonus above, inflicts M.D. with punches and kicks. (S.D.C. damage in S.D.C. environments.)

Weapons:
Laser: Lasers can be fired from the eyes: 3D6 M.D. per blast. Range: 150 feet (46 m) per level of the Tattooed Defender inside. Each blast counts as one melee attack.
Magic Tattoos: The Tattooed Warrior inside the Crystal Super-Guardian can still access all his magic tattoos. Weapon and Magic Weapon Tattoos created while merged with the Super-Guardian are proportional to the Super-Guardian's large size and do an extra 1D6 M.D. as a result of it.

Magical Environmental Features: Breathe Without Air, Impervious to Cold, and Impervious to Fire. Electricity, lasers and light-based attacks do half damage. All protections are always in effect.

● The Super-Guardian is resistant to physical attacks and takes *half damage* from Mega-Damage punches, M.D. melee weapons, rail guns, M.D. explosions, etc. Normal, S.D.C. weapons do no damage. (In an S.D.C. setting, the Super-Guardian has a Natural A.R. 15.)

● The Crystal Super-Guardian is resistant to energy attacks like electricity, lightning, ion, plasma and particle beams, as well as Rune Weapons, TW weapons and other magic weapons, all of which inflict *half damage*.

● Impervious to normal cold and fire, but magic and M.D. fire and cold do *half damage*.

Penalties and Limitations: Additional armor or magical armor cannot be placed on this giant Golem-like automaton. It is -40% to Prowl, Climb, Swim or perform most other Physical skills due to its size and crystal body. Glints and reflects sunlight.

Vulnerabilities: Sonic-based attacks inflict double damage, including Vibro-Blades. Magic Crystal Weapons, whether artifacts or created via spell magic, inflict full damage.

Level 12

Create Crystal Golem (Ritual)

Range: Touch.
Duration: Exists until destroyed.
Saving Throw: None.
P.P.E.: Seven Hundred; ritual magic.

A Golem is a sort of soulless automaton or robot created from clay and magic, and animated to do the bidding of his creator. The most well known are stone and iron Golems. The Crystal Golem is variation of the same magic and idea.

The mage draws a pentagram made of ground crystal made from semi-precious stone. Second, a human-sized Golem is sculpted in clay and covered in crystals stuck into the clay. The crystals and gems must be worth at least 2,000 credits. A heart made from iron ore crystals is placed inside the chest, two red or violet rubies or sapphires are placed as eyes, and two small hollows are dug into the chest of the clay human form where a heart would be in a human. During the ritual, these hollows are filled with the mage's own blood. In addition to the 700 P.P.E. required to bring the creation to life, the spell caster permanently loses six S.D.C. points (or three Hit Points) _and_ 1D4 P.P.E. points. At the conclusion of the ritual, the clay figure becomes giant and rises as a Crystal Golem.

The Crystal Golem is made of solid crystal and is a Mega-Damage construct that is impervious to many magic spells, psionic attacks, and the weapons of mortals. It is faster than the Stone and Iron Golems, and has a few additional immunities and vulnerabilities.

Crystal Golem

- Horror Factor: 16
- I.Q. 6, Supernatural P.S. 22, Speed 24, Height: 10-14 feet (3 to 4.3 m). Weight: 1D4+8 tons.
- Five attacks per melee round. Damage is per Supernatural P.S.: 2D6 M.D. punch or kick, 4D6 M.D. from a power punch or full speed ram attack. (Double S.D.C. damage in S.D.C. environments.)
- Fires laser beams from its eyes (2D6 M.D. per blast). Range: 30 feet (9.1 m) per level of the spell caster who created it. Each blast counts as one melee attack.
- The Crystal Golem is surprisingly fast and agile and is +2 to strike, parry, and dodge.
- Resistant to physical attacks and takes _half damage_ from Mega-Damage punches, M.D. melee weapons, rail guns, M.D. explosions, etc.
- Magic that inflicts physical damage such as electricity, lightning, and energy attacks, as well as Rune weapons, TW and other magic weapons, inflict _half damage._
- Impervious to lasers and light-based magic.
- Impervious to normal cold and fire (magic fire and cold does only 20% their usual damage).
- Impervious to psionics and magic spells that affect the mind or the nervous system (doesn't have either); impervious to any forms of mind control and mental or emotional attacks. Others spells like turn dead and banishment are also useless.
- Impervious to possession and Horror Factor.
- Does not breathe air or need nourishment, thus impervious to gas attacks, poison, disease and can survive underwater at any depth.
- M.D.C.: 50 per level of the spell caster. (Double as S.D.C. in S.D.C. environments and has a Natural A.R. of 16.) Regenerates 2D6 M.D. (or 4D6 S.D.C.) per melee round in sunlight; 1D6 M.D. (or 2D6 S.D.C.) in darkness.
- **Nearly Indestructible.** Destroyed limbs regenerate in one hour and the entire Golem _regenerates completely_ in 24 hours when seemingly blown to bits and completely destroyed. **Note:** The only way to permanently destroy any Golem is to remove its iron heart from the chest cavity while it is still largely intact.
- **Vulnerabilities:** Sonic based attacks, including Vibro-Blades, inflict double damage. Magic Crystal Weapons, whether artifacts or created via spell magic, inflict full damage.

Level 13

Crystal Arch (Ritual)

Range: Theoretically unlimited. The mage or the mage and two others can be teleported at the same time.
Duration: Instant, when activated.
Saving Throw: None.
P.P.E.: Eight Hundred P.P.E. to construct and enchant each Crystal Arch on the same world. Two Thousand to make an inter-dimensional Crystal Arch with access to another planet or dimension. HALF the P.P.E. cost when built on a ley line or nexus point. An Arch needs to be created and enchanted/activated at each desired location, world or dimension to travel there via this magic. **Note:** Once the arches are in place, it costs only 50 P.P.E. to Teleport to an arch at another location on the same world, and 200 P.P.E. to Dimensional Teleport to an arch on another world. And that is the benefit of the Crystal Arch. Flawless teleportation, inexpensive P.P.E. cost (after it is built), and no opening up of a Rift.

The Crystal Arch is a teleportation device that can whisk the mage thousands of miles away on the same world, or to another planet or dimension. There is a catch, there must be a corresponding arch at the intended destination, otherwise the spell does not work (no P.P.E. is expended, nothing happens). So while a mage may have a single crystal arch within his residence or hideout, he needs to construct one or more of them at whatever additional locations he would like to teleport to. Another secret lair, a location in the mountains, a place on the beach, or among some standing stones on another planet, etc. A reciprocal arch must be somewhere on the world or dimension the mage desires to visit.

When there are two or more Crystal Arches, all the spell caster has to do is pump 50 P.P.E. into a Teleportation arch to travel to another arch elsewhere on the same planet, or 200 to travel to another Crystal Arch on a different world or dimension. Speaking the destination out loud and thinking about the location as you step under the arch has you appearing at the other arch. It is as simple as that. Each Crystal Arch can connect to any of the other Crystal Arches the mage may have created. It simply costs more to perform a dimensional teleport than it does to teleport to someplace else on the same world.

Of course, the crystal arches take time and cost money to construct, plus the mage has to travel to the destination desired in order to construct a receiving arch. The ritual is rather simple and only takes 2D6x10+15 minutes to complete. It is the building of the Arch, at least the size of a conventional doorway, that takes time and costs money. Each arch (any design) must be made of slabs of stone or crystal, or even concrete, with a crystal or gem imbedded in each. Transporting and setting up the slabs of stone or crystal, like Stonehenge, to create the arch costs money and requires manpower (or magic) all by itself. Plus it must be located on a ley line that is, itself, connected to a nexus point. That alone could take several weeks and cost money to arrange. (1D4+1) months. Once completed, the arch has 200 M.D.C. +30 M.D.C. per level of the spell caster; double the M.D.C. if built on a ley line, nexus point or inside a Stone Pyramid.

Level 14

Crystal Cocoon Prison (Ritual)

Range: Self or 10 feet (3 m); line of sight required.
Duration: 10 years per level of the spell caster, double if created and left (buried, perhaps?) on the same lay line.
Saving Throw: Standard.
P.P.E.: Nine Hundred

This powerful ritual must be conducted within a cave and it must be large enough to enclose the ritual area, as in there has to be a roof. Next, two dozen crystals are placed around the subject to be cocooned. A charcoal line is drawn connecting all the crystals as if they were dots to be connected. At the conclusion of the ritual, a diamond worth no less than 1,000 credits must be placed on the forehead or breast over the heart of the subject.

This spell is commonly used to place a prisoner or monster into stasis slumber and holding him captive for years, without actually killing him/it. The Crystal Cocoon can also be used to survive a disaster until rescue is possible or until a cure can be found for a terminal illness or injury. Other uses include transporting and preserving one a live specimen, especially if dangerous, a valuable artifact, or as a sort of time capsule. The spell caster must dictate during the ritual how long the victim is to remain in suspended animation. At the end of the duration, the crystal cracks open to release whoever or whatever is inside.

The creator of the cocoon can open it at any time and he can program a date in which the cocoon should open without him. Otherwise it can be opened by force. However, cutting into the cocoon or using explosives could kill the life form inside. Extreme care is required.

The Crystal Cocoon Prison has 1,000 M.D.C. regardless of its size. (In S.D.C. settings, it has 10,000 S.D.C. and a Natural A.R. of 15.)

Level 15

Crystal Tower (Ritual)

Range: The spell caster must stand within a magic circle comprised of crystals until the conclusion of the ritual.
Duration: Two years per level of the spell caster, double if built on a ley line.
Saving Throw: None.
P.P.E.: Two Thousand to create. 10,000 P.P.E. to extend the duration to 20 years per level of the spell caster (double if built on a ley line).

The mage is able to conjure forth a tower made of a bluish crystal that has green energy crackling about the tower. The tower has 500 M.D.C. (750 S.D.C. with an armor rating or 18 in S.D.C. environments) per level of the spell caster, and is a sturdy and solid structure.

There is one critical condition when casting the spell, it must be cast over earth/ground, preferably with a rocky terrain. Once cast, the tower magically rises up from the ground and is ready to be occupied.

The preparations for the ritual is a daunting task. First, an exact replica of the tower must be carved out of topaz or other light colored crystal in exact detail (remember, Crystal Mages can grow, shape and carve crystal). This alone can take several weeks or longer unless a professional artist can be found to carve the tower for the mage. Windows, doorways, stairs, fireplaces, rafters, and individual rooms with their walls in place must be made inside the replica.

Next a circle must be drawn defining the width of the tower. The circle must have a gemstone spaced out evenly at four points along the circle.

Once all the preparations are finished, the tower replica is placed in the exact middle of the circle and the ritual begins. It last for 2D4+2 hours. At the conclusion of the ritual, the earth swallows up the replica and moments later the tower begins to rise out of the ground. The tiny replica dictates the exact size, number of floors and interior details. The actual doors, windows and furnishings need to be installed after the completion of the tower.

When the spell duration ends, large cracks begin to form and the inhabitants have 3D4 hours to vacate before it all comes crashing down. All debris from the tower melts like candy in the sun and is absorbed back into the earth. All of the other original components are burned up during the creation of the circle. Contents left inside the tower are destroyed and also swallowed up by the earth.

Spell of Legend

Crystal Palace (Ritual)

Range: The spell caster must stand within a magic circle comprised of crystals until the conclusion of the ritual.
Duration: One year per level of the spell caster, double if built on a ley line.
Saving Throw: None.
P.P.E.: Eight Thousand to create. 24,000 P.P.E. to extend the duration to 10 years per level of the spell caster (double if built on a ley line). Crystal Towers, as per the previous spell, can be added to it over time.

This rare Spell of Legend functions the same way as the Crystal Tower, only a one piece palace or castle keep is sculpted in miniature, complete with stairs, windows, kitchen, dining hall, throne room, ballroom, dungeon, bed chambers, guest rooms, bathrooms, etc. When the ritual is completed, the earth swallows up the replica and moments later the palace begins to form, rising out of the ground. The palace, as small and simple or as large and elaborate as desired. Defensive walls around the palace with a moat and drawbridge, etc. can be added later via conventional construction. Doors, tapestries, furnishings, and similar must be added or built later, but the core structure of the palace is all there. The more detailed the miniature, the more ready it is to move in and finish. When in sunlight the palace sparkles like a new diamond, sunlight bouncing off the many faceted angles. Like something out of fairy tale.

The ritual is far more grueling than the Crystal Tower. First, an exact replica of the palace must be carved in crystal. Next five gemstones worth more than 500,000 credits each must be used within the magic circle, the circle itself must be drawn with one thousand precious and semi-precious stones worth no less than 200 credits each. Twelve hours of chanting must be done from midnight till noon of the following day. Any interruption during the ritual means that all components are ruined and the spell fails. Regardless of the size of the palace, it has 1,000 M.D.C. per level of the spell caster. The exact size is in direct proportion to the replica. Towers may be added via the Crystal Tower spell.

When the spell duration ends, large cracks begin to form and the inhabitants have 4D6 hours to vacate before it all comes crashing down. All debris from the tower melts like candy left in the sun and is absorbed back into the earth. Most of the gems and semiprecious stones used in circle are burned up during the creation of the circle, but the five main gems are buried someplace in the earth below. Contents left inside the palace are destroyed and swallowed up by the earth when it collapses.

Atlantean Crystal Artifacts

Water Crystal

A Water Crystal is a small, handheld gem about the size of a golf ball. It is clear or light blue in color and seems to have water sloshing around inside of the gem. When the Atlantean concentrates and spends **one P.P.E.** point, the liquid forms an arrow and points to the closest natural source of fresh water. The arrow continues to point toward a body water for two hours for every P.P.E. point spent. **For 8 P.P.E.** the crystal can magically produce a gallon of drinking water. It pours out of the crystal like a faucet. For **2 P.P.E.** it points to a body of salt water/sea or ocean. The water crystal has 4 M.D.C. (400 S.D.C.) and can be damaged via non-M.D.C. weapons.
Cost: 10,000 credits.

Campfire Crystal

A Campfire Crystal is about the size of an apple and is shaped like a pyramid. Inside the crystal appears to be flickering fire. The crystal is always mildly warm to the touch, but never hot and never burns. When **four P.P.E.** is channeled into the Campfire Crystal it glows with the light and warmth of a campfire, lighting and heating a 20 foot (6.1 m) area. The advantages include no risk of starting fire to dry underbrush, carpeting, etc., or anyone getting accidentally burned, easy portability, and instant light and heat.

The light and warmth lasts for two hours for every four P.P.E. spent, indefinitely when on a ley line or until turned off. The crystal can be held and carried while activated without the person carrying it or any object touching it being burned, so it can func-

tion as a torch or portable heater. The brightness of the pyramid crystal can be dimmed to the equivalent of a 40 watt lightbulb up to 100 watts, and flickers like a campfire. The light is not sunlight and will not keep vampires or Shadow creatures at bay. One P.P.E. turns it off/cancels the effect before the duration ends. The Fire Crystal has 8 M.D.C. (800 S.D.C.) and can be damaged via non-M.D.C. weapons.
Cost: 8,000 credits.

Sheltering Crystal

This is a small, brown or orange crystal pyramid. When activated creates a *Sheltering Force* as per the spell. The Sheltering Crystal is activated with **20 P.P.E.** and lasts for 6 hours. If on a ley line the Sheltering Crystal lasts indefinitely! The crystal has 6 M.D.C. (600 S.D.C.) and can be destroyed via non-M.D.C. weapons.
Cost: 45,000 credits.

Crystal Climber

The Crystal Climber is a unique but effective climbing tool. It is a simple, spiked metal rod or stake with five small crystals: two mounted at the bottom above the pointed end, two at the top and one in the middle. The rod is the width of a staff but a quarter its length. Etched in a spiral going up the staff are two, intertwined ivy vines snaking around the whole rod. To use the Crystal Climber, the Atlantean channels **10 P.P.E.** into one of the two crystals at the pointed end of the metal stake by touching them. Then he pounds the rod into the ground, stone, base of a concrete wall, etc. A moment later, two strands of ivy, strong as rope, grow out of the rod, and snake their way up straight up the side of a ravine, a mountain cliff, wall, side of a building, tower, tree, etc.; the vines weaving between each other to create plenty of hand and footholds. The latticework of vines climbs the surface at a rate of 10 feet (3 m) per melee round (15 seconds) and can go as high as 1,000 feet (305 m), or roughly 100 stories. Another rod pounded into the surface where the first latticework of vines stops, go up from there to enable mountain climbers to scale greater heights.

Each one foot length of vine has a damage capacity of two M.D.C. (200 S.D.C.), so the structure is very strong and remains in place for 14 days or until the magic is broke. Climate has no impact on the magic vines, so they work fine in deserts and arctic conditions. To cancel the magic, the two vines at the base of the rod are severed and the rod is pulled out of the ground. Even then, the vines remain for 14 hours before withering and crumbling to dust. To end the enchantment in seconds, the rod needs to be pulled from the ground and 10 P.P.E. placed into one of the top crystals by touch, to cancel the magic, the vines crumbling to dust in four melee rounds (60 seconds).
Cost: 15,000 credits.

Crystal of Civility

Atlanteans consider themselves civilized and sophisticated people. The pyramid-shaped, pink Crystal of Civility helps bring a measure of calm and civility to every situation. A 12 foot (3.6 m) radius of effect, everyone in the radius remains cool-headed and fairly reasonable. Situations can still get heated and people can become angry and even fight, but it takes longer before tempers flare, and hopefully before then, a more amicable accord can be reached. Those with strong opposing views actually hear the other point of view. They may not agree with it, but they hear it and leave before throwing angry words, punches or gunfire. If everyone is feeling warm and friendly, deals and bartering will be fair for all parties involved; not a steep discount, but fair and reasonable. People having a rousing good time feel alert, positive and open to new ideas. This air of civility costs **20 P.P.E.** per 30 minutes. The Crystal of Civility has 6 M.D.C. (600 S.D.C.) and can be damaged via non-M.D.C. weapons.

Cost: 30,000 credits.

Crystal Healing Wand

The Healing Wand is made of emerald or other green crystal. The Crystal Healing Wand is seldom longer than six inches to one foot (0.15 to 0.3 m) and can be a life saver. Thus, it is highly sought after, not just by Atlantean healers, but by all healers, Nomads, Tattooed Voyagers, and adventurers. The crystal wand is as thick as the narrow end of a pool stick and is crafted from a single piece of emerald or green crystalline stone. At the one end is a sculpted rose, the symbol for healing among Atlanteans.

15 P.P.E. to heal wounds. When 15 P.P.E. is pumped into the wand and it is waved over a wound it magically closes and heals the wound and restores 5D6 Hit Points (or 3D6 M.D.C. if a Mega-Damage being). This can be repeated a often as needed at the cost of 15 P.P.E. each time, for as long as P.P.E. is available to power the magic. When Hit Points are fully restored (or two-thirds of M.D.C.), the Healing Wand can be used to restore S.D.C./bruising, stiffness and discomfort at a rate of 2D6 S.D.C. (or 1D6 M.D.C.) per every additional 15 P.P.E. spent. The cost is higher even thought the healing is less, because the individual is no longer seriously injured and should be able to heal nicely without magical intervention. That's how this magic device works.

30 P.P.E. to heal broken bones, burns or other serious internal injury, or to snap an individual out of a coma (90% success), the wand is placed over the injury or the patient's heart and the injury is repaired at the amount listed above.

10 P.P.E. to Cure Minor Disorders, same as the spell of the same name.

20 P.P.E. to Cure Illness, same as the spell. This includes curing fever, the flu, sore throat, the common cold, rashes, and similar. It cannot cure chronic illnesses like cancer, heart disease, blood disease, diabetes, mental illness, etc., only illnesses caused by bacteria or viral infection.

20 P.P.E. can also be spent to purify up to 10 gallons (38 liters) of water to make it safe to drink or 50 pounds (22.5 kg) of food, cleansing it of harmful bacteria, disease, poison or toxin by placing the wand in the container with the water or tapping the wand on the food.

Cost: 275,000 credits.

Crystal Rod of Light

The Crystal Rod of Light (and Hope) is half as thick as a staff, and more resembles a cane. In fact, it is as long as a cane and many use it as such. Many are covered in beautiful etchings of vines and flowers or the sun and other designs that represent life, hope and goodness, while others are quite plain. The rod may have a metal or wood handle like that of a cane, attached or not.

When **20 P.P.E.** is pumped into the Crystal Rod of Light, it pulses and releases a bolt of magic energy that reproduces the powerful invocation **Lifeblast.** This can be used on a person to restore hope and optimism (and instill him with bonuses) or as a weapon to be used against animated dead, zombies, Banshees and Grave Ghouls, vampires/undead and Necromancers. Same as the spell described in the **Rifts® Book of Magic,** page 108.

Cost: 375,000 credits.

Communications Crystal

These crystals are small, handheld smoky quartz crystals the size of a golf ball but in the shape of a cube. Atlantean symbols are carved into each face of the cube, but the top and bottom have a pyramid etched into them with a tiny crystal in the center. These crystals allow two-way communications like a cell phone, but with a 3D holographic display. Range is limited to 20 miles (32 km). When on a ley line, the range is doubled, triple at a nexus point or stone pyramid. One P.P.E. provides up to 10 minutes of use. The Communication Crystal has 5 M.D.C. (500 S.D.C.) and can be damaged by non-M.D.C. weapons.

Cost: 40,000 credits.

Crystal Eye

This crystal tool looks like a short rod or gun scope made of blue or clear crystal. It is 6 inches (0.15 m) long and two inches in diameter. An eye of Mystic Knowledge is carved along the side of the crystal and glows when **5 P.P.E.** is pumped into it. Atlanteans use it like a telescope with a few options.

1. Can be used anytime and it acts like a normal spyglass and magnifies up to 20 times. No P.P.E. necessary.

2. **Five P.P.E.** enables the Crystal Eye to see the invisible with it. Duration: Five minutes.

3. Spending **one P.P.E.** per minute, the Crystal Eye can record whatever the person is seeing through the crystal and is able to zoom in using the telescopic feature via mental or spoken command. By spending the same amount of P.P.E., it will play back the image (no sound) on the eyepiece of the scope. An additional 5 P.P.E. projects the recording onto a wall or screen. The images can also be relayed with the same range and limitations as the Communications Crystal, but cost 5 P.P.E. per minute to transmit. A maximum of six hours can be recorded.

The Crystal Eye has 5 M.D.C. (500 S.D.C.) and can be damaged by non-M.D.C. weapons.

Cost: 90,000 credits.

Magic Crystal Weapons

Crystal weapons are old Atlantean constructs from a bygone era. Many consider them to be antiques and archaic. Most Atlantean Tattooed Warriors prefer to rely upon their magic tattoo weapons these days. That said, many Magic Crystal Weapons are passed down from one generation to the next. Most Atlanteans consider it an honor to carry such a unique weapon and look forward to the day they pass it on to their own children.

Magic Crystal Weapons have always remained popular among Crystal Mages and Stone Masters, and are gaining renewed respect and interest from Atlantean adventurers like Nomads and Voyagers, and especially from non-Atlanteans who value and desire magic weapons and artifacts of all kinds. Tattooed Defenders are also starting to take another at look at these old, reliable weapons of the past with an eye toward the future. Many Defenders already use the Crystal Deflector Gauntlet and/or Crystal Stun Mace, and the melee weapons also hold an appeal.

Crystal melee weapons always resemble the classic weapons made of steel, except that they have a much higher degree of sheen to them. Upon closer inspection it becomes clear they are made of crystal.

Magic crystal melee weapons have two damage settings: They do normal S.D.C. damage like any weapon of steel until energized with P.P.E., at which point they become deadly Mega-Damage weapons.

Damage Note: In an S.D.C. setting, when energized with P.P.E., the weapon does double its normal S.D.C. setting.

Cost Note: The price listed is what Atlanteans pay for such items. Outsiders, if sold these items at all, pay 2-3 times the list price. Non-Atlanteans who prove themselves to be valuable and trusted allies are sometimes give a Crystal Weapon as a boon, gift or reward.

Magic Crystal Melee Weapons

Crystal Dagger

This weapon can be thrown 30 feet (9.1 m), x3 when the thrower has Supernatural P.S.
Weight: One pound (0.45 kg).
Damage: 1D6 S.D.C. or 1D6 M.D. when energized.
P.P.E. to Energize: 4 P.P.E. per 20 minutes.
Cost: 25,000 credits.

Crystal Short Sword

Weight: Three pounds (1.35 kg).
Damage: 2D6 S.D.C., 2D6 M.D. when energized.
Bonus: +1 to parry.
P.P.E. to Energize: 8 P.P.E. per 15 minutes to energize.
Cost: 50,000 credits.

Crystal Large Sword

Weight: 6 pounds (2.7 kg).
Damage: 3D6 S.D.C., 3D6 M.D. when energized.
Bonus: +1 to strike and parry.
P.P.E. to Energize: 10 P.P.E. per 10 minutes to energize.
Cost: 72,000 credits.

Crystal Battle Axe

Weight: 6 pounds (2.7 kg).
Damage: 3D6+2 S.D.C., 3D6+2 M.D. when energized.
P.P.E. to Energize: 12 P.P.E. per 10 minutes to energize.
Cost: 75,000 credits.

Crystal Hatchet/Tomahawk

This weapon can be thrown 40 feet (12.2 m), x3 when the thrower has Supernatural P.S.
Weight: 3 pounds (1.35 kg).
Damage: 2D4 S.D.C., 2D4 M.D. when energized.
Bonus: +1 to parry.
P.P.E. to Energize: 6 P.P.E. per 10 minutes to energize.

Cost: 40,000 credits.

Crystal Morning Star

Weight: 5 pounds (2.25 kg).
Damage: 3D6+2 S.D.C., 3D6+2 M.D. when energized.
P.P.E. to Energize: 10 P.P.E. per 10 minutes to energize.
Cost: 80,000 credits.

Crystal Mace

Weight: 5 pounds (2.25 kg).
Damage: 2D6 S.D.C., 2D6 M.D. when energized.
P.P.E. to Energize: 8 P.P.E. per 15 minutes to energize.
Cost: 60,000 credits.

Crystal Mace and Chain

Weight: 5 pounds (2.25 kg).
Damage: 3D6 S.D.C., 3D6 M.D. when energized.
P.P.E. to Energize: 10 P.P.E. per 10 minutes to energize.
Cost: 65,000 credits.

Crystal Staff

Weight: Five pounds (2.25 kg).
Damage: 1D6+2 S.D.C., 1D6+2 M.D. when energized.
Bonus: +1 to parry.
P.P.E. to Energize: 5 P.P.E. per 15 minutes to energize.
Cost: 30,000 credits.

Crystal Spear

This weapon can be thrown 150 feet (45.7 m), x3 when the thrower has Supernatural P.S.
Weight: Five pounds (2.25 kg).
Damage: 1D6+4 S.D.C., 1D6+4 M.D. when energized.
Bonus: +1 to strike.
P.P.E. to Energize: 8 P.P.E. per 15 minutes to energize.
Cost: 40,000 credits.

Crystal Trident

This weapon can be thrown 60 feet (18.3 m), x3 when the thrower has Supernatural P.S.
Weight: Six pounds (2.7 kg).
Damage: 2D6+3 S.D.C., 2D6+3 M.D. when energized.
Bonus: +1 to parry and disarm.
P.P.E. to Energize: 10 P.P.E. per 10 minutes to energize.
Cost: 70,000 credits.

Crystal Stun Mace

Often used by Atlantean law enforcement officers and sometimes, adventurers. The stun effect delivers a non-lethal jolt that temporarily stuns its victim.
Weight: 5 pounds (2.25 kg).
Save vs Stun: 16 or higher. Mega-Damage beings are +2 to save in addition to their bonuses, and duration is half. Does not work on demons, gods and supernatural monsters, but the sting of it will make them angry. Stun is ineffective against environmental M.D.C. body armor, power armor, robots, and Guardian Armor, but is effective against body armor without a helmet and armor not fully environmental.

Duration: 2D4+1 melee rounds, and extend by an additional 2D4 melee rounds for every hit by the Stun Mace for which the character does not save.

Damage & Stun Effect: 2D6 S.D.C. + Stun when energized. Victims who do not save are -8 to strike, parry, and dodge plus reduce the character's speed and number of attacks per melee round by half.

The accumulative effect on the nervous system of the body being repeatedly struck and stunned may knock the victim unconscious, even if he has previously saved. After being struck more than four times, the unprotected character may be stunned into unconsciousness for 2D4 melee rounds. When he recovers, he will suffer the stun penalties for 1D4 minutes. Roll to save, a failed roll means there is a 01-42% chance of being rendered unconscious.

P.P.E. to Energize: 10 P.P.E. per two minutes of use.

Cost: 45,000 credits.

Shard Launcher

The Shard Launcher is a device built into a leather vambrace or gauntlet. Mounted on top is a solid white crystal shaped like a triangle. The Atlantean infuses the crystal with P.P.E., and on command, it launches deadly crystal shards.

Weight: 2 pounds (0.9 kg).

Range: 600 feet (183 m).

Duration: One melee round. Each single shard fired or triple shard blast counts as one melee attack.

Damage: 1D6 M.D. per each single crystal shard or 3D6 M.D. for a rapid-fire triple shard blast. Point and shoot.

Bonus: +1 to strike.

P.P.E. to Activate: 20 P.P.E.

Cost: 90,000 credits.

Crystal Energy Weapons

Specific crystals were used along with technological weapons to form a hybrid of technology and magic. This is not true Techno-Wizardry. The results are weapons that are magic based and can fire a variety of different types of energy.

These weapons do not use clips but rather recharge from ambient P.P.E. at ley lines and stone pyramids at a rate of 20 P.P.E. per melee round (15 seconds) until their payload is filled to capacity. Or can be charged via the P.P.E. of its user or any mage or Atlantean willing to temporarily expend their own P.P.E.

Some people may charge for P.P.E. recharging. Rates vary and are almost non-existent on worlds with high P.P.E., and are exorbitant on low P.P.E. worlds, and may even require a ritual and blood sacrifice to acquirer the necessary P.P.E. to recharge a crystal weapon even with a fraction of its full payload.

All Crystal Energy Weapons are designed in such a way that the P.P.E. contained in them can NOT be accessed. Cracking the containment compartment cause the crystal(s) inside to immediate disintegrate and the weapon to explode, destroying the weapon and inflicting 1D6x10 M.D. to a 4 foot (1.2 m) radius.

In all cases, damage is S.D.C. in S.D.C. environments and M.D. in Mega-Damage settings.

Cost Note: The price listed is what Atlanteans pay. Outsiders, if sold these items at all, pay 3-5 times the list price.

Crystal Laser Pistol

A sleek looking laser pistol with a yellow or red crystal built into the top of the weapon where you might expect the slide of an automatic weapon to be. The weapon is an elegant design. Magic/P.P.E. and Crystal magic are its source of power.

Weight: 2 pounds (0.9 kg).

Range: 900 feet (274.3 m).

Duration: One melee round whether all the shots are fired or not.

Mega-Damage: 2D6 M.D. per single blast.

Rate of Fire: Each blast counts as one attack.

P.P.E. to Energize: 20 P.P.E.

Payload: 120 P.P.E. or six melee rounds of combat before needing recharging.

Cost: 60,000 credits.

Crystal Laser Rifle

A rifle version of the laser pistol except it has two yellow or red crystals built into the top of the weapon where you might expect the slide of an automatic weapon to be. The weapons is an elegant design. Magic/P.P.E. and Crystal Magic are its source of power.

Weight: 2 pounds (0.9 kg).

Range: 2,000 feet (610 m).

Duration: One melee round whether all the shots are fired or not.

Mega-Damage: 2D6+2 M.D. per single blast.

Rate of Fire: Each blast counts as one melee attack.

P.P.E. to Energize: 30 P.P.E. for one melee.

Payload: 240 P.P.E. or eight melee rounds of combat before needing recharging.

Cost: 100,000 credits.

Crystal Multi-Pistol

The Crystal Multi-Pistol looks like a heavy-duty laser pistol except it has a clear, blue and red colored crystal built into the top body of the weapon starting where you would expect the slide of an automatic pistol to be and up toward where the barrel meets the body. The weapon has a decidedly advanced, high-tech look, upgraded a millennia ago from the style that more resembled a flintlock pistol. The weapon can fire three types of blasts: A telekinetic force blast or fiery plasma blast, or an electric bolt. The type of blast is selected by voice command.

Weight: 4 pounds (1.8 kg).

Range: 300 feet (91 m).

Duration: One melee round whether all the shots are fired or not.

Mega-Damage: 3D6 M.D. per telekinetic (TK) blast or 4D6 M.D. from a plasma blast or lightning bolt!

Rate of Fire: Each blast counts as one melee attack.

P.P.E. to Energize: 40 P.P.E. for one melee.

Payload: 240 P.P.E. for six melee rounds of combat before needing recharging.

Cost: 135,000 credits.

Crystal Multi-Rifle

The Atlantean crystal multi-rifle has a similar look and style as the small multi-pistol with a larger, clear, blue and red colored crystal built into the top body of the weapon. The weapon can fire three types of blasts: A telekinetic force blast or fiery plasma blast, or an electric bolt. The type of blast is selected by voice command.

Weight: 10 pounds (4.5 kg).

Range: 2,000 feet (610 m) for the telekinetic blast and 1,600 feet (488 m) for the plasma and lightning/electric blast.

Duration: One melee round whether all the shots are fired or not.

Mega-Damage: 4D6 M.D. per telekinetic (TK) blast or 5D6 M.D. from a plasma or electric blast.

P.P.E. to Energize: 44 P.P.E. for one melee.

Rate of Fire: Each blast counts as one melee attack.

Payload: 320 P.P.E. for seven melee rounds of combat before needing recharging.

Cost: 170,000 credits.

Crystal Energy Sword

Crafted from a single piece of crystal, the energy sword is a medium or large crystal blade but with crystals also built into the handle and a large gem in the pummel at the end of the handle. It has all the properties of a Crystal sword, but can also be energized to crackle with electricity or plasma, and fire both.

Weight: 6 pounds (2.7 kg).

Range: 120 feet (36 m) for electrical blast or plasma blast.

Duration: One melee round whether all the shots are fired or not.

Damage: Sword 3D6 S.D.C., 3D6 M.D. when energized.

Damage: Electrical or Plasma Charged Blade or Energy Blast: 4D6 S.D.C., or 4D6 M.D. when the blade is energized, and same damage when fired as a blast of energy.

Bonus: +1 to strike as blade and ranged weapon.

P.P.E. to Energize: 40 P.P.E. for one melee.

Rate of Fire: Each blast counts as one melee attack.

Payload: 320 P.P.E. for eight melee rounds of combat before needing recharging.

Cost: 200,000 credits.

Crystal Deflector Pistol

As Atlanteans started to explore the Megaverse, not everyone they encountered was peaceful. In response, the Atlantean Crystal Mages and Alchemists developed a number of defensive items using their crystal technology. The Deflector Pistol is one of them. It unleashes a burst of TK (telekinetic) energy that strikes its target with enough force to knock him off his feet or stop bullets, arrows, spears and thrown items in their trajectory as if they hit a wall, knocking them 2D6 feet (0.6 to 3.7 m) down and off to the side. **Note:** There is a 01-20% chance that the deflected bullets, etc., may hit a bystander in the immediate area of deflection.

The weapon has a single barrel as wide as a double-barreled shotgun, and a clear crystal built into the top of the weapon where you might expect the slide to an automatic weapon. In fact, it rather resembles a sawed-off shotgun.

Weight: 2 pounds (0.90 kg).

Range: 120 feet (36.6 m).

Duration: One melee round whether all the shots are fired or not.

Damage: 1D6+1 S.D.C. per single blast plus stops projectiles and knocks down people and knocks over animals weighing under 400 pounds (180 kg). Those knocked down take 1D6 S.D.C. damage, lose initiative and one melee attack. Animals, even predators, are startled by getting hit hard by an invisible force and are likely (01-66%) to run away and hang back for 1D6 melee

rounds. Victims of the blast of force feel like their whole body just ran into a wall or they were tackled by a 300 pound (135 kg) linebacker.

Blasting bullets, shotgun blasts, arrows and thrown objects requires a roll to strike that beats the strike roll of the attacker. This is hard to do, which means the shooter of the Deflector Pistol suffers a penalty of -2 to strike and stop the incoming projectile attack. Success means it was stopped and deflected it in mid-air.

Firing at a vehicle causes the driver to make a piloting skill roll at -10%. A failed roll means the vehicle swerves and slows down 1D4x10%, but probably does not crash. Against mini-missiles, there is a 01-60% chance the mini-missile is knocked 2D6 feet (0.6 to 3.6 m) off course. Against large missiles, there is only a 01-10% chance it is knocked off course.

Rate of Fire: Each deflector blast counts as one attack.

P.P.E. to Energize: 10 P.P.E.

Payload: 120 P.P.E. or twelve melee rounds of combat before needing recharging.

Cost: 80,000 credits.

Crystal Deflector Rifle

A bigger version of the pistol that resembles a shotgun. With all the same effects, just a longer range and higher P.P.E. cost.

Weight: 5 pounds (2.25 kg).

Range: 800 feet (244 m).

Duration: One melee round whether all the shots are fired or not.

Damage: Same as Deflector Pistol, above.

Rate of Fire: Each deflector blast counts as one attack.

P.P.E. to Energize: 15 P.P.E.

Payload: 220 P.P.E. or 15 melee rounds of combat before needing recharging.

Cost: 140,000 credits.

Crystal Deflector Gauntlet

The gauntlet has a large crystal surrounded by six smaller crystals embedded in a leather gauntlet. Three smoky quartz crystals each have a carving. It can fire a Deflector blast (same a the pistol but a much shorter range), or create an opaque energy field that is used as a shield.

Weight: One pound (0.45 kg).

Range: 30 feet (9.1 m) for the force blast or touch with shield.

Duration: One melee round whether all the shots are fired or not.

Damage: Blast damage and knockdown effect is the same as Deflector Pistol, above.

Special Deflector Shield Defense: The Deflector shield functions as a protective energy shield that stops incoming attacks, and can even parry bullets and energy blasts, but with a -2 penalty.

A push-back effect occurs when an attacker strikes the shield with his own body or a melee weapon, requiring he make a saving throw roll of 14 or higher. A failed save means striking the shield pushes him back 1D6 feet (0.3 to 1.8 m) and he loses one melee attack!

Bonus: +2 to parry with the shield.

Rate of Fire: Each deflector blast counts as one attack. Using the Deflector Shield to parry does not use up an attack.

P.P.E. to Energize: 15 P.P.E.

Payload: 220 P.P.E. or 15 melee rounds of combat before needing recharging.

Cost: 145,000 credits. Always sold as a single gauntlet, not a pair. Combatants seldom wear more than one gauntlet of any kind.

Crystal Combat Gauntlet

The gauntlet is made of leather, but the top is completely covered in crystal, the fingertips end in short claws, and four short spikes protrude from the knuckles.

Weight: Two pounds (0.90 kg).

Range: Laser blast 100 feet (30.5 m) and melee combat.

Duration: Four melee rounds when energized.

Damage: 1D6 S.D.C. from laser blast, +2D4 S.D.C. from claw strike in addition to usual P.S. damage, and +2D6 S.D.C. added to usual punch damage when the combat gauntlet. All damage becomes M.D. when the gauntlet is energized! Remember, Tattooed Men have Supernatural P.S. and already do Mega-Damage punches. The Combat Gauntlet adds to that damage.

Bonus: +1 to disarm and +5% to Climbing skill.

Rate of Fire: Each laser blast counts as one attack.

P.P.E. to Energize: 15 P.P.E.

Payload: 220 P.P.E. or 15 melee rounds of combat before needing recharging.

Cost: 165,000 credits. Always sold as a single gauntlet, not a pair. Combatants seldom wear more than one gauntlet of any kind.

Crystal Powered Armband

The Crystal Powered Armband is worn around one of the upper arms. It is composed of leather, chain mail and four magic crystals, one of them being a P.P.E. battery. Each crystal bears various Atlantean symbols inscribed upon it. The magic device is designed to give Atlantean non-combat personnel, rescue personnel and adventurers who are not Tattooed Men with Supernatural Strength, Endurance and M.D.C. bodies, similar temporary abilities.

The user can activate any or all of the powers as needed, assuming they have the P.P.E. available to activate them all. Actually the same basic device with the same enchantments may be built into a similar looking necklace.

Weight: One pound (0.45 kg).

Spells and P.P.E. to Activate: Superhuman Endurance (12), Superhuman Strength (10; increases P.S. to 24 and makes it Supernatural), and Armor of Ithan (10) that provides 40 M.D.C. per activation.

Duration: Superhuman Endurance lasts for two hours per activation while Superhuman Strength and Armor of Ithan both only last only for 8 minutes per activation.

Payload: 64 P.P.E. for two activations that engage all three abilities before needing recharging or activation from personal P.P.E. The spell abilities can be activated one at a time as desired, or all three at once for 32 P.P.E.

Cost: 250,000 credits. Always sold as a single armband.

Crystal Head Band

This is another stylized piece of leather and chain magic artifact with four select crystals, one being a P.P.E. battery. Its worn as a headband or part of a headdress, cap or head wrap. Most people are likely to perceive it as a piece of jewelry and not a magic item.

Weight: Half a pound (0.22 kg).

Spells and P.P.E. to Activate: See the Invisible (5), Breathe Without Air (5), and Sense Evil (5). All function the same as the spell.

Duration: 8 minutes each per activation.

Payload: 64 P.P.E. for four activations that engage all three abilities before needing recharging or activation from personal P.P.E. The spell abilities can be activated one at a time as desired, or all three at once for 15 P.P.E.

Cost: 170,000 credits.

Tattoo Magic

Magic tattoos can only be created by Atlantean Alchemists, Atlantean Tattoo Masters, the Splugorth, the Splugorth High Lords (a combination priest and alchemist), and the occasional ancient dragon. However, it was a breed of dragon known as the *Chiang-Ku*, believed to be extinct (or nearly so), who is credited with the creation of Tattoo Magic and passing it on to their Atlantean friends and allies.

Although magic tattoos can be instruments of great power, the acquisition of them is difficult. First, it is a rare mystic art whose secrets are closely guarded by those who know them. Second, they are incredibly painful, causing physical and emotional damage that can actually lead to insanity. It is interesting to note that magic tattoos are known to work on only a few races: Humans, Ogres (further supporting the apparent biological similarity between humans and the giant Ogres), True Atlanteans (humans), and, to a lesser degree, Elves. The magic also works on its inventors, the Chiang-Ku dragons. Magic tattoos do not instill magic powers nor cause the suffering when applied to members of any other race. Humans are uniquely suited for this magic, which may indicate that the origin of the magic, and possibly the Chiang-Ku, is ancient Earth.

The magic tattoos augment the recipient and when seven or more are applied, make him into a superhuman with Supernatural Strength and Endurance and an M.D.C. body. Historically, the so-called "Tattooed Men" have served the Atlantean people as warriors, defenders and knights errant. The Splugorth managed to steal the secrets of Tattoo Magic many millennia ago and use T-Men as warrior slaves, assassins, guards, protectors, and spies. As slaves, the Splugorth also use Tattooed Men in gladiatorial games as well as sell them as slave stock like human guard dogs and attack dogs to non-human beings on Rifts Earth and other dimensions. However, they keep the majority for their own insidious purposes. Sadly, there are generations of Atlantean warrior slaves, as well as humans and Ogres, who have been bred and raised to be loyal slaves and minions for the Splugorth. Such slaves know little if anything about their Atlantean heritage or past, and serve their monstrous masters with loyalty and dedication. Tattooed Men hold a special place among the Splugorth as elite slaves and minions and as such, receive many special privileges, including women and breeding. (See **Rifts® World Book 2: Atlantis** and **Rifts® World Book 21: Splynn Dimensional Market** for more details about T-Men who are Minions of Splugorth, as well as other slave stock, symbiotic organisms and other Splugorth magic and weapons.)

Atlantean T-Men. Tattoo Magic has been used by True Atlanteans since before Atlantis vanished. It came into prevalent use

for the **Vampire Crusades** when the *Undead Slayer* was first invented. Other Tattooed O.C.C.s like the *Tattooed Defender* (warriors/police) and *Tattooed Voyager* (dimensional traveler) came later. After much experimentation, it became accepted practice that only the special, combat oriented trades would receive a sufficient number of magic tattoos to make them superhuman Mega-Damage beings in the service of their people.

To outsiders, it may not seem like much of a sacrifice because Tattoo Magic makes these special combat classes supermen, but magic tattoos come with a price. And for Atlanteans, who value the natural world, becoming something more than human is difficult. Though they consider magic to be part of that natural world, for humans to be Mega-Damage beings with Supernatural Strength is not. Moreover, receiving magic tattoos is an agonizing process, and all Atlanteans who submit to becoming Tattooed Men (a term used whether it is a male or female enhanced warrior) take their responsibilities very seriously. On one hand, being a T-Man is an honor and makes you an instant hero in the eyes of many people, not just Atlanteans. On the other, they are also something of a freak whose job it is to fight not just criminals and humanoid enemies, but vampires, demons and supernatural horrors no one should ever have to face, let alone do so on a regular basis.

For these reasons, the majority of True Atlanteans in all clans comply with receiving their two Marks of Heritage and no more than 1-4 additional magic tattoos. The average citizen seldom gets more than one additional. Atlantean clan elders and Alchemists/Tattoo Masters strictly enforce this law.

Using Magic Tattoos

Activation of a Magic Tattoo. To activate any of the magic tattoos, the Tattooed Man touches the desired image and concentrates, focusing his P.P.E. to bring the tattoo to life. Sometimes a simple chant is used to help with the focusing process. At seventh level and higher, Tattooed Men are so skilled that they can activate any tattoo by concentration alone, and do not need to touch the skin art in order to activate it. An important ability when your hands are full or bound, or your body is covered in body armor or a spacesuit.

The time spent to activate any magic tattoo is a matter of two or three seconds and counts as one melee attack. Thus, the activation of five or six tattoos by a T-Man is likely to use up all of his melee attacks for one entire melee round.

All magic tattoos are permanent and can be used endlessly, provided the individual has enough P.P.E. available to him. The only restriction is that each specific magic tattoo can create only *one* of whatever the tattoo depicts. If the item or creature is currently in use, an identical article cannot be created by activating the same tattoo again. It is not available until its duration ends and the weapon, creature or effect comes to an end.

Each magic tattoo on the body must be different – no duplicates, thus it is impossible to create two Gryphons or two magic axes, etc. But a Gryphon and a tiger is no problem, or a battle axe (ordinary axe) and a flaming axe (magic and suitable for battling the supernatural), or a large sword and a short sword, or two knives but with different blades or handles.

Also, certain tattoos can build upon each other to enhance the powers. See Enhancement Tattoos for details.

143

Tattoo Activation Limit (6). There is an upper limit to the number of tattoos that can be active at a time. Your average *Tattooed Defender* (or *Splugorth Tattooed Warrior*) can have dozens of magic tattoos, but the maximum number of tattoos that can be active at any given time is **six**. Individuals with six or fewer magic tattoos are not categorized as Tattooed Men.

P.P.E. Needed to Power Magic Tattoos. Of course, the Tattooed Man must have sufficient P.P.E. to activate any of his tattoos. Each type of magic tattoo requires different amounts of P.P.E. (Potential Psychic Energy) for activation. This means Tattooed Men need to learn to build, preserve and channel their P.P.E. in a way similar to practitioners of magic. Another reason magic tattoos are not easy for ordinary Atlanteans to master and use to their full effectiveness. **Note:** Each O.C.C. description will indicate how much P.P.E. the character starts with and gains with experience. In addition, each magic tattoo gives Atlanteans six additional P.P.E. points. The typical Atlantean citizen has around 22 P.P.E. The average Tattooed Man has 4-5 times that even at low levels. They can also channel P.P.E. at ley lines and stone pyramids.

Channeling ambient P.P.E. at Ley Lines and Nexus Points. All Atlantean Tattooed O.C.C.s are able to draw energy from ley lines and nexus points up to a certain amount of P.P.E. every melee round to activate a magic tattoo, rather than use their own P.P.E., or to power and use a magic device. The exact amount is described under each specific O.C.C., but is typically around 20 P.P.E. points, sometimes more, occasionally less.

Tattoo Magic by Type

Note: *Italics indicate new tattoos.* The number in parenthesis is the P.P.E. required to activate.

Animals

Small animals with 12 Hit Points or less (10 P.P.E.)
Medium-sized animals with 13 to 30 Hit Points (15)
Medium-sized animals with 31 to 50 Hit Points (20)
Large animals with over 50 Hit Points (30)

Monsters

Minor monsters with 50 M.D.C. or less (50)
Major monsters with 51 to 150 M.D.C. (80)
Giant monsters with 151 to 300 M.D.C. (100)
Super monsters with 301 to 500 M.D.C. (150)

Note: 500 M.D.C. is now the cap. Even if a creature has more in real life, it cannot exceed 500 M.D.C. as a magic tattoo.

Monster-Shaping Tattoos

Monsters with 1,000 S.D.C./Hit Points or less (30)
M.D.C. Races with 60 M.D.C. or less (60)
M.D.C. Races with 61-200 M.D.C. (90)
M.D.C. Races with 201-1,000 M.D.C. (120)
M.D.C. Races with 1,001-3,000 M.D.C. (200)

Animal/Monster Enhancements

Military Saddle (2/5)
Animal/Monster Breathing Fire/Ice/Lightning (select one) (12/25)
Flaming (claws, hoofs, fangs or tail) (7/15)

Mounted Weapon (30; Monsters only)
Fiery Streaks (10/15)
Barding (10/25)

Simple Weapons

Simple Weapons (2)
S.D.C. Shield (4)

Magic Weapons

Flaming Shield (15)
Weapon Covered in Flames (10)
Flaming Weapon Dripping Blood (25)
Weapon Covered in Flames and a Coiled Snake/Serpent (20)
Weapon Impaling or Smashing a Baal-Rog's Head (Demon Slayer) (30)
Weapon Impaling or Smashing a Deevil Beast's Head (Deevil Slayer) (30)
Weapon Smashing or Impaling a Heart; Anti-P.P.E. (20)
Weapon Smashing or Impaling a Skull: Anti-I.S.P.(10)

Magic Weapon Enhancements

Weapon Dripping Blood (5)
Blood Splatter (around the weapon) (20)
Two Weapons Crossed (5)
Weapon Covered in Electrical Arcs (20)
Weapon with a Flaming Gout Shooting Out (20)
Weapon Wrapped with Green or Black Thorns (Poison) (25)
Weapon with Wings (+5, +10, +20 or +30)

Power Tattoos

Black Sun (40)
Beautiful Dancer (15)
Bleeding Heart (20)
Chain Encircling a Skull or Brain (25)
Chain with a Broken Link (30)
Chain Wrapped Around a Cloud (50)
Cracked or Broken Skull (25)
Cross (15)
Eye with a Dagger In It (25)
Eye of Knowledge (15)
Eye of Mystic Knowledge (20)
Eye with Tears (15)
Eyes: Three (20)
Flaming Eye (20)
Heart Encircled by Chains (40)
Heart with Large Wings (20)
Heart with Tiny Wings (10)
Heart Pierced by a Wooden Stake (15)
Heart of Steel (25)
Heart in Two Pieces (30)
Heart Wrapped in Thorns (35)
Knight in Full Body Armor (25)
Lightning Bolts (30)
Rose and Thorny Stem Dripping Blood (30)
Phoenix Rising from the Flames (124)
Shark or Dolphin (20)
Skeleton in Chains (20)
Skull with Bat Wings (30)
Skull Coiled with Thorns (40)

Skull Engulfed in Flames (45)
Thorns or Ball of Thorns (15)
Wolf's Head with Glowing Eyes (30)
Orb with a Flame Within It (40)
Red Lightning Bolt (Impervious to Energy) (40)
Blazing Comet (Space Flight as per spell in Fleets of the Three Galaxies) (40)
Eye of Mystic Knowledge Encircled by Chains (Magic Resistance) (20)
Eye of Mystic Knowledge with a Red Slash Through It (Negate Magic) (40)
Eye of Mystic Knowledge on a Broken Shield (Dispel Magic Barriers) (45)
Fire Dragon's Head (Impervious to Fire) (20)
Fire Dragon's Head Breathing Fire (30)
Gas Mask or Air Breathing Mask (Impervious to Vacuum) (15)
Ice Dragon's Head (Impervious to Cold) (20)
Ice Dragon's Head Breathing Ice (30)
Nuclear Symbol (Sub-Particle Acceleration) (40)
Power Matrix (Energize Tattoo) (5+)
Rose Encircling a Heart (Bio-Regeneration) (50)
Star Field – Zero Gravity Movement (10)
White Skull on a Black Shield – Sense Evil (5)

Defender Tattoos

Crystal Guardian Armor (25 + life energy)
Crystal Super-Guardian (40 + life energy)

Sunaj Assassin Power Tattoos

Black Hooded Cloak (Cloak of Darkness) (12)
Camouflaged Cloak (Chameleon) (12)
Closed Eye (Invisibility: Superior) (30)
Coiled Rope or Rappelling Gun (10)
Explosion – Self-Destruction (20 or 40)
Porcelain Mask (Mask of Deceit) (25)
Silver or Gold Key (Escape) (15)

Dimension Tattoos

Pyramid with Atlantean Clan Symbol or Clan Crest (30 plus 2 P.E. points)
Open Rift with a Small Pyramid in the Rift (Redirect Rift) (50 P.P.E. and 1D4 P.E. points, +25 P.P.E. per additional person)
Pyramid with a Rift at the Apex of the Pyramid (Communication Rift) (50 P.P.E. and 1 P.E. point)
Eye of Knowledge Within a Rift (Dimension Sense) (25 P.P.E. and 1 P.E. point)
Two Pyramids Connected by a Rift (Rift Teleportation) (100 or 50 P.P.E. and 4 P.E. points)
Chain Wrapped Around a Rift (Close Rift) (40 P.P.E. and 2 P.E. points)
Rift on a Stone Wall (Mystic Portal) (40 P.P.E. plus 1 P.E. point)
Heart Within a Rift (Sustain) (12)
Pair of Chains Pulling a Rift Open (25 P.P.E. per minute)
Silhouettes of People in a Rift (Dimensional Teleport) (200 P.P.E. and 1D4+4 P.E. points or 125 P.P.E. and 12 P.E. points)
Crossing Ley Lines with an Open Rift (Dimensional Portal) (400 P.P.E. and 1D4+8 P.E. points)

Animal Tattoos

Animal tattoos have the magic ability to come to life, leap off the body, become full size, and fight for their maker. The animals, including insects and arachnids, are completely obedient to their creator and fight to the death. Only the Tattooed Man who created the animal can command it. They respond to verbal commands. Like most tattoos, the user of the animal tattoos may cancel the magic at any time with a mere thought. Until then, or until the animal is slain or the magic's duration expires, the tattoo animal continues to exist, even when its creator is rendered unconscious, possessed, or mind controlled.

In the case of possession or mind control, the controlling outside force cannot activate any new tattoos nor cancel any already activated. Tattoos that were activated at the moment that control was initiated remain in place until the end of their duration or the animal is slain/depleted of S.D.C. points.

None of the animal's powers can be transferred or extended to the T-Man or other living beings.

As many as six tattoos can be activated at any one time unless the O.C.C. states otherwise. All effects and abilities are cumulative.

To Activate an Animal Tattoo, the T-Man merely touches the desired tattoo, focuses his concentration (counts as one melee attack), the tattoo glows, disappears from his arm, and reappears as a dull gray, life-sized animal protector. The animals aren't actually alive, but composed of magic and an ectoplasm-like substance.

P.P.E. Cost to Activate Animal Tattoos: Small animals (12 Hit Points or less): 10 P.P.E. Medium-sized animals (13 to 30 Hit Points): 15 P.P.E. Medium-sized animals (31 to 50 Hit Points): 20 P.P.E. Large animals (over 50 Hit Points): 30 P.P.E.

Duration: One hour per each level of the Tattooed Man, or until the animal is destroyed/slain by depleting its S.D.C. and Hit Points, or until the magic is canceled. When canceled or destroyed, the creature glows, disappears, and reappears on the T-Man's body as a tattoo.

The tattoo is instantly reusable if the magic was canceled or the duration time has expired. However, if the animal was destroyed, meaning all of its S.D.C. was depleted, the T-Man must spend twice the number of P.P.E. points to re-create it or wait four hours.

Destroying a Tattoo Animal as a living entity causes its owner to suffer 3D6 points of damage *direct to Hit Points* or 2D6 M.D.C. if he is a Mega-Damage being, which all Tattooed Men are. Damage is cumulative for the destruction of each living tattoo. No damage if the tattoo is canceled or the duration ends. Damage heals as normal or can be restored by magical or psionic means. T-Men heal from physical injury and recover P.P.E. quickly via meditation.

S.D.C.: Magic animals are S.D.C. and Hit Point creations. No tattoo animal is a Mega-Damage creature. See animal descriptions.

Animal Characteristics: The magic animals act like the creature illustrated in the tattoo in every way, and possesses all the abilities that the real animal would have. Birds fly, peck and claw; canines bite and run; felines stalk, climb, claw and bite; bulls and bovines charge and ram; snakes slither and bite; and so on.

Damage: Animals are S.D.C. creations and inflict only S.D.C. damage. Animals created by Tattoo Magic are typically intended for use in combat (attack and defense) or as a pack animal or riding animal. They do not function like a wizard's familiar, but as a trained pet. The T-Man is not mentally linked to the creature and does not see, hear or know what the creature is experiencing other than suffering Hit Point damage at the moment of its destruction.

Animal Stats: A great resource for animal information is the **Monsters & Animals sourcebook** for the **Palladium Fantasy RPG®**. This book contains around 200 different animals and can be a terrific sourcebook for any Palladium RPG. Using this reference book enables you to play specific animals using their appropriate stats without any work on your part. There are also numerous monsters that can be dropped into most any game setting. **Note:** You do not need **Monsters & Animals** to play a Tattooed Man in **Rifts®**. You should be able to wing it using common sense and the basic, general data that follows under Animal Tattoo Descriptions, below. Since animal tattoos are used primarily as a fighting ally, all one typically needs to know is how much damage the creature can endure and what kind of damage it inflicts. Remember, all animals are S.D.C. creatures and inflict S.D.C. damage.

Animal Tattoo Descriptions

Ape: Chimpanzee: The same size and behavior as the real animal. 48 Hit Points and 40 S.D.C. Bite inflicts 2D4 S.D.C. damage, slashing and tearing hands do 2D4 +3 damage. Three attacks per melee. +3 to strike, +2 to parry and dodge, and can use simple weapons such as clubs, rocks, knives, and similar, but not guns. Average Spd is 10. Nightvision 15 feet (4.6 m), Climb 88%, Prowl 60%, leap up to 10 feet (3 m).

Ape: Gorilla: The same size and behavior as the real animal. 80 Hit Points and 80 S.D.C. Bite inflicts 2D4 S.D.C. damage, slashing and tearing hands do 2D6+6 damage. Four attacks per melee. +3 to strike, +3 to parry, +1 to dodge, and can use simple weapons such as clubs, rocks, knives, and similar, but not guns or tech. Average Spd is 12. Nightvision 15 feet (4.6 m), Climb 40% and Prowl 40%.

Baboon: The same size and behavior as the real animal. 48 Hit Points and 10 S.D.C. Bite inflicts 2D6+3 S.D.C. damage, slashing and tearing hands do 2D4+2 damage. Three attacks per melee. +3 to strike, +2 to parry and dodge. Average Spd is 12. Nightvision 40 feet (12.2 m), exceptional vision and hearing, track by smell 65%.

Badger & Wolverine: The same size and behavior as the real animals. 30 Hit Points and 10 S.D.C. Bite or slashing claws do 1D6+2 S.D.C. damage. Three attacks per melee. +1 to strike and parry, and +3 to dodge. Average Spd is 12. Nightvision 50 feet (15.2 m), track by smell 65%, and dig 5 feet (1.5 m) per minute.

Bear: Black and Brown: The same size and behavior as a real bear. 66 Hit Points, 80 S.D.C. Bite does 1D8+2 S.D.C. damage, slashing claws 2D6+6 S.D.C. damage, pouncing/ram does 1D6+4 and has a 1-50% chance of knocking its opponent down (victim loses initiative and one melee attack), but counts as two attacks. Three attacks per melee. +2 to strike and parry, +1 to dodge. Average Spd is 22 but can run in bursts of speed at 30 mph (48 km) for up to 15 minutes. Climb 40%, Swim 80%.

Bear: Grizzly or Polar: The same size and behavior as a real bear. 120 Hit Points, 80 S.D.C. Bite does 1D8+6 S.D.C. damage, slashing claws 2D6+8 damage, pouncing/ram does 2D6+4 and has a 01-62% chance of knocking its opponent down (victim loses initiative and one melee attack), but counts as two attacks. Four attacks per melee. +2 to strike and parry, +1 to dodge. Average Spd is 16 but can run in bursts of speed up to 20 mph (32 km) for up to 15 minutes. Climb 40%, Swim 70% (+25% to Swim for polar bears).

Bird: Hawk or Falcon: The same size and behavior as the real animals. 16 Hit Points and no S.D.C. Bite 1D6 S.D.C. damage, slashing claws inflict 1D4+2 damage, and a diving claw attack 2D4+2 damage, but counts as two attacks. Three attacks per melee, +2 to strike and parry and +3 to dodge. Average speed flying is 50, about 35 mph (56 km). Nightvision 300 feet (91.4 m), exceptional vision and hearing, and track by smell 65%.

Bird: Eagle: The same size and behavior as the real animal. 24 Hit Points and 10 S.D.C. Bite 2D4 S.D.C. damage, slashing claws inflict 2D6+4 damage, and a diving claw attack 4D6+4 damage, but counts as two attacks. Four attacks per melee, +2 to strike and parry and +3 to dodge. Average speed flying is 50, about 35 mph (56 km), but can attain a speed of 75 mph (120 km) and maintain that speed for an hour. Nightvision 400 feet (122 m), exceptional vision and hearing, and track by smell 60%.

Boar or Wild Pig: The same size and behavior as the real animals. 40 Hit Points and 40 S.D.C. Bite/slashing tusks does 1D8+2 S.D.C. damage, head butt does 1D6+2, ram does 2D6+4 and has a 1-55% chance of knocking its opponent down (victim loses initiative and one melee attack), but counts as two attacks. Three attacks per melee. +1 to strike, and +2 to dodge. Average Spd is 22 but can run in bursts of speed at 35 mph (56 km) for up to 30 minutes.

Canine: Fox, Coyote, Jackal, or Small Dogs: The same size and behavior as the real animals. 24 Hit Points, 10 S.D.C. Bite does 1D6+4 S.D.C. damage, slashing claws 1D4 damage, three attacks per melee. +1 to strike and parry, +4 to dodge. Average Spd is 50, about 35 mph (56 km) and can run at that speed for 1D6 hours. Track by smell 70%, Swim 50%, Prowl 50%, keen vision and hearing.

Canine: Wolf or Large Dogs: The same size and behavior as the real animals. 48 Hit Points, 40 S.D.C. Bite does 2D6+8 S.D.C. damage, slashing claws 1D4 damage, three attacks per melee. +3 to strike, +1 to parry, +6 to dodge. Average Spd is 50, about 35 mph (56 km), and can run at that speed for 2D4 hours. Track by smell 85%, Swim 65%, Prowl 50%, keen vision and hearing, and nightvision 30 feet (9 m).

Elephant: The same size and behavior as the real animal. It can be ridden by the Tattooed Man who created it. 90 Hit Points and 100 S.D.C. Three attacks per melee. Tusks inflict 2D6+6 S.D.C. damage, strike from trunk 1D6, leg kick/stomp 3D6+6 damage, head butt does 3D6+6, and a ramming charge and trample inflicts 6D6+6 damage and has an 80% likelihood of knocking opponents weighing less than 1,000 lbs (450 kg) to the ground, causing them to lose one melee attack and initiative (counts as two attacks). Average Spd is 10, about five mph (8 km), but can run as fast as 35 mph (56 km) for 30 minutes. Keen hearing and sense of smell, good vision, nightvision 40 feet (12.2 m), Swim 90% and has a prehensile trunk.

Feline: African Lion: The same size and behavior as the real animal. 52 Hit Points, 80 S.D.C. Bite does 2D4 S.D.C. damage, slashing claws 2D6+6 damage, four attacks per melee. +3 to strike and parry, +4 to dodge. Average Spd is 22, about 15 mph (24 km), but can run in bursts at a speed of 25 mph (40 km) for 1D4 minutes. Track by smell 70%, Swim 50%, Prowl 70%, Climb 30%, leap up to 15 feet high (4.6 m) and 20 feet long (6 m), keen vision and hearing, and nightvision 60 feet (18.3 m).

Feline: Bobcat, Lynx, Mountain Lion: The same size and behavior as the real animals. 42 Hit Points, 40 S.D.C. Bite does 1D6 S.D.C. damage, slashing claws 2D4+3 damage, four attacks per melee. +3 to strike and parry, +4 to dodge. Average Spd is 22, about 15 mph (24 km), but can run in bursts of 30 mph (48 km) for 1D4 minutes. Swim 44%, Prowl 86%, Climb 90%, leap up to 20 feet high (6 m) and 20 feet long (6 m), keen vision and hearing, and nightvision 200 feet (61 m).

Feline: Cheetah: The same size and behavior as the real animal. 48 Hit Points, 40 S.D.C. Bite does 1D6 S.D.C. damage, slashing claws 2D4+6 damage, four attacks per melee. +4 to strike and parry, +6 to dodge. Average Spd is 22, about 15 mph (24 km), but can run in bursts of incredible speed – 80 mph (128 km) for 1D4 minutes. Track by smell 50%, Swim 55%, Prowl 50%, Climb 45%, leap up to 10 feet high (3 m) and 15 feet across (4.6 m), keen vision and hearing, and nightvision 50 feet (15.2 m).

Feline: Leopard & Panther: The same size and behavior as the real animals. 48 Hit Points, 40 S.D.C. Bite does 1D6 S.D.C. damage, slashing claws 2D4+3 damage, four attacks per melee. +3 to strike and parry, +4 to dodge. Average Spd is 22, about 15 mph (24 km), but can run in bursts at a speed of 35 mph (56 km) for 1D4 minutes. Track by smell 50%, Swim 80%, Prowl 90%, Climb 75%, leap up to 3 feet high (9 m) and 40 feet across (12.2 m), keen vision and hearing, and nightvision 200 feet (61 m).

Feline: Tiger: The same size and behavior as the real animal. 68 Hit Points, 80 S.D.C. Bite does 2D6 S.D.C. damage, slashing claws 2D6+8 damage, four attacks per melee. +3 to strike and parry, +4 to dodge. Average Spd is 22, about 15 mph (24 km), but can run in bursts at a speed of 35 mph (56 km) for 1D4 minutes. Track by smell 50%, Swim 80%, Prowl 70%, Climb 50%, leap up to 20 feet high (6 m) and 25 feet long (7.6 m), keen vision and hearing, and nightvision 200 feet (61 m).

Ferret, Mink, or Marten: The same size and behavior as the real animals. 12 Hit Points and no S.D.C. Bite and slashing claws inflict 1D4 S.D.C. damage. Three attacks per melee, +1 to strike and parry and +4 to dodge. Average Spd is 10. Nightvision 40 feet (12.2 m), exceptional vision and hearing, track by smell 65%, Climb 50%, Prowl 65%, and Swim 70%.

Horse: The same size and behavior as the real animal. It can be ridden by the Tattooed Man who created it. 48 Hit Points and 80 S.D.C. Three attacks per melee, bite inflicts 1D4 S.D.C. damage, front leg kick 2D6 damage, hind leg kick 4D6 damage, charging head butt does 2D4+10 and has an 80% likelihood of knocking opponents weighing less than 300 lbs (135 kg) to the ground, causing them to lose one melee attack and initiative (counts as two attacks). Average Spd is 33, about 22 mph (35 km), but can run as fast as 45 mph (72 km) for 1D4 hours. Can also leap up to six feet high (1.8 m) and 12 feet long (3.7 m), keen hearing, and swim 50%.

Monkey: The same size and behavior as the real animal. 32 Hit Points and 10 S.D.C. Bite and slashing/tearing hands inflict 1D6+1 S.D.C. damage. Three attacks per melee, +3 to strike and parry and +5 to dodge. Average Spd is 12. Nightvision 25 feet (7.6 m), exceptional vision and hearing, Climb 95%, Acrobatics 95%, leap 8 feet high (2.4 m) and 20 feet (6 m) across in trees, prehensile tail.

Rhinoceros: The same size and behavior as the real animal. It can be ridden by the Tattooed Man who created it. 84 Hit Points and 80 S.D.C. Two attacks per melee, jab with horn inflicts 2D6+4 S.D.C. damage, leg kick/stomp 3D6+4 damage, head butt with horn does 3D6 +4, and a ramming charge and trample inflicts 4D6 +6 damage and has an 80% likelihood of knocking opponents weighing less than 1,000 lbs (450 kg) to the ground, causing them to lose one melee attack and initiative (counts as two attacks). Average Spd is 14, about seven mph (11 km), but can run as fast as 30 mph (48 km) for 12 minutes. Keen hearing and sense of smell, poor vision, and Swim 40%.

Scorpion: The same size as a common scorpion, it behaves as a living scorpion would, its sting is poisonous. 2 Hit Points. Three attacks per melee, +2 to strike and dodge, Spd 8, and can Climb (90/75%) most surfaces except glass or highly polished metal.

Spider (non-poisonous): One to three inches (76 mm maximum) in diameter. 2 Hit Points. Bite does one point of damage. Two attacks per melee, Spd 10, and can Climb (95/90%) most surfaces except glass or highly polished metal.

Spider (poisonous): Three inches (76 mm) in diameter. 4 Hit Points. Bite does one point of damage plus 4D6 damage (roll to save vs poison – a successful save means no damage). Three attacks per melee, Spd 12, and can Climb (95/90%) most surfaces except glass or highly polished metal.

Snake (poisonous): About four to six feet long (1.2 to 1.8 m). 13 Hit Points and 6 S.D.C. Moves and behaves as a normal snake. Bite inflicts 1D4 S.D.C. damage and releases a poison that causes an additional 4D6 damage (roll to save vs poison – no damage if save is good). Two attacks per melee. +3 to strike and dodge.

Wasp or Bee: The same size as the common insects, it behaves as a living bee or wasp. 1 Hit Point. Its sting is painful, causing one S.D.C. point of damage per every two stings. Two attacks per melee, +2 to strike and dodge, Spd walking 8, Spd flying 37 (25 mph/40 km) and can Climb (98/96%) most surfaces except glass or highly polished metal.

Monster Tattoos

Monster magic tattoos function very similarly to animal tattoos. The main difference is that the monster is a Mega-Damage creature and inflicts Mega-Damage with its attacks. Only animal-like predatory monsters such as the Fury Beetle, Rhino-Buffalo, Chimera, dinosaurs, Dragonsaurus, Grigleaper, Gryphon, Harpy, Leatherwing, Peryton, Teepowka, Yazhing Multipede, Worms of Taut and similar, can be created. Intelligent monsters like dragons, werebeasts, demons, Elementals, etc., are NOT possible.

To Activate a Monster Tattoo, the T-Man merely touches the desired tattoo, focuses his concentration (counts as one melee attack), the tattoo glows, disappears from his arm, and reappears as a dull gray, life-size monster. **Note:** The monsters are not actually alive, but composed of magic and an ectoplasm-like substance.

P.P.E. Cost to Activate Monster Tattoos: Minor monsters (50 M.D.C. or less): 50 P.P.E. Major monsters (51 to 150 M.D.C.): 80 P.P.E. Giant monsters (151 to 300 M.D.C.): 100 P.P.E. Super monsters (301 to 500 M.D.C.): 150 P.P.E. with 500 M.D.C. now the cap. Even if a creature has more M.D.C. in real life, it cannot exceed 500 M.D.C. as a monster tattoo brought to magical life.

Duration: 30 minutes per each level of the Tattooed Man, or until the monster is destroyed by depleting its M.D.C., or until the magic is canceled. When canceled or destroyed, the creature glows, disappears, and reappears on the T-Man's body as a tattoo.

The monster tattoo is instantly reusable if the magic was canceled or the duration time has expired. However, if the monster was destroyed, meaning all of its M.D.C. was depleted, the T-Man must spend twice the number of P.P.E. points to re-create it or wait eight hours.

Destroying the Tattoo Monster as a living entity causes its owner to suffer 5D6 points of damage direct to Hit Points or M.D.C. if Mega-Damage being, which all Tattooed Men are. Damage is cumulative for the destruction of each living tattoo. The damage will heal as normal or can be restored by magical or psionic means. T-Men heal from physical injury and recover P.P.E. quickly via meditation.

M.D.C.: Magic tattoo monsters are M.D.C. creations. No monster tattoo is an S.D.C. creature. Tattoo monsters have the maximum amount of M.D.C. possible for that particular type of creature. Remember that super-monster M.D.C. cannot exceed 500 M.D.C.

Monster Characteristics: The magic monster acts like the real monster would in every way and has all the abilities of that creature. Only its creator can command or ride it.

Damage: Monsters are M.D.C. creations and inflict Mega-Damage. Monsters created by Tattoo Magic are designed for combat: attack and defense. They do not function like a familiar; the Tattooed Man is not mentally linked to the creature and does not see,

hear or know what the creature is experiencing other than suffering M.D.C. loss at the moment of its destruction.

Monster Stats: Just pick an animalistic monster from a World Book or sourcebook and assume the Monster Tattoo that is brought to life is basically that creature. **Rifts® Conversion Book One**, **Vampire Kingdoms™**, **New West™**, **Dinosaur Swamp™**, **Rifts® Sourcebooks 3** and **4**, among others, offer a variety of suitable monsters.

Enhancements & Modifications to Monster and Animal Tattoos

Just like weapon tattoos, animal and monster tattoos can also be modified and enhanced. The base requirement is the monster or animal. Like the weapons, the tattoo enhancements count as a *second active tattoo*, and *add to the overall cost* of activating the animal or monster tattoo with the enhancement/modification.

A maximum of three enhancements can be added to a monster or animal tattoo. An animal or monster with three enhancements would count as *four tattoos* when active (the creature and the three enhancements).

Military Saddle

P.P.E. to Activate with this Enhancement: 2 for animal and 5 for a monster.
Duration: The same as the creature being activated.
Power: Adding a saddle to any animal or monster makes the beast easier to control and ride like a horse. Tattooed Men gain a +10% bonus to their Horsemanship skill (or have a base riding skill of 50%). One requirement is that the animal or monster must be capable of having a rider and that a saddle can be reasonably added. Example, a ferret, dog, cougar or eagle cannot be saddled and ridden.

Animal/Beast Breathing Fire/Ice/Lightning (select one)

P.P.E. to Activate with this Enhancement: 12 for animals or 25 for monsters.
Duration: The same duration as the creature being activated.
Power: The tattooed warrior should select one breath weapon (fire/ice/lightning) when he receives the tattoo.
Damage: Select one. **Note:** Damage is S.D.C. for animals.
    Fire: Damage: 3D6 M.D. Range: 60 feet (18.3 m).
    Ice Shards or Frost: Damage: 2D6+2 M.D. Range: 80 feet (24.4 m).
    Electrical: Damage: 3D6 M.D. Range: 60 feet (18.3 m).
Attacks per Melee: The animal or monster has a breath weapon it can fire equal to the number of attacks per melee it possesses, but each breath attack counts as one of its melee attacks.

Flaming Claws, Hoofs, Fangs or Tail

P.P.E. to Activate with this Enhancement: Costs an additional 7 P.P.E. for animals (S.D.C. damage bonus) or 15 for monsters (M.D.C. damage bonus).
Duration: The duration is the same as the creature being activated.

Power: Whichever one of the animal or monster's natural weapons (claws, talons, hooves, teeth/fangs or tail if appropriate as a weapon like a scorpion) is covered in flames to indicate it does more damage than usual. Add 2D6 M.D. (or 2D6 S.D.C. to animals that inflict S.D.C. damage) to whatever the normal damage is for that creature's weapon (teeth, claws, etc.). So if a claw strike normally inflicts 1D6 M.D., it now does 3D6 M.D. (Or S.D.C. as the case may be.) In the case of most creatures, this is a set of teeth/fangs or the front two claws, or bird talons, or front hooves (or two back hooves), one scorpion tail, and so on. Only a pair of appendages can have this enhancement (i.e. upper and lower teeth, front paws for claws, etc.). If the creature has more limbs, for example eight tentacles, only two tentacles can have this enhancement.

Mounted Weapon

Requirement: Also requires a Military Saddle if the weapon is to be fired by a rider.
P.P.E. to Activate with this Enhancement: Applicable to monster tattoos only and costs an additional 30 P.P.E. to activate.
Duration: The duration is the same as the creature being activated.
Power: This is an addition to the creature. An energy weapon that is mounted on the monster, though it may have an organic appearance that fits the monster. It fires a mystic energy bolt (similar to the Power Bolt spell).
Damage: 5D6 M.D. per blast.
Range: 1,600 feet (487 m).

Attacks per Melee: The weapon can be designed to be fired like a mounted weapon on a vehicle or power armor by the T-Man rider (only the T-Man can ride the monster and fire this weapon), or by the creature itself. Each blast by the rider counts as *one of his melee attacks.* Shooting while moving has a -1 strike penalty, -3 when the monster is running at full tilt or dodging.

If the monster can fire the weapon on its own, as if it were one of its own natural weapons, the mounted weapon counts as *ONE extra melee attack* for the creature, but it can only be fired once per melee round.

Fiery Streaks

P.P.E. to Activate with this Enhancement: Costs an additional 10 P.P.E. for animals or 15 P.P.E. for monsters.
Duration: The duration is the same as the creature being activated.
Power: Fiery Streaks are added near wings or legs. Increases the animal or monster's speed by 50%. This includes flight and/or ground speed.

Barding (Animal Body Armor)

Requirement: Also requires a Military Saddle tattoo if the armor is to accommodate a rider.
P.P.E. to Activate with this Enhancement: Costs an additional 10 P.P.E. for S.D.C. barding or 25 for M.D.C. barding.
Duration: The duration is the same as the creature being activated.
Power: The animal or monster has a complete set of barding/protective body armor. Damage is first subtracted from this armor before it does damage to the magical construct. Only applicable to animals the size of a large dog or wolf, or larger.

S.D.C. Barding: 60 S.D.C. +15 S.D.C. per level of the Tattooed Man.

M.D.C. Barding: 60 M.D.C. +15 M.D.C. per level of the Tattooed Man.

Monster-Shaping Tattoo Magic

Original concept by C.J. Carella

Monster-Shaping tattoos are a special category of super-rare tattoos that seemingly transform the user into a member of any monster species. These tattoos do not grant "true" shape-shifting abilities, but create an ectoplasm-like substance that surrounds the character's true body, disguising his appearance and making him appear to be a monster he is not.

True Atlanteans cannot be transformed by any means, magical or technological, but the magical Monster-Shaping tattoos do NOT physically transform the character. Instead they create a magical *false body around him.* One might consider the monster shape created by the tattoos to be a mystic monster *costume* or exoskeleton that changes his appearance. The monster shape adds to the Tattooed Man's M.D.C., scent and physical P.S., P.P. and P.E., but does NOT grant the user any of the special powers of the monster race he or she is disguised as (although they *may* be able to simulate certain powers and abilities through other means).

Note: This tattoo type is exclusive to the *Skellian Clan Monster Hunter*. (See O.C.C. in this book for details.) Once in a great while it is bestowed as a reward to Skellian *Tattooed Defenders* and *Undead Slayers* of high rank or for heroic service above and beyond the call of duty. Monster-Shaping tattoos are used to get close to monstrous enemies. Only members of Clan Skellian and a few Chiang-Ku dragons associated with Clan Skellian know the secrets of Monster-Shaping tattoos (a particular group of Chiang-Ku helped the Skellian clan design the magic tattoos). Atlantean player characters must be affiliated with Clan Skellian to get a Monster-Shaping tattoo. **Note:** The Splugorth are beginning to suspect that a new category of tattoo has come into existence. Once they find proof of it they will spare no effort to obtain its secrets for themselves.

Shape-Shifting Capabilities of Monster-Shaping Tattoos

To activate a Monster-Shaping tattoo, the Monster Hunter merely touches the tattoo and focuses his concentration on it (counts as one melee action/attack). The tattoo glows with a blinding aura that completely covers the Atlantean. When the aura dissipates, the Monster Hunter has a new, monstrous shape.

An added advantage to this unique tattoo is that nobody suspects there is an Atlantean Tattooed Man concealed inside, because Atlanteans cannot shape-change. That's the beauty of this particular magic tattoo, it creates a sort of magical costume or armor that looks like a specific type of monster, but is really made of ectoplasm and worn like a suit of light power armor. The Atlantean is not, himself, transformed in any way, he is clad in a light M.D.C., magical disguise!

Monster-Shaping Tattoo per Type of Monster: A single Monster-Shaping tattoo does not enable the Atlantean heroes to turn into an endless array of monsters of any variety. It is limited to that "type" of creature. However, that enables them to create a variety of creature disguises when the monsters look very similar to one another. For example, a *Reptilian Monster-Shaping tattoo* means the Monster Hunter can turn into a large variety of large, humanoid Lizard Men. Likewise, a Monster-Shaping tattoo of a Xiticix enables the Monster Hunter to create a Monster-Shaping disguise of ANY type of Xiticix, from Drone to Hunter, all of them except for the Queen. That same tattoo can be used to make a Pincer Warrior of Cibola and many other insectoid species that have a similar appearance. But NOT Arachnoid species because arachnids are different from insects. Likewise, a canine Monster-Shaping tattoo enables the warrior to assume the disguise of most humanoid canine species, including werewolves in their humanoid-wolf form, the Dark Hound, Space Wulfen, and a wide range of large Dog Boys and other canine mutants and monsters. However, though related on the evolutionary scale, a canine tattoo would not enable the Monster Hunter to create a humanoid *bear* disguise, nor a feline. It has to be a similar looking creature of the same type: Canine, feline, avian, reptilian, saurian (dinosaur-like), amphibian, fish, and other broad ranges of species. Of course, some beings are unique enough that they require a monster specific tattoo for a Monster-Shaping disguise to be possible. This applies to beings like the Brodkil, Lyn-Srial, Worm Wraiths and Oborous-Slitherers found in the New West.

P.P.E. needed to activate the Monster-Shaping Tattoo: The P.P.E. cost depends upon the M.D.C. associated with the monster being mimicked by the magic. The lower the M.D.C. of the monster, the lower the P.P.E. cost.

Monsters with 1,000 S.D.C./Hit Points or less: 30 P.P.E.

M.D.C. races with 60 M.D.C. points or less: 60 P.P.E.

M.D.C. races with 61 to 200 M.D.C.: 90 P.P.E.

M.D.C. races with 201 to 1,000 M.D.C.: 120 P.P.E.

M.D.C. races with 1,001 to 3,000 M.D.C.: 200 P.P.E. (the limit).

P.P.E. Cost Note: Reduce P.P.E. cost by 10% when on a ley line, and reduce by 20% when the tattoo is activated at a ley line nexus.

M.D.C. Armor from Monster-Shaping Disguise: Treat the magical Monster-Shaping construct/disguise as a suit of M.D.C. or S.D.C. body armor (varies with the creature being imitated). When its structural capacity is depleted, the shell/shape is destroyed, its armor protection gone, and the person inside is revealed. The M.D.C. of the faux monster exterior corresponds with the M.D.C. of the creature being mimicked and the amount of P.P.E. spent (see above). Use the average M.D.C. of the monster being imitated as if it were 6th level +1D6x10 M.D.C. (or Hit Points and S.D.C. combined as the case may be) to determine the M.D.C. of the ectoplasmic covering.

For example, an ectoplasmic disguise to look like a 7 foot Felinoid Mutant Jaguar of Omagua would have 70 S.D.C. +1D6x10 S.D.C. from the magic tattoo. S.D.C. because the Jaguar people are Hit Point/S.D.C. based beings. 70 because the "average" Hit Points for a 6th level Jaguar mutant is 35 Hit Points + 35 S.D.C. = an average total of 70. Thus, the disguise generated by the Monster-Shaping disguise is 70 S.D.C. and costs 30 P.P.E. All S.D.C. constructs have a *Natural Armor Rating of 14,* so only rolls to strike of 14 or higher inflict damage.

By comparison, if disguised as the supernatural *Pincer Warrior* (see page 136 of **Rifts® South America**), the average M.D.C. for the disguise is 325 points + 1D6x10 M.D.C. at a cost of 120 P.P.E. to create. **Note:** "Average" M.D.C. is the midpoint between minimum and maximum M.D.C. for that 6th level creature. The **maximum Mega-Damage Capacity** of the disguise generated cannot exceed *800 M.D.C.* or *twice the Character's own natural M.D.C.* total, whichever is *less,* even if the creature being imitated could have much greater M.D.C. in real life.

Duration: 30 minutes per each level of the Monster Hunter's experience, or until destroyed. **Note:** Duration of the disguise becomes doubled starting with the day the Monster Hunter reaches 6th level experience and forward.

If the S.D.C. or M.D.C. of the shell is destroyed, so is the disguise, turning into floating globs that quickly fade away into nothing, and revealing the Monster Hunter underneath. The disguise also globs and fades away should the Monster Hunter concealed by the disguise be killed. The convincing ectoplasmic disguise continues to remain in place when the Atlantean wearing it is rendered unconscious, is possessed, or falls victim to mind control.

Mimic Basic Physical Attributes: The monster form works like a power armor, providing the wearer with the equivalent of the maximum P.S., P.P., and P.E. attributes of the creature the disguise is mimicking – or – the Monster Hunter's own, whichever is *higher.* While the physical disguise enables the Monster Hunter to use horns on his head, extra limbs, a tail, etc., he cannot fly even if the Monster Shape has wings, nor breathe fire, etc. See Attacks, below, for more details.

Many monsters, particularly those with animal traits and abilities, rely on scent to help them navigate the world. Somehow, the Monster-Shaping tattoo imbues the disguise with the proper scent to fool creatures with the keenest of senses.

Attacks per Melee and Possible Extras from Monster-Shaping: The Monster Hunter also gains any extra natural hand to hand attacks his disguise may offer from an additional appendage, such as a tail strike, or extra pair of arms or tentacles, as well as corresponding damage from a bite or claw attack. The monster shape, however, does NOT grant the tattoo user any of the creature's natural abilities or skills, such as heightened senses of smell, hearing, superior vision, see the invisible, etc., nor flight, climbing or leaping abilities, resistance to fire or cold, Bio-Regeneration, natural shape-shifting abilities, breath or energy attacks, magic, psionics, and so on.

Limitations: The Monster-Shaping tattoo only gives the Monster Hunter the general shape, size and features of a particular race or type of humanoid monster, including demons and supernatural creatures. It cannot be shaped to assume the features of a specific individual. The True Atlantean may look like a typical Troll or Devilkin, but cannot make himself look like a specific leader or war chief of a particular tribe or any other individual.

When a Monster-Shaping magic tattoo is activated, wisps and strands of ectoplasm appear and seem to cocoon around the Atlantean, completely covering his body, light armor, clothing and gear he may have been wearing. Any weapons and equipment the Atlantean intends to use as "the monster" should be taken off before the spell is cast and put back on over the monstrous exterior. Likewise, a bulky backpack or sword hilt is going to stick out as an odd growth or hunchback on the monster unless it is removed and stowed away first.

The ectoplasm quickly takes the shape of the inhuman monster race desired. The racial disguise desired must be inhuman and monstrous, not human or human-like and attractive. The shape must be humanoid and larger than the Monster Hunter.

Size matters: Since most Atlanteans are between six feet, two inches (1.9 m) and 7 feet (2.1 m) tall, only larger than human species of mutants, monsters and D-Bees can be imitated by the magic. Large mutants and D-Bees like the Anti-Monster, Arkhon and Aunyain of South America, most Felinoids and Fallam of South America, Blucies, Bruutarsaur, Demon-Dragonmage, Ewaipanomas of South America, Fennodi, Grackle Tooth, Greot Hunter, Lanotaur, Larmac, Mastadonoid, Pincer Warrior of South America, (a short) Pogtal Giant, Sasquatch, Splugorth Conservator, Erta, Kydian, many Splugorth slave races, Dark Hound, werebeasts, large Dog Boys, Ogres, Trolls, Brodkil, many aliens and monsters of the Three Galaxies, many demons and Deevils, and similar beings up to 12 feet (3.7 m) tall can all be mimicked by Monster-Shaping tattoos.

Note: Though some rumors claim giant races and large monsters like dragons, sphinxes, centaurs and others can also be mimicked, it is not true because they are not humanoid enough or are much too large. Remember, this monstrous exterior is worn by the Monster Hunter like a suit of power armor, so it can only be so large.

Tattoos remain visible: Even disguised as a monster, the magic somehow preserves the Atlantean's other magic tattoos and they *remain visible* on the character's false hide or scales. The tattoos can be covered under clothing, a robe, cloak, rags, mud, war paint or armor, but doing so may restrict the Monster Hunter's access to them. Since most people, especially D-Bees, cannot use Tattoo Magic, unless they have witnessed Atlantean Tattooed Men using them they probably know nothing about magic tattoos. Consequently, most people are likely to assume any tattoos are decorative markings or paintings, and have no reason to suspect the character is an impostor or spy just because of the tattoos. However, other Atlanteans, the Minions of Splugorth and others familiar with True Atlanteans know about Tattoo Magic and may be instantly suspicious or realize there is an invader in their midst.

The advantage of the magic tattoos being visible on the monstrous hide is that the Atlantean Monster Hunter can activate and use them while in disguise. Activating magic tattoos in plain sight will, of course, reveal the character to be a dangerous impostor and intruder.

Simple Weapon Tattoos

Simple weapons are magic tattoos that create a seemingly real, physical weapon out of thin air. The type of weapon is limited to those used in hand to hand combat, like an axe, boomerang, ball and chain, club, mace, war hammer, knife, sword, spear, staff, pole arm, and even a bow and arrow. Any of the weapons typically considered melee weapons or which fall under the category of W.P. Ancient Weapons can be a magic tattoo. The weapon inflicts the normal amount of S.D.C. damage for that specific type. However, the weapon is lightweight, perfectly balanced, and never dulls nor breaks.

Note: All types of ancient weapons used in hand to hand combat can be made into a magic tattoo, including exotic weapons like tiger claws and shurikens. Although a good list of basic ancient weapons are described in **Rifts®** and other Palladium RPGs, players and Game Masters might want to take a look at Palladium's **Weapons and Armor** sourcebook with more than 700 kinds of ancient weapons. This is an inexpensive sourcebook with stats that can be used with any game system.

Simple Weapons

P.P.E. to Activate: All Simple Weapons require only 2 P.P.E. to activate.

Duration: 30 minutes per level of experience or until canceled.

Power: Creates the weapon illustrated in the tattoo out of thin air, right down to every detail, ornate or plain hilt, inscription, etc. The weapon is lightweight, perfectly balanced, and indestructible. Vanishes when the magic is canceled or the duration ends.

Weapon Skill Bonuses: W.P. skills and bonuses are applicable, but such weapon skills must be selected separately.

Size: The weapon is always proportional to the size of the T-Man and the type of weapon it is.

Notes: The user of the Simple Weapon tattoo can cancel the magic at any time with a mere thought and the weapon disappears. The tattoo weapon continues to exist even when the user is rendered unconscious, possessed, or mind controlled. In the case of possession or mind control, the controlling outside force cannot activate any new tattoos nor cancel any already activated. Tattoos that were activated at the moment that control was initiated remain in place until the end of their duration. Anybody can pick up and use a tattoo weapon as long as the T-Man allows it. Remember, the T-Man can cancel the magic in the twinkle of an eye, leaving the person suddenly weaponless.

As many as six tattoos can be activated at any one time. All effects and abilities are cumulative.

Limitation: Modern weapons, revolvers, rifles, automatic and energy weapons are NOT possible.

None of the weapon's powers can be transferred or extended to living beings or to modern weapons.

A List of Some Common Melee Weapons:

Arrow for a Short Bow: 1D6 S.D.C.

Arrow for a Long Bow or Cross Bow: 2D6 S.D.C.

Throwing Knife, Throwing Spikes or Shurikens: 1D6 S.D.C. (1D4 for small knives and most pocket knives).

Throwing Axe: 2D4 S.D.C.

Battle Axe (large): 3D6 S.D.C.

Knife/Dagger: 1D6 S.D.C.

Survival Knife: 2D4 S.D.C.

Double-Bladed Claw: 2D4 S.D.C.

Triple-Bladed Claw: 3D4 S.D.C.

Machete: 1D6 S.D.C.

Short Sword, Saber, Cutlass, Scimitar or Sickle: 2D4 S.D.C.

Large Sword (most). 2D6 S.D.C.

    Bastard Sword: 2D6+2 S.D.C.; two-handed.

    Broadsword: 2D4+1 S.D.C.

    Claymore: 3D6 S.D.C.; two-handed.

    Flamberge and Executioner's Swords: 4D6 S.D.C.; two-handed.

    Long Sword: 2D6 S.D.C.

    Rapier: 2D4 S.D.C.

Spear (short) or Javelin: 1D6 S.D.C.

Spear (long): 2D6 S.D.C.

Pick: 2D4 S.D.C.

Pole Arm (long): 3D6 S.D.C.

Blunt Weapons:

    Ball and Chain: 2D4 S.D.C.

    Cane or Scepter: 1D6 S.D.C.

    Club/Cudgel/Pipe: 2D4 S.D.C.

    Flail: 2D6 S.D.C.

    Hercules Club (large mace): 3D6 S.D.C.

    Mace: 2D4 S.D.C.

    Mace and Chain: 3D6 S.D.C.

    Morning Star (spiked): 2D6 S.D.C.

    Staff (short): 1D6 S.D.C.

    Staff (long): 2D4 S.D.C. (+1D6 if iron).

    Bo Staff (long): 2D6 S.D.C.

    Warhammer: 2D6 S.D.C.

    Scythe: 4D6 S.D.C.; two-handed.

Simple S.D.C. Shield

P.P.E. to Activate: 4

Duration: 30 minutes per level of experience or until canceled.

Power: Creates the shield illustrated in the tattoo out of thin air. The shield is lightweight, perfectly balanced, and has 200 S.D.C. and an A.R. of 13. The shield takes damage only when an attacker is trying to destroy it, which is rare. Vanishes when the S.D.C. is depleted or the magic is canceled or the duration ends.

The size of the shield is always proportional to the size of the T-Man and based on the type of shield depicted in the tattoo. Some are small, some medium, some large. Some are round, others V or heart-shaped, rectangular and so on.

Bonus: +1 to parry in addition to any W.P. skill or P.P. bonuses. **Note:** As always, the user of the tattoo can cancel the magic at any time with a mere thought and the shield disappears. The shield continues to exist even when the user is rendered unconscious, possessed, or mind controlled.

M.D.C. Flaming Shield

P.P.E. to Activate: 15

Duration: 30 minutes per level of experience or until canceled.

Power: Creates the shield illustrated in the tattoo out of thin air. The shield is lightweight, perfectly balanced, and is completely *indestructible!* Vanishes when the magic is canceled or the duration ends. The size of the shield is always proportional to the size of the T-Man.

Bonus: +2 to parry in addition to any W.P. skill or P.P. bonuses.

Note: The user of the tattoo can cancel the magic at any time with a mere thought and the shield disappears. The tattoo shield continues to exist even when the user is rendered unconscious, possessed, or mind controlled.

Magic Weapon Tattoos

Just like a Simple Weapon, activation of a Magic Weapon tattoo creates a real, physical weapon out of thin air. The difference is this weapon possesses magical properties and is indestructible.

P.P.E. Cost to Activate: Varies depending on the magic imbued upon the weapon, plus the cost of any applicable Magic Weapon Enhancements. Each Enhancement adds to the cost to activate as the final magic weapon. *Two enhancements per weapon, maximum.* Each enhancement adds to the cost of activation, so if the T-Man got a Flaming morning star (meaning it inflicts M.D.C. and costs 10 P.P.E. to activate) and the *Wings enhancement* added (throwing range tripled plus the weapon returns to the thrower, costs 20 P.P.E. to add to a Flaming weapon), the total activation cost is 30. Add another 20 P.P.E. if also enhanced with *Weapon Covered in Electrical Arcs,* for a total of 50. This high cost is why many T-Men do not add more than one enhancement or even no additional enhancements to their Magic Weapon tattoos. Or have a range of tattoos or one or two favorites.

Duration: All Magic Weapons (and Enhancements) last 15 minutes per level of the T-Man or until the Tattoo Magic is canceled and the weapon is dispelled.

Weapon Type: Melee weapons just like Simple Weapons. As usual, Modern weapons, revolvers, rifles, automatic and energy weapons are not possible as a Magic Weapon tattoo.

Weapon Skill Bonuses: The character's usual W.P. skills and bonuses are applicable when using any weapon created via magic tattoo.

Size: The weapon is always proportional to the size of the T-Man and the type of weapon.

Power: Varies with each type of Magic Weapon Tattoo and 1-2 possible additional enhancements.

Notes: As always, the tattoo user can cancel the magic at any time with a mere thought and the weapon disappears. The magic weapon tattoo continues to exist even when the user is rendered unconscious, possessed, or mind controlled. In the case of possession or mind control, the controlling outside force *cannot* activate any new tattoos nor cancel any already activated. Magic Weapon tattoos that were active at the moment that control was initiated remain in place until the end of their duration.

Anybody can pick up and use weapons created by a magic tattoo as long as the T-Man allows it. Remember, the Tattooed Man can cancel the magic in the twinkle of an eye, leaving the person suddenly weaponless.

As six tattoos can be active at any one time, all effects and abilities are cumulative. Each Magic Weapon Enhancement, like wings, added to the tattoo when it is initially created counts as part of that ONE tattoo even if there are two enhancements.

Enhancements Over Time: If a Magic Weapon Enhancement is added to a Magic Weapon tattoo at a later date – days, months, even centuries after the main Magic Weapon tattoo was first created – EACH new enhancement counts as a separate and unique tattoo. That means that, although they are all activated together in one melee attack, a weapon with two enhancements added later would count as *three* tattoos toward the maximum of six tattoos that can be active at any one time. So it is best to figure out and get the Magic Weapon tattoo and any enhancement(s) done at the same time so they all count as ONE tattoo. And remember, two enhancements, maximum, regardless of when the enhancements are added.

Weapon Covered in Flames (Mega-Damage)

This is the standard when it comes to Magic Weapon Tattoos, because of its low P.P.E. cost and M.D. capabilities.

P.P.E. to Activate: 10

Duration: 15 minutes per level of experience or until canceled.

Power: The weapon, whether it be a dagger, sword, club, arrow, etc., inflicts the Mega-Damage equivalent of the usual S.D.C.

damage, point for point in M.D.C. settings. That is to say if the weapon, like a short sword, normally does 1D6 S.D.C. damage, the Magic Weapon inflicts 1D6 M.D., if the weapon normally does 2D6 S.D.C. it does 2D6 M.D., and so on. **Notes:** 1. The flames indicate it inflicts Mega-Damage (M.D.) in Mega-Damage environments. Since the magic tattoo creates a "magic" weapon, against an S.D.C. opponent (or in an S.D.C. environment) it does its normal S.D.C. damage +8 (its magical bonus), and the M.D. damage noted above against M.D.C. opponents.

2. The tattoo is covered in flames, but the weapon that physically manifests is not. It looks like an ordinary weapon, perhaps with a very faint glow to indicate it is a "magic" weapon that inflicts M.D.

Flaming Weapon Dripping with Blood (M.D. Double Damage)

P.P.E. to activate: 25
Duration: 15 minutes per level of experience.
Power: The weapon inflicts the Mega-Damage equivalent of the usual S.D.C. damage x2 in M.D.C. settings. That is to say if the weapon, like a short sword, normally does 1D6 S.D.C. damage, this Magic Weapon inflicts 2D6 M.D., if the weapon normally does 2D6 S.D.C. it does 4D6 M.D., and so on. **Notes:** Notes are the same as *Weapon Covered in Flames,* above. **Note:** Damage is S.D.C. against S.D.C. opponents, and M.D. against Mega-Damage opponents.

Weapon Covered in Flames and a Coiled Snake/Serpent (Serpent Slayer)

P.P.E. to Activate: 20
Duration: 15 minutes per level of experience or until canceled.
Power: The weapon inflicts its normal M.D. to most opponents, but does THREE times Mega-Damage when used against ser-

pents/snakes, dinosaurs, reptiles, reptilian D-Bees and monsters, dragons, sea serpents, Worms of Taut, and supernatural reptilian beings like the Dybbuk, Sowki, Serpent Beast and Gargoyles. If the weapon normally inflicts 2D6 S.D.C., the weapon with this tattoo does 2D6 M.D. against normal foes and 6D6 M.D. against a reptilian creatures. **Note:** Many dinosaurs, dragons and Gargoyles are not, strictly speaking, reptiles, but are associated with serpents and reptiles so they are included in this magic. Also note that damage is S.D.C. against S.D.C. opponents, and M.D. against Mega-Damage opponents.

Weapon Impaling or Smashing a Baal-Rog's Head (Demon Slayer)

P.P.E. to activate: 30
Duration: 15 minutes per level of experience or until canceled.
Power: This tattoo of a melee weapon does its usual damage to most creatures. As a Demon Slayer it does the weapon's usual damage +8 damage to all types of demons, including Deevils, etc., but inflicts double the weapon's usual damage +12 to the Demons of Hades, specifically. **Note:** Damage is S.D.C. against S.D.C. opponents, and M.D. against Mega-Damage opponents.

Weapon Impaling or Smashing a Deevil Beast's Head (Deevil Slayer)

P.P.E. to activate: 30
Duration: 15 minutes per level of experience or until canceled.

Power: This tattoo of a melee weapon does its usual damage to most creatures. As a Demon Slayer it does the weapon's usual damage +8 damage to all types of demons, including Hades demons, etc., but inflicts double the weapon's usual damage +12 to the Deevils of Dyval, specifically. **Note:** Damage is S.D.C. against S.D.C. opponents, and M.D. against Mega-Damage opponents.

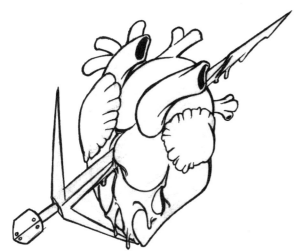

Weapon Impaling or Smashing a Heart (Anti-P.P.E.)

P.P.E. to Activate: 20
Duration: 15 minutes per level of experience or until canceled.
Powers: Instead of physical damage, this weapon inflicts damage to the target's P.P.E. base! Only affects living creatures.

Damage is equal to the normal S.D.C. damage for that weapon, except this amount is subtracted from the victim's P.P.E. For example, a tattoo of a knife which would normally inflict 1D6 S.D.C. would instead take 1D6 P.P.E. from its victim. The attack can be parried or dodged as usual, and a successful saving throw vs magic of 15 or higher will resist the attack (no P.P.E. loss). Cannot be combined with the Dripping Blood or Covered in Flames tattoo effects.

The magical tattoo weapon can also be used against magic force fields and magic barriers. The weapon does its normal S.D.C. damage in M.D. against the magical barrier. Only defenses composed entirely of magic energy (P.P.E.), such as Armor of Ithan, Energy Field, and magic walls/barriers, can be damaged in this way. Bio-Wizard or Techno-Wizard enchanted armor, magically hardened steel, Millennium Tree armor, and similar items will NOT be harmed by this magic weapon.

Weapon Impaling or Smashing a Skull (Anti-I.S.P.)

P.P.E. to Activate: 10
Duration: 15 minutes per level of experience or until canceled.
Powers: This weapon inflicts no physical damage. Instead, it inflicts damage to the target's I.S.P. base.

Damage is equal to the normal S.D.C. damage for that weapon, except this amount is subtracted from the victim's I.S.P. For example, a tattoo of a knife which would normally inflict 1D6 S.D.C. would instead take 1D6 I.S.P. from its victim. The attack can be parried or dodged as usual, and a successful saving

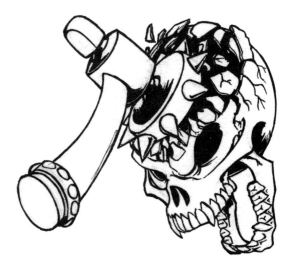

throw vs magic of 14 or higher will resist the attack (no I.S.P. loss). Cannot be combined with the Dripping Blood or Covered in Flames tattoo effects.

The weapon can also inflict damage equal to its S.D.C. damage as M.D. to defenses composed entirely of psionic energy, such as the Telekinetic Force Field and Psi-Shield. This does not include physical matter which has been strengthened through the use of psionic powers, like the stone weapons of the South American Pucara Giants.

Magic Weapon Enhancement Tattoos

In addition to the seven types of Magic Weapon tattoos, above, there are some *enhancements* or features that can be added on to the Magic Weapon, such as Wings to increase the range it can be thrown (or fired if an arrow), or Two Weapons Crossed to provide combat bonuses, and so on. Each enhancement adds to the cost to activate a particular Magic Weapon tattoo. For example, adding Wings to a Weapon Covered in Flames (10) adds 20 P.P.E., for a total cost of 30. The maximum number of enhancements that can be added to any weapon tattoo is two. If done when the tattoo is first made, they all count as one tattoo, e.g. a flame covered sword with wings, or whatever one or two enhancements are desired.

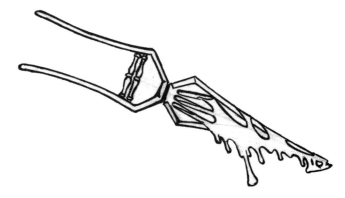

Weapon Dripping Blood (S.D.C.)
(Double S.D.C. Damage of Simple Weapons Only!)

Additional P.P.E. to Activate: 5
Duration: 15 minutes per level of experience.

Power: The weapon, whether it be an arrow, dagger, sword, club, etc., inflicts double its usual amount of S.D.C./Hit Point damage for that particular weapon. Applicable to Simple Weapons only.

Blood Splatter Around the Weapon

Additional P.P.E. to Activate: 20
Duration: 15 minutes per level of experience or until canceled.
Power: This tattoo augments that specific Magic Weapon tattoo to be far more deadly in combat for the duration. When active, the weapon does a Critical Strike (double damage) on every roll to strike that is a Natural (unmodified) 18, 19 or 20. If hand to hand skill or other bonuses already give the T-Man a Critical Strike on an 18-20, this tattoo would improve the Critical Strike of the weapon to a Natural 17-20.

Two Weapons Crossed (Combat Bonus)

Additional P.P.E. to Activate: 5
Duration: 15 minutes per level of experience or until canceled.
Power: This enhancement makes the T-Man +1 to strike and +2 to parry with ANY type of weapon that falls into the category of the weapons depicted in the tattoo (e.g. knives, clubs/maces/hammers, or axes, or swords, or spears, etc.). The weapons must be identical or similar, such as two crossed knives, two swords, etc. The bonus applies whether the T-Man is using one or both of the weapons in the tattoo, or a normal S.D.C. or M.D. weapon of the same type. The bonuses are in addition to any combat or W.P. skills the character may also possess. Crossbows and bows and arrows are NOT included with this particular type of tattoo.

Weapon Covered in Electrical Arcs

Additional P.P.E. to Activate: 20
Duration: 15 minutes per level of experience or until canceled.
Power: The enhancement gives the weapon an electricity attack. A successful strike delivers a nasty electrical jolt to his opponent, and inflicts +2D6 M.D. extra damage from the electricity. No damage occurs when the weapon is successfully parried. It can also fire an electrical blast that does 2D6 M.D.; range: 60 feet (18.3 m), each blast counts as one melee attack. Can be combined with a Weapon Covered in Flames to make the weapon inflict M.D. in all modes of attack. **Note:** Electricity damage is 2D6 S.D.C. in S.D.C. against S.D.C. opponents and 2D6 M.D. against Mega-Damage opponents.

Weapon with Flaming Gout Shooting Out

Additional P.P.E. to Activate: 20
Duration: 15 minutes per level of experience or until canceled.
Power: This enhancement enables the weapon to fire a gout of M.D. fire like a flamethrower, in addition to its normal weapon capabilities. Each flame blast counts as one of the T-Man's melee attacks and does 5D6 M.D. Range: 100 feet (30.5 m). Can be combined with a Weapon Covered in Flames to make the weapon inflict M.D. in all modes of attack. **Note:** Fire damage is 5D6 S.D.C. in S.D.C. settings and 5D6 M.D. against Mega-Damage opponents and S.D.C. against S.D.C. opponents. If combined with Flames and Dripping Blood, the fire damage remains at 5D6 M.D. and the range remains 100 feet (30.5 m).

Weapon Covered with Green or Black Thorns (poison)

Additional P.P.E. to Activate: 25

Duration: 15 minutes per level of experience or until canceled.

Power: A Magic Weapon covered with thorns inflicts contact poison. When the weapon strikes flesh, the victim must make a saving throw vs lethal poisons/toxins (a roll of 14 or better is needed to save). Cannot be combined with Dripping Blood, but can be combined with Weapon Covered in Flames (M.D.C.).

Green: On a successful save, the victim suffers an additional 1D4 M.D. (or S.D.C. damage), but is otherwise okay, no penalties nor full damage from the poison.

On a failed saving roll, green thorns impairs its victim: -3 on Perception Rolls, -2 on initiative, -2 to strike, parry, dodge, disarm, and pull punch, -1 melee attack, -20% on skill performance and reduce speed 30%. Duration is 10 minutes. The victim feels weak and focus is hazy. The penalties from multiple poisonous strikes are not cumulative, but the duration is (10 minutes for each failed save) and so is damage: +2D6 M.D. (or S.D.C. depending on the nature of the victim) from the poison per each strike. This is in addition to the weapon's usual damage.

On a failed saving roll, black thorns inflict 6D6 M.D. (or S.D.C./Hit Point damage) per each successful weapon strike. This is in addition to the usual damage inflicted by the weapon. On a successful saving throw there is only 1D4 M.D. damage.

Note: Those who have the tattoo Thorns or Ball of Thorns (protection from poison) activated prior to taking any damage are protected and automatically save from this weapon's attack. This tattoo upgrade is a favorite of Sunaj Assassins and Tattooed Archers of the Splugorth. Damage is S.D.C. against S.D.C. opponents, and M.D. against Mega-Damage opponents.

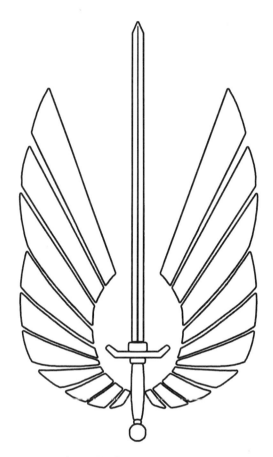

Weapon with Wings

Additional P.P.E. to activate the wing feature: 5 if a Simple Weapon (S.D.C. damage), 10 if Dripping Blood (double S.D.C. damage) or Impaling a Heart (anti-P.P.E.) or a Skull (anti-I.S.P.), 20 if Weapon Covered in Flames (an M.D. weapon), 30 if Serpent Slayer, Demon Slayer or Deevil Slayer, or Flaming and Dripping with Blood.

Duration: 15 minutes per level of experience or until canceled.

Power: The weapon can be thrown, or arrows fired, three times farther than the usual effective range and it automatically returns to the Tattooed Man immediately afterwards! Typically four arrows in the tattoo; one of any other type of weapon.

Power Tattoos

Power Tattoos bestow *magic powers* upon the Tattooed Man or gives him the ability to impose an effect upon, or attack, others. Some are utilitarian, some defensive, and others offensive in nature.

P.P.E. Cost to Activate: Varies depending on the magic imbued upon the tattoo user or his victim. Each Power Tattoo lists the cost.

Duration: As indicated under each specific Power tattoo. As always, the tattoo user may cancel the magic at any time with a mere thought. The Power tattoo remains in effect even when its creator is rendered unconscious, possessed, or is mind controlled.

Unless noted otherwise, the user of the tattoo can cancel the effects of the magic at any time with a mere thought. The effects of the tattoo magic continue even when the user is rendered unconscious, possessed, or mind controlled. In the case of possession or mind control, the controlling outside force can NOT activate any new tattoos or cancel tattoos that were activated at the moment that control was initiated. Active tattoos remain in place until the end of their duration.

Power: Varies with each type of Power Tattoo. *None* of the powers can be transferred or extended to other people, they only effect the T-Man.

Attacks per Melee: Each activation of a tattoo as well as each use of the power bestowed counts as one melee attack.

Saving Throw: Opponents trying to save versus Power tattoo magic such as the Death Touch, Empathic Transmission, etc., must roll a 16 or higher, unless stated otherwise. A successful save usually means no damage or effect. Failure to save means the victim suffers full penalties and damage.

Note: Remember, as many as 6 tattoos total can be activated at any one time unless stated otherwise in the O.C.C. or tattoo description. All effects and abilities are cumulative.

Black Sun (Darkness Powers)

P.P.E. to Activate: 40
Duration: Five minutes per level of experience.
Range: Self or a 5 foot (1.5 m) radius per level of experience
Number of Attacks: Each use of a Darkness power counts as one of the tattoo user's melee attacks.
Power: The tattoo user is given the following (limited) powers over darkness:

- Nightvision 600 feet (182.9 m), see in magic darkness, and the ability to recognize Shadow Beasts and other creatures from

the Shadow Dimension even when they are melded into the shadows. (Does NOT include Shadow Vision.)
- Shadow Meld; same as the spell.
- Cloak of Darkness; same as the spell

Beautiful Dancer (Hypnotic Gaze)

P.P.E. to Activate: 15
Duration: Duration of the effects varies with the command. The T-Man retains the ability for two minutes per level of experience.
Range: 12 feet (3.65 m) and eye contact.
Number of Attacks: Each Hypnotic Suggestion counts as two of the tattoo user's melee attacks.
Power: The tattoo user is given the psionic ability of Hypnotic Suggestion, equal to the Super-Psionic power of the same name.

Bleeding Heart (Power Punch)

P.P.E. to Activate: 20
Duration: Two minutes per level of experience or until canceled.
Power: The tattoo user is able to inflict Mega-Damage with his bare hands as if his P.S. attribute was Supernatural. Note that only the hands, arms and strength are affected, and that lifting and carrying abilities are NOT boosted to Supernatural by this magic, nor is the P.S. attribute number increased. Its sole purpose is to allow the user to inflict Mega-Damage with his bare hands.

Parry Bonus: This Magic Tattoo is sometimes called "Steel Hands," because the Power tattoo also enables the enchanted individual to parry Mega-Damage blades, flaming weapons and

even energy blasts with his bare hands! The character's usual parry bonuses apply when parrying melee weapons and attacks. No parry bonuses apply when attempting to parry energy blasts and projectile attacks and he is -5 to parry them.

For Tattooed O.C.C.s who are already M.D.C. beings with Supernatural P.S.: +6 M.D. to their physical punches, and +12 on power punches, but the latter counts as two attacks. And of course, they can parry M.D. weapons with their bare hands.

Note: Damage is S.D.C. against S.D.C. opponents, and M.D. against Mega-Damage opponents.

Chain Encircling a Skull or Brain (Bonus to Save vs Psionics)

P.P.E. to Activate: 25
Duration: One minute per level of experience or until canceled.
Power: Impervious to mind control of all types and +3 to save vs psionic attacks of any kind.

Chain with a Broken Link (Supernatural P.S.)

P.P.E. to Activate: 30
Duration: Five minutes per level of experience or until canceled.
Power: Instills or boosts Supernatural Strength (+6 to P.S. for duration of the magic). Mega-Damage is inflicted from all physical attacks, punches, kicks, head butt, power punch, etc., and lifting and carrying abilities are also boosted. Remember, +6 to P.S. is likely to bump a T-Man's Supernatural P.S. up to the next level which inflicts greater damage. **Note:** Damage is S.D.C. against S.D.C. opponents, and M.D. against Mega-Damage opponents. See Supernatural Strength list in the core rule book.

Chain Wrapped Around a Cloud (Air Powers)

P.P.E. to Activate: 50
Duration: One minute per level of experience or until canceled.
Power: Influence the elemental force of air.

- See the Invisible, the same as the spell (see *Rifts Ultimate Edition*, page 199).
- Float in the Air, same as the spell (see *Rifts Ultimate Edition*, page 202).
- Wind Rush, same as the spell (see *Rifts Ultimate Edition*, page 214).
- Call Lightning twice per melee round/every 15 seconds; same as the spell (see *Rifts Ultimate Edition*, page 209).
- Calm Storms, same as the spell (see *Rifts Ultimate Edition*, page 223).
- See Air Elementals.
- Communicate with Air Elementals.

Cracked or Broken Skull (Mental Blast)

P.P.E. to Activate: 25
Duration: Victims suffer the effects for one melee round per level of the tattoo user. The T-Man retains the ability for one minute per level of experience.
Range: Touch or 100 feet (30.5 m) plus 10 feet (3 m) per level of experience. The intended target must be visible.
Number of Attacks: Each Mental Blast counts as one of the tattoo user's melee attacks.
Saving Throw: The intended victim must roll 14 or higher to save. A successful save means no damage, no penalties.
Powers: The T-Man using this magic can cause a victim to be overcome with mind-splitting headache pain with a mere touch. The effects are as per the spell *Mental Blast.* 5D6 damage plus disorientation: -2 on initiative, -2 to strike, parry, dodge, -20% on all skills. Multiple blasts have cumulative effect. See **Rifts® Book of Magic**, page 109, for details.

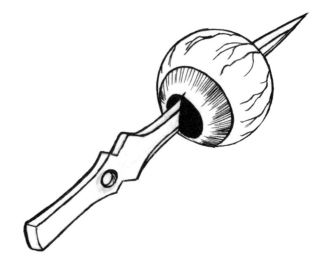

Eye with a Dagger in It (Blind)

P.P.E. to Activate: 25
Duration: The effect is instant and the victim is blinded for one melee round per level of the T-Man's experience.

The Tattooed Man possesses the blinding touch for one melee round (15 seconds) per level of his experience.
Power: Blinds an opponent by activating the tattoo and touching the intended victim. Victim needs to save vs magic, 16 or higher. A failed save means blinded (-10 to strike, parry, dodge) for one melee round (15 seconds) per level of the tattoo user.

Each blinding touch counts as one melee attack. It works on beings with natural armor, cyborgs, creatures of magic and supernatural beings, as well as those clad in M.D.C. armor and power armor with less than 350 M.D.C. or less. Power Armor with 350 M.D.C. or more blocks the magic. Cannot be used to blind people inside a vehicle by touching the vehicle or the window.

Cross (Turn Dead)

P.P.E. to Activate: 15
Duration: One minute per level of experience or until canceled.
Power: Turn Dead, equal to the invocation of the same name.

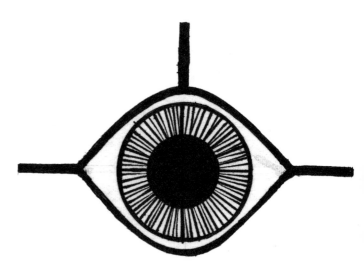

Eye of Knowledge (Language)

P.P.E. to Activate: 15
Duration: 15 minutes per level of experience or until canceled.
Power: Understands and speaks all languages equal to a skill of 96%.

Includes Literacy equal to a skill of 82% and can read and understand most written languages, but that does not include magic symbols, runes, wards or circles.

Eye of Mystic Knowledge (Magic)

P.P.E. to Activate: 20

Duration: 10 minutes per level of experience or until canceled.

Power: Can recognize magic circles, symbols, wards, and runes as being genuine articles involved in magic. 86% skill in reading and using magic scrolls, 74% skill in recognizing enchantment and possession, 62% skill of being able to read/identify specific wards and magic symbols. 50% skill in correctly identifying magic circles. 40% skill in accurately reading runes. 30% chance of correctly identifying a magic item, including weapons and artifacts.

This knowledge does not enable the character to cast spells, perform rituals or operate circles.

Note: The tattoo is an eye in a circle with two equal length lines. In many cases the eye may be inside a pyramid. A pyramid point-side up means the knowledge is only available for doing good works. A pyramid with its point facing downward means it works only when used for evil purposes. The pyramid often indicates the Tattooed Man's alignment (at least at the time he received the tattoo) and/or that it was designed to restrict a warrior slave's use of the knowledge as intended by his master/tattoo creator. The magic tattoo with this pyramid restriction does not work when contrary to its alignment, and will not work for selfish motives either.

Eye With Tears (Empathy & Transmission)

P.P.E. to Activate: 15

Duration: Two minutes per level of experience.

Power: Empathy equal to the psionic sensitive power and can perform one Empathic Transmission once per melee round; each

use counts as one melee attack. See the Rifts® core rule book for details.

Eyes: Three (Supernatural Vision)

P.P.E. to Activate: 20

Duration: Ten minutes per level of experience.

Power: Perfect vision plus the following:

- Nightvision: 1,200 feet (366 m); sees in total darkness.
- See the Invisible, including the supernatural.
- See Aura (same as psionic sensitive power).
- Bonuses: +1 on initiative and +1 to strike.

Flaming Eye (Fire Projection & Thermo-Imaging)

P.P.E. to Activate: 20

Duration: Five minutes per level of experience.

Range: 100 feet (30.5 m), plus 50 feet (15.2 m) per level of experience for the flame attack.

Number of Attacks: Each fiery blast counts as one melee attack.

Damage: 1D4 M.D. per level of experience.

Bonuses: +2 to strike with flame from the eye, but no other bonuses apply to the fire bolt shot from the eye. Each fire blast counts as one melee attack.

Powers: Provides the tattoo user with the ability to see infrared radiation (heat waves) equal to a thermo-imager with a range of 600 feet (183 m), as well as the power to fire an M.D. bolt of fire from his eyes. Range: 60 feet (18.3 m). 1D4 M.D. per level of the T-Man's experience. Damage is S.D.C. against S.D.C. opponents, and M.D. against Mega-Damage opponents.

Heart Encircled by Chains (Invulnerability)

P.P.E. to Activate: 40

Duration: 10 minutes per level of experience or until the total number of M.D.C. is depleted. The user of the tattoo can cancel the magic at will. The effects of the magic continues even when the user is rendered unconscious or mind controlled.

Power: Limited Invulnerability: A faint but visible, light blue magic aura encircles the character rather like a force field protecting him and everything on his body. Ordinary S.D.C./Hit Point damage does NO damage! The aura also provides 75 M.D.C. per level of the tattoo user. Subtract any M.D. caused by Mega-Damage attacks from the character's magical M.D.C. aura. This includes damage from falls, collisions, explosions, energy blasts, Supernatural P.S. punches, and even poison, gas, and drugs. When the M.D.C. is used up and gone, the limited invulnerability magic continues to protect against S.D.C. attacks until the duration elapses or the magic is canceled.

Vulnerabilities: It does not protect against magic clouds, psionic attacks or many types of magic, only those that do physical damage. The character is, of course vulnerable to magic that immobilizes, entangles, and influences the mind and senses, like Domination and Blind, for example. Physical attacks created by psionics such as Psi-Sword or spells that do damage like Call Lightning and Fire Ball, do damage to the magic aura until it is whittled down to zero. Likewise, spells such as Light Target, Befuddle and Charm are not stopped by invulnerability since they do not cause direct physical damage.

Heart with Large Wings (Fly)

P.P.E. to Activate: 20

Duration: 30 minutes per level of experience or until canceled by the user of the tattoo.

Power: The tattoo user can fly at a speed of 50 mph (80 km) plus 10 mph (16 km) per level of experience. Maximum height is limited to 4,000 feet (1,219 m) above the ground. The effects of the magic continues even when the user is rendered unconscious or mind controlled, which means he will float 2D6 feet (0.6 to 3.6

m) above the ground and float in the direction of the wind at a rate of about five miles (8 km) an hour.

Bonuses when Flying: +1 to strike and dodge, +1 when the tattoo user reaches levels 4, 8 and 12, and +3 to damage from hand to hand attacks due to height and speed advantage. **Note:** Damage is S.D.C. against S.D.C. opponents, and M.D. against Mega-Damage opponents.

Heart with Tiny Wings (Speed)

P.P.E. to Activate: 10

Duration: 30 minutes per level of experience or until canceled by the user of the tattoo. The magic remains in place when the user is rendered unconscious, possessed or mind controlled.

Power: Run at Superhuman Speed: 30 mph (48 km) plus 10 mph (16 km) per level of experience. He can also leap up to 20 feet (6 m) high or 30 feet (9 m) lengthwise from a running start and at a speed of at least 30 mph (48 km).

Bonuses: +1 to dodge (when running) at levels 1, 4, 8 and 12; +2 to damage in melee combat due to speed advantage. Supernatural beings, like Undead Slayers, inflict an extra +1D4 M.D. for every 30 mph (48 km).

Heart Pierced by a Wooden Stake (Protection)

P.P.E. to Activate: 15

Duration: One hour per level of experience or until canceled.

Power: The T-Man gains the following power:

● Immune to the Pheromone Induced Seduction.

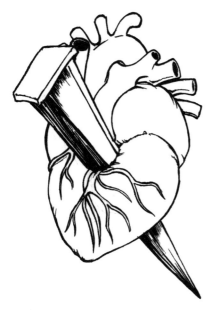

- The character is impervious to the slow kill bite, and cannot be turned into a vampire or enslaved.
- Impervious to all the mind control powers of vampires and related species of undead.
- When the magic tattoo is first activated, a wooden stake and a cross appears, one in each hand. Both disappear when the duration ends or the tattoo magic is cancelled.

Note: Though greatly protected by this magic tattoo, the vampire can hurt and even kill a Tattooed O.C.C. like the Undead Slayer by using killing bite attacks, the brute force of punches, claws, etc., and via weapons or magic.

Heart in Two Pieces (Strength Drain)

P.P.E. to Activate: 30
Duration: Victims suffer the effects for one melee round per level of the tattoo user's experience.

The Tattooed Man retains the ability for one minute per level of experience.
Range: Touch.
Number of Attacks: Each use counts as two melee attacks.
Powers: At first, the victim of this attack feels nothing but a simple touch or the strength of a punch. But when he attempts to return the blow, its effects are apparent. Unless the victim makes a successful saving throw vs magic of 14 or higher, he finds his P.S. attribute temporarily reduced by half! Reduce all damage stats and bonuses appropriately, and even lesser supernatural creatures and creatures of magic suffer from the loss of strength. Greater Demons, Demon Lords, Godlings, gods, the undead and adult dragons, *are immune* to this magic.

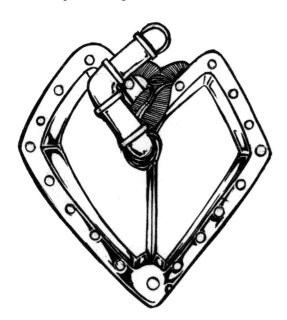

Heart of Steel (Courage)

P.P.E. to Activate: 25
Duration: Five minutes per level of experience.
Range: Self.
Powers: Provides the tattoo user with resistance to fear and the following bonuses:

+4 to save vs Horror Factor and all fear inducing attacks.
+2 to save vs illusions and mind control.
+5 to save vs possession.

Heart Wrapped in Thorns (Poison Touch)

P.P.E. to Activate: 35
Duration: Effects last one minute per level of experience. The tattoo user retains the ability for two minutes per level of experience.

Range: Touch.

Number of Attacks: Each poisonous touch counts as one melee attack.

Powers: This magic can cause a victim to feel as if he has been poisoned. Potential victims may roll a saving throw vs magic of 14 or higher. A successful save means the attack fails and no penalties are inflicted. A failed saving throw means the victim believes he has been poisoned and suffers from the following psychosomatic penalties: Attacks per melee and speed are reduced by half, -4 to all combat bonuses, is -4 to save vs real poisons and toxins, is -30% on all skills and feels dizzy, nauseous and ill.

Lightning Bolts (Shoots Lightning)

P.P.E. to Activate: 30

Duration: One minute (4 melee rounds) per level of experience or until canceled.

Range: 200 feet (61 m) plus 100 feet (30.5 m) per level of experience; +3 to strike and only bonuses from the P.P. attribute can be added to this strike bonus; hand to hand and W.P. bonuses are not applicable.

Number of Attacks: Each bolt counts as one melee attack.

Damage: 2D6 M.D. plus 1D6 M.D. per every two levels of experience; i.e.: 2D6 at first level, 3D6 at second level, 4D6 at fourth level, 5D6 at sixth level and so on. The user can regulate the amount of damage a lightning bolt can inflict in increments of 1D6. **Note:** Damage is S.D.C. against S.D.C. opponents, and M.D. against Mega-Damage opponents.

Power: The tattoo user can fire lightning bolts from his hands. The character simply points and mentally releases the lightning bolt.

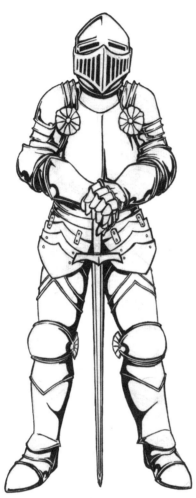

Knight in Full Body Armor

P.P.E. to Activate: 25

Duration: 30 minutes per level of experience, or until M.D.C. is depleted, or until the magic is canceled, or duration time ends.

Power: Magic, M.D.C. body armor appears on the body of the tattoo user. The armor is transparent so the other tattoos can still be seen. The T-Man's hand can pass right through the armor, like air, in order to touch and activate other tattoos, but to all others the armor is as solid as M.D.C. alloys! The armor is weightless and does not restrict movement in any way.

M.D.C. of the Armor: 35 M.D.C. per level of the tattoo user's experience. **Note:** The armor cannot be placed on another person; it magically appears on the tattoo user. The armor is not like modern environmental suits and does not protect the wearer from toxic air, fumes, gases, or foul smells. **Note:** Armor is S.D.C. with an A.R. of 17 in S.D.C. environments and M.D.C. in Mega-Damage environments.

Rose and Thorny Stem Dripping Blood (Healing)

P.P.E. to Activate: 30

Duration: One minute per level of experience or until canceled. As many as three healing touches can be performed every minute. Each healing counts as two of the character's melee attacks.

Range: Touch.

Power: With the touch of his hand the tattoo user is able to heal wounds and injuries; restoring 1D6 Hit Point damage and 3D6 S.D.C. (or 1D6+3 M.D. to Mega-Damage beings) per each touch. Three healings per melee round are possible.

Shark or Dolphin (Swim)

P.P.E. to Activate: 20
Duration: 30 minutes per level of experience or until canceled.
Range: Self.
Power: The tattoo user can swim like a fish at a speed of 20 mph (32 km), breathe without air, swim at a proficiency of 98%, at a maximum depth of two miles (3.2 km). Underwater combat bonuses: +2 to parry and dodge in water.

Phoenix Rising from the Flames (Resurrection)

P.P.E. to Activate: 124 and see note.
Duration: Instant, with permanent results.
Range: Touch or within 12 feet (3.7 m).
Power: Super-healing and resurrection of others! Using the power to super-heal will restore up to 50 Hit Points and 50 S.D.C. points, or 100 M.D.C. if the character being healed is a Mega-Damage creature. Furthermore, the super-healing cures all types of common diseases, Magic Minor Disorders, Magic Sickness, Minor Curse, and turns a victim of Petrification back to flesh. Forms of insanity, magic insanity and addiction are not cured via this magic.

Resurrection is possible only if performed within six hours after the moment of death. The magical resurrection costs 124 P.P.E. and brings the dead person up to three Hit Points and restores/regenerates missing limbs and organs and completely heals all wounds without scarring.

Resurrection Costs: 124 P.P.E., plus the cost of performing a resurrection has a lasting effect on the tattoo user. *The character permanently loses* 1D6 Hit Points or M.D.C., 2D6 P.P.E. points, and one P.E. attribute point of his own each time a resurrection is performed. However, he permanently gains one M.A. point. There are no penalties for performing a super-healing.

Skeleton in Chains (Constrain the Undead)

P.P.E. to Activate: 20
Duration: One minute per level of experience.
Range: Touch or up to 200 feet (61 m) away.
Number of Attacks: Each use of this ability counts as one melee attack.
Powers: The tattoo user can keep the undead at bay. With the wave of a hand, he can cause any one undead to freeze in its tracks for 1D4 melee rounds. Only one undead can be affected at a time. Mummies, zombies, and similar unintelligent undead have no saving throw against this magic. Most others, like vampires, can attempt to resist the magic and have a saving throw of 14 or higher. Master Vampires and other superior undead are immune to the magic's effects.

Skull with Bat Wings (Animate Dead)

P.P.E. to Activate: 30
Duration: Five minutes per level of experience or until canceled.
Power: Animate and Control Dead, same as the spell invocation of the same name.

Skull Coiled with Thorns (Death Touch)

P.P.E. to Activate: 40
Duration: Two minutes per level of experience or until canceled.
Power: Limited power over death (well, sort of). The tattoo user is enveloped in an eerie, pale white glow. The aura instills in him the following: +25% to save vs coma/death, +6 to save vs poison and deadly gases/vapors, +6 to save vs Horror Factor, +1 to save on all other saving throws, one super bio-regeneration (self: restores 1D4x10 S.D.C. and 6D6 Hit Points, or 1D6x10+10 M.D.C. if a Mega-Damage being).

Upon others, the tattoo user can inflict the Death Touch.
Death Touch Number of Attacks: Each Death Touch counts as two melee attacks.
Range: Touch and will penetrate M.D. body armor and magic armor, but not robots, vehicles or power armor with 160 M.D.C. or more.
Bonuses: +1 to strike and parry in addition to normal bonuses.
Damage from Death Touch or Death Blow: Each punch that strikes or even a gentle touch inflicts an additional 1D6 points

of damage directly to Hit Points or 3D6 M.D. to Mega-Damage creatures like dragons, demons, fellow Tattooed O.C.C.s, etc. Potential victims roll to save vs magic (needs a 16 or higher to save). A successful saving throw means NO damage is caused by the Death Touch – this time. If a character is killed by a Death Touch (six or more touches that inflict damage), he is -12% to save vs coma/death.

Note: The Death Touch will awaken victims who are sleeping and even unconscious characters get an automatic saving throw. Characters of a good, and even selfish alignment seldom select this power. Assassins (Sunaj) on the other hand, love it.

Skull Engulfed in Flames (Fire Powers)

P.P.E. to Activate: 45
Duration: Five minutes per level of experience or until canceled.
Power: The tattoo user is enveloped in an eerie, red glow that resembles heat vapors and wisps of fire that appear and disappear in a random pattern across the body. The magic makes him impervious to fire and heat, including magic and Mega-Damage fires (no damage). Lasers and all other forms of energy do half damage, and the glowing aura provides 60 M.D.C. points of protection. When the bonus 60 M.D.C. is depleted, the other powers remain.

The tattoo user can also shoot bolts of fire from his finger-tips. He simply points and mentally releases the fiery blast.
Number of Attacks: Each fire blast counts as one melee attack.
Damage: 1D4 M.D. per level of experience. The user can regulate the amount of damage a fire bolt can inflict in increments of 1D4.
Range: 100 feet (30.5 m) per level of experience.
Bonuses: +2 to strike. Only bonuses from the P.P. attribute can be added to this strike bonus, hand to hand and W.P. bonuses are not applicable.
Note: Damage is S.D.C. against S.D.C. opponents, and M.D. against Mega-Damage opponents.

Thorns or Ball of Thorns (Protection from Poison)

P.P.E. to Activate: 15
Duration: 10 minutes per level of experience or until canceled.
Power: Impervious to all forms of poison and +2 to save vs all types of drugs, chemicals, and gases.

Wolf's Head with Glowing Eyes (Hunting Prowess)

P.P.E. to Activate: 30
Duration: Five minutes per level of experience.
Range: Self.
Bonuses: +1 to initiative.
Powers: Similar to the magic spell, Eyes of the Wolf, but with some modifications.
- Nightvision 100 feet (30.5 m)
- Recognize and track animals by sight: 01%-50%
- Identify edible plants, fruits and meat: 01%-75%
- Sense traps: 01%-35%

New Power Tattoos

Over the millennia, Atlanteans have created new Power tattoos. Alchemists and Tattoo Masters regularly collaborate and share their newest creations with their fellow Atlanteans. The following are new tattoos created in recent decades. Naturally, the Splugorth have been able to get their tentacles on these new tattoos, so it is likely many, if not all, may be seen on Splugorth Tattooed Warrior Slaves as well.

Orb with a Flame Within It (Fire Globe)

P.P.E. to Activate: 40
Duration: The Fire Globe lasts one hour per level of experience or until it is used.
Damage: 5D6 M.D. at the moment of impact and 5D6 additional M.D. per melee round for 1D4 minutes (4-14 melees).
Power: Activating the tattoo creates one portable globe containing a magical fire. Like the spell of the same name, this "Fire Globe" is about the size of a grapefruit and flickers as if a fire burns inside (which it does), but no heat or significant amount of light radiates from it. The globe can be handled and put in a bag or backpack for later use without fear of starting a fire until it is thrown and it ignites. Upon impact, the fire inside erupts like napalm, covering the surface body of its target in flame. It burns for 1D4 minutes and then vanishes or until it is extinguished. It can be put out with magic or by rolling in dirt or being covered in dirt, sand, or other substance to smother the flame. The use of water to extinguish the fire hurts, creates steam and inflicts 2D6 M.D. (scalding) before the fire is extinguished.

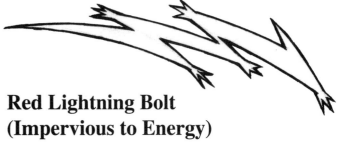

Red Lightning Bolt (Impervious to Energy)

P.P.E. to Activate: 40
Duration: One melee round per level of experience.
Power: This temporarily makes the tattoo user impervious to all energy based attacks. Physical attacks such as punches, kicks, arrows, bullets, rail gun rounds, and explosives do full damage.

Blazing Comet

(Space Flight as per spell in Fleets of the Three Galaxies)

P.P.E. to Activate: 40

Duration: 30 minutes per level of experience.

Power: The tattoo user can hover and fly in space totally protected from the elements and can move as easily as a Cosmo Knight. Flight speed is Mach One (767 mph/1,227 km) per level of experience and the individual has zero-G movement and a protective aura with 20 M.D.C. per level of experience. The T-Man appears to be wearing a blue, glowing force field. The protection from vacuum remains in place even if all the M.D.C. protection is depleted. This tattoo is most common for Atlanteans who travel in the Three Galaxies and engage in space exploration.

Eye of Mystic Knowledge in a Red Circle with a Slash Through It (Negate Magic)

P.P.E. to Activate: 40

Duration: Instant.

Power: When a T-Man is attacked magically and fails his saving throw, this tattoo can be activated to cancel the effect of the enchantment. Works the same as the Negate Magic spell. The T-Man can try to negate any magical effects cast upon him, or another by touch, by activating this tattoo.

Eye of Mystic Knowledge Encircled by Chains (Magic Resistance)

P.P.E. to Activate: 20

Duration: Five minutes per level of experience.

Power: This tattoo allows the tattoo user further resistance to magic attacks. The T-Man is +2 to save vs all types of magic and enables him to see the invisible.

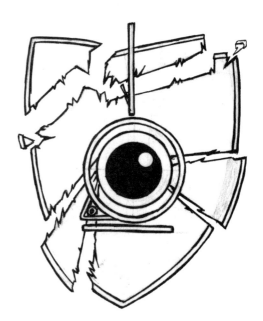

Eye of Mystic Knowledge on a Broken Shield (Dispel Magic Barriers)

P.P.E. to Activate: 45

Duration: Instant.

Power: The T-Man can attempt to dispel a magic barrier that bars his path by touching it and activating this tattoo. The effects are the same as the spell Dispel Magic Barriers.

Fire Dragon's Head
(Impervious to Fire)

P.P.E. to Activate: 20
Duration: Ten minutes per level of experience.
Power: Activation makes the tattoo user impervious to all forms of heat and fire, including magic fire, M.D. plasma, lava, etc.

Fire Dragon's Head Breathing Fire

P.P.E. to Activate: 30
Duration: Five minutes per level of experience.
Power: Activation gives the tattoo user control over the element of fire and can perform ONE of the following powers. Only one power can be selected and used whenever this tattoo is activated.

1. Breathe Fire: Four times per melee round, the tattoo user can breathe fire doing 5D6 M.D. Range is 5 feet (1.5 m) per level of experience. Each breath attack counts as one melee attack. The ability can be used for five minutes per level of experience.

2. Wall of Flame: The T-Man can create a wall of flame that is 10 feet (3 m) long, by 5 feet (1.5 m) thick, by 10 feet (3 m) high per level of experience. Damage from the flames is 4D6 M.D. for every 5 feet (1.5 m) traveled through the fire. The size of all dimensions increases by 5 feet (1.5 m) every level of experience. The wall remains for five minutes per level of experience.

Note: Damage is S.D.C. against S.D.C. opponents, and M.D. against Mega-Damage opponents.

Gas Mask or Air Breathing Mask
(Impervious to Vacuum)

P.P.E. to Activate: 15
Duration: Ten minutes per level of experience.

Power: This tattoo shields the tattoo user from the effects of a vacuum. The T-Man can breathe and function normally in a vacuum without needing any sort of space suit for protection. However, if there is no gravity the individual must find a way to secure/anchor himself or move in space, otherwise he drifts away.

This tattoo also protects the tattoo user from toxic air, poisonous gas and for breathing in environments without air, including underwater (and survive ocean depths up to two miles/3.2 km). It also negates the effects of any spells that create vacuums.

Ice Dragon's Head
(Impervious to Cold)

P.P.E. to Activate: 20
Duration: Ten minutes per level of experience.
Power: Activation makes the tattoo user impervious to all cold-based attacks, including magic spells, ice breath attacks, ice-cold water, the vacuum of space, and sub-zero environments, etc.

Ice Dragon's Head Breathing Ice

P.P.E. to Activate: 30
Duration: Five minutes per level of experience.
Power: The tattoo user can manipulate the ice on several levels with this tattoo. Only ONE power can be used when this tattoo is activated, pick one.

1. Breathe Frost: Four times per melee, the tattoo user can expel an icy frost breath that does 4D6 M.D. Range is 5 feet (1.5 m) per level of experience. Each breath attack counts as one melee attack. The ability can be used for five minutes per level of experience.

2. Ice Blade: The T-Man can fire a large, machete-sized shard of ice from his hand that does 3D6 M.D. +1 M.D. per level of experience. Range is 20 feet (6.1 m) per level of experience. Each ice dagger blast counts as one melee attack.

Nuclear Symbol
(Sub-Particle Acceleration)

P.P.E. to Activate: 40
Duration: One melee round per level of experience.
Power: The tattoo user is impervious to radiation of all kinds.

The T-Man can fire energy blasts from his hands. The damage is 1D4x10 M.D., +2 M.D. per level of experience. Range is 30

feet (9.1 m) per level of experience. Each energy blast counts as two melee attacks.

Note: Damage is S.D.C. against S.D.C. opponents, and M.D. against Mega-Damage opponents.

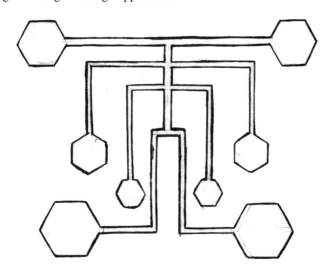

Power Matrix (Energize Tattoo)

P.P.E. to Activate: Five to activate Power Matrix, plus the P.P.E. cost of the magic tattoo the user wants to extend via the Power Matrix. Or 5 P.P.E. to activate and make available the P.P.E. stored in the Power Matrix for casting spells or the activation of other tattoos or magic devices.

Duration: Doubles or continues for another full duration the powers/abilities and duration of another tattoo, or immediately makes available energy stored in the Power Matrix to activate one or more magic tattoos within the usual limitation of no more than six magic tattoos active at any one time.

Power: There are situations where the tattoo user may not want an active magic tattoo's duration and abilities to end. The P.P.E. stored in the *Power Matrix tattoo* can be used to extend the duration of that tattoo with but a thought. Applicable to any type of magic tattoo.

It is used only to extend the duration of an active tattoo and as an energy reserve with which to activate other magic tattoos when he has used up his own P.P.E. or extra P.P.E. is required.

P.P.E. Reserve: The Power Matrix can hold 10 P.P.E. per level of the tattoo user. It can be recharged with P.P.E. two ways. One, by the T-Man channeling his own P.P.E. into the Matrix via med-

itation at the rate of 10 P.P.E points an hour, or by channeling the ambient P.P.E. of a ley line or nexus point at a rate of 20 P.P.E. per hour. The energy is available until spent. When used up, the tattoo user must consciously channel new P.P.E. into it or the Power Matrix remains empty or with whatever is left.

Rose Encircling a Heart (Bio-Regeneration)

P.P.E. to Activate: 50
Duration: One minute per level of experience.
Power: Activation of this tattoo Bio-Regenerates physical damage at a rate of 4D6 M.D.C. per melee round (once every 15 seconds). S.D.C. beings see 4D6 Hit Points or 4D6 S.D.C. restored, whichever needs regeneration. Hit Points are restored first, then S.D.C.

Star Field (Zero Gravity Movement)

P.P.E. to Activate: 10
Duration: Ten minutes per level of experience.
Power: This tattoo grants the T-Man the skill of Zero Gravity Movement at 98%. See **Rifts® Dimension Book 2, Phase World®** for complete details.

White Skull on a Black Shield (Sense Evil)

P.P.E. to Activate: 5

Duration: Five minutes per level of experience.

Power: This tattoo lets the T-Man sense the presence of evil as per the Sense Evil psionic ability. Range is 25 feet (7.6 m) per level of experience.

Defender Power Tattoos

These two powerful tattoos have been specifically developed for the defense and protection of Atlantean settlements from supernatural foes and other enemies by creating the magical equivalent of a light power armor (Crystal Guardian) and a large combat robot (the Crystal Super-Guardian). The mystic energy of the Guardian and Super-Guardian Power Tattoos integrate with the crystal armors created by a Crystal Mage and/or Atlantean Alchemist (or Chiang-Ku dragon). Both are formidable combat units with excellent M.D.C. and armor with regenerative capabilities. They both also allow the warrior to access and continue to use his magic tattoos while inside them.

Both tattoos are exclusive to the *Tattooed Defender O.C.C.*, imparted to them in a secret ritual that only Tattooed Defenders are trained to use. Part of that training involves a willingness to use magical constructs that are killing you – draining you of your life essence – while you wear them. Like true heroes, Tattooed Defenders are blasé about the whole situation, pointing out that everyone who goes to battle whether it's on foot or inside a combat vehicle is putting their life on the line. True enough, but they are not being slowly killed by the combat vehicle they pilot.

Crystal Guardian Armor

Exclusive to the Tattooed Defender

P.P.E. to Activate: 25 plus life energy of the wearer!

Duration: One hour per level of experience of the Defender; double on ley lines, at stone pyramids and in sunlight (solar and magic powered). Deactivates when taken off.

Range: Armor by touch.

Number of Attacks: Same as the Tattooed Defender inside +1.

Damage: As per the *Create Crystal Guardian Armor spell.*

Bonuses and Limitations: As per the *Create Crystal Guardian Armor* spell, page 132, includes laser fire.

Powers: The tattoo user is able to don Crystal Guardian environmental armor to combat invaders and the forces of evil. The Guardian armor functions as a magical, light power armor. It is solar energy and ley line powered, which is perfect for the Tattooed Defender whose job description includes defending stone pyramids which are always located along ley lines and harness their energy.

As a rule, a Tattooed Defender is issued a Crystal Guardian (or Crystal Super-Guardian) for special missions and as necessary for the defense of an Atlantean colony, pyramids, or clan. Like fighter pilots, the Tattooed Defender leaps into his Crystal Guardian and charges into battle. Most Tattooed Defenders do not own their own Guardian Armor, however, some officers and renowned Defender heroes are awarded Guardian Armor for outstanding service to their city or clan.

See the *Create Crystal Guardian Armor spell* for complete stats, details and abilities, page 132.

Crystal Super-Guardian

Exclusive to the Tattooed Defender

P.P.E. to Activate: 40 plus life energy of the wearer!

Duration: 30 minutes per level of experience; double in sunlight, on ley lines and at stone pyramids (solar and magic powered). It also draws on the Defender's own life force, so the warrior needs to be conscious of this. It is recommended not to be worn for more than 6-8 hours at a time. The magic tattoo combines with the magic in the Golem-like body to make it fully powered and energized the entire time it is worn. Deactivates when the Tattooed Defender steps out of it.

Range: Armor by touch.

Number of Attacks: As per the *Create Super-Guardian spell,* which includes bonus attacks added to the character's own.

Damage: As per the *Create Super-Guardian spell.*

Bonuses: As per the *Create Super-Guardian spell*; includes laser fire.

Powers: The tattoo user is able to merge with the powerful Crystal Super-Guardian Armor to combat invaders and the forces of evil. The Super-Guardian armor functions as a sort of magical crystal combat robot or Golem operated by a pilot inside, i.e. the Tattooed Defender. It is solar energy and ley line powered, which is perfect for the Tattooed Defender whose job description includes defending stone pyramids which are always located along ley lines and harness their energy.

As a rule, a Tattooed Defender is issued a Super-Guardian (or Guardian armor) for special missions and as necessary for the defense of an Atlantean colony, pyramids, or clan. Like a giant robot pilot, the Tattooed Defender leaps into his Crystal Super-Guardian and charges into battle. Most Tattooed Defenders do not own their own Super-Guardian, however, some officers and renowned Defender heroes are awarded a Super-Guardian Pseudo-Golem for outstanding service to their city or clan.

See the *Create Super-Guardian Pseudo-Golem spell* for complete stats, details and abilities, page 133.

Sunaj Power Tattoos

The Alchemists and Tattoo Masters of the Aerihman clan have been working overtime to come up with unique variations of power tattoos that give their legions of Sunaj an edge with assassinations. So far, they are meeting with some success, but unfortunately they had to share this knowledge with their Splugorth Masters to keep up the facade that they are willing minions. So the Splugorth now also possess these tattoos for their T-Men minions. These tattoos are limited to the Aerihman clan's Sunaj Assassins, Sunaj Shadow Assassins and Shadow Mages, and the Tattooed Minions of Splugorth.

Black Hooded Cloak (Cloak of Darkness)

P.P.E. to Activate: 12
Duration: Four minutes per level of experience.
Power: Like the Cloak of Darkness spell, the tattoo user is cloaked in a field of darkness that follows him everywhere. The character can see perfectly from within the darkness, but those outside the radius of magic cannot see in. At night, it renders the cloaked individual virtually invisible, although he can still be detected by infrared and/or heat sensors, thermo-imaging optics, motion detectors and similar sensor systems. Furthermore, the aura of darkness may noticeably obscure a particular part of the area around him, making it obvious to visual detection, especially in daylight or when bathed in light – the magic darkness cannot be dispelled by ordinary light. Consequently, this cloaking spell is ideal in darkness for hiding, escape and setting up an ambush.

In combat, opponents who attack a character cloaked in darkness from any distance (beyond the 5 feet/1.5 m area of magic) are -3 to strike, unless guided by thermo-optics or similar heat-based optic systems, and even then are -1 to strike. Those who step into the darkness for hand to hand combat will see their quarry without difficulty; no penalty unless they step outside the 5 foot (1.5 m) radius of effect.

Camouflaged Cloak (Chameleon)

P.P.E. to Activate: 12
Duration: Five minutes per level of experience.
Power: Like the Chameleon spell, the color and pattern of the tattoo user's clothes and physical body magically change to blend into the surrounding environment and disappear from sight. Movement destroys the effectiveness of this magic. The character is 90% undetectable if unmoving. 70% undetectable if moving 2 feet (0.6 m) per melee round or slower. 20% undetectable if moving 6 feet (1.8 m) per melee round. Totally ineffective if moving any faster. The magic is effective against normal vision, see the invisible and most optic systems. A thermo-imager is likely to reveal the character, especially if he is hiding in a cold environment. However, if the air temperature or a machine he is hiding against is around the same temperature as his body temperature (within five degrees), the character is concealed even from it. Movement will register on motion detection systems.

Closed Eye (Invisibility: Superior)

P.P.E. to Activate: 30
Duration: 10 minutes per level of experience.
Power: Like the Invisibility: Superior spell, the tattoo user is invisible on the prowl and totally undetectable by all types of electronic equipment. He becomes visible only when engaging in a hostile action. The T-Man can activate any tattoo while invisible, unless it directly relates to a hostile action/attack, turning him visible.

Coiled Rope or Grappling Hook

P.P.E. to Activate: 10
Duration: On hour per level of experience.

Power: Once activated, the T-Man points his hand and a magical grappling hook is fired. It sticks/catches to its intended target and has 200 feet (61 m) of length per level of experience. It automatically reels in the rope, raising the Sunaj to the location of the hook. The Sunaj is pulled along at a rate of 50 feet (15 m) per melee round.

Explosion (Self-Destruction)

P.P.E. to Activate: 20 (self) or 40 (self and collateral damage).
Duration: Permanent; instant effect.
Range: Self only for the cost of 20 P.P.E., or with a blast radius of 10 feet (3 m; half as far if the Sunaj is wearing armor at the time).
Damage: Self or area effect. <u>Self</u>: At 20 P.P.E. the tattoo wearer immolates in a matter of 1D6 seconds as if on fire from the inside out. The remains of the body quickly turn into burned ash and start to collapse in on itself when a small explosion sends ash and charcoalized bits of ash flying in a poof of energy. If inside armor at the time, the suit is filled with ash and all electronics are burned to a crisp. There is nothing left to identify the body; the remains too cremated to provide any usable DNA. This is a painful but quick death (seconds). There is no collateral damage except to those who may have been touching or leaning over the body as it burns up. They take 1D6 M.D.

<u>Area Effect Explosion</u>: At a cost of 40 P.P.E., the explosion is greater and does damage to an area. The body is vaporized in a sudden explosion. Everything within a 10 foot (3 m) blast radius suffers 4D6 M.D. If the Sunaj is wearing armor, it blows apart, suffers 2D4x10 M.D. from the inside, and electronics are completely fried. Death is instant and there is absolutely nothing left to identify. The area effect explosion is used whenever the Sunaj has enough P.P.E. to completely vaporize himself and to hurt his enemies in one last defiant moment.

Power: This tattoo causes the wearer's body to explode, killing him instantly and disintegrating his body so that nothing is left behind to identify him; no blood, hair, teeth or even skin cells. This usually destroys the Sunaj's armor as well, sending it flying into many pieces and rendered useless and difficult to study.

Needless to say, this tattoo can only be activated once, and it is only ever used if capture is imminent or more likely, has already occurred. And even then, if there is any hope of escape, rescue, or otherwise preventing the Sunaj's identity from being revealed,

the self-destruct tattoo is not used until the last moment. This tattoo is reserved for only the most hopeless situations, and it is one of the reasons the identity of the Sunaj remains such a mystery.

This tattoo is exclusive to the Sunaj. Other Atlanteans, Tattooed Men, and even the Chiang-Ku are completely unaware of its existence, let alone how to create it. Even if the Splugorth had knowledge of it, they would never put it on their warrior slaves; the last thing they want is to give them a way to kill themselves.

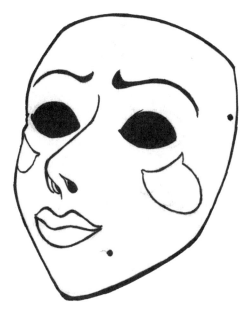

Porcelain Mask (Mask of Deceit)

P.P.E. to Activate: 25
Duration: One hour per level of experience.
Power: Like the Mask of Deceit spell, the tattoo user can mold a mask to cover his face with a thought. Skin tone, hair color, eye color and facial hair are all part of the disguise. He can attempt to imitate a specific person at 20% +3% per level of experience (+10% to the disguise skill) or simply make himself look like Joe Average. Only the face is disguised by the mask. Everyone who encounters the disguised character gets a save vs magic, but is -4 to succeed. A successful save means the true features are seen, not the mask. However, those who don't really pay attention or care who the character might be, are automatically fooled by the deception (no chance to save).

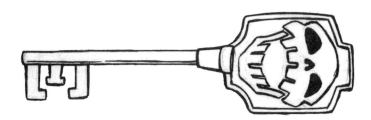

Silver or Gold Key (Escape)

P.P.E. to Activate: 15
Duration: Instant.
Power: Like the Escape spell, activation of tattoo enables the T-Man to escape any bond or open any locking mechanism that bars his way.

This includes being tied with rope, handcuffs, doors, etc.

Dimension Tattoos

Dimension Tattoos are fundamentally the same as other magic tattoos, but with a focus on dimensional travel and teleportation. These specialized Power tattoos are typically reserved for *Atlantean Tattooed Voyagers* as they are best trained in how to utilize them to their fullest potential. Should a Dimension tattoo be placed on anyone other than an Atlantean Voyager, it costs 50% more P.P.E. and P.E. points to activate the tattoo. The only exception being *Chiang-Ku dragons* as they are the creators and masters of magic tattoos.

It should be noted that some of the tattoos drain more than P.P.E. In some instances, they drain the Tattooed Voyager of Physical Endurance (P.E.) points. This drain is temporary and all spent P.E. points do return after complete rest at a rate of one point per hour of sleep or rest, or two points per hour of meditation.

Remember to adjust P.E. bonuses accordingly when they are spent. If the Tattooed Voyager's P.E. dropped to half or less, the character functions as fatigued and exhausted. All combat bonuses are temporarily reduced by half, and -2 attacks per melee until the T-Man can rest and recover (must have half or more of his P.E. number). If P.E. is dropped to zero or below, the Voyager collapses into a coma, is vulnerable and could die without receiving medical attention. Magical Healing touch only restores one P.E. point per spell casting!

The process of receiving a Dimension Tattoo is similar to receiving a Power Tattoo. The only difference is that the debilitating effects last longer. Damage is 6D6 S.D.C./Hit Points (or M.D.C. as the case may be) and it causes severe pain for 1D4 days. The limb where the tattoo is located is black and blue, stiff and painful to the extent it can barely move. For the duration there is a throbbing ache accompanied by stabbing pain that shoots through the whole body, and the recipient suffers from nausea and weakness from the pain and physical exhaustion. Reduce speed by 80%, combat bonuses to zero (no bonuses for the 1D4 days duration), attacks per melee by half, and suffers a -40% to the performance of all skills for the duration (1D4 days).

At the end of the 1D4 days, the Tattooed Man is well on the road to recovery and normalcy. The pain is a dull throb and only hurts when the individual exerts himself in combat or heavy work, not in normal activity. All penalties, above, are reduced by half, and after another 1D4 days, they are back to full health and performance. **Note:** No magic, psionics or Healing Pyramid, reduces the pain or its duration. The recipient of the magic tattoo needs to tough it out. In fact, all True Atlanteans (and Chiang-Ku) know that because the tattoo and accompanying pain and damage is *magical in nature*, trying to stop the pain or shorten its duration with healing magic or by other means risks undoing the magic ritual to create the tattoo, and therefore rendering the tattoo powerless. All Tattooed Men know that to receive a magic tattoo they must endure the debilitating recovery process.

Atlanteans do not know if the Splugorth possess Dimension Magic tattoos. It is assumed they do, but they do not give these tattoos to common slaves like the Maxi-Man or T-Monster Men. Which suggests they may reserve them for elite minions only, or they do *not* know the secrets to these tattoos. Or perhaps, do not trust slaves and lesser minions with them.

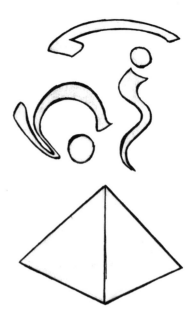

Pyramid with Atlantean Clan Symbol or Crest
(Dimensional Teleport to a Stone Pyramid)

P.P.E. to activate: 30 +2 P.E. points.
Duration: Instant.
Power: This tattoo is created in the Atlantean's home pyramid where the magic ritual binds the recipient of the tattoo to this specific pyramid and its connecting ley lines. No matter what dimension the Atlantean is in, he can activate the magic tattoo and Dimensional Teleport to that pyramid. This connection is to a specific pyramid location and the Tattooed Man always appears at that one location every time the tattoo is activated. The Atlantean can bring with him an additional 30 pounds (13.5 kg) per level of experience, so experienced Atlantean Voyagers may be able to take anther person or some equipment or loot back with them when they D-port back home; depending on the weight and level of the Tattooed Man.

In the event that something happens to the pyramid, the tattoo will bring the user to the nexus point the pyramid once controlled.

Open Rift with a Small Pyramid in the Rift (Redirect Rift)

P.P.E. to activate: 50 +1D4 P.E. attribute points. It costs an additional 25 per additional person and there must be an open and active Rift.

Duration: One minute per level of experience.

Power: This tattoo enables the character to subvert an existing, active Rift or a dimensional portal at a stone pyramid (not one under another being's control, like a Shifter) and redirect it to another dimension. This is typically how the Atlantean Voyager travels from one dimension to another. He finds an existing Rift and takes momentary control of it to redirect it to a different world or dimension that is known to him. The Tattooed Man must have visited the location in the past or have significant knowledge of the desired destination, otherwise the Rift opens to a random location within that dimension. If the tattoo user has been to a particular world or dimension they can redirect the Rift to any known nexus point in that environment.

Like a Shifter, the tattoo user must be the last person through the Rift. It is also possible for someone to go through the Rift while it is open, and as always, an opened Rift may attract 1D6 Entities and other supernatural beings.

Pyramid with a Rift at the Apex of the Pyramid (Communication Rift)

P.P.E. to activate: 50 +1 P.E. attribute point.

Duration: Two minutes per level of experience.

Power: The tattoo user is able to open a small Communication Rift on a ley line nexus. This allows for two-way communications with someone in another dimension to make a report, send a message or warning, etc. If the Communication Rift is opened at a stone pyramid, duration is doubled and the Communication Rift can be turned into a normal-sized, dimensional Rift, with the stone pyramid taking control of the dimensional portal. The tattoo user has to expend the initial 50 P.P.E. for the Communication Rift, and an additional 50 P.P.E. to have it expand to a dimensional Rift. The pyramid pays any additional P.P.E. cost to further expand the Rift to allow travel. This is often used when a lone dimensional traveler needs to return from a scouting mission or when reinforcements are needed.

Eye of Knowledge within a Rift (Dimension Sense)

P.P.E. to activate: 25 +1 P.E. attribute point; a temporary loss.

Duration: 1D4 minutes.

Power: This tattoo when activated, places the tattoo user into a trance for the duration, during which he can sense the dimensional vibrations and elements of the world or dimension he is

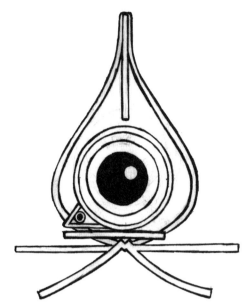

on. He can do likewise while a Rift is open to scan the world or dimension it is linked to before stepping in. He gleans the following information (or most of it, the G.M.'s discretion) in just 1D4 minutes.

Base percentage for Success: 60%+3% per level of experience. Getting this information is not automatic. On a failed roll, the tattoo user only gets the first three lines of information, and needs to wait eight hours before he can try again to learn more.

Knowledge Acquired from Dimension Sense:

Type of dimension or world: Infinite, Parallel or a Pocket Dimension.

Density of dimensional fabric: Weak, permeable, strong or impenetrable.

Can the dimension support human life?

Is it rich or poor in magic?

S.D.C. or Mega-Damage environment?

Is it a mortal or supernatural realm? Meaning an Earth-like world of mortals or a place like Hades or Dyval dominated by demons and supernatural evil, a dimension filled with Entities or spirits, or a realm of magic inhospitable for mortal life, like the Elemental Plane.

Are there one or more Alien Intelligences present? But not where they can be found.

Are there any dimensional quirks and what kind?

Are there ley lines and nexus points?

Is there much dimensional activity? Meaning are there one or more active, open Rifts within a 100 mile (160 km) radius per level of his experience or stone pyramids? Are there dimensional anomalies within the same radius and the general direction to find them.

Last Passage: At a ley line nexus or stone pyramid, the tattoo user can sense the last time a Rift was opened and where it led to, i.e. what world or dimension.

Note: See **Rifts® Dimension Book 8: Megaverse® Builder** for details about the Dimensional Fabric, traveling to other worlds and dimensions and creating them.

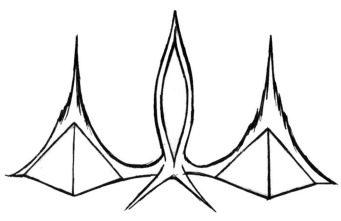

Two Pyramids Connected by a Rift (Rift Teleportation)

P.P.E. to activate: 100 (or 50 P.P.E. and 4 P.E. points) for an Atlantean Voyager, Shifter or Temporal Raider and Temporal Wizard; 200 P.P.E. for other practitioners of magic.

Duration: One melee round (15 seconds).

Power: As per the *Rift Teleportation* spell (see page 222 of **Rifts® Ultimate Edition**). Upon activation at a ley line nexus, the tattoo user can make a one-way teleport from one ley line nexus point (or stone pyramid located at a nexus) to another nexus point. Maximum range is 200 miles (320 km) per level of the tattoo user. Always to a ley line nexus on the same planet. As many as one additional human-sized person per level of experience can be teleported with him as long as they are all clustered together and holding onto each other.

Chain Wrapped Around a Rift (Close Rift)

P.P.E. to activate: 40 +2 P.E. attribute points.
Duration: 1D4 minutes.

Power: The activation of this Dimensional tattoo *temporarily closes* an open, active Rift for 1D4 minutes. This is typically used to buy time for the tattoo user, because the Rift will reopen after the 1D4 minutes duration elapses.

The Rift gets to save vs magic, but needs a 17 or higher to save. (1-16 means the Rift temporarily closes). The G.M. may roll this save or let the player character deploying the tattoo roll to save. A roll of 1-16 means the Rift temporarily closes. Seventeen

or higher means the Rift saves and does not close, but the Voyager still loses the P.P.E. and P.E. he spent to activate the tattoo. The spent P.E. points return at the rate of one point per each hour of rest. If the character is fighting or on the move, the points will not return until he is able to rest. **Note:** This Dimensional Tattoo does not work on permanent Rifts like the St. Louis Gateway.

Rift on a Stone Wall (Mystic Portal)

P.P.E. to activate: 40 +1 P.E. attribute point.
Duration: One melee round per level of experience.

Power: Like the Mystic Portal spell, when activated by the Tattooed Man this enchantment creates a sort of mini-Rift on whatever surface he is touching. Press the palm of his hand (or lean into it with his shoulder, forehead or even his buttocks), activate the Rift through Wall tattoo, and the area on the wall shimmers brightly and a portal or passage appears, as if cut out of the very stone and rimmed with energy like a mini-Rift that cuts through solid material. The magic portal does no damage to the wall (or floor, or ceiling), it simply rearranges dimensional space and time to create an opening through which people can walk through. When the magic's duration ends or the portal's maker wants it closed, the opening vanishes and the wall reappears just as it was.

The portal can be to the adjoining room, or create a 12 foot (3.6 m) deep passage/tunnel per each level of the spell caster in any substance, S.D.C. or M.D.C., but stops when it reaches the other side of the barrier. Creating an opening in just one wall. Looking into it reveals what is on the other side. Stepping through it instantly places the character in that location. How many people can pass through the opening depends on how long the mini-Rift remains open and how quickly people pass through it. It is fair to assume 1D6+6 people moving quickly can go through an opening in a typical wall (6 inches to 3 feet/0.15 to 0.9 m) in one melee round/15 seconds. When the spell duration ends, the mini-Rift Mystic Portal vanishes, but the maker of the Rift on a Stone Wall can close it at any time.

One-way passage. Once a character(s) steps through the portal, the opening behind him/them is gone. To return to the other side, a new portal must be made or another way around found. The portal can be placed on a vertical wall, the floor or ceiling, in each case creating portal to what lays beyond.

A Negate Magic spell can be used by an opponent to close the portal if the negation spell is successful. The tattoo user can close it as quickly as he desires.

Note: This tattoo cannot be used to create an opening through any living creature, including the trunk of live trees or a tangle of vines or brush. Nor can it be used to teleport or move a stationary object, unless it is to drop it straight down through a floor. This tattoo does not work on the magical Impenetrable Wall of Force nor against a Wall of Wind, Fire or Water, but will work on a Wall of Stone, Wall of Clay or Wall of Ice, the side of a car, truck, APC, aircraft, spaceship, or any, hard, physical wall-like barrier.

Heart within a Rift (Sustain)

P.P.E. to activate: 12
Duration: 24 for hours per level of experience.
Power: When activated, this tattoo sustains the tattoo wearer up to 24 hours per level of experience, without food, water, or breathable air! The magic keeps the Tattooed Man's energy level up and removes the need for any outside source for these vital things to live. In addition, the individual only needs two hours sleep per night for the duration of the magic. The enchantment can help the individual survive in many hostile environments without breathable air or food, but he remains vulnerable to external conditions such as heat, cold, wind, etc., and physical attacks. Fatigues from exertion as normal. A must for serious explorers and dimensional travelers.

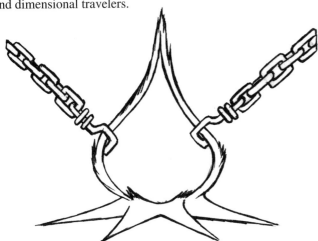

Pair of Chains Pulling a Rift Open

P.P.E. to activate: 25 P.P.E. per minute.
Duration: One minute, but additional P.P.E. can be pumped into the enchantment to keep it open longer. 25 P.P.E. per each minute.

Power: The tattoo user is able to increase the duration a Rift is open. This can be a natural Rift or one opened by another being. This can be important to rescue the innocent or pursue an enemy.

Silhouettes of People Inside an Opened Rift (Dimensional Teleport)

P.P.E. to activate: 200 +1D4+4 P.E. points (or 125 P.P.E. and 12 P.E. points).
Duration: Instant.
Power: This powerful tattoo allows the Tattooed Man to do a Dimensional Teleport for himself and an additional 200 pounds (90 kg) per level of experience, whether that additional weight be material goods or people. This tattoo is so powerful that it temporarily drains 1D4+4 points of the character's P.E. attribute. Adjust P.E. bonuses appropriately. The spent P.E. points return at the rate of one point per each hour of rest. If the character is fighting or on the move, the points will not return until he is able to rest or meditate.

The tattoo user must have some knowledge of the world or dimension he wishes to teleport to.
Base Level of Success: 20% +5% per level of experience (+15% to Atlantean Nomads, +30% to Tattooed Voyagers, +50% to Chiang-Ku dragons).

On a successful roll the tattoo user and anyone touching him is instantly Dimensionally Teleported to the dimension known to the user.

On a failed roll, roll percentile dice to determine what happened and where the character(s) appears.

01-20% The tattoo user did not go anywhere and is still in the exact same location and dimension when he activated the tattoo! P.P.E. and P.E. are spent with no result.

21-40% The tattoo user did not achieve the desired result but did move 1D4x10 yards/meters away from where he had started. This is probably of little help, though he (and those touching him) may have teleported out of the line of sight of an enemy.

41-80% Arrived at the intended dimension, but not at the intending location. Game Master's choice as to how far the character(s) is off course.

81-100% Ends up in a random dimension or at a different location in the same dimension or a different part of the world from which this journey began. This could be the start of a new adventure!

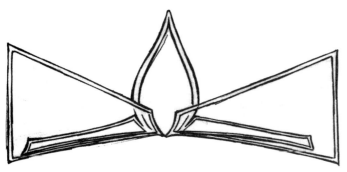

Crossing Ley Lines with an Open Rift (Dimensional Portal)

P.P.E. to activate: 400 plus 1D4+8 P.E. points.
Duration: Two melee rounds (30 seconds) per level of the tattoo user.

Power: Like the Dimensional Portal (Rift) spell, this magic tattoo opens a two-way door to another dimension. The tattoo user can open a Rift to a specific world he is familiar with or a random one. Once the Rift closes, the only way back is to open another Rift. One of the real dangers of using this magic is that some "thing" unwanted often slips through along with the person who opens the Rift.

This tattoo is typically used at a ley line nexus or stone pyramid where the T-Man can draw on the extra P.P.E. available there. The high P.P.E. cost drains the Tattooed Man of P.P.E. as well as physically depriving him of 1D4+8 P.E. points. Adjust P.E. bonuses and fatigue appropriately. The spent P.E. points return at the rate of one point per each hour of rest. If the character is fighting or on the move, the points do not return until he can stop and rest.

Atlantean Pyramids

Most travelers who are familiar with Atlantean culture assume that all stone pyramids are the same. This could not be further from the truth. While pyramids are in just about every Atlantean city, they are not all the same. There are in fact three distinct types of stone pyramids.

The most common is the **Dimensional Pyramid**. These pyramids are plugged into the Megaversal ley line grid and can provide all sorts of benefits such as controlling the local weather, access to other dimensions, extended life spans and increased healing. These pyramids tend to be the largest of all the pyramid types.

The second most common pyramid type is the **Power Pyramid**. These pyramids are found only on ley lines and never on a nexus point. These pyramids use a combination of stone magic and Techno-Wizardry to transmit electrical power throughout Atlantean cities.

The least common of the pyramids, and often the smallest, is the **Healing Pyramid**. While the Dimensional Pyramid heals to a limited degree, it is at the Healing Pyramids where all the miracles occur. These pyramids serve as *healing centers* and are often the source of the Atlantean's renowned healing knowledge.

What all the pyramids have in common is that they are all constructed of stone. 100% of the main structure in all pyramids must be made of stone. No other material can be used. Once the main pyramid structure is in place other material can be brought in to build other pieces such as doors, additional rooms and so on.

Internal Pyramid Features
Common to all Atlantean Pyramids

Internal Lighting: The majority of the lighting within stone pyramids is provided from **Globe of Daylight** spells. They are built into crystals along the upper walls and ceilings of each room and hallway. They appear as glass orbs or even sconces which emanate light. All Atlanteans know how to control these lights and using them is second nature. All lights are simply voice activated. Like a light with a dimmer switch, the level of the light can vary and individuals can adjust this intensity upon command. The *day/night cycle* follows the late spring pattern of Earth, so the light actually starts and dim during the evening hours and slowly turns to night. However, at a command, the light can be brought up to full intensity in as little as 4 seconds, or at whatever level is desired. Since the illumination is *true sunlight,* creatures such as vampires and Shadow beings are repulsed, trapped or even destroyed by the light.

Visiting Techno-Wizards can figure out how the mechanisms and devices inside a stone pyramid work in a fairly short time. So can most other practitioners of magic. They realize quickly that the devices draw power directly from the pyramid, which draws its energy from the nexus, and that there is no need for them to use their own P.P.E. reserves. Anyone, even guests, can operate the lights via voice command, but some "guest rooms," however, are built with light switches and knobs for faucets for those who are not accustomed to using magic.

Some areas may have security restrictions. In these cases, the light only work for specific individuals. The internal lighting also doubles as a built-in security elements. The specifics are discussed below under *Pyramid Security Features.*

Water Works: As the Atlanteans left Earth to settle on other dimensions, the first structure built on a new world is a Dimensional Pyramid. As such it has to sustain its builders and colonists, so it needs to have many of the basic necessities we take for granted in our homes. For example, Pyramids are not constructed like conventional buildings with scores of pipes running through them. Rather the Atlanteans have come to rely heavily on the creations of Stone Magic, Crystal Magic, Techno-Wizard devices and magic items collected across the Megaverse. Rooms with running water, like kitchens and bathrooms, have a basin similar to today's modern sinks. These basins are filled via a magical device that creates just the right amount of water, at whatever temperature is desired. With a command, the basin is drained and fresh water refills it instantly (takes about 7 seconds or half a melee). The same holds true of bathroom facilities. Certain rooms essentially have a TW toilet that takes care of the dirty business of disposing of waste. Showers and bathtubs also have TW water faucets. Like the basins, they can provide water at whatever temperature desired. Thanks to the constant level of magic these devices can be run without the user having to expend their own P.P.E. Again, a small percentage of guest rooms have knobs and switches to control the flow of water, but they are the exception.

Electrical Outlets and Devices that Run on Electricity: Pretty much all electrical devices that operate in Atlantean Pyramids are TW in nature. Since they are constructed to draw P.P.E. directly from the pyramid there is no need to have outlets and plugs. Also, the most likely devices found in Pyramids will be cooking devices, food storage and perhaps communications equipment. Atlanteans don't need P.D.D.'s or televisions to entertain themselves and as such, none are likely to be found in a pyramid. However since most Atlanteans are likely to have used alien technology, Mega-Damage weapons for instance, there can be a need for electrical power. To account for this, most pyramid will have 1D4 solar powered generators and a few electrical backup systems on hand to convert P.P.E. into electricity. There are also facilities to allow visitors and adventurers with alien technology to recharge E-Clips and other common items used in traveling the Megaverse.

Pyramid Security Features: Dimensional incursions do happen and Atlantean clans have learned to be ever vigilant. Tattooed Defenders are stationed on all levels and are usually the primary guards. Other Atlantean O.C.C.s such as Undead Slayers or Tattooed Voyagers, may be on hand as well, however Tattooed Defenders are in the majority. Stone pyramids are never left defenseless and in addition to the normal security force, there are often 2D6 visiting warriors on hand to assist in the pyramids defense in a pinch.

Each stone pyramid is equipped with a variety of defenses. The first and most subtle of the defenses is a simple alarm for intruders. The devices to activate the alarms are often innocuous looking things that non-Atlanteans would never suspect. Each Atlantean clan has their own style, but whatever is chosen is pretty much the same throughout their pyramids. For instance, some clans will have a simple pull rope that may be disguised with hanging rugs or tapestries. Certain icons could be enchanted along the walls or even simple switches and dials. Once activated a very loud and obvious alert sound reverberates throughout the pyramid. Once an alarm is activated, the Pyramid Control Center (or security station) is immediately alerted and a holographic representation of the entire floor appears, complete with occupants. What few people realize is that each of the lighting orbs doubles as the equivalent of a Ley Line Observation Ball. A protective cover around the light feature retracts and the normal sunny daylight globes take on a bluish hue as security begins to actively scan the area. Security can then direct guards to the locations where defenders are needed.

There is a different alarm for fires, and the **Pyramid Control Center** and **Security Center** are alerted and respond accordingly, usually in less than one minute. While it's unlikely that the Pyramid will burn to the ground, fire and smoke could still pose a threat to the occupants. Major locations like control centers and labs will have a built-in fire suppression system. It's a TW device that uses the enchantment, Extinguish Fire. It's effective and activates within 15 seconds of detecting smoke. For other locations, TW Fire Extinguishers are stored nearby. Each has 10 charges, with a single charge able to put out a fire in a 100 foot (30.5 m) area.

In addition to the alarm, each of the major corridors has stone walls that can be slid into place. They are not magical per se, as they don't just magically appear; instead a TW mechanism is responsible for raising, lowering, or sliding the stone walls. Each wall has 120 M.D.C. and takes a full melee to open and close. The walls can be raised, lowered, or slid at the whim of those in the Pyramid's Control Center. A common tactic is to isolate foes or for those who pose a real danger and herd them to an exit by closing off select corridors. The security walls are often found in major corridors and intersections. They are not depicted on the maps and can be placed at the discretion of the Game Master.

Secret corridors and private rooms are typically not monitored nor do they have sliding security walls. It's unlikely that most security forces are even aware of hidden rooms and corridors.

Dimensional Pyramids

Most Atlantean cities and colonies are built around a Dimensional Pyramid which is the first pyramid to be constructed and serves as the city's hub. During their construction, the core Dimensional Pyramid is always placed on a ley line nexus point for maximum power and control of ALL connecting ley lines. Smaller, connected Dimensional Pyramids and Healing and Power Pyramids maybe built nearby within the area of the nexus (ley lines are one or more miles wide so more than one pyramid can be built upon it), but they are versatile enough to be placed elsewhere on a ley line rather than at the nexus point. This means there may be a cluster of stone pyramids at a nexus junction, with satellite pyramids elsewhere. The larger the city or community, the more pyramids there are likely to be scattered along ley lines and other, probably smaller, ley line nexus points. The Dimensional Pyramid is always built on the most powerful nexus unless terrain/environment dictates otherwise.

Dimensional Pyramids, as the name suggests, are connected to the Megaversal ley line grid. Atlanteans use Dimensional Pyramids to control a powerful network of ley lines and to travel from one location to another on that world as well as from one world or dimension to another. This means the Dimensional Pyramid is the first core structure to be constructed when Atlanteans settle in an area. It connects the colonists or explorers to numerous other Atlantean settlements where a Dimensional Pyramid also exist, and it enables them to bring in supplies, building materials and people from other worlds. Dimensional Pyramids also have a dramatic calming effect on the ley lines and nexus, and all but eliminates random Rifts, dimensional anomalies and Ley Line Storms.

Powers of the Dimensional Pyramid

1. Slows the Aging Process: Sleeping overnight inside a Dimensional Pyramid removes stress and fatigue, renewing the body and any creature within its confines. True Atlanteans are physically rejuvenated to such a degree that they remain youthful in appearance, and they actually increase their life span; add one year for every 365 days of sleep in a pyramid located at a nexus or 730 days in a pyramid located on a ley line.

P.P.E. Cost: Negligible – effectively none.

2. Healing (Limited): Laying or resting inside a Dimensional Pyramid for 24 hours will completely remove stress and fatigue and increase healing. Stone Masters heal three times faster than normal and P.P.E. is restored at twice the normal rate. True Atlanteans, humans, Ogres and dragons will heal twice as fast and P.P.E. recovery is 20 points per half hour. Other races will heal at one and a half times faster than usual. P.P.E. recovery is the same as being on a ley line or nexus.

Increased healing occurs at Dimensional Pyramids located on a ley line or nexus point. For treatment of wounds, diseases and other medical needs, True Atlanteans use the Healing Pyramid (described below).

P.P.E. Cost: Negligible – effectively none.

3. Stasis Sleep: Any Atlantean can place themselves into a state of suspended animation that can last for days, years or decades. All they must do is go inside the pyramid, relax and meditate; focusing on the amount of time they wish to remain in stasis. During stasis, the Atlantean ages one week for every ten years, requires no food or water, is unaffected by changes in temperature, and is completely healed of any wounds or minor illness.

The character will be woken from the stasis if he or the pyramid is attacked. There is no means of protection like a force field. Special arrangements must be made to have some sort of guardian. **Note:** There are often several secret chambers, with some specifically set up for stasis sleep. They are so well hidden that the average visitor or invader looking for any is -20% to locate them.

Stasis sleep is possible at all Dimensional Pyramids whether it is located on a ley line or nexus.

P.P.E.: Cost: Negligible – effectively none.

4. The Focus and Control of P.P.E.: The Dimensional Pyramid might be thought of as a mystic dam used to harness, control, and direct ley line energy. This means that the energy and bonuses of increased power normally available from untapped ley lines is <u>not</u> available from ley lines or nexus point with a pyramid on them. These normal bonuses are available only when actually on or inside the controlling pyramid. Only the Stone Masters enjoy super increased abilities and even they cannot tap that energy unless they actually stand on or inside the pyramid. Ley Lines cannot be tapped either for a range of five miles (8 km) in either direction of the pyramid.

To free a ley line or nexus of the pyramid's control, it must be destroyed! All Dimensional Pyramids are Mega-Damage structures. Even a small pyramid is typically the equivalent to a five to ten story building (never any smaller). This M.D.C. applies to all pyramid types described below.

Small Pyramid: 100-200 feet (30.5 to 61 m) tall: 2D4x1000 M.D.C.

Medium Pyramid: 300 to 500 feet (91.4 to 152 m) tall: 1D4x10,000 M.D.C.

Large Pyramid: 600-1,000 feet (183 to 305 m) tall: 2D6x10,000 M.D.C.

Huge Pyramid: 1100 feet (335 m) or taller: 2D4x100,000 M.D.C.

5. Harmonious Effect on Ley Line Storms and Random Rifts: The construction of a Dimensional Pyramid directly on a ley line nexus enables the builders to control the nexus and the two or more ley lines that cross at the nexus point. This has a calming effect on all the connecting ley lines, and reduces the number of Ley Line Storms by 70% and virtually eliminates the possibility of a Rift randomly appearing (1% chance of an annual occurrence along the ley line or 4% at a ley line nexus).

When a Ley Line Storm does occur, the pyramid's controllers are able to change its direction or stall the storm in one spot to avoid population centers and reduce its speed, intensity and duration by half. That part is easy, but a skilled Control Center manager (usually a Stone Master, Voyager, or Ley Line Walker) has a 15% chance, +5% per level of experience, of stopping the Ley Line Storm and make it dissipate completely within 1D4 minutes.

The pyramid's controllers can also close a Dimensional Rift that has begun to randomly open within 2D4 melees (30 to 120 seconds), but must expend 500 P.P.E. to do so. This P.P.E. is tapped from the pyramid's massive P.P.E. reserve.

6. Increase the Power of Stone Magic: Stone Masters and Crystal Mages inside or on the outside of a Dimensional Pyramid enjoy a dramatic increase in power, in large part because the pyramid is built on a ley line nexus point and it and they tap *earth energy*. The increased power level is first used for the construction of the Dimensional Pyramid and then other buildings and stone pyramids around it. The finished Dimensional Pyramid is used to channel and control the magic energy, manage the weather, bring in building materials and workers from other worlds, and to prevent random Rifts from opening.

A stone pyramid built at a nexus point triples and sometimes quadruples *Stone Magic*, and doubles the powers drawn from gems and crystals. It doubles and sometimes triples Crystal Magic (usually noted in the specific spell), and doubles the power (duration, range, etc.) of Tattoo Magic.

A stone pyramid built on a ley line, but not at a nexus, doubles the power of Stone Magic and Crystal Magic, but only when the mages are within the radius of the nexus where the stone pyramid rests, or are inside or on the pyramid itself.

Reduce Ley Line Benefits for Most Magic Users. Other practitioners of magic do not enjoy their usual power boost or the availability of ambient P.P.E. unless they are right at the stone pyramid or the nexus it controls. **Here is why:** The Dimensional Pyramid controls and channels that energy like a dam channels and holds water. The ley lines controlled by a stone pyramid no longer radiate with their full strength, greatly reducing the usual level of ambient magic energy that can be used by other magic users. This means spell casters do NOT see an increase in the power, range, duration or damage of their spells and the availability of ambient P.P.E. on a ley line is a meager *1D4 points per melee round*. This also means recovery of P.P.E. and healing is reduced by half on these tapped ley lines! HOWEVER, when they are within the radius of the ley line nexus (usually a 1D4 mile/1.6 to 6.4 km radius where two or more ley lines cross to create a nexus point), they are able to tap the nexus as usual and are back up to full power. The same is true when they are on or inside the stone pyramid itself.

Important Note: *Stone Masters, Crystal Mages, Earth Warlocks, Earth Elemental Fusionists,* and *Earth Elemental beings* are not affected by the weakened ley lines tapped by the stone pyramid(s). These mages can still draw the full range of ambient P.P.E. and benefits of the ley lines because they draw upon *earth energy* (ley lines) for their earth-based magicks. Their link to the earth keeps them linked to its energies and able to draw upon them regardless of the number of stone pyramids also tapping the same earth energy via the ley lines.

7. Storage Reserve of Potential Psychic Energy (P.P.E.): All stone pyramids are constantly using P.P.E. to maintain a constant flow of energy to provide and maintain many magic effects of the pyramid and surrounding community as previously described. Even so, the pyramid becomes charged with a reservoir of magic energy. The amount of P.P.E. available on ley lines and nexus points has a natural ebb and flow so there is never a consistent amount of energy throughout the day, with even larger spikes during certain times of the year and celestial events.

The range of available extra P.P.E. at any six hour interval is 5D6x100 (that's 500 to 3,000 points) from each pyramid located on a ley line nexus. 2D4x100 from Dimensional Pyramids located on a ley line but away from a nexus. Double these numbers when the nexus has three or more ley lines running through it, quadruple if part of an uncommon, *ley line triangle.*

When the energy reserve is depleted, six hours is required for the stone pyramid to renew its P.P.E. reserve (roll the dice previously indicated). However, none of that new energy is available until the full six hours has passed. In a pinch, P.P.E. energy can be drawn from a **Power Pyramid**, but for only a limited amount at a time. 100 P.P.E. per melee round can be drawn to replenish a Dimensional Pyramid's reserves. No more than 3,000 P.P.E. can be stored and if more than 100 P.P.E. per melee round is transferred, there is a risk of an *uncontrolled Rift opening.* For every 20 P.P.E. points above 100 there is a 10% chance of creating a huge, uncontrolled Rift.

Note: Depletion of *the energy reserve* will not negate or lessen the basic functionality and capabilities of the Dimensional Pyramid (Numbers 1-6), but insufficient P.P.E. may make teleportation or Rifting impossible. It should also be noted that each different pyramid has a different amount of magical energy is stored. See the specific types for details.

8. Pyramid Defensive Systems: Over the millennia, True Atlanteans had to evolve from a peaceful society full of high ideals to one that has become more pragmatic and prepared to defend itself. The stone pyramids of ancient Atlantis lacked many of the defenses they have today. The Vampire Scourge helped change that. The following can be considered weapon systems built into the stone pyramid. It should be noted that the P.P.E. cost is the P.P.E. required to activate a specific function. This energy is drawn from the pyramid's reserve, described under number 7. Additional P.P.E. can be used from those in the pyramid or drawn from a Power Pyramid. See Power Pyramids for specifics.

9. Summon Storms: These defenses can be dangerous as the stone pyramids are designed to prevent dangerous storms from threatening the pyramid and surrounding community. As a consequence, the unleashing of any of these storm attacks directed at the enemy are deployed with great care. Since the Dimensional Pyramid is on a nexus or a ley line it can summon a storm from another dimension, or even invoke dangerous dimensional anomalies. Since these storms tend to affect a large area, there is a chance that a portion of the city or pyramid can become damaged, even when the storm is controlled as best as possible. So summoning any type of storms has the likelihood of some collateral damage. The following storm can be summoned for defense.

- Dimensional Vortex: This is similar to the Displacement Storm in that pyramid controllers can select a 200 foot (61 m) area and 1D6 random Rifts will open. These Rifts have the same effect as a Dimensional Vortex and will suck in every-

one around them. Dimensional Vortex is described in **Rifts® Dimension Book 7: Megaverse® Builder,** page 29.

P.P.E. Cost: 500 and can be activated once every 30 seconds (every other melee).

- Displacement Storm: Pyramid controllers can target a 10 foot (3 m) area where a random Rift teleports all in the area of affect into a displacement storm. A saving throw vs ritual magic of 16 or higher can resist the magic. Those who save are not caught in the displacement storm, but are teleported 2D8x100 feet (60 to 488 m) away from the area targeted. They are sent to a random location around the pyramid, but appear on the ground, never hundreds of feet in the air. Displacement storms are described in **Rifts® Dimension Book 7: Megaverse® Builder,** page 26.

P.P.E. Cost: 100 per activation. It can be activated once per melee.

- Fire Storm: Summoned from the pits of Hades, brown clouds and flickers of fire form in the sky. The smell of sulfur and brimstone fills the air for miles around. Damage is inflicted upon everything in the sky within a 6,000 foot (1828 m) diameter. The pyramid controllers can direct this anywhere around the pyramid up to 15,000 feet (4572 m) away from the pyramid. Any enemies flying through these low-hanging clouds a mile thick, suffer *1D4 M.D. per melee round.*

The Atlanteans have such control over the storm that the controller can unleash 1D6+4 massive fire bolts per melee round at a specific target or spread the number of fire bolts out among several targets. *Each fire bolt does 1D4x10 M.D.*

Fire Rain Option: This is exactly what it sounds like. The Fire Rain from the clouds covers on an area without discrimination, hurting the enemy and innocent people and property alike. Damage is *3D6 S.D.C. per melee round* and it rains for 2D6 minutes at a time. There is a 01-45% chance combustibles catch fire.

The storm can last for as long as 1D6x10+6 minutes, but can be cancelled at any time.

P.P.E. Cost: 200

- Ley Line Bolt: It can be directed at larger targets, 10 feet (3 m) long or tall or larger, similar to an artillery shell. Damage to targets on a nexus is 2D6x10 M.D., on a ley line it is 2D4x10 M.D., but 1D4x10 M.D. to targets not on the ley line. Range: 10,000 feet (3048 m). The pyramid can fire a maximum of six attacks per melee round, but the bolts seem to emanate from the tip of the pyramid. There can be up to four different operators firing off Ley Line Bolts, but each one costs 100 P.P.E.

P.P.E. Cost: 100 P.P.E. per minute per operator. If there were four gunners it would cost 400 P.P.E. per minute.

- Ley Line Fade Shift: This is perhaps the ultimate weapon in terms of its sheer intimidation value. Pyramid controllers can shift one of the connecting ley lines so that all targets within the ley line become slightly out of phase with the current dimension. For the duration, they are intangible and unable to affect anything around them. They are like ghosts, and anything they touch (even other victims) they pass right through. All targets can save vs ritual magic of 16 or higher. On a successful save they are unaffected. Those with teleport abilities can teleport out of this limbo as can those with dimensional teleporting abilities, but they must go to another dimension.

While insubstantial, the victim cannot attack enemies nor can they be attacked unless by magic or psionics. They are also trapped and cannot leave the ley line or enter the pyramid while in this phased state.

P.P.E. Cost: 100 points per melee round.

● Ley Line Tendril Bolt: This weapon is meant for troops and to defend against mass attacks. A series of ley line tendril bolts can be sent down the length of any of the connecting ley lines. Damage is limited to 3D6 M.D., but affects all targets on the ley line. This makes using this weapon a tricky proposition as it will affect friend and foe alike. Range is 2000 feet (610 m). Those that save vs magic of 14 or higher only suffer half damage.

P.P.E. Cost: 50 per blast. Up to four blasts per melee can be unleashed.

● Lightning Storm: The pyramid charges the air so that lightning shoots down. This affects a 1000 foot (305 m) area away or around the pyramid. Damage is 4D6 M.D. per bolt with 6D6 bolts per minute. There is a 1-40% chance per melee of getting hit with a single bolt for individuals. Large vehicles and airborne creatures have a 1-40% chance per melee to be hit by 1D4 bolts. The lightning storm will last for 4D6 minutes.

P.P.E. Cost: 400

● Summon (and Control) Fog: Pyramid controllers can create a fog at various degrees of thickness to obscure targets and confound the enemy. Same as the Summon Fog spell at 5th level proficiency, but duration is quadrupled, or as long as needed. Can be cancelled at any time.

P.P.E. Cost: 100

● Summon and Control Storm: This is a good defense to have when fighting vampires. The effects are the same as the spell of the same name and is equal to 5th level proficiency. Duration is quadruple or as long as needed. Can be cancelled at any time.

The Atlanteans have such control over the storm that the controller can unleash *1D6+4 lightning bolts* per melee round at a specific target or spread the number of fire bolts out among several targets. *Each lightning bolt does 1D4x10 M.D.*

In the alternative, a directed windstorm can be unleashed. See Summon and Control Storm spell for details.

P.P.E. Cost: 300

● Summon Ley Line Storm: Pyramid controllers can discharge ALL of the pyramid's energy reserve to instantly create a Ley Line Storm. The controllers can then control and direct the storm's movement, but it is limited to traveling along the connecting ley lines. All of the storm's effects/powers/damage can be turned on or off, they can select special effects, and direct energy blasts at specific targets/individuals or area.

The storm lasts for two minutes per 100 P.P.E. points spent to create it. The storm's creator can stop it at any one place or make it disappear at any time. If the creator is killed or knocked unconscious, the storm runs wild for the maximum possible duration plus 2D4 minutes. See the Summon Ley Line Storm spell for details.

P.P.E. Cost: All of the pyramid's P.P.E. reserve, and duration is two minutes per 100 P.P.E. points spent.

10. Control the Weather Around the Pyramid: The Dimensional Pyramid's controllers are able to use the channeled and controlled magic energy of the ley lines and nexus to influence the local weather. This is done to protect and help cities and communities around the pyramid by creating rain for crops and during droughts, preventing storm damage, general protection, and creating an idyllic living place. Weather controlling abilities are identical to the following spells, except the range, area of effect and duration are increased by four times: Call Lightning, Calm Storm, Summon Fog, Summon Rain, Summon and Control Storm and Extinguish Fire.

P.P.E. Cost: 200

11. Pyramid Communications: Any True Atlantean or Stone Master can magically communicate with people at all types of stone pyramids. A holographic-like image appears to a specific individual or to everybody present if a general call/message is sent. If the message is sent to a specific person, the individual making the transmission can see and hear the other person at the other pyramid. Otherwise, they see whoever answers the call at the other end. The line of communication can remain open for 20 minutes per 10 P.P.E. when on the same planet. Multiple pyramids can also engage in a conference call at a cost of 15 P.P.E. per 20 minutes per each pyramid.

A two-way transmission between dimensions is also possible, but at a cost of 40 P.P.E. per 20 minutes, and conference calls cost 60 P.P.E.

The character making the transmission to another pyramid can also leave a recorded message. The message plays the moment the intended recipient arrives at the pyramid. The message is stored for 200 years or until received by the intended person, whichever comes first. P.P.E. cost is the same as above.

P.P.E. Cost: As described above.

12. Teleportation via Pyramids: Dimensional Pyramids built on ley lines or on nexus junctions are connected by an invisible grid of magic energy that spans the universe. This means an individual with the right knowledge or taken care of by onsite personnel, can Teleport from one Dimensional Pyramid to another. The only requirements are that the pyramid be in the same dimension and the person teleporting (or the personnel operating the pyramid) know the location of the other pyramid. The process takes about three seconds (one melee attack/action) regardless of distance. To travel to a different dimension, a Rift must be opened, which is also possible with a Dimensional Pyramid.

All True Atlanteans know how to Teleport using the Dimensional Pyramid. The teleportation process is so exact that most people can teleport themselves, and can take as many as two dozen people, or 50 tons, along with them. Back when it was only the Atlanteans who possessed the knowledge to build Dimensional Pyramids, there was no need for security. Now, with powerful and monstrous creatures like the Splugorth who also possess Dimensional Pyramids, there is the threat of spies, bandits, raiders and entire armies appearing at Atlantean pyramids. As a result, there is always tight security at Dimensional Pyramids, and teleportation and where it is done is limited to specific, designated areas. This way guards can be placed where trouble is most likely to happen.

Another security feature is being able to identify where the teleporting person is arriving from. All friendly pyramids are noted in the pyramid's control room. When the Teleport occurs, it sends a unique ripple that identifies the location and world.

If an unknown ripple is received, an alarm sounds, alerting the Atlantean Defenders that an unknown traveler is en route and could spell trouble. Defenders and a squad or two of Defenders in Guardian Crystal Armor and Super-Guardians are stationed in the pyramid at "teleportation landing zones" and respond to all potential threats within 1D4 melee rounds (15-60 seconds). More Defenders, Undead Slayers and other defenders can be scrambled in a moment's notice.

Due to the instantaneous nature of Teleports, there is often little warning. At most, there is one melee round (15 seconds) to act before possible problems occur. This is a contingency that all Tattooed Defenders train for, and they are very good at responding to these unusual kinds of situations and managing all manner of danger and threats.

P.P.E. Cost: 100 per Teleport.

13. Dimensional Teleportation at Stone Pyramids: The concept is identical to the conventional Teleport process described in Number Twelve, above, except on a dimensional scale. The same type of mystic grid connects all the dimension pyramids in other dimensions across the Megaverse. If the Atlantcan knows the location of one of these other Dimensional Pyramids he can momentarily open a Dimensional Rift and Teleport from one dimension to another. A character can find any dimension he has visited in the past or knows has a stone pyramid. Furthermore, there are Tattooed Voyagers on staff that can open the Rifts that allows dimensional travel for those authorized to travel to that location. Which is most people. Atlanteans have a very open and free society, so its citizens are allowed to go pretty much anywhere, provided it does not represent a danger to the city-state they are leaving.

An experienced Voyager, Stone Master and even a Nomad can open a Rift, instantly link up to all the available Atlantean Dimensional Pyramids. They can mentally scan and search the dimensions for Dimensional Pyramids connected to a desired world or different dimension without having ever been to it or having any prior knowledge about it. The searching process takes 1D4 minutes.

The opening of a Dimensional Rift to another Dimensional Pyramid takes 30 seconds (two melee rounds). Once opened, the character simply steps through and the dimensional doorway instantly closes. This means if there are groups of people, the person opening the Rift must be the last to go through, especially if there are non-Atlanteans among them. The Rift can remain open for one melee per level of the person who opened it. This is a very safe way to travel to other worlds and dimensions, because there is zero risk of opening the Rift to the wrong dimension or letting in an undesirable or undetected monster into the world you are leaving. Why? Because the stone pyramids are all linked on a cosmic grid of ley lines. The activation of the Dimensional Rift instantly activates that link to the other Dimensional stone pyramids on other worlds and in other dimensions, and makes them available to the D-travelers.

All True Atlanteans understand dimensional teleportation using Dimensional Pyramids. The big difference is that to Dimensional Teleport, the person must enter the Rift. Vehicles and multiple individuals can enter if the Rift is held open longer than a few seconds. The average True Atlantean can hold the portal open for one melee per level of experience, while a Stone Master, Tattooed Voyager and Atlantean Nomad can hold the Rift open for one minute per level of experience.

Prior to the sundering of Ancient Atlantis, all Dimensional Teleports could be done anywhere in the pyramid. Now due to added security features, Dimensional Teleports are limited to select areas of the pyramid. The security features are the same as those described in Number 12.

P.P.E. Cost: 500 points each time a Rift is opened regardless of how long it is held open; seconds or minutes.

14. Dimensional Rifts/Portal: This is your classic Dimensional Rift, a two-way door to another dimension that is not linked to any pyramids. The portal can be opened to a specific world or random dimension and not to a stone pyramid. All the usual dangers and difficulties of creating a Rift apply.

The Rift remains open for 60 seconds per level of the portal opener. However, there is a 1-40% chance that the doorway will get stuck, staying open for 3D4 minutes longer than the character desires. There is also a 1-53% chance that a being from another dimension may usurp control of the dimensional portal if the portal connects to the being's home dimension or plane of existence. This is especially true of powerful alien intelligences(s) like the Splugorth, vampires, demon princes, Deevil regents and gods. Having a Rift usurped means that the character who originally opened the portal has completely lost all control over it. The alien intelligence who dominates that world controls the portal and can instantly close it, or keep it open and/or send its minions into the Rift and into the world connected by the portal. See the Table for Usurped Rifts at the end of this section.

Note: All conventional Rifts can only connect two worlds at a time. Multi-dimensional Rifts connecting three or more worlds simultaneously are not possible. The few attempts to link several worlds by using one Rift have been experiments and have always resulted in disaster (see the Janus Experiment for more details).

P.P.E. Cost: 1000 each time a Rift is opened regardless of how long it is held open, seconds or minutes. Creating a dimensional portal is not possible at pyramids located on a ley line unless at peak power (800 P.P.E.) and even then the mage will be required to use his own energy and possibly additional P.P.E. to get the 1000 P.P.E. points necessary to create the Rift.

Typical Atlantean Dimensional Pyramid Layout

The Atlantean Pyramid is an icon of their culture. The crafting that goes into each pyramid is very labor intensive, but the end results are worth the enormous effort. All Atlantean Dimensional Pyramids share a similar structure in their makeup, but often the exact layout will vary from clan to clan. For instance, some of the more reclusive clans will have more secret rooms, doors and vaults than say a clan that is more open. The pyramid described below is just one example of what could be considered a "typical" Atlantean Dimensional Pyramid, typical in that they share many of the same types of rooms with similar functions. The exact layout can vary, and often does, from clan to clan.

Game Masters, please feel free to redefine the various rooms and functions to suit their own games. In fact, these pyramids could also double for Splugorth pyramids. You are only limited by your imagination.

Pyramid Symbols

Spiral Staircases: For non-Atlanteans these spiral staircases go from floor to floor throughout the pyramid. Each staircase is roughly 5 feet (1.5 m) wide, allowing for two people to walk side by side.

Wooden Doors: Most doors are constructed of oak or a similar hardwood. Thanks to magical enchantments and the magic that courses through the pyramid, wooden doors will have 20 M.D.C. each. The doors do have locks and are locked as needed. Most are conventional locks, although it is not unheard of to have electronic locks as well. Some are even TW in nature using the Seal spell to keep them secure.

Stone Doors: Areas that may require higher security will have stone doors. They are not hidden like secret doors, but to visitors who don't frequent Stone Pyramids, they may as well be concealed. Characters that make a successful Detect Concealment will be able to identify the door and know where the mechanism is to open it. Stone doors have 50 M.D.C. each. The stone doors have conventional locks where needed as well as electronic or TW locks.

Double Steel Doors and Single Steel Doors: Such doors are used in high security areas. They are magically reinforced and have 75 M.D.C. each. These doors are also locked via magic and a password or even a magic key is needed to gain access.

Secret Doors: All secret doors blend in and resemble the stone walls of the pyramid. All secret doors are magically reinforced steel doors with 100 M.D.C. Secret doors require a Detect Concealment roll to find and even then is a -20% penalty due to the superior Atlantean craftsmanship. True Atlanteans are only -10% while Stone Masters are actually +10% to locate these hidden doors. These doors are also automatically locked and the locking mechanism is often hidden as well. The doors can be locked via a key, via technological means, or via magic.

Pyramid Levels

Commons Floor Level One

In the early days of the Atlantean migration from earth, when clans settled on other worlds, the Dimensional Pyramid was one of the first structures built. Whole clans would often need to seek refuge inside the pyramid, so the largest floor was the ground level. Here the majority of the clan gathered, and it's where the majority of the socialization took place. It could be considered a town square of sorts with many of the clan's necessities located somewhere on the main floor. Today, however, the Commons Floor has become more of a "Grand Central Station" and it is the common place for all visitors to pass through.

The floor has several highlights which include numerous teleport chambers as well as chambers for creating Rifts. Other features include medical facilities and a place for large clan gatherings. All dimensional visitors are likely to arrive somewhere on the commons floor.

1. Central Chamber: The central chamber is often one of the largest and most ornately decorated rooms in the entire pyramid. It has a 60 foot (18.3 m) vaulted ceiling and along the sides of the room are stone pillars that provide support.

This room's only function is to create Dimensional Portals. Many people are sent and received in this chamber and it can be considered the *public entrance* to an Atlantean community in terms of dimensional travel. There are other rooms where dimensional portals can be created, but the Central Chamber is considered the primary location for such activity.

2. Teleport Chambers: Atlanteans use these chambers to teleport from pyramid to pyramid be it on the same dimension or another. There are six altogether, with three on either side of the Central Chamber. Due to pyramid security features, those teleporting to a particular pyramid will always arrive in one of these six chambers.

3. Large Teleport Chamber: These chambers are used when very large parties need to teleport at once or when large quantities of goods need to be brought to and from the pyramid. Essentially, it's for teleporting cargo and only used as such. Arrangements are often made ahead of time. In the case of unexpected dimensional merchants, the pyramid can route visitors to an unoccupied chamber or the other large teleport chamber when needed.

4. Grand Foyer: The Grand Foyer is where local visitors often arrive to meet with various Atlantean clan members. It is often open to the elements; however some clans have sliding doors in case the pyramid needs to be sealed. This room comes close to the beauty of the Central Chamber with its elaborately carved pillars or exotic artwork like large murals or paintings. This room is typically representative of the clan that built the pyramid.

5. Large Medical Ward: Atlantean Pyramids are renowned for their powers of healing. Most Atlantean pyramids have a large medical area that is the equivalent of an emergency room. Any dimensional traveler or Atlantean that appears at the pyramid (those that are non-hostile) can request medical aid and expect to be well cared for. The level of care can vary, although it is typically equal to being treated in a hospital with trained physicians

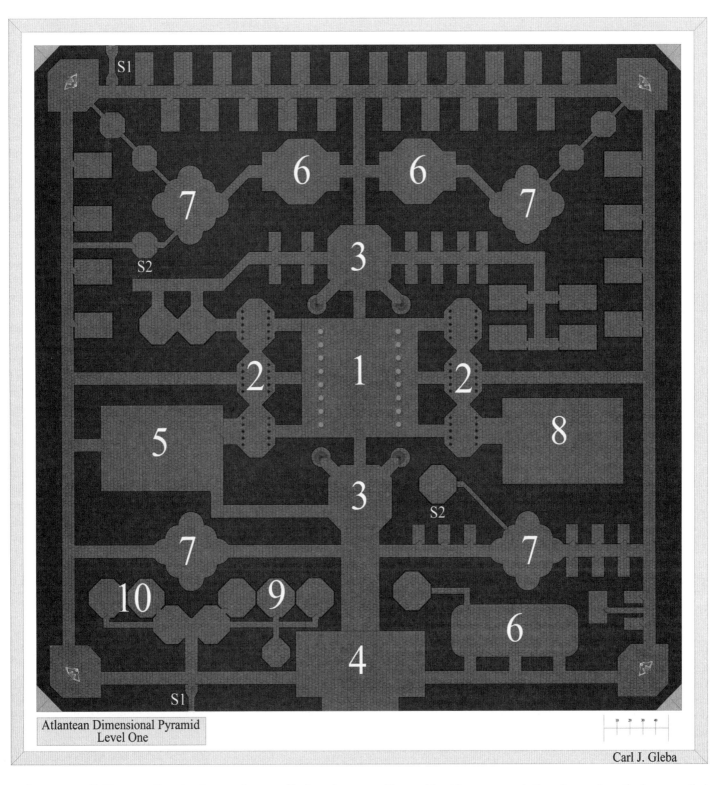

**Atlantean Dimensional Pyramid
Level One**

Carl J. Gleba

and nurses available as well as having modern medical equipment.

Atlanteans typically do triage here and will teleport the critically wounded to a Healing Pyramid. In Atlantean settlements where they do not have a Healing Pyramid, this large medical ward would be equipped in a similar capacity as the Healing Pyramid. See the Healing Pyramid later in this section for more details.

In the event there is no Healing Pyramid, the Dimensional Pyramid would likely have 1D6+2 healing pools (described under the Healing Pyramid) and have access to 3D4 medical beds as described below under the Healing Pyramid. Dimensional Pyra-

mids would not have access to the advanced medical powers that most Healing Pyramids have.

6. Clan Eating and Kitchen Chambers: Atlanteans that gather in large numbers often have large social gatherings. As such, they often enjoy dining together. These rooms serve as a combination dining and food preparation area – essentially, a large cafeteria where visitors can expect to get a free meal and a drink depending on the generosity and protocols of the particular clan.

7. Clan Common Rooms: These large rooms are for clan gatherings when not dining. These rooms are often adorned with comfortable furniture and many other amenities depending on the clan. Some will be kept simple while others can be very lavishly decorated with fountains, and artwork to the latest in electronic media and games, all TW of course. These rooms are meant to be comfortable and inviting.

8. Teleportation Storage Chambers: These large chambers are used to hold potable supplies in vast quantities, like food, water and medical supplies. They are supplies that are often meant for the pyramid's occupants and can be conveniently teleported from one pyramid to another as needed. A secondary use of this chamber is to turn it into a secondary medical ward in the event of emergencies. In the safer dimensions, sometimes this chamber is even used as a place for dimensional merchants to set up shop.

9. Learning Chambers: Young Atlanteans are often here learning how to meditate, how to use their magic tattoos, as well as to learn how to use the powers of the pyramid. Some of the learning chambers are set up like classrooms while others appear as large meditation chambers.

10. Tattoo Parlors: These parlors are often reserved for the clan's senior tattoo artist. This person will often dedicate their time teaching the next generation of tattoo artists. Each parlor can hold up to ten tattoo artists. When not is use, these rooms are sealed tight to protect the magical components needed in the creation of magic tattoos.

S1 & S2 secret chambers and doors. Each Pyramid is likely to have one or two secret entrances. The same holds true for secret chambers. These hidden chambers are often reserved for Atlantean clan leaders who require a place of solitude to retire to, or when specific clan members can be put into stasis in a secret location. The secret doors that lead to these areas are nearly impossible to discern from the rest of the stonework. One must be actively looking for them and the skill Detect Concealment will have a -20% skill penalty. On a successful roll, the secret door is found as well as the means to open it.

Level Two

Science and Learning Center

The Atlantean society has always advanced their knowledge through the study of science. The same holds true even today. The second level tends to have numerous science and medical labs. It is also one of the few levels with an active security presence. Known clan members are seldom questioned, however anyone not from the clan is often stopped and asked to move along to a different level. As a rule, 2D4+4 Tattooed Defenders guard these levels. There is often one guard at each check point (see Number 6) and a few wandering guards. The security is more for the safety of others than to concern about the various labs. Most clans prefer to only grant access individuals who already have scientific and medical knowledge. It is not a location for the curious or outsiders.

1. Isolated Lab: This is where any kind of lab work that is needed for the medical center on the first floor is done, including blood tests, DNA testing, drug tests and similar lab work that requires an isolated environment. When there is a Healing Pyramid nearby, isolated laps are moved there and this location becomes prime real estate for an Atlantean scientist or alchemist. With the permission of clan elders, a teleport link can be established with a nearby Healing Pyramid that allows the Atlantean scientist to instantly teleport between his labs. This link is specific to an individual and allows them to bypass pyramid security and appear directly in their specified labs.

2. Security for Level Two: While Atlantean clans are very open, there is still a need for security where safety (and secrets) may be of concern. Security often includes 8-16 Tattooed Defenders, four with Crystal Guardian Armor and two Super-Guardians. High-ranking clan members are automatically granted clearance as are specific clan members such as known Stone Masters and Clan Alchemists. Guests and younger clan members are often escorted off the level.

3. Small Labs: These are small, isolated labs typically used for the research and the study of magic or science. Each room has several feet of stone around them to protect the pyramid and its occupants from accidents or from letting anything escape. These labs are typically reserved for individuals. It is customary in Atlantean culture to ask the clan elders' permission to conduct experiments that may last longer than a few weeks. It is generally assumed that these rooms are open to academics for the sole purpose of being shared.

4. Isolated and Secure Lab: This floor has a large, isolated laboratory that requires people to pass through a security checkpoint. This lab is reserved when the experiment may pose a danger and it can be sectioned off in the event that the entire lab is not needed. A heavy wall can be erected to separate the room in half or into smaller sections. The wall is activated via a control panel along the wall that takes a full melee to slide into place. Or a Stone Master can create custom designs.

5. Unsecured Labs: These are larger labs where teams can work together, or where several people can work at a time like in a classroom, if necessary. Studies include Xeno-Botany, Xenology, and Xeno-Archeology, as well as arcane studies. These facilities are open and expected to be shared by all who use them.

6. Security Checkpoints to Secure Labs: Just because of the nature of this level, a small security force is kept at the four corners just in case.

7. P.P.E. Storage and Transfer Points: P.P.E. that is siphoned off of the Ley Line is channeled and stored through these chambers. The statue in the middle of the chamber has a focus and control crystal that regulates the magic energy. Every few decades, these crystals need to be changed as part of a regular maintenance cycle. If they don't get changed the pyramid will lose many of its powers over time. Only Atlantean Stone Masters and clan elders even know what these statues are for. This is not common knowledge even among Atlanteans. Destroying these statues reduces all pyramid powers by 25%. Destroying all four effectively disables the pyramid. It can run on reserve P.P.E. until it is used up and all pyramid powers are at 1/10th their normal level until the P.P.E. runs out. Each statue has 500 M.D.C. and is not easy to destroy, and Tattooed Defenders are only a minute away.

8. Multi-Purpose Rooms: These rooms can serve several purposes. Most are used as conference rooms where clan scientists/alchemists can meet in a private location to hash out problems or to meet and discuss their discoveries. Others use them as additional private studies, while others convert them into small labs. The exact function will vary depending on the clan's needs. One is often always a unisex washroom.

9. Library: The library is a secured chamber where the clan will store most of their written knowledge. The medium will vary from books and scrolls to computer discs. A clan elder is often in

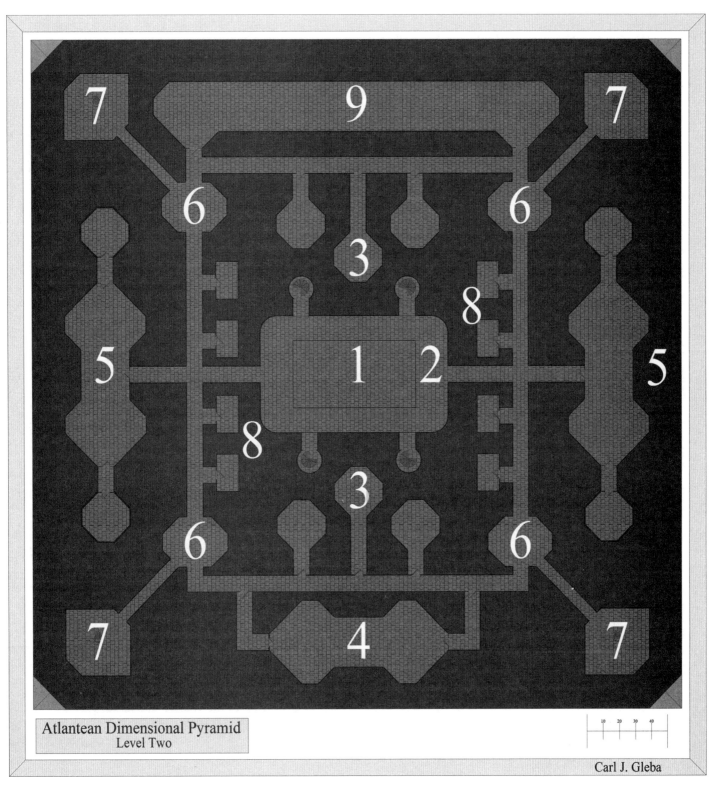

Atlantean Dimensional Pyramid
Level Two

Carl J. Gleba

charge of keeping all the information organized and easily found. Any kind of knowledge is likely to be found here, from forgotten spells to the latest on dimensional travel. What information is available is at the discretion of the Game Master. While Atlanteans have amassed a lot of knowledge, even they do not know everything. Perhaps clues could be found that would lead the group to a place to search.

Note on Secret Rooms for Level Two: Because experiments can sometimes run amok, many Atlantean designers purposely do not construct any secret labs on level two. That is not to say they never exist, but it is uncommon.

Level Three

Control Center

Many of the pyramid's functions are monitored and controlled from the third level. The magic abilities of the pyramid pretty much run automatically with little need for Atlantean intervention. Still, after the Janus experiment, many Atlanteans feel the need for a tight grip on their creations and now all functions are monitored constantly.

Security is lax on this level for a few reasons. First, only Atlanteans can operate the equipment and powers of each pyramid.

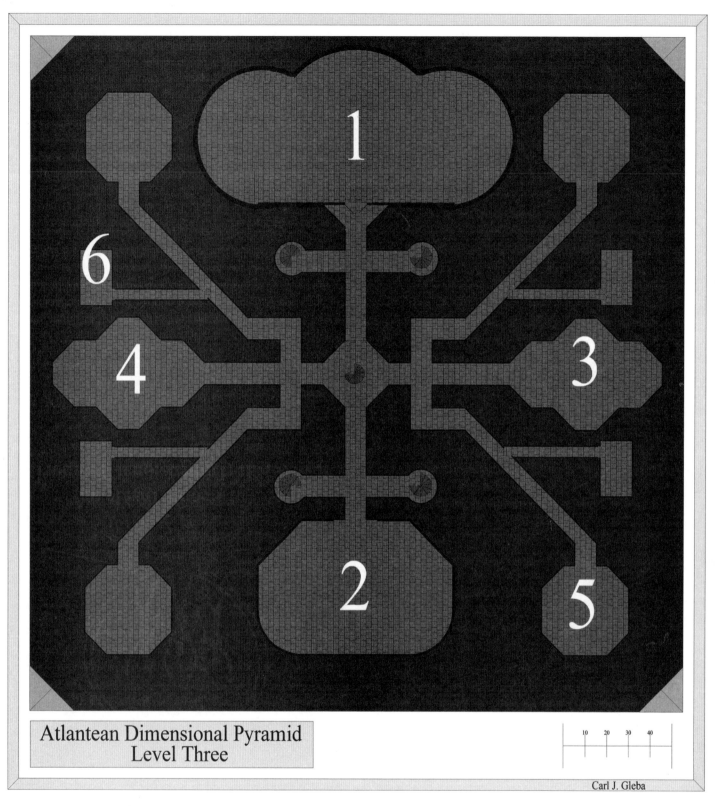

Atlantean Dimensional Pyramid
Level Three

10 20 30 40

Carl J. Gleba

Second, outsiders really do not have a clue as to what the exact function of each room is anyway. As a precaution there are seven Tattooed Defenders (two clad in Crystal Guardian Armor, one in Super-Guardian armor), and two Undead Slayers or Tattooed Voyagers who patrol this level to keep it safe and secure.

1. Pyramid Control Center: The pyramid control center has two primary functions. First is to monitor all Rift activity and the second is pyramid security.

Rift activity for the pyramid is monitored, recorded, and can be controlled from here. Scattered around the room are sever-al small control stations. Each station has a variety of multi-colored control gems. Depending on where a Rift opens, the corresponding control station will become active and a holo-graphic representation of the Rift appears. Atlanteans monitor the Rifts for any dimensional instability that might occur. While no anomalies can happen in the pyramid itself (the controllers see to that), they can occur on outbound Rifts that do not go to other pyramids. In these cases, controllers attempt to stabilize the Rift(s). Atlantean player characters should roll their *Operate*

Dimensional Pyramid skill if allowed to operate any controls in the dimension control center.

The control center can also monitor other Rifts that open along the ley lines if and when they occur. This is only likely if there are no other pyramids on the connecting ley lines. Controllers can attempt to take control of those Rifts, but at half their Operate Dimensional Pyramid skill.

Security is effectively the same, as most incursions happen as the result of an unexpected Rift, or if a Rift is usurped by a powerful being or Alien Intelligence. This is rare, but does happen. There are also Dimensional Raiders who may know about an Atlantean pyramid and decide to take a run at it. Many desire to have such a powerful mechanism under their control. They know if they make a blitzkrieg assault they may be able to open a Rift to another world or dimension (their real target), or they know there are valuable Atlantean weapons, magic and valuables that could be grabbed in a quick raid. Thus, on more than one occasion, small groups of D-Raiders have tried to take over Atlantean pyramids or run through them trying to scoop up whatever goods they can before making their escape. Sometimes D-Raiders target personnel to capture and hold captive, and some just enjoy the thrill of the action.

In addition to having a set of steel doors, the Pyramid Control Center also has a reinforced wall between the stairs and the door that can be slid into place. This wall has 200 M.D.C. and is meant to keep the control room safe in case of incursions. The wall can be activated and only takes seven seconds (a half a melee) to slide closed. The wall can only be opened and closed from within the control room.

2. Weather Control Hub: Atlanteans can control the weather on and around the pyramid. Holographic maps of the surrounding area are depicted on the walls and work stations around the control hub. Like a satellite they display weather that is in the surrounding area. While weather can only be controlled immediately around the pyramid, it can read the ley lines out to 50 miles (80 km) expanding the visual range and helping to warn of any impending weather concerns to surrounding communities.

This room also doubles as a defense center. It is here that pyramid operators can direct many of the weapons of the pyramid. Each controller has a holographic representation of the battlefield. From here they can coordinate their attacks to maximum effect.

3. Communication Hub: This room is essentially a major communications center for the pyramid. It has a powerful TW computer that can store and route messages to various individuals. Messages are often routed directly to the individual requested and if they are not in the pyramid, the message can be stored for later viewing, up to 100 years. Individuals only monitor this room to ensure that the source of the message is authentic. They can also help individuals send secured messages when secrecy is of the utmost importance.

Atlanteans typically carry a communications crystal. The crystal comes in many shapes and forms and can be placed in a necklace or ring if desired. The crystal acts like a cell phone and alerts Atlanteans of incoming messages as well as allows them to communicate with anyone without having to go directly to the communications hub. Range is unlimited within an Atlantean city. Range when not in a city is limited to 5 miles (8 km) from the pyramid or connecting ley lines. Communication Crystals are described below under Crystal Artifacts.

4. P.P.E. Flux Control: The P.P.E. levels of the pyramid are constantly monitored. This is mostly to ensure that the pyramid has enough magic energy to control its normal functions; however various magic experiments that use excessive amounts of magic energy can also be monitored here as well. In an instant, they can divert the P.P.E. to prevent large buildups or instances where great harm could result from the excess P.P.E. being released. This room can also detect the subtle (or not so subtle) increases in ley line activity that can lead to a Ley Line Storm. Notification is immediately sent to the weather hub where the storm can be quickly brought under control.

5. Stone Master Workshops. The corners of the pyramid are reserved as places of honor for the Stone Masters who crafted the pyramid. These corner rooms are typically workshops where they can work in peace. For pyramids that have been around for generations, some clans turn these workshops into tombs for honored Atlanteans, especially for those who constructed the pyramid. Some even serve as grand stasis chambers and are decked out like a pharaoh's tomb.

6. Stasis Chambers. These are secured chambers for Atlanteans who wish to go into stasis. These rooms are reinforced, and while the doors are not hidden, they may not be obvious to see to non-Atlanteans, and sometimes they are concealed with secret doors in the walls. Depending on the clan, each room may be sparse or ostentatious. Some clans use simple stone slabs while others use a sealed coffin or fancy sarcophagus to hold those who lie in stasis.

Level Four

Royal Chambers

The Royal Chambers are meant for higher ranking clan members such as clan elders, representatives, diplomats, heroes of renown and the clans' ruling class. While there is no royalty anymore in Atlantean culture, the tradition has stuck, and those in charge of the clans are looked up to in a similar capacity as kings, princes, ladies and lords. They are offered larger accommodations and direct access to the pyramid's conveniences.

1. Private Teleport Chamber: High-ranking clan members have access to a private teleport chamber. They can use the chamber to teleport to any connecting pyramid or anywhere within the pyramid. The special properties of this chamber make it possible to bypass pyramid security for the convenience of the clan rulers. It is also large enough to accommodate large groups of Atlanteans. The chamber can also create a dimensional Rift should the need arise.

2. Private Dining Area: These dining chambers are typically used for honored guests, high-ranking Atlanteans from other clans or other honored dignitaries. There are two dining chambers and one large kitchen.

3. Private Rooms: These can be considered executive suites for honored guests or where high-ranking clan members stay. These rooms are typically decked out with the best amenities available.

4. Private Labs: These labs are typically reserved for the clan's senior alchemists or high-ranking mages. They are equipped with the best materials and equipment.

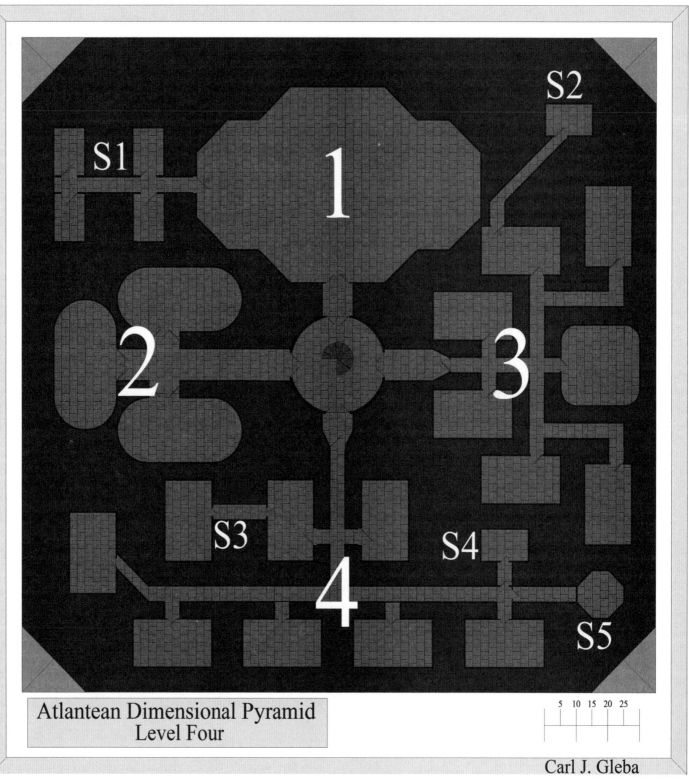

Secret rooms S1 to S5: The secret rooms on this level serve a variety of purposes. Some are secret labs or vaults, others are sleeping chambers or private studies for select individuals and some are even private teleport chambers or safe rooms. The exact purpose will vary from pyramid to pyramid and user to user.

Level Five

Clan Elders Level

Clan Elders are revered for their experience and wisdom. Leadership of a clan will vary. Some will use the royals, while others rely on the clan elders. In either case, clan elders are still provided a level of their own. Like the royal chamber, the elders' level can be considered an executive suite with the best amenities available.

1. Grand Meeting Chamber: This room can serve a dual purpose. It can be a large meeting chamber for the clan elders, or it can serve as a greeting chamber for the elders of other clan, foreign dignitaries, or important visitors. Any important gathering of clan elders takes place here, whether it is to discuss clan business and issues, and for VIP parties and celebrations.

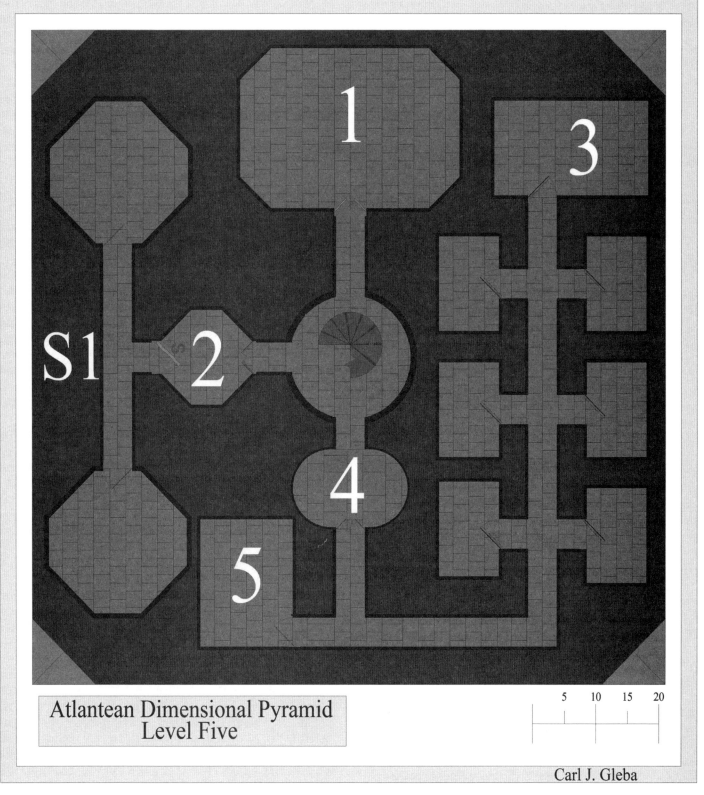

Atlantean Dimensional Pyramid Level Five

5   10   15   20

Carl J. Gleba

2. Clan Elders' Private Teleport Chambers: These rooms are where clan elders or guests to the pyramid would arrive if teleporting to the pyramid's top chamber. It's separated from the other rooms so that individuals that arrive must go through the security on level 5.

3. Clan Elder Private Chambers: These chambers are equivalent to the presidential suite at any grand hotel with all the amenities one would need, including a bathroom and small study. Most clan elders simply use them as private studies while others use them as private stasis chambers.

4. Clan Elders' Personal Guards: Clan elders typically have a small retinue of Tattooed Defenders who stand guard and provide protection. This guard station is intended to be used for the whole level with guards making patrols as needed. To get to the elders' private chambers one must pass through the guard station. There are typically two Tattooed Defenders to each clan elder.

5. False Vault: Atlanteans often have many secrets to guard and they need a safe place to hide them. The false vault is meant to mislead any would-be thieves from finding the actual vault.

There are often some items of value in there to mislead and distract thieves and to keep the actual items of value safe.

S1. Hidden Vaults: The pyramid's actual vaults are always hidden behind secret doors somewhere in the pyramid. The secret door is as difficult as any other secret door to locate and it is magically reinforced, plus they often have magic alarms or even wards protecting them.

Optional Usurped Rift in a Dimensional Pyramid Table

If a random Rift in a stone pyramid is usurped, Game Masters can roll on the random table below to see who has control of the Rift. This could be used for a single encounter or could lead to a whole new adventure.

01-20% Usurped Pyramid Rift by Unknown Intelligence: Characters sense a very powerful intelligence probing all those around them. There is no immediate threat of danger. Empathic characters or those who use the psionic power of empathy will at first sense curiosity for a few moments. It then changes to indifference and the Rift is released to the pyramid controller. The Rift remained under the control of the unknown intelligence for 1D4+1 minutes.

21-25% Vampire Intelligence: A random Rift was inadvertently opened to a realm where vampires exist. Possibly even in Mexico on Rifts Earth. Atlanteans will sense that a Vampire Intelligence has control of the Rift. Within 2 melees (30 seconds), 1D6 Wild Vampires start pouring into the pyramid via the Rift every melee round until control of the Rift is regained and it is closed. One Secondary Vampires will enter every minute. If the Rift is open for five minutes or more, a Master Vampire comes through. The Rift remain under the Intelligence's control for 2D4 minutes unless shut-down sooner!

26-35% A Portal to Rifts Earth: The exact location is up to the Game Master. This could be an opportunity to send the player characters to someplace they have been wanting to visit.

36-40% Demon Prince or Deevil Regent: A powerful demonic being has taken control of the Rift. It starts sending 1D4 Lesser Demons/Deevils/Chaos Demons/Daemonix or other demonic creatures, through the Rift to explore. Every other melee round, 1D4 Lesser Demons of Deevils (or sub-demons) come through. Every minute one Greater Demon arrives. The Rift remains open for 2D4 minutes.

41-50% The Minion War: The Rift is stuck open at a place where demons AND Deevils and their minions are doing battle. Every minute for 2D4 minutes 1D4 Lesser Demons (and or minions) and 1D4 Deevils (and/or Host) appear in the pyramid still fighting each other. At the end of the battle, the winning side will stay and try and claim the pyramid unless defenders chase them through the Rift in which they came.

51-55% A Rift to the Courts of Light: A Rift to the dimension of angelic or other good supernatural beings opens up. 2D6 come through before the Rift closes. They could be allies or create problems. Who knows what chaos they will unleash?

56-60% A Rift to an Inhospitable Dimension: The Rift is stuck open for 3D4 minutes to a strange dimension that is leaking in a toxic gas. Everyone near the Rift has to evacuate or suffocate due to lack of oxygen.

61-70% The Shadow Realm Invades: Forces from the Realm of Shadows send in 1D4 Shadow Beasts (and/or other denizen)

per melee round. The Rift remains open for 1D6 minutes before it is closed on the other side. The Shadow Beasts try to fight their way to get out of the pyramid and into the world.

71-75% The Realm of the Undead Invades: 1D4 zombies stumble through the Rift per melee looking for fresh meat. The Rift remains open for 3D4 minutes.

76-85% Splugorth Dimension: The Rift is being controlled by a Splugorth stone pyramid. Every 30 seconds a Splugorth Slaver with four Blind Warrior Women appear through the Rift. They are hunting for slaves or combatants in their gladiatorial arena, and try to capture as many Atlanteans as possible. The Splugorth hold the Rift open for 4D6 minutes. In the alternative, this could be a portal to someplace on Atlantis and it could be Kittani or Kydians warriors coming through, or Sunaj(!) or D-Bee slave races, or even runaway slaves who have come to the Atlanteans for asylum from the Splugorth. Their master and his forces may not be far behind.

86-90% Sunaj Surgical Strike: A planned strike by the Sunaj is launched through the Rift, with 1D4+1 Sunaj Assassins, 1D4 Shadow Assassins, and one Shadow Mage, arriving per melee round for 2D4 melee rounds. Their goal is to secure the pyramid or to capture a key person or two (and clan leader, elder, scientist, mage, etc.) for reasons unknown. Is this a prelude to a full-scale invasion? When the battle is done, can all the Sunaj be accounted for? Could this assault have been a distraction to let one or more assassins slip into the Atlantean compound or city-state?

91-92% Greater Elemental or Elemental Intelligence: A curious Elemental Entity comes through the Rift. It is only in its energy form and is harmless at the moment. It will look around the pyramid occasionally using Telekinesis to throw small objects around after it examines them. If someone tries to stop the Greater Elemental or Elemental Intelligence, they will try to possess the nearest thing it can find; a person, a tree, an open fire pit or water basin, dirt from a potted plant or even the air. It will then retaliate against the person who attacked it. If left unmolested it leaves after 1D6+2 minutes.

93-94% Minor Elemental: Roll for a Minor Earth, Air, Fire or Water Elemental that emerges from the Rift after holding it open for 1D4 minutes. It tries to escape into the world unless stopped and sent back to its own dimension.

95-96% Entities Swarm In. Several Entities come through the Rift. There will be 1D6 of the same type. Roll to determine which type of entity comes through: 01-10% Poltergeist, 11-20% Syphon, 21-30% Haunting, 31-40% Tectonic, 41-50% Possessing (all described in **Rifts® Dark Conversions**), 51-60% Gluttonous Entity, 61-70% Beautiful Ghost, 71-75% Harmful Ghost, 76-80% Conglomerate Entity, 81-90% Contagion Entity, 91-100% Rotting Entity. (The latter group can be found in **Rifts® World Book 29, Madhaven**.)

97-99% Monster Rush! The Rift unleashes a horde of 1D6+6 of the following: 01-25% Xiticix, 26-50% Black Faeries, 51-75% Brodkil, 76-100% Witchlings. (All are described in **Rifts® Sourcebook One, Revised & Expanded**.) Other monsters from across the Three Galaxies or the Megaverse may be substituted. That might even include monsters and beings from other game settings!

100% Possession! 6+1D4 Atlanteans have become possessed and are starting to take control of the Pyramid. In less than 20 minutes they will lock-down the pyramid and be able to Rift in more creatures like themselves or its minions. The possessed Atlanteans need to be stopped, preferably not killed. What is possessing them? Whatever you would like, Possessing Entity, Mindolar (see **Rifts® Dark Conversions**), some sort of demon, spirit, etc.

Atlantean Healing Pyramids

The Atlantean Healing Pyramid is the Atlantean version of a hospital, trauma center and advanced biological research center all rolled into a single building. The primary focus is on healing, so these pyramids lack many of the dimension-spanning qualities of their larger brothers.

Most Healing Pyramids are small or medium in size, large ones being the exception. Their most distinguishing feature is the top of the pyramid flattens out. Each clan tends to adorn the top with some kind of medical symbol; some use the caduceus which is slowly becoming a Megaversal symbol of medical treatment, while others use the traditional "white rose," or an emerald or emerald green color in some way – all of which signify healing among the Atlantean clans. the remaining clans use a variation of it. The flattened roof supports airborne vehicles when teleportation is not available.

It would seem that with the miracles that an Atlantean Healing Pyramid could accomplish that there would be one in every Atlantean settlement, but that is not the case. First, constructing them is a great undertaking that often involves a dozen experienced Stone Masters and months of preparation and building time. Second, is having the right location. While Dimensional Pyramids can be built on ley lines or nexus points, Healing Pyramids can only be built on a nexus that has at least two or more intersecting ley lines. It has nothing to do with the amount of P.P.E. surging through this kind of nexus, but rather it is about the placement, like the practice of *feng shui* on Earth's China. Finally, there are some exotic components needed in the construction. This is where the crystal powers come into play and are combined with the Stone Magic. Healing centers possess a host of magical healing abilities that are accessible by most Atlanteans. In the case of certain healing apparatus, a trained Atlantean healer would be on hand to administer treatment.

There is one final note about Atlantean Healing Pyramids, most are small by the standards of 21st Century hospitals. The reasons for this is the majority of Atlanteans have excellent health and magical and psionic healing methods and procedures are fast and simple. Recovery from treatment is very quick, if not instant. Most patients can go home the same day.

Medical problems are very rare among Atlanteans and one could say as a society, they have become somewhat complacent. Regular medical visits are unheard of, and those who do are often the elderly or warriors and adventures who picked up a new injury or alien "bug." Atlanteans have managed to correct 99% of all genetic defects and most diseases are stopped quickly due to their advanced medical and magical knowledge. There has not been a need for larger Healing Pyramids since the days of the Vampire Scourge. So not every Atlantean clan has a Healing Pyramid and then they tend to still be on the small side. Those that do have a Healing Pyramid often open it up to passing dimensional travelers or those Atlanteans who do medical and biological research. As dimensional conflicts like the Minion War and increased attacks from the Sunaj occur, the need for larger or more numerous Healing Pyramids *may* be necessary.

Powers of the Healing Pyramid

1. Slows the Aging Process: This power is the same as described under the Dimensional Pyramid, except it also affects everyone within a five mile (8 km) radius as well.

2. Healing (limited): This is the same as the Dimensional Pyramid described above. Healing Pyramids also have an array of healing powers at their disposal described below.

3. Stasis Sleep: This is the same as the Dimensional Pyramid. Patients that need critical care can be put in stasis by a trained Atlantean healer. Stasis can help halt or slow down many afflictions. For example, if a patient needs to be isolated due to a contagious disease, the stasis will stop all progression of the disease and allow the Atlanteans time to study the disease and find a cure. Only P.P.E. and I.S.P. afflictions cannot be put in stasis. See the seven deadly plagues in Megaverse in Flames. The stasis sleep is exactly the same as described under the Dimensional Pyramid with the exception that the patient is often monitored with an array of medical equipment. Also, the trained healer can bring the patient out of stasis when needed.

4. The Focus and Control of P.P.E.: This is exactly the same as described under the Dimensional Pyramid.

5. Storage of Potential Psychic Energy (P.P.E.): Healing Pyramids can store 3D4x100 P.P.E. This fluctuates every six hours. This P.P.E. is used to access the various healing powers. In an emergency, power could be drawn from a Power Pyramid (see below) if needed.

6. Pyramid Communication: This power is the same as described under the Dimensional Pyramid.

7. Teleportation via Pyramids: Because there is the possibility of contamination or even releasing a disease, not every room in the Healing Pyramid can be teleported from or to. There are designated areas for this. Except for being limited to specific areas of the pyramid, this power is exactly the same as the Dimensional Pyramid.

8. Dimensional Teleport via Pyramids: Healing Centers can receive dimensional travelers, but are not capable of sending. One must teleport to another pyramid for to dimensional teleport. There is a specific receiving area for those who are teleporting in from another dimension.

9. Healing Abilities: The following powers are available in all Healing Pyramids.

Healing Pools: Atlantean Stone Masters are able to craft healing pools using a combination of Stone Magic and Crystal Magic. The pools are often very ornate. The healing pools are for Atlanteans who come in with cuts, scrapes, bruises and minor injuries. Serious trauma like broken bones and organ or brain injuries must be brought to one of the emergency centers within the pyramid. The pools are always heated and are in hot, steamy rooms. Each pool can hold four to eight people at a time. While resting in the pool, 3D6 S.D.C. or Hit Points are recovered every 15 minutes. Supernatural beings like Undead Slayers recover 1D6 M.D.C. every ten minutes. Healing is considered magical and it leaves no scars. It should be noted that the water is mystically charged but only heals while in a pyramid. It does no additional damage to vampires and has no healing properties if removed from the pyramid. There are often three dozen healing pools in a Healing Pyramid. While using a healing pool, patients are +10% to save vs coma/death and treatment is equal to a hospital. These pools do not need to be activated and are considered "on" at all times.

Emergency Center Healing Beds: In the emergency centers there are at least a dozen stone daises that are ornately decorated with gems courtesy of the power of a Stone Master. The Atlantean healers are trained in the use of these healing beds and have access to the following magical powers. All spells are performed at the level of the healer. Only Atlantean healers are trained in the use of these beds and are able to access the spells listed below. To access the magic powers of the healing beds, players should roll their operate pyramid skill. On a successful roll the healer is able to access the assorted magic spells and begin treatment. Treatment even with these magic powers is never guaranteed, although patients do enjoy a +20% to save vs coma/death and treatment is considered the same as being done in a hospital. The following spells are pretty standard and can be expected to be found in all Atlantean Healing Pyramids. On a failed roll, the power cannot be accessed at that moment and the Atlantean must concentrate for 1D4 melees before trying again. If time is critical, another Atlantean can try. It should be noted that P.P.E. is drained from the pyramid in order to use these powers.

Cleanse (6): Used to sterilize wounds and the general area.

Manipulate Objects (2+): Used by doctors as an extra set of hands when doing delicate work like surgery.

Cure Illness (15): Just like the spell, most minor illnesses can be treated.

Cure Minor Disorder (10): Used to cure most minor disorders.

Breathe Without Air (5): When a patient has damage to their throat or lungs, this spell can be a life saver and ensures that oxygen can be delivered to the brain.

Fortify Against Disease (15): This is used primarily by healers and nurses to prevent spreading illness.

Heal Wounds (10): This is the most commonly used power as it will treat a variety of injuries for those who are wounded. It will not heal Mega-Damage beings, just S.D.C. creatures.

Greater Healing (30): This is used to treat critically wounded patients.

Life Blast (15): This is used when the patient is fading. It can act like a defibrillator and give the patient that extra bit they need to survive.

Light Healing (6): This is mostly utilized via the Healing pools, but can also be accessed from a healing bed.

Sense Evil (2): This is just a precautionary ability that Atlantean healers have access to. It is used primarily to detect possession or determine if someone might do harm to the healing staff.

Sleep (10): This can be used to anesthetize patients for surgery or to calm those in distress. Typically a vial of water is enchanted and the recipient must ingest it or it can be delivered via a hypodermic needle.

Sustain (12): This can be used to help patients who are not critical and it will sustain them long enough until they can be treated. It usually prevents their conditions from getting worse, although it will not stop internal or external bleeding.

Exorcism (30): This power is used when patients are possessed.

Negate Poison/Toxin (5): An all-purpose ability that can quickly save most patients who are suffering from exposure to toxins or poisons.

Super-Healing (70): This is used to treat Mega-Damage beings like Undead Slayers or Tattooed Defenders and similar Mega-Damage patients.

Advanced Healing Abilities: The following spells vary per Atlantean Clan. Not every Atlantean Clan has access to these spells and some clans that do are not willing to share, though they may lend aid at their Healing Pyramid. Roll percentiles for each spell to determine if the Healing Pyramid has these spells.

Purification (Food/Water) (20) 1-50%
Purge Other (100) 1-50%
Remove Curse (140) 1-24%
Restore Limb (80) 1-60%
Restore Life (275) 1-25%
Restoration (750) 1-35%
Resurrection (650) 1-10%
Stone to Flesh (30) 1-25%

Healing Pyramid Layout

The following details the various levels of what can be considered a "typical" Atlantean Healing Pyramid. Pyramids can and will vary from clan to clan.

Level One

General Treatment Center

1. Central Chamber: This is a meeting and gathering area where Atlanteans teleport into. The chamber is typically not as ornate as those of Dimensional Pyramids and is often decorated with symbols of healing. To avoid the spreading of diseases and to protect wounded individuals, the pyramid limits teleportation on this level to and from this room. Beyond the confines of the room it will not work save for actually casting spells and expending the appropriate P.P.E. There are two sets of stairs in opposite corners of the chamber to allow access to upper chambers.

2. Urgent Care Chambers: Two urgent care chambers are set up on the first floor to treat a variety of ailments. They are often small and not meant to handle large-scale emergencies. They have a full array of healing apparatus at their disposal as well as a small lab in the rear of the room. Usually, two Atlantean healers are on hand at any given time to treat these non-life threatening problems. In an emergency additional healers can be called in.

3. Healing Pools: There are often four chambers set up as communal healing pool rooms. Any Atlantean citizens can walk into a Healing Pyramid and go to one of the pools for minor scrapes, bruises and so on. The pools can hold four adults while the large pool in the center can hold up to ten. The type and amount of healing is described above.

4. Large Healing Pools: The large pools are meant for larger beings such as Chiang-Ku dragons as well as other Atlantean allies who are welcome to use the pools. The pools can also be used for humanoids and in an emergency, up to 20 can fit into the pool. The healing is the same only the pool size is larger.

5. Private Chambers: The private chambers are used for a variety of purposes. Some are sleeping quarters for the Atlantean

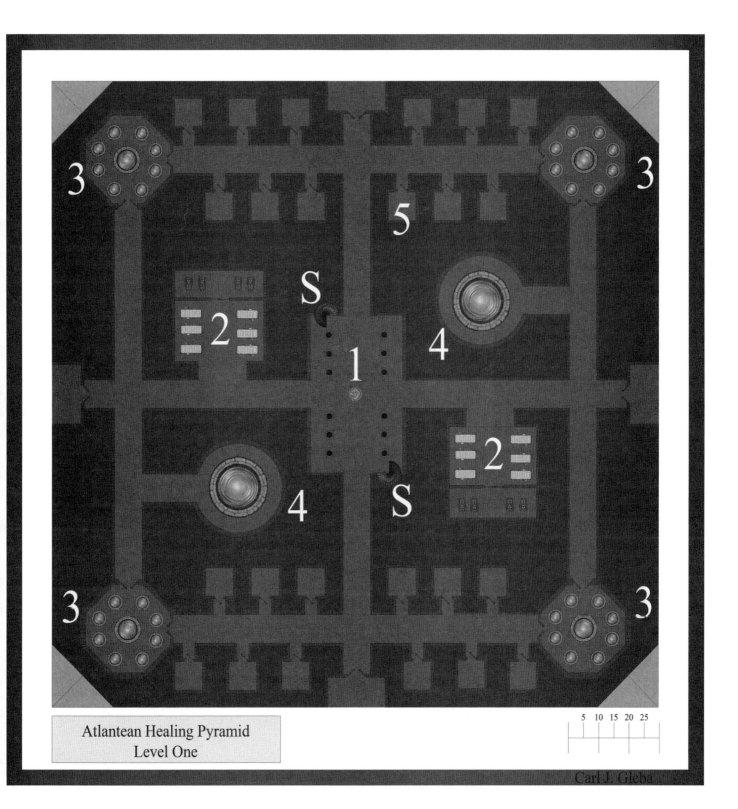

Atlantean Healing Pyramid
Level One

5　10　15　20　25

Carl J. Gleba

healers on call. Others are used by those who wish to rest after being healed. They typically get converted to makeshift labs, storage rooms, meeting rooms or eating areas. They are meant as all-purpose room, for a variety of functions. Each pyramid typically has two dozen.

Level Two

Urgent Care Center

Level Two is the equivalent of an urgent care facility. It is not an emergency room, but it is capable of taking care of those that are sick, have a broken bone and other serious, but non-life threatening injuries.

1. Main Teleport Chamber: Most Atlanteans can teleport directly to this chamber. It the equivalent of a waiting room for family members.

2. Medical Examination Rooms: There are two medical exam rooms where injured people can be examined by an Atlantean doctor. The room is typically divided by hanging curtains.

3. Urgent Care Monitoring Rooms: When patients need to be monitored overnight or for an extended period, it is done in these rooms.

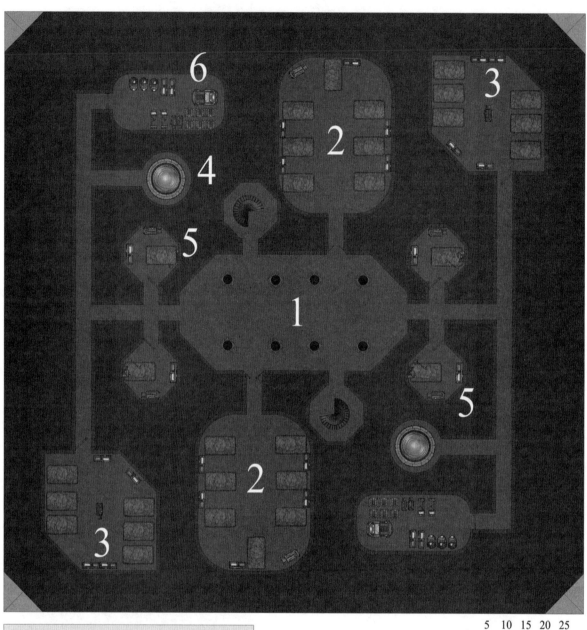

**Atlantean Healing Pyramid
Level Two**

5 10 15 20 25

Carl J. Gleba

4. Healing Pools: These pools are a follow-up to whatever treatment a Healer decides is needed. This allows the individual to heal up often without scars and in a calm relaxing environment.

5. Private Examination Rooms: There are four rooms where patients can be seen in private.

6. Medical Supply Storage: Extra supplies are stored here.

Level Three

Advanced Diagnostic, Research & Treatment Level

1. Surgical Rooms: When suffering from a critical wound or when magic can not help, a trained medical doctor or psychic sur-geon/Psi-Healer can use one of these rooms to perform surgical procedures. These rooms also double as advance diagnostic for D-Bee and life forms unknown to Atlanteans.

2. Various Medical Labs: Any kind of medical or biological research can be done in these labs to include blood work, genetics and molecular science.

3. Storage Rooms: These rooms often contain perishable medical supplies, such as artificial blood, various saline solutions, perishable drugs and a variety of other medical supplies.

4. Conference Room: This is the primary meeting room used by all medical staff at the Healing Pyramid. This room has access to any electronic medical records and data stored in the pyramid.

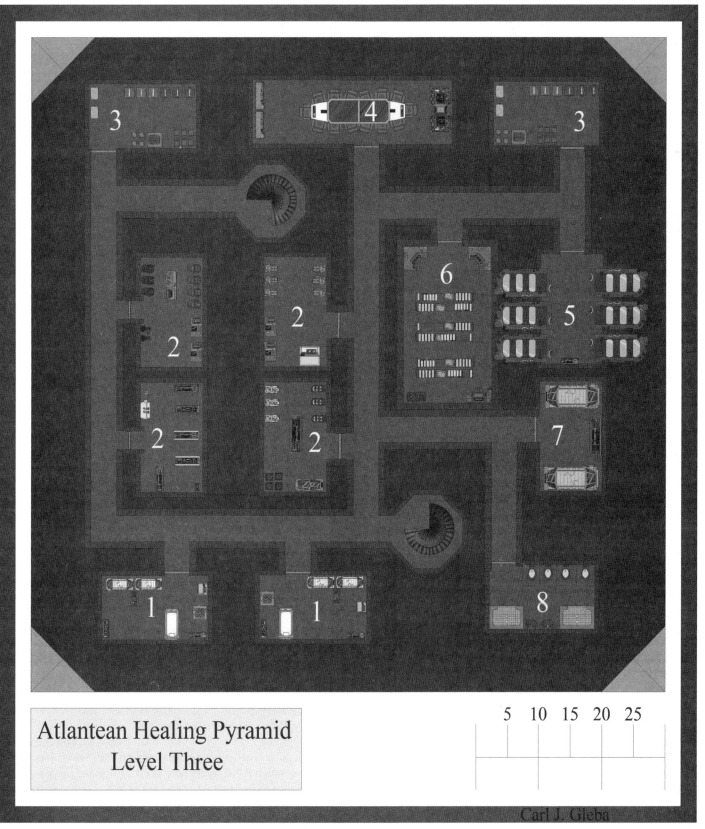

**Atlantean Healing Pyramid
Level Three**

Carl J. Gleba

5. Emergency Medical Stasis and Morgue: This room has advanced TW chambers to preserve the dead or assist Atlanteans who are unable to put themselves into stasis. Slabs extend out of the wall and retract to store the dead or those in stasis when needed.

6. Medical library and Records Room: Most Healing Pyramids have extensive medical libraries and records for those who have been treated at the pyramid. All data can be accessed here if needed, but this room is typically locked and only specific in-

dividuals on staff have access. Atlanteans also believe in patient-doctor confidentiality.

7. D-Bee Medical Exam Room: This room is special in that it is able to simulate different environments if needed. Sometimes, D-Bees need to be treated under conditions that mimic their home world. The room uses some of the most advanced magic devices to simulate several hundred conditions to different gravity to dense, toxic atmospheres.

8. Washroom and Showers: Many of the Atlantean medical staff spend more than their fair share of time in a Healing Pyramid. They have the facilities available to refresh themselves when needed.

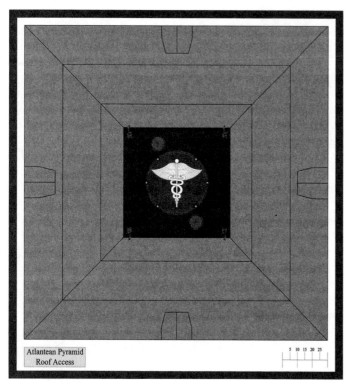

Atlantean Pyramid
Roof Access

5 10 15 20 25

Roof Access: Most Atlanteans are able to ley line phase as needed. However, there are times when they are not able to ley line phase such as when they have non-Atlantean visitors. In these cases, the roof of an Atlantean pyramid can serve as a landing pad for medical vehicles. Mystic alarms automatically alert medical staff of when a ship or people land on the roof. This way medical staff can be ready to treat the injured.

Power Pyramids

A Power Pyramid is the Atlantean equivalent to a modern day nuclear power plant. The difference is that the stone pyramid uses magic energy (P.P.E.) and not fissionable material. It is also able to transmit the power over a wide area without the need for power lines. The exact range and amount of power available depends on the size of the Power Pyramid or the number of them present. Small Power Pyramids can supply energy to all Atlantean structures in a five mile (8 km) radius, medium pyramids an 16 mile (25.6 km) radius, and a large Power Pyramid to a 35 mile (56 km) radius.

Power Pyramids are almost always located at a ley line nexus, but can also be built on a ley line connected to a nexus or a solitary ley line with no nexus point. Those built on a ley line rather than a nexus point are usually small Power Pyramids to supply a community on the outskirts or to provide supplemental energy. Remember, a nexus point is typically 1-4 miles in diameter, so there is plenty of room for multiple pyramids. Atlanteans never build any more Power Pyramids than they need simply for safety concerns. They have also built in additional safety features because they never want to see what happened to ancient Atlantis, happen again. And in the many millennia since that tragedy, it never has.

Monitoring and redundant safety features are designed to catch problems even if something should slip by those in the control room, which is a rare event. There are a number of safety features that can kill the power in seconds. The Power Pyramids of today are safer than they have ever been. Any attempts at sabotaging a Power Pyramid suffer a -40% penalty to any skills that could be used to sabotage, and even then, damage is likely to comparatively minor and have no serious or lasting complications whatsoever on the Power Pyramid, the community or the environment. Skill that might be used in an attempt at sabotage include, Electrical Engineering, Electricity Generation, or Mechanical Engineering; there are numerous pieces of equipment that are not magical in nature or that require th Techno-Wizardry skill. The penalty is not due to alien construction, which would impose an additional -30%, but they due to the numerous safety features and redundant features and failsafes built into the pyramid. Each system has three or four redundant backups that would need to be bypassed in order to cause a serious problem. If by some miracle a saboteur was successful, it would reduce operations and power supply by 1D4x10%. Severe sabotage like that is unlikely, but it is possible, especially to by those who have some understanding of how a Power Pyramid work, like some agents within the Sunaj.

Key Features of Power Pyramids:

1. The Focus and Control of P.P.E.: This is crucial for a Power Pyramid as the energy is shunted to TW generators and then distributed to the surrounding city and/or countryside.

2. Harmonious Effect on Ley Line Storms and Random Rifts: As with Dimensional Pyramids, Power Pyramids have a harmonious effect on ley lines. Ley Line Storms are reduced by 50%, although additional Power Pyramids on the same ley line will increase the calming effect by 5% per Power Pyramid with a maxim of an 80% reduction. Random Rifts are reduced to a 5% chance per annual occurrence.

3. Increase the Power of Stone Magic: This is the same as listed under Dimensional Pyramids.

4. Storage of Potential Psychic Energy (P.P.E.): Power Pyramids are a storehouse for P.P.E., but it can only be used by the respective Power Pyramid on any of the connecting ley lines. The primary reason for storing the P.P.E. is to keep a reserve on tap when ley line energy is low or magically diverted. The P.P.E. storage capacitors can be slowly charged with P.P.E., however they can only hold their maximum capacity for 96 hours and then they heat up and can possibly explode, releasing an uncontrolled Mega-Rift. Typically, no more than two banks of capacitors are kept at full charge and it is the job of those who work at the Power Pyramid to shunt power between the capacitors on a daily basis. Some clans vary how much P.P.E. is actually stored. For game purposes, each bank of capacitors can hold 1D6x1,000 P.P.E. There are four banks per pyramid so P.P.E. can range from 6,000 to 24,000 P.P.E. When needed, the P.P.E. can be directed to a Dimensional Pyramid, Healing Pyramid or any of the stone weapons used for defense.

5. Pyramid Communications: Communications is limited to within the same dimension only. This is primarily a security feature to prevent dimensional incursions into the Power Pyramid.

6. Teleportation via Pyramids: This is restricted to a particular level and room in a Power Pyramid. Teleporting into the wrong location can have catastrophic results for the person teleporting in, especially if one were to teleport near a power conduit that is actively charging or discharging P.P.E. The effect would be the same as a failed Teleport. Roll under the *Teleport: Superior spell*. The secured Teleport Chamber is the primary way in and out of the Power Pyramid as there are no external doors for security reasons. The Teleport Chamber has 6-12 (roll 2D4+4) Tattooed Defenders on guard to inspect all arrivals, four of them have with access to Crystal Guardian Armor and two .

7. Ley Line Redirection: Power Pyramids have the capability of redirecting ley line energy. Atlanteans only do this when absolutely necessary and it is always temporary, in part, because they can only maintained redirection for 8 hours, and require a full 24 hours to charge before the ley line can be redirected again. This is

sometimes done as a security measure to deny someone access to the ley line or the ley line is redirected for a tactical advantage. It should be noted that a Power Pyramid can NOT redirect a ley line if it part of a ley line triangle. This is more of a safety feature and it has never actually been tried for fear disrupting a ley line triangle would have catastrophic results, causing all kinds of dimensional disturbances similar to those felt during the last days of Atlantis.

Power Pyramid Layout
Level One

Atlantean Power Pyramid
Level One

5 10 15 20 25

Carl J. Gleba

Power Generation Equipment

1. Pyramid Power Storage Units: In the event that there is a low ebb in P.P.E., these units release P.P.E. to keep the power plant running. They cannot charge any of the P.P.E. capacitors, but each bank of three can keep the Power Pyramid running for three weeks. They only provide power for the key abilities described above except for number 7.

2. The Pyramid has four P.P.E. Electro-Current Reactors: These devices turn P.P.E. into a form of energy that can easily be transmitted. Energy is funneled up to one of the four attached obelisks. The air is supercharged with electrical energy. Energy

constantly moves up the obelisk chamber. Anyone making direct contact with the reactor suffers severe damage (2D6x10 M.D.) per contact. When the reactors need to be repaired or serviced, they can be shut down while the other reactors continue to operate. If necessary, as many as three of the reactors can be shut down, for repairs. For each reactor shut down, the range that the pyramid can supply power is reduced by 25% per reactor.

3. Primary P.P.E. Collector: This large TW device is the primary collector and distributor of P.P.E. absorbed by the pyramid. The P.P.E. is channeled to the four reactors where it is converted into usable energy. Energy constantly sparks between the col-

Atlantean Power Pyramid
Level Two

Carl J. Gleba

lector and the power conduits leading to the four reactors. This energy is exposed and anyone caught between the collector and power conduits will take 1D6x10 M.D. each time they touch it.

4. Emergency Control Rooms: In the event that the main control room is damaged or unable to shut down the reactors, they can be shut down in one of four emergency control rooms. These rooms also provide access to each of the individual reactors.

Level Two

Clockwork Internal Operations

Since most of the machinery on the base level is 20 to 30 feet (6.1 to 9.1 m) in height, most of the equipment needs to be ac-

cessed via scaffolding. Each chamber has two sets of stairs to access the scaffolding. This area is typically off limits and only occasionally does pyramid staff come onto these levels. It is typically never more than twice a month and then those tours are to review the equipment for wear and tear.

Level Three

Pyramid Access and Control Center

1. Secured Teleport Chamber: This is the only access to the pyramid via teleportation. The rest of the pyramid is secured against dimensional Rifts and teleportation. Regardless of where one wants to Teleport into the Power Pyramids they always ap-

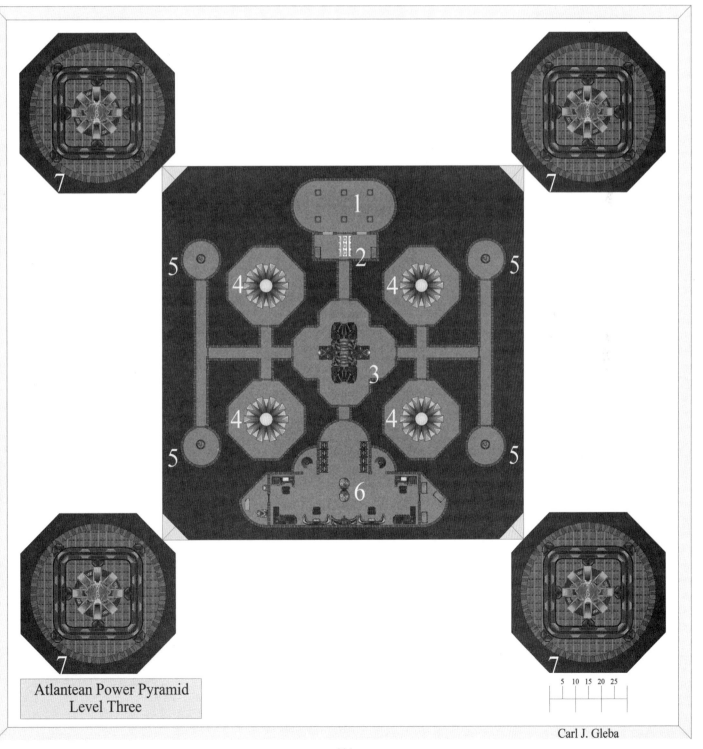

Atlantean Power Pyramid
Level Three

5 10 15 20 25

Carl J. Gleba

pear in the teleport chamber. This is a built-in security and safety measure that can only be overridden in the control center.

2. Guard Station: Because of the sensitive nature of the Power Pyramids, 8-12 Tattooed Defenders, two Undead Slayers, and a Stone Master or Crystal Mage are stationed in this guard station. The guards have a small computer terminal which allows them to identify who should have access to the pyramid. Typically only expected visitors or those who work in the Power Pyramid are allowed access. Visitors are rare and must be accompanied by a high ranking member of the clan.

3. Central Power Core: This is the workhorse of the whole Power Pyramid. P.P.E. is fed into the power core and turned into transmittable electrical energy. This device is constantly monitored from the control room and checked to ensure there are no power build-ups which could damage or destroy the pyramid.

4. P.P.E. Storage Capacitors: These devices are a combination of TW device and crystal artifact. Each P.P.E. Storage Capacitor is able to store between 1,000 and 4,000 P.P.E. These devices are crafted from a single large crystal that is shaped by a Crystal Master and turned over to a Techno-Wizard who adds the final components that links the capacitor to the rest of the pyramid's systems.

5. Access to Lower Power Levels: These rooms provide stairs that allow access to the emergency control rooms on the

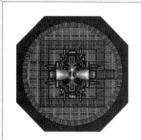

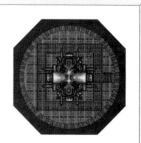

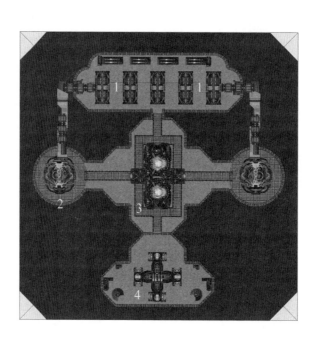

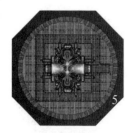

Atlantean Power Pyramid
Level Four

5 10 15 20 25

Carl J. Gleba

first level. These rooms are sealed by a TW lock and the corridors are periodically patrolled by one of the guards from the guard station.

6. Command Center Access and Controls: This is the whole nerve center of the Power Pyramid. Despite the pyramid's complexity, the control room is rather simplistic with only four major control interfaces. The sophisticated TW computer used runs most of the major functions of the pyramid. All of the interface consoles have a 3D interface that each user can physically manipulate. In the center of the control center is a hologram projector that shows the various power levels and power flows within the pyramid. Just like the other interfaces, this model can be physi-

cally manipulated to make changes to the power flow and P.P.E. levels.

7. Power Transmitter Obelisks Access. People rarely need to go into the pyramid's obelisks, but if they do, this level allows for maintenance on the power transmitters.

Level Four
Magic Control Center

1. Mystic Generators: The pyramid's mystic generators are used to transmit P.P.E. energy when needed to other Atlantean structures. While most can use the transmittable electrical energy, some like the defense obelisks require a direct infusion

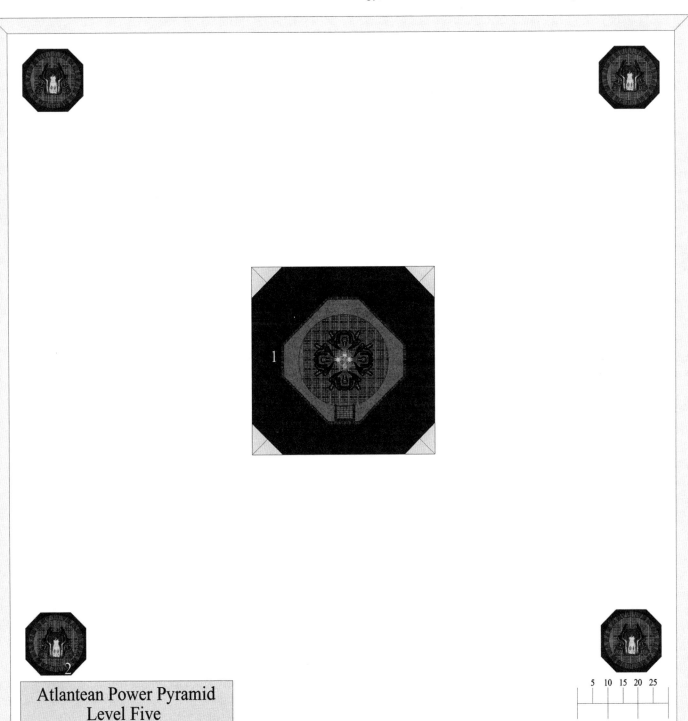

Atlantean Power Pyramid
Level Five

5 10 15 20 25

Carl J. Gleba

of P.P.E. to operate. This bank of mystic generators can syphon P.P.E. from the storage capacitors and transmit it using the mystic power conduits that lead to the tip of the pyramid.

2. Mystic Power Conduits: These two chambers tap the mystic generators and move the power to the central power core. Operators can access these chambers via the central power core to conduct repairs or to check on the equipment.

3. Central Power Core Access Grid: The central power core channels all of the pyramid's P.P.E. when needed to the pyramid power apex shunt in the level above.

4. Auxiliary Control Room: A small team is typically stationed in the auxiliary control room. Their task is to check the equipment from signs of wear and tear. They can also access the control terminals to run diagnostics on equipment. The Power Pyramid can be controlled from here if necessary and would require a computer hacker level of abilities to do so. This room also provides access to the level above it.

Level Five

1. Pyramid Apex Power Shunt: This piece of equipment can direct the P.P.E. to the specific location that needs it.

2. Power Transmitters Power Shunts: These power shunts transmit the correct amount of energy to avoid overloading Atlantean equipment. Each power shunt can be accessed from the level below. If these power shunts are damaged or inoperable, power output range is reduced by 25% per power shunt.

Other Notable Atlantean Structures

Atlantean Oubliette

As Atlanteans traveled the Megaverse, they have encountered many powerful foes and even more powerful weapons and artifacts. Some items are best left hidden but in some cases, the Atlanteans felt the item was so powerful that they had to safeguard it to keep the Megaverse safe. That is where the Atlantean Oubliettes come into play. An Oubliette can be best thought of as a dimensional vault used to safeguard very powerful items or people. It is meant to keep intruders out, and whatever is inside, trapped. Dimensional Raiders that come across Atlantean Oubliettes often consider them death traps and avoid them at all costs.

An Oubliette creates a pocket dimension with an impenetrable dimensional barrier. The barrier is often one-way, keeping those who sneak in trapped until freed by an Atlantean. If trapped inside an Oubliette, the dimensional barrier prevents the use of Teleportation spells, Mystic Portals, D-Phasing and similar dimensional and temporal spells. In theory, someone could shoot their way out, but this is likely to create a lot of noise. Some Atlanteans can reverse the field to keep people out, but the side-effect is to prevent all kinds of teleportation and dimensional spells (the same as

those mentioned above) from being used within a one mile (1.6 km) radius of the Oubliette. To those who can sense dimensional anomalies, like Shifters, this would stand out. When the field is focused inward, a Shifter passing by is unlikely to notice it unless he is actually touching the building in question, in which case the dimensional anomaly would become apparent, but he wouldn't be able to guess the exact nature of the anomaly, just that one exists.

Each Oubliette only has one way in and one way out, similar to a dimension with a dimensional focal point. This entrance has a series of keyholes, although they don't look like keyholes. They are often shapes carved into a stone wall that look like ornate patterns, but they are hollows for Atlantean crystals to be placed in them. These crystals are the keys to the Oubliette. One crystal is the key that opens the door, and the other can activate, deactivate and reverse the dimensional barrier on the Oubliette. More elaborate Oubliettes will have pass codes and similar elaborate locks, with some magical while others are technological in nature. While a crystal key is often needed to access an Oubliette, a skilled lock picker with mystic knowledge could pick the lock. This would require the combination of P.P.E. from the Escape spell combined with a successful Pick Locks at -30%. Keep in mind that to non-Atlanteans, the keyholes are often inconspicuous. Consider it a high Perception Roll to even realize that they are keyholes.

In Atlantean cities, Oubliettes do not stand out like a pyramid. Rather they are constructed in such a way as to blend into the rest of the city. It is a philosophy of hiding something in plain sight. A facade is often in the front of the building like some kind of low-key business, a florist for example. Some are even built into affluent Atlantean homes. Just keep in mind that Oubliettes are never built into any of the pyramids. The magicks used to construct each are incompatible. Atlantean Oubliettes come in all shapes and sizes and there is no standard Oubliette.

Stone Defensive Weapons

Atlanteans did far more with stone than just create their homes and pyramids out of it. Stone weapons are now the basic defenses found in any Atlantean city, especially with the threat of dimensional raiders as well as old enemies like the Splugorth or vampires.

Stone Obelisk

Stone Obelisks often appear in many Atlantean cities. Many are decorated with elaborate sculptures, bas-reliefs, or even act as street signs. They are often 20 to 80 feet (6.1 to 24.4 m; roll 2D4x10) tall, and the tip has the constant glow of ley line energy. These devices are deadly weapons that are a hybrid of Techno-Wizardry and Stone Magic. Operators in Dimensional Pyramids control these devices, which can deliver a nasty jolt via the Lightning Arc spell. The power of the Stone Obelisk is equal to a sixth level caster, but with a superior range.

<u>M.D.C. of Obelisk:</u> 350

<u>Weight:</u> Each Obelisk weighs 10 tons.

<u>Range:</u> 600 feet (188 m) away from a ley line. 1,200 feet (366 m) on a ley line. 2,400 feet (732 m) within the radius of a nexus.

<u>Mega-Damage:</u> 4D6 M.D. away from a ley line. 6D6 M.D. on a ley line and 1D6x10 M.D. for Stone Obelisks locate at a nexus.

Rate of Fire: Equal to the combined number of attacks of the operator, typically 4 to 6 shots per melee.

Payload: Each Obelisk has a small reserve of P.P.E., enough for five castings. Additional P.P.E. can be directed to any and all Obelisks at a rate of 30 P.P.E. per melee. Each Obelisk typically stores 150 P.P.E. This is enough P.P.E. to keep the weapon running for 30 melees before it requires a recharge. The maximum P.P.E. that can be held is 300 per Obelisk.

Cost: 2.5 million credits, but they are never sold.

Note: A typical Atlantean city could have 40 to 50 Stone Obelisks. They will be scattered about the city to form a defensive grid.

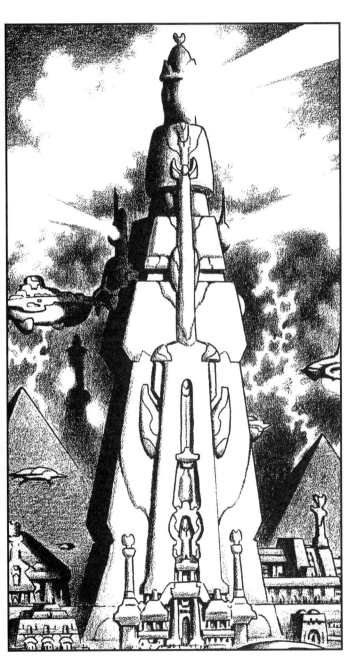

Mega-Obelisk

The Mega-Obelisk is a souped-up version of the regular Obelisk found in Atlantean streets. Each Mega-Obelisk is 500 feet (152.4 m) tall and serves as a defensive structure to battle demons and creatures from the Rifts, or even aggressors outside the city.

Each Mega-Obelisk can create a massive force field to encircle the Atlantean city, fire deadly bolts of mystic energy, or create a massive Globe of Daylight that can fire beams of pure solar light. However, only one feature can be used at a time, and none of the others can be used if a force field is up.

M.D.C. of the Mega-Obelisk: 2,500

Weight: Each Mega-Obelisk weighs 200 tons.

Powers:

1. Force Field: The force field has 20,000 M.D.C. and can regenerate M.D.C. at a rate of 1D4x100 M.D. per melee round. Each Mega-Obelisk can project a force field that covers a five mile (8 km) radius, so it may be necessary to have numerous Mega-Obelisks to cover an entire city or city-state.

2. Mystic Blast. The Mystic Blast takes ley line energy and projects it in a concentrated beam that lasts for eight seconds. This weapon is the Atlantean equivalent of artillery and is best used against large targets. Humanoid targets 20 feet (6.1 m) tall or smaller are +5 to dodge the beam.

Range: 1,200 feet (366 m) away from a ley line. 2,400 feet (732 m) on a ley line, and 4,800 feet (1,463 m) when located within the radius of a nexus.

Mega-Damage: 1D6x10 M.D. away from a ley line. 2D6x10 M.D. on a ley line and 1D4x100 M.D. for Mega-Obelisks located at a nexus. It can also fire a wide, area effect blast that inflicts 4D6 M.D. to all targets within a 25 foot (7.6 m) radius.

Rate of Fire: The beam can only be fired twice per melee. Operators firing from one of the pyramids are +3 to strike large opponents, giant robots, and military vehicles with the beam, but they are -2 to strike if they try to hit a small target under 10 feet (3 m) in size.

Payload: Effectively unlimited, but each Mega-Obelisk requires a dedicated Power Pyramid. All reserve P.P.E. must be diverted to the Mega-Obelisk in order for it to operate. If the Power Pyramid is disabled or destroyed, the Mega-Obelisk will not work.

3. Globe of Daylight Projector. The tip of the Mega-Obelisk glows like a lighthouse and projects a massive spotlight that is 100 feet (30.5 m) wide and has a range of up to 6,000 feet (1828 m). This intense beam of solar energy and light inflicts 6D6 damage direct to Hit Points for every melee that a vampire is in the light. Vampires will have their typical reaction as they do to Globe of Daylight. Non-vampires in the light require sunglasses, polarized vision or some kind of eye protection or else they are partially blinded by the light and are -3 to strike, parry, and dodge.

Cost: 150 million credits, but they are never sold.

Atlantean Stone Lions

Remotely Operated Defenders

One of the innovations that the Atlanteans have come up with is remotely operated defenders based on the magic used to create Stone Golems. The creation is a closely guarded secret among Atlantean Alchemists who have a specialty in Stone Magic and spell magic. The statues appear to be carved from a single piece of stone. They are often very elaborate and ornate in appearance. Most will be found around major stone structures like any of the stone pyramids or even the homes of important individuals.

Operators can safely control these automatons from a safe room inside a pyramid, and can see through the eyes as if they were actually there. If the Stone Lion is destroyed, they simply take control of another one. Stone Lions are very popular because no one can tell the difference between a regular stone statue and an R.O.D., as they do not register as magic when they are not activated. This makes it easy to hide these defenders in plain sight.

Most clans have adopted the Stone Lion as their protector, but the actual animal used can vary (stats still remain the same) from clan to clan. The typical Atlantean city can have an average of 80 to 100 R.O.D.s throughout the city. At any given time there are a dozen operators, and another dozen can be brought in within 1D4 melees thanks to Ley Line Phasing.

Model Type: ASG-77

Class: Automated Stone Golem.

Crew: None, controlled remotely by an operator.

M.D.C. by Location:

Legs (4) – 150

* Head – 125

** Main Body – 250

   * A single asterisk indicates a small or difficult target to hit. These can only be struck when the attacker makes a Called Shot, and even then, the shooter is -3 to strike. Destroying the head will blind the operator, making the R.O.D. useless.

   ** Depleting the M.D.C. of the Main Body destroys the Stone Lion.

Speed:

Running: 120 mph (192 km) maximum.

Leaping: The Stone Lion can leap 20 feet (6.1 m) high or across, and add 30 feet (9.1 m) with a running start.

Flying: Not possible.

Underwater Capabilities: The Stone Lion can walk along the bottom of the body of water at one third its running speed. Maximum depth is 4,000 feet (1,219 m).

Statistical Data:

Height: 6.5 feet (2 m) at the shoulder.

Width: 5.2 feet (1.6 m).

Length: 19 feet (5.8 m) including the tail.

Weight: 1.5 tons (1,350 kg).

Physical Strength: Strength is equal to a Supernatural P.S. 33.

Cargo: None.

Power System: Magical and draws on ley line energy.

Market Cost: 500,000 credits in raw material is needed. Atlanteans do not sell Stone Lions, as a pyramid is needed to control them anyway. Without the control panel, the Stone Lion is a massive paperweight.

Operating Stats: The R.O.D. is +5 to strike, parry and dodge, +2 to roll with impact/fall, +5 to pull punch, +4 to strike with the eye lightning bolts, fire breath and water breath.

Attacks per Melee: The number of attacks when controlled by an operator is four per melee, +1 at levels 4, 8, and 12.

Weapon Systems:

1. Eye Lightning Bolts: The Stone Lion can fire the equivalent of the Electric Arc spell from its eyes.

Primary Purpose: Assault.

Secondary Purpose: Defense.

Range: 150 feet (45.7 m).

Mega-Damage: 3D6 M.D.

Rate of Fire: Up to five shots per melee.

Payload: Unlimited while on or within a half mile (0.8 km) of a ley line or nexus point. When away from a ley line, the Stone Lion has a limited payload with enough P.P.E. for five melee rounds total before it needs to be recharged. The Stone Lion can recharge at a stone pyramid or by being within a half mile (0.8 km) of a ley line. If totally depleted, it takes one melee of recharging before it can fire again, but the battery reserve will be fully charged within one minute.

2. Fire Breath: The Stone Lion has a built-in mystical flame thrower based on the Flame Gout spell.

Primary Purpose: Assault, Anti-Personnel.

Secondary Purpose: Defense.

Range: 150 feet (45.7 m) long and 10 feet (3 m) wide.

Mega-Damage: 4D6 M.D.

Rate of Fire: The fire breath can be used up to four times per melee.

Payload: Unlimited while on or within a half mile (0.8 km) of a ley line. If off the ley line, the lion holds enough P.P.E. to use the fire breath for 10 melees total before it needs to be recharged. Recharging is the same as the Eye Lightning Bolts.

3. Water Breath: This is a dual purpose function that the lion has built in. It can fire blasts of water which can be used to fight vampires or used to put out any fires. Since the lions are very fast, relatively small and agile (compared to a fire truck), they can be on most fire scenes in a matter of minutes.

Primary Purpose: Anti-Vampire.

Secondary Purpose: Fire Control.

Range: 120 feet (36.6 m).

Mega-Damage: None, but does 5D6 damage direct to Hit Points if fired at a vampire.

Rate of Fire: Six shots maximum per melee.

Payload: Unlimited while on or within a half mile (0.8 km) of a ley line. If off the ley line, the lion holds enough P.P.E. to use the water breath for 10 melees total before it needs to be recharged. Recharging is the same as the Eye Lightning Bolts.

4. Hand to Hand Combat: The lion can engage directly in hand to hand combat if necessary. Damage from a restrained swat is 5D6+18 S.D.C. A bite does 3D6 M.D., a full strength swat inflicts 4D6 M.D., a claw inflicts 6D6 M.D., a power claw does 1D6x10 M.D. (but counts as two attacks), and a leap where the lion can strike with all four claws does 2D4x10 M.D., but it counts as three attacks.

5. Sensor Systems Note: Operators are linked to their lions and as such, see through their eyes. The lion has the following built in spells: *See the Invisible, See Aura, Sense Magic* and *Globe of Daylight*. Any can be active up to three times per day for 30 minutes at a time at no P.P.E. cost.

6. Mystic Abilities: The Lion regenerates damage at a rate of 5D6 M.D.C. every 10 minutes as long as it is on a ley line or within half a mile (0.8 km) of a ley line. Healing is double at a ley line nexus. Also see *#5 Sensor Systems* above.

The Shadow Dimension

Many dimensional travelers assume that the Shadow Dimension, or Plane of Shadows, is one all-encompassing dimension, but it is not. Just as each person gives off a shadow, so do dimensions. For each dimension, there is a corresponding Shadow Dimension – a shadowy duplicate of the original but devoid of color and light. For example, the Shadow Dimension connected to Rifts Earth resembles the Earth, complete with a mega-sized city where Chi-Town is located, but instead of being populated with Coalition citizens, the population size is half and people are replaced with Shadow Beasts and other Shadow beings, all subservient to a council of Shadow Lords. The ruins of Tolkeen on Shadow Earth are ruins in the Shadow Dimension that are mostly devoid of life except for a few shadow monsters and small gangs of Shadow Beasts. Likewise, the city of Center on Phase World has a shadowy duplicate, but none of the fantastic technology that exists in Phase World exists in its shadow duplicate. Rather it is a large, dilapidated city falling into ruins and haunted by Entities and a variety of shadow monsters.

Each dimension, under the correct conditions, has a direct connection to its twisted shadow duplicate. In dimensions rich in magic, these portals are more prevalent. In dimensions low in magic, the connection is more like a massive wall that keeps them separated, but it is still there. However, opening a doorway to the shadowy doppleganger world of darkness is only possible during significant mystical events such as planetary alignments, or the summer or winter solstice, and even then you may need a magical ritual and human sacrifice.

Of all these Shadow Dimensions, the most powerful is the one connected to Rifts Earth. While there are no ley lines on this Shadow Rifts Earth in the conventional sense, there are dimensional doorways that allow the resident Shadow Beasts and Shadow Lords access to our dimension. Once on Earth, they lurk and observe from the shadows, hunting mortals for food and pleasure, and watching for the right opportunity to cause havoc. Such creatures may function as solitary hunters or hunt in small groups, or serve a Shadow Lord with his own plans for the people of Earth. Other shadow monsters may willingly join forces with beings, mortal and otherwise, that are more powerful than they, and with offer them an opportunity for murder and mayhem. Shadow Beasts and other denizens of the Shadow Plane are sometimes summoned and enslaved by Shifters, Witches and other beings who call upon the forces of darkness to serve them. Even such a lowly position may be satisfying if the shadow monster is allowed to kill and unleash its fury, or if it admires its wicked master.

On the parallel Shadow Earth, the power level of Rifts Earth has sparked fighting and competition on a global level among the Shadow Lords and their minions. This is fortunate for Earth's inhabitants, because these powerful and wicked beings, if organized, could pose a serious threat. However, chaos demons such as these live up to the chaos part of their name, and are undisciplined, disorganized and combative even among their own. For now, the Shadow Lords try to accumulate as much power as possible in their own shadow realm where they amass armies of Shadow Beasts and other shadow creatures, and spend their time waging war upon their neighbors to expand their sphere of power and influence, or to settle countless (and often pointless) squabbles.

General Dimensional Makeup for a Shadow Dimension

This is a model for Game Masters to use to create other Shadow Dimensions. Just follow the dimension outline below. See **Rifts® Dimension Book Seven, Megaverse® Builder** for more details on creating dimensions.

Type of Dimension: The Plane of Shadows (or Shadow Dimensions) are all Parallel Dimensions cast in eternal twilight. Each is a twisted, dark mirror image of the dimension inhabited by mortals.

Primary Dimensional Medium: This will always be the same as the parent dimension.

Secondary Dimensional Medium: This too is always be the same as the parent dimension.

Dimensional Fabric: This will mimic the parent dimension in the mortal realm, but access between the parent dimension and Shadow Dimension is considered *permeable* with a +20%.

Magic Level: A duplicate of the parent dimension.

Dimensional Energy Matrix: Another extension of the parent dimension and will be the same.

Time Flow: Time flows in the same manner as the parent dimension.

Dimensional Quirks: The dimensional quirks are the same as the parent dimension, with one addition. There will always be 2D6 permanent *Shadow Doors* connecting to the parent dimension that has spawned the shadow world. These doors may be small and will not always be open all the time, but they do open and close at regular intervals. These Shadow Doors are what Shadow Denizens use to cross between dimensions. The size of the door varies and at times may be too small to go through.

Final Note: All Shadow Worlds and Dimensions are filled with *Shadow Beasts* and other denizens of shadows, some of which are described in this section. In addition to the creatures of shadows, which are the most common and numerous, other powerful beings can also rule. Game Masters should feel free to use other demons, Deevils, Alien Intelligences, ancient dragons, powerful sorcerers and perhaps creatures from other Palladium game lines such as the *Nightlords*. See the **Nightbane® RPG** and the **Nightlands sourcebook** for more details about the Nightlords and their demonic minions, all of whom can be easily adapted to Rifts® or most any Palladium game setting.

Dimensional Makeup for the Shadow Dimension Connected to Rifts Earth

This is the specific makeup of the Shadow Dimension connected to Rifts Earth.

Type of Dimension: Parallel Dimension.

Primary Dimensional Medium: Space/Vacuum.

Secondary Dimensional Medium: Galaxies full of stars and planets.

Dimensional Fabric: Weak (+20% to dimensional teleports).

Magic Level: Super High.

Dimensional Energy Matrix: Negative.

Time Flow: Normal time flow.

Dimensional Quirks: Fracture Points, Multi-Rift, numerous Dimensional Triangles.

Notable Inhabitants: The Shadow Lords and their shadow denizens are described below.

The geography of the Rifts Earth Shadow Dimension is not all that different from Rifts Earth. The continents have the same general appearance including Atlantis, but other elements are quite different. The various environments are also similar, hot or cold, forested or desert, etc., so where there are vast tracts of forests, lakes, deserts, jungles, and cities, they also exist in this shadowy duplicate. Skies are usually clear. When the sun rises, it always casts long, deep shadows. The only time there are no shadows is the short periods before dusk and dawn. Even when the sun is in the sky, it seems a more distant star and a mottled yellow color. At night the moon and the stars are the primary source of light, but the nights are dark and filled with shadows. During a full moon, the landscape is comparatively bright, making shadows very long and dark. When a new moon and when the moon is just a sliver, the worlds of the Shadow Dimension are at their darkest and safest for the denizens of shadows. The remainder of the month the moon casts its pale light upon a dark, dead domain of shadow play.

The weather is roughly the same, but generally less humid, less cloudy and always 20 degrees Fahrenheit (6.6 C) cooler, day and night. At night, it is very dark and any light source sticks out like a sore thumb. During the day, the world is a contrast of light and dark, with deep shadows and a haze in the sky. A bit of fog or mist hugs the ground in the mornings but burns off within an hour. There are only two additional natural sources of light visible at night, anti-ley lines and the small ley line pools. Anti-ley lines exist in place of the ley lines found on Rifts Earth. These resemble conventional ley lines except they are dark purple in color with swirls of black and blue energy mixed in. Anti-ley lines are the opposite of ley lines in the sense that instead of being sources of magic power, they *absorb magic energy*. Where the anti-ley lines intersect, a dark Rift may appear. To open a Rift or perform magic along an anti-ley line, 20% more P.P.E. is necessary than usual.

Entering the Plane of Shadows

On Rifts Earth and many other worlds, there is a time of the day when shadows grow long and dark. This is usually 2-3 hours after dawn and 2-3 hours before dusk, when the sun is just high enough and bright enough to create long, deep shadows. On most days, this is an ordinary sight. However, there are certain times of the year when some of these long, deep shadows become portals to the Shadow Dimension. At dusk, during times of high magic usually associated with the solstice, equinox, eclipse or planetary alignment, the dimensional fabric in these shadows becomes weak and shallow. It is at such moments that someone not careful could accidentally step into the Shadow Dimension, and a Shadow Beast or other shadow creature could step out into our world, as if to take the person's place. On most worlds, this occurrence only happens at a few locations, usually where magic is strong or dark forces conspire. On Rifts Earth, such places exist at the corners of the

Bermuda Triangle. Another is the **Black Forest** of Germany, but there are other places too. One of the most notorious is the **Shadow Forest** located on the western edge of the *Magic Zone*. There, magic energy is so strong and the dimensional fabric is so weak, that there are particular locations – so called Shadow Doors – that open to become portals to the Shadow Dimension. Dimensional doorways that open and close daily. In the Shadow Forest, Shadow Beasts and their ilk come and go as they please and keep the western borders relatively free of Coalition patrols. This region is under the watchful eye of the Federation Lord known as **Grey**. Rumors suggest he is a Shadow Lord who has made some kind of alliance with Lord Dunscon. (See **Rifts® World Book 16: Federation of Magic** for more information about Lord Dunscon.) Whatever the case, he remains in his domain in the Magic Zone and is content to rule the Shadow Forest. For now.

If there is any thread of truth to the rumors that *Lord Grey* is a Shadow Lord, then he must have some link to the Shadow Dimension. Those adventurers who have traveled to the Shadow Forest and returned have reported that access to another dimension is indeed true, and it is not a place of splendor or light. No, it is a shadowy nightmare.

Magic has a unique characteristic in the Shadow Plane and is not the same as in the realm of mortals. Ley lines and nexus points do not have their signature light bluish glow, and magic users report they cannot draw magic energy from them. The lines of energy in the Shadow Dimension are a dark purplish color and crackle with thin lines of violet energy that feel somehow malevolent and dangerous. They are not calm and subdued like the ley lines we know, but seem to constantly crackle and surge like a violent electrical storm. Instead of glowing faintly, they cast more shadows.

The anti-ley lines, as they are called by some, also do not give up their P.P.E. but rather they absorb it from others. Magic users find if they rest anywhere on the purple lines of the shadow world, that their P.P.E. is drained at a rate of 4D6 P.P.E. points per hour! Casting spells on a purple anti-ley line also reduces the potency of the spells (duration, range, damage, etc.) by HALF. Even Shadow Lords and their minions are affected by these conditions and avoid these energy streams, leaving the surrounding area desolate and uninhabited. Dimensional Rifts do open at nexus points along anti-ley lines, and may lead anywhere in the Megaverse, including its parent world and other domains of mortals. However, the Rifts are violent, stay open for half the time one would expect, and crackle in a threatening manner with purple magic energy.

People who pass through such a Rift at an anti-ley line lose 20% of their current P.P.E. supply and suffer 2D6 points of physical damage. Those with high levels of P.P.E. feel the loss most. Damage is proportional to the being afflicted, so M.D.C. creatures take Mega-Damage and S.D.C. beings take S.D.C./Hit Point damage. Creatures of magic and supernatural beings take triple damage, but P.P.E. loss remains at 20%. Those resistant to energy take half damage and those impervious to energy take no damage, but still lose P.P.E.

Ley lines and ley line nexus points in the Shadow Dimension become small pools of magic energy located along the anti-ley lines. Here the familiar blue energy is found in a small, shimmering circle or slight oval-shaped energy pool. The largest of those, located in places where you would find a nexus in the world of mortals, are 1D4x100 feet (30.5 to 122 m) in diameter. Smaller pools are 2D6 feet (0.6 to 3.6 m) in diameter, and are usually located at the equivalent of what is the middle of a ley line in the parent world. The small size of these ley line pools in the dark world of the parallel Shadow Dimension makes ley lines difficult to locate there. When found, however, the pool can be used just like a ley line or nexus point back home. A sort of magical oasis in the middle of an anti-ley line in the Shadow Dimension. Likewise, a stone pyramid located on an anti-ley line where one rests at a ley line nexus in the real world, still taps and draws upon ley line energy and can be used the same as a stone pyramid to open Rifts, heal, etc., like always. Another oasis on the energy draining anti-ley line network.

Denizens of the Shadow Dimension

Shadow Wraith
Shade Hunter
Shadow Beast
Shadow Behemoth
Shadow Lord

The Plane of Shadows has a variety of creatures as varied as any world. Shadow Beasts happen to be in the majority and are very common. Few other creatures dominate the land as they do. Only the Shadow Lords hold more sway over the land and from all accounts, are the undisputed masters of it. Fortunately, they are power-hungry beings and are too busy squabbling and fighting against each other to have any grandiose Megaverse-conquering schemes. Still, they involve mortals and beings from other dimensions as their pawns and henchmen, as well as slaves and playthings when it suits them.

Shadow Wraith

The Shadow Wraith is a life force vampire that lives in the Shadow Dimension. These creatures feed upon the life force of other beings, including any of the shadow denizens. They start out feeding on a person/creature's P.P.E., but the sweet dessert is the victim's life essence (Hit Points). A Shadow Wraith must feed on at least 20 Hit Points or 40 P.P.E. per week. When given the opportunity, most gorge themselves, which allows them to go for 1D4+4 weeks without needing to feed again, as they can absorb and hold eight to ten times what they need to sustain themselves.

The Shadow Wraith resembles a shadow version of a Hades Gargoyle minus the tail. They have the same general build, but are a bit smaller. In the dark, they could be easily mistaken for a winged gargoyle. They can fly, though the wings are filled with holes and tears. Damage that does not impair the monster's ability to fly. The general appearance is where their similarities end. The Shadow Wraith has blood red eyes that glow when it is feeding. The eyes also glow when the creature is angry or when casting Shadow Magic. They have mouths full of razor sharp teeth and while some eat flesh or drink blood, they do not gain any sustenance from it. They eat their prey to enjoy the suffering and the taste of the flesh and blood like a dessert.

Many Shadow Wraiths have been recruited by the Obsidian Council and they serve as lieutenants in their armies of Shadow Beasts. They tend to be bullies who like to be in a position of power and most are not content unless they are in charge. Shadow Wraiths under the command of the Obsidian Council are in positions where they have a squad of troops to command, which make them content even if answering to a Shadow Lord. Those Shadow Wraiths not under the command of the Obsidian Council may gather in small flocks or hunt as lone predators or in pairs or groups of three or four.

Shadow Wraith Stats

Intelligent Humanoid Shadow Monster

Alignment: Miscreant or Diabolic.

Attributes: I.Q. 1D6+8, M.E. 1D6+10, M.A. 1D6+9, P.S. 1D6+33 (Supernatural), P.P. 1D6+14, P.E. 1D6+18, P.B. 2D6, Spd 1D6+16 on foot or 1D4x10+48 flying (45 mph/72 km on average).

M.D.C.: 5D6x10 + P.E. attribute number. (On S.D.C. worlds, Shadow Wraith have 1D6x10+60 Hit Points plus 2D6x10+40 S.D.C. and a Natural A.R.: 14.) Reduce by half in daylight!

Horror Factor: 14

Size: 2D4+12 feet (14-20 feet/4.3 to 6.1 m) tall, wingspan is 18-24 feet (5.5 to 7.3 m) and weigh 1,000-1,800 pounds (450 to 815 kg).

Average Life Span: Unknown. It is said Shadow Wraiths can live up to 1,000 years, but most tend to die a violent death long before they are they reach the end of their life span. Others claim they are archaic demons and as such, are immortal until slain.

P.P.E.: 1D4x10 plus P.E. attribute number. Since they are life force vampires, they do not have a high base P.P.E., but they can hold the P.P.E. of their slain victims for nourishment.

Natural Abilities: Supernatural P.S. and P.E. in darkness only (becomes Robotic P.S. in sunlight), impervious to cold, heat, fire, disease, drugs and poisons, can see in total darkness, nightvision 2,000 feet (610 m), turn invisible in darkness and shadows, Bio-Regeneration 3D6 M.D.C. per melee round, and magically understands and speaks all languages at 88%. Shadow Wraiths are cannibals and attack and feed on their own kind when easier prey is not available.

Winged Flight (special): Maximum altitude of 10,000 feet (3,048 m), glide (silent, +10% to Prowl), and hover stationary. Glide assisted leap up to 120 feet (37 m) up and across without actually flying.

Power Dive (special): Counts as three attacks, but is +3 to strike, inflicts damage equal to Power Punch +1D6 M.D., and is silent (+10% to Prowl) unless the monster lets loose with a screech or battle cry.

Shadow Meld (special): The natural ability to blend into any shadow, same as the Shadow Meld spell, at will with no limitation to duration and no P.P.E. cost.

Remember, when melded with shadow, the Shadow Being is completely invisible to optic systems and sensors. Thermo-optics, infra-red, passive night optics, motion and heat sensors, Techno-Wizard magic readers, etc., none of them detect or read the Shadow Being. It is invisible to it all of them when they are inside a shadow. When out outside of a shadow, its can be seen in all its frightening glory and detected by motion

sensors and detect magic. They do not give off any heat or thermo signatures. **Note:** This is true of ALL Shadow Beings.

Slow Walk (special): Like all beings spawned of the Shadow Dimension, the creature can go into what the denizens of shadows call *the Slow Walk*, a sort of semi-conscious state of stasis. When food or energy is not available, the metabolism of the creature's body slows down to a crawl. Unlike a bear that hibernates, or a vampire that curls up and closes down into complete stasis sleep, Shadow Beings keep moving, but very slowly, as if in a trance. The creature may stop and perch itself someplace, staring off into space or ever so slowly moving its head to cast its gaze elsewhere. Others slowly walk about at a snail's pace. When prey or a threat appears, the creature snaps out of the Slow Walk, anxious to attack and feed or vent its pent up frustration. It is only then that the monster feels hunger pangs and is motivated to kill and feast upon another living creature, be it from the Shadow Dimension or elsewhere. The Slow Walk can be an endless agony, as Shadow Beings cannot die of starvation.

R.C.C. Equivalent Skills: Prowl on foot 65% (add bonuses for gliding or dive attack), Climb 80/75%, Land Navigation 70%, Wilderness Survival 80%, Track (by sight) 40%, Detect Ambush 45%, Detect Concealment 40%, Intelligence 40%, Swim 40%, Tailing 50% (+20% from the sky), Lore: Demons & Monsters 60%, native language is Whisper (90%; the language of the Shadow Lords). All skills advance at 2% per level of experience. Reduce by half in sunlight.

Equivalent Level of Experience: 1D6 or as set by the Game Master for Non-Player Characters. Not recommended as a Player Character. Use the same experience table as the Ley Line Walker.

Vulnerabilities/Penalties: Daylight hurts their eyes and forces them to squint. Shadow Wraiths can only see clearly up to 200 feet (60.9 m) away in sunlight (double in overcast conditions). Worse, Shadow Wraiths lose all flight capabilities in daylight, even when overcast, because sunlight causes their wings to shrivel up and become useless.

If forced to fight in full daylight, the creature's strength drops from Supernatural to Robotic P.S., they lose the ability to fly, and skills, natural abilities, number of attacks, combat bonuses, attributes and M.D.C. are all reduced by half.

A Globe of Daylight will not shrivel wings or cause them to fall out of the sky, but the light is bright and painful, and forces them to leave the area or be forced to fight at half power the same as sunlight.

Weapons made of silver or light (not fire) do double damage in S.D.C. environments. On Mega-Damage worlds, silver-plated weapons do the Mega-Damage equivalent, so if a silver blade normally does 1D6 S.D.C., it inflicts 1D6 M.D. to the Shadow Wraith. M.D. light weapons, including lasers, do double damage.

Attacks per Melee: Five attacks per melee round, +1 attack at levels 3, 6, 10, 15 and 20. Reduce the number of attacks by half in sunlight, but the Shadow Wraith is not blinded.

Mega-Damage: As per Supernatural P.S., typically 5D6 M.D. full strength punch (or 2D6 M.D. for Robotic P.S. in sunlight); +2D6 M.D. for claw strike, bite does 3D6 M.D., or by weapon (probably giant-size with an extra 1D6 or 2D6 M.D. due to its size).

Bonuses (in addition to attribute bonuses and skills): +2 on Perception Rolls when in darkness, +2 to initiative when attacking come from above, +2 to strike and parry, +4 to dodge when in flight only, +1 to disarm and entangle, +2 to pull punch and roll with impact, +2 to save vs mind control, +2 to save vs psionics, and +5 to save vs Horror Factor. Reduce by half in sunlight.

Magic: Shadow Wraiths know the following Shadow Magic spells: Whispered Voice, Shadow Skin, Shadow Globe, Shadow Pools, and two shadow spells of choice from any level. They cannot teach or learn any additional spells once selected. Remember, P.P.E. is only 1D4x10 plus P.E. attribute number.

Psionics: None.

Alliances and Allies: Other Shadow Wraiths and Shadow Beasts, and they serve the Shadow Lords. They sometimes work with evil practitioners of magic and powerful evil supernatural beings when it suits them or if that being has the power to enslave them.

Enemies: All creatures of light, Champions of Light, Atlantean Monster Hunters and Undead Slayers, and Atlanteans in general. They see humans and most mortal life forms as prey, pawns and playthings.

Shade Hunter

Animal Predator

The Shade Hunter is the sky-borne predator of the Shadow Dimension. These creatures resemble a hammerhead shark with bat-like wings and a pair of demonic arms. Instead of a shark's tail, the creature has two long, barbed tails that can be used to strike and entangle prey. Along the back are bony plates to protect them from attacks from above. If they have any vulnerability it is the numerous photo-receptors on the head. They have no eyes in the conventional sense. Rather the head is black with complex patterns that look like the compound eyes of insects. These eyes allow them to see very well in the dark and with amazing detail.

Shade Hunters have a high animal intelligence which enables them to lay in wait, pick off people one by one, hide from hunters, and when gathered in small packs, coordinate their attacks and plan ambushes. The monster may hunt as a lone individual, but more often as a mated pair, a family unit of 1D6+2, or in small packs of 1D6+6. The largest alpha female is always the pack leader. The other pack members are males and she only allows the strongest males to be part of her pack. Other females are chased away or killed and eaten by the pack. Their high intelligence and size means Shade Hunters can be trained like dogs by Shadow Lords and used as bloodhounds, hunting packs, and attack and guard animals. Shadow Beasts also sometimes train one or two Shade Hunters to be a riding animal or companion/bloodhound.

Shade Hunter Stats

Intelligent Animal Predator

Alignment: Miscreant.

Attributes: I.Q. 1D4+7 (animal intelligence; +3 for alpha female), M.E. 2D6+10, M.A. 1D6+6, P.S. 1D4+16 (Supernatural; +10 for alpha female), P.P. 1D6+18, P.E. 1D6+18, P.B. 1D4+4, Spd 2D6+6 on the ground, scurrying along on

E. WALTON 2017

their arms or sliding on their belly. 1D6x10+80 flying (70-80 mph/112 to 128 km). Reduce speed by half in sunlight.

M.D.C.: 1D6x10 + P.E. attribute number for most males and beta or juvenile females. 2D6x10 M.D.C. + P.E. attribute for the alpha female. (On S.D.C. worlds, 6D6+20 Hit Points and 1D4x10 S.D.C., double for the alpha female. Natural A.R. 10 in the shadows and 5 in the light.) Reduce M.D.C. by half in daylight.

Horror Factor: 13 for an individual, 16 for a pack of 6 or more.

Size: Males: 6-11 feet (1.8 to 3.3 m) long, 2-3 feet (0.6 to 0.9 m) in diameter and a wingspan of 18-24 feet (5.5 to 7.3 m). The average female is 20% larger than the male, while the big, alpha female is 30% larger.

Weight: Males and typical females: 400-700 pounds (180-315 kg). Alpha female: 800-900 pounds (360-405 kg).

Average Life Span: 2D6x10 years.

P.P.E.: 4D6 (+10 for alpha female).

Natural Abilities: Supernatural P.S. and P.E. in darkness only (becomes Augmented P.S. in sunlight), can see in total darkness, nightvision 17,000 feet (5,182 m) and owl-like sight (can see a rabbit up to three miles/4.8 km away), turn invisible in darkness and shadows, Bio-Regeneration 1D6 M.D.C. per melee round (double for females), and magically understands all languages at 75%. Animal, so it cannot speak.

Slow Walk (special): Like all beings spawned of the Shadow Dimension, the creature can go into what the denizens of shadows call *the Slow Walk*, a sort of semi-conscious state of stasis. When food or energy is not available, the metabolism of the creature's body slows down to a crawl. Unlike a bear that hibernates, or a vampire that curls up and closes down into complete stasis sleep, Shadow Beings keep moving, but very slowly, as if in a trance or sleepwalking. The creature may stop and perch itself someplace, staring off into space or ever so slowly moving its head to cast its gaze elsewhere. Others slowly walk about at a snail's pace. When prey or a threat appears, the creature snaps out of the Slow Walk, anxious to attack and feed or vent its pent up frustration. It is only then that the monster feels hunger pangs and is motivated to kill and feast upon another living creature, be it from the Shadow Dimension or elsewhere.

Track by Scent (special): Can track by scent at 65% (+15% to follow blood scent), and can smell blood up to 4 miles (6.4 km) away unless the wind is blowing away from the creature. Reduce by half in sunlight.

R.C.C. Equivalent Skills: Gliding Prowl 90%, Winged Prowl 60%, Climb 80/75%, Land Navigation 85%, Wilderness Survival 95%, Track 65%, Detect Ambush 30%, and understands Whisper (the language of the Shadow Lords) 90%. Reduce by half in sunlight.

Equivalent Level of Experience: Not applicable, because it is an animal.

Vulnerabilities/Penalties: Their photo-receptors are very sensitive to light and it hurts their eyes. Blind in sunlight, even on overcast days.

A *Globe of Daylight* is just too bright and holds them at bay 300 feet (91.5 m) from the furthest edge of the light, probably circling like a shark. Entering the light blinds them (-10 penalty to strike, parry and dodge). Likewise, they are -2 to save against a Blinding Flash, and on a failed roll to save, the

monster suffers a Horror Factor response and flees the area for 1D6 minutes or until the blindness ends.

Weapons made of silver or light (not fire) do double damage in S.D.C. environments. On Mega-Damage worlds, silver-plated weapons do the Mega-Damage equivalent, so if a silver blade normally does 1D6 S.D.C., it inflicts 1D6 M.D. to the Shade Hunter. M.D. light weapons, including lasers, do double damage.

Attacks per Melee: Four attacks per melee round. Two in sunlight and will fight blind (-10 to strike, parry and dodge).

Six attacks for the alpha female only. Three in sunlight and fights blind.

Mega-Damage: For males and young females: As per Supernatural P.S., typically 1D6 M.D. on a full strength punch, butt or body strike (or 1 M.D. for Augmented P.S. in sunlight). A bite does 2D4 M.D. and a striking blow from one of the two barbed tails inflicts 1D6+3 M.D. or 2D6+4 M.D. from a simultaneous strike from both tails. Entanglement from one or both tails inflicts 1D4 M.D., double damage every time someone tries to free himself from the entanglement. The same damage for anyone trying to pull the tail tentacles far enough away to free their teammate. Reduce by half in sunlight.

For the alpha female: As per Supernatural P.S., 3D6 M.D. on a full strength punch, butt or body strike (or 1D6 M.D. for Augmented P.S. in sunlight). A bite does 2D6+6 M.D. and a striking blow from one of the two barbed tails inflicta 2D6+4 M.D. or 4D6+6 M.D. from a simultaneous strike from both tails. Entanglement from one or both tails inflicts 2D4 M.D., double damage every time someone tries to free himself from the entanglement. Reduce by half in sunlight.

Bonuses (in addition to attribute bonuses): +2 on Perception Rolls and on initiative in darkness, +3 to strike, parry, dodge, +2 to pull punch or bite, +2 to roll with impact, and +4 to save vs Horror Factor. Reduce by half in daylight.

Magic: None.

Psionics: None.

Alliances and Allies: Pack creature that considers its pack to be allies. Sometimes they serve as guard dogs for Shadow Lords.

Enemies: All creatures of light, Champions of Light, Atlantean Monster Hunters and Undead Slayers, and Atlanteans in general.

Shadow Beast

The Shadow Beast is one of the most common denizens of the Shadow Dimension. So common, in fact, that it is they who are most thought of or magically summoned at the hands of many a Summoner or powerful magic user. They are also the minion Shadow Lords are most likely to use to carry out their cruel and vicious orders, and do so with great pleasure. These large, brutish beasts seem to dominate the Shadow Dimension. Dimensional travelers must be wary as one or more Shadow Beasts may lurk in the shadows.

Shadow Beasts are the eyes and ears of the Shadow Lords. Each Shadow Lord commands thousands of them and they make up the bulk of their forces. Shadow Beasts are used in just about every capacity, from front line troops, to cannon fodder, to scouts and spies. They are ideal minions that carry out their orders with a perverse pleasure.

Shadow Beast who are not claimed as servants to a Shadow Lord and forced to do his bidding, roam freely across the Shadow Dimension. Though they may walk together in groups and there may be tens of thousands of them in a Shadow city, they are, as a rule, lone predators. They do not hunt in packs and do not usually establish lairs or dens. Shadow Beast only gather in numbers and work together toward the same goal when they are summoned and forced to serve a more intelligent and powerful being such as a practitioner of magic, Demon Lord, Shadow Lord, dark god, etc.

Shadow Beast Stats

Intelligent Humanoid Shadow Monster

Alignment: Miscreant or Diabolic.

Attributes: I.Q. 1D4+5, M.E. 1D4+5, M.A. 1D4+5, P.S. 1D6+24, P.P. 1D4+20, P.E. 1D4+26, P.B. 1D4+1, Spd 1D6+18.

M.D.C.: 1D6x10+25 plus an additional 1D6 M.D.C. per level of experience. (On S.D.C. worlds, Shadow Beasts have 1D4x10+20 Hit Points, 1D4x10 S.D.C. and a Natural A.R.: 10 in the shadows and 5 in the light.) Reduce by half in daylight!

Horror Factor: 13

Size: 9-12 feet (2.7 to 3.6 m) tall.

Weight: 300 to 500 pounds (135 to 225 kg).

Average Life Span: Unknown. Thought to be immortal.

P.P.E.: 6D6

Natural Abilities: Supernatural P.S. and P.E. in darkness only (becomes Augmented P.S. in sunlight), nightvision 2,000 feet (610 m), impervious to cold, heat, disease, drugs and poison, turn invisible in darkness and shadows, Bio-Regenerates 2D6 M.D.C. per melee but only in the shadows, and magically understands and speaks all languages at 88%. Shadow Beasts are cannibals and may attack and feed on their own kind when easier prey is not available. They may also feed upon those they vanquish in battle.

Shadow Meld (special): The natural ability to blend into any shadow, same as the Shadow Meld spell, at will with no limitation to duration and no P.P.E. cost.

Remember, when melded with shadow, the creature is completely invisible to optic systems and sensors. Thermo-optics, infra-red, passive night optics, motion and heat sensors, Techno-Wizard magic readers, etc., none of them detect or read Shadow Beasts. They are invisible to all of them when they are inside a shadow. When out outside of a shadow, Shadow Beasts can be detected by motion sensors and detect magic. They do not give off any heat or thermo signatures. **Note:** This is true of ALL Shadow Beings.

Slow Walk (special): Like all beings spawned of the Shadow Dimension, the creature can go into what the denizens of shadows call *the Slow Walk*, a sort of semi-conscious state of stasis. When food or energy is not available, the metabolism of the creature's body slows down to a crawl. Unlike a bear that hibernates, or a vampire that curls up and closes down into complete stasis sleep, Shadow Beings keep moving, but very slowly, as if in a trance. The creature may stop and perch itself someplace, staring off into space or ever so slowly moving its head to cast its gaze elsewhere. Others slowly walk about at a snail's pace. When prey or a threat appears, the creature snaps out of the Slow Walk, anxious to attack and feed or vent its

pent up frustration. It is only then that the monster feels hunger pangs and is motivated to kill and feast upon another living creature, be it from the Shadow Dimension or elsewhere. The Slow Walk can be an endless agony, as Shadow Beings cannot die of starvation.

Track by Scent (special): They can track by smell at 46% (+14% to follow blood scent), and can smell blood up to 2 miles (3.2 km) away. Reduce by half in sunlight.

R.C.C. Equivalent Skills: Prowl 90%, Climb 80/75%, Land Navigation 60%, Wilderness Survival 80%, Track 40%, understands Whisper (the language of the Shadow Lords 86%), and magically understands and speaks all languages 80%. Reduce by half in sunlight.

Equivalent Level of Experience: 1D6 or as set by the Game Master.

Vulnerabilities/Penalties: Daylight hurts their eyes and forces them to squint. Shadow Beasts can only see clearly up to 200 feet (61 m) away in sunlight (double in overcast conditions). Worse, Shadow Beasts see all their skills, abilities, bonuses and M.D.C. reduced by half in daylight, even when overcast. If forced to fight in full daylight, the creature's strength drops from Supernatural to Augmented P.S.

A Globe of Daylight has the same effect and the light is bright and painful, forcing the Shadow Beast to leave the area or be forced to fight at half power.

Weapons made of silver or light (not fire) do double damage in S.D.C. environments. On Mega-Damage worlds, silver-plated weapons do the Mega-Damage equivalent, so if a silver blade normally does 1D6 S.D.C., it inflicts 1D6 M.D. to the Shadow Beast. M.D. light weapons, including lasers, do double damage.

Attacks per Melee: Six attacks per melee round, +1 attack at levels 5, 10 and 15. Three in sunlight and fights at half power.

Mega-Damage: As per Supernatural, typically 5D6 S.D.C. on a restrained punch, 3D6 M.D. on a full strength punch, head butt or body strike (or 1D6 M.D. for Augmented P.S. in sunlight), a power punch does 6D6 M.D. but counts as two melee attacks, a claw strike does 4D6+2 M.D., and a bite inflicts 3D6+3 M.D. Reduce by half in sunlight.

R.C.C. Bonuses (in addition to any likely attribute bonuses): +2 on Perception Rolls and initiative in darkness, +3 to strike, +4 to parry, dodge, and disarm, and +8 to save vs Horror Factor; fearless. Reduce by half in sunlight.

Magic: None.

Psionics: None.

Alliances and Allies: Other Shadow Beasts and Shadow Wraiths, and they serve the Shadow Lords. Shadow Beasts sometimes work with evil practitioners of magic, particularly Shifters and Shadow Mages, as well as powerful, evil supernatural beings when it suits them or if that being has the power to enslave them. Many are aligned to a specific Shadow Lord and serve as his obedient foot soldiers and minions.

Enemies: All gods of light, Creatures of Light, Champions of Light, Atlantean Monster Hunters and Undead Slayers, as well as Atlanteans, Lemurians, humans and mortals in general. Mortals are seen as prey and playthings. Hates being summoned and forced to serve mortals, but may warm up to beings who have it kill, torture and hurt others.

Shadow Behemoth

Animal Predator

The Shadow Behemoth is a large, bulldog-like creature that stalks the lands of the Shadow Dimension. It has a pair of large, oversized front legs, a barrel chest, a large head and a large maw full of teeth. Its large upper body tapers off to a pair of smaller hind legs. It black fur is short and fine, giving it a sleek or wet appearance.

Shadow Behemoths attack and eat anything that comes within the range of their senses. They prefer live prey, but will eat carrion, organic garbage, and dried bones. Thankfully, Shadow Behemoths are not very smart and can be easily tricked and outwitted. In the Shadow Dimension, Shadow Beasts sometime ride them or command 1D6 of them as attack dogs or hunting animals. Shadow Lords easily control and command these hounds and use packs of them as trained guard dogs, attack dogs and animals. Shadow Behemoths instinctively accept Shadow Beasts as their superiors and Shadow Lords as their pack leader and master.

In the wild, Shadow Behemoths hunt as a lone individual, a mated pair, 1D4+2 family group or as small packs of 1D6+6 animals.

Shadow Behemoth Stats

Animal Predator

Alignment: Diabolic.

Attributes: I.Q. 1D4+4 (animal intelligence), M.E. 1D6+8, M.A. 1D6+6, P.S. 1D6+30 (Supernatural), P.P. 1D6+15, P.E. 1D6+20, P.B. 1D4+3, Spd 2D6+50 (40 mph/64 km on average).

M.D.C.: 1D4x100 M.D.C. + P.E. attribute number. (In S.D.C. worlds, the Shadow Behemoth has 3D6x10 Hit Points, and 120 S.D.C. with a Natural A.R. of 13.) Reduce M.D.C. by half in daylight.

Horror Factor: 12 for an individual or pair, 14 for a pack.

Size: 9-12 feet (2.7 to 3.7 m) at the shoulder. 10-15 feet (3-4.6 m) long.

Weight: 1-2 tons.

Average Life Span: Unknown, assumed to be immortal.

P.P.E.: 2D6

Natural Abilities: Supernatural P.S. and P.E. in darkness only (becomes Augmented P.S. in sunlight), can see in total darkness, nightvision 5,000 feet (1,524 m) and owl-like sight (can see a rabbit up to one mile/1.6 km away), turn invisible in darkness and shadows, Bio-Regeneration 1D6 M.D.C. per melee round, and magically understands all languages at 50%. Animal, so it cannot speak.

Sense the Supernatural (special): It can sense supernatural creatures and creatures of magic (including mages and Atlanteans who possess 100 P.P.E. or more) up to one mile (1.6 km) away, and is able to track them at 60% (+20% if it is a Greater supernatural creature, Demigod, Godling, adult dragon, deity or other very powerful being). Reduce by half in sunlight.

Slow Walk (special): Like all beings spawned of the Shadow Dimension, the creature can go into what the denizens of shadows call *the Slow Walk*, a sort of semi-conscious state of stasis. When food or energy is not available, the metabolism of the creature's body slows down to a crawl. Unlike a bear that hibernates, or a vampire that curls up and closes down into complete stasis sleep, Shadow Beings keep moving, but very slowly, as if in a trance. The creature may stop and perch itself someplace, staring off into space or ever so slowly moving its head to cast its gaze elsewhere. Others slowly walk about at a snail's pace. When prey or a threat appears, the creature snaps out of the Slow Walk, anxious to attack and feed or vent its pent up frustration. It is only then that the monster feels hunger pangs and is motivated to kill and feast upon another living creature, be it from the Shadow Dimension or elsewhere.

Track by Scent (special): Can track by scent at 60% (+10% to follow blood scent), and can smell blood up to one mile (1.6 km) away unless the wind is blowing away from the creature.

R.C.C. Equivalent Skills: Climbing 45%/0%, Dowsing 70%, Land Navigation 86%, Prowl 50%, Swimming 60%, Track 60%, Wilderness Survival 90%, and understands Whisper (the language of the Shadow Lords) 70%. Reduce by half in sunlight.

Equivalent Level of Experience: Not applicable, animal.

Vulnerabilities/Penalties: Very sensitive to light and it hurts their eyes. Blind in sunlight, even on an overcast day.

A Globe of Daylight is just too bright and holds them at bay 200 feet (61 m) from the furthest edge of the light, probably circling like a wolf pack. Entering the light blinds them (-10 penalty to strike, parry and dodge). Likewise, they are -2 to save against a Blinding Flash, and on a failed roll to save, the monster suffers a Horror Factor response and flees the area for 2D6 minutes or until the blindness ends.

Weapons made of silver or light do double damage in S.D.C. environments. On Mega-Damage worlds, silver-plated weapons do the Mega-Damage equivalent, so if a silver blade normally does 1D6 S.D.C., it inflicts 1D6 M.D. to the Shadow Behemoth. M.D. light weapons, including lasers, do double damage.

Attacks per Melee: Four attacks per melee round. Two in sunlight and will fight blind (-10 to strike, parry and dodge).

Six attacks for the alpha male of a pack. Three in sunlight and it fights blind.

Mega-Damage: As per Supernatural P.S., typically 4D6 M.D. on a full strength pounce, head butt or body block (or 1D4 M.D. for Augmented P.S. in sunlight). Bite does 5D6 M.D. (2D6+2 M.D. in sunlight). A power bite does 1D6x10 M.D. but counts as two attacks (4D6 M.D. in sunlight). Add +1D6 M.D. to all attacks by the alpha male.

R.C.C. Bonuses (in addition to any likely attribute bonuses): +4 on initiative, +3 to strike, +1 to parry, +3 to dodge, +1 to roll with impact, +4 to pull bite, pounce or body block, and +4 to save vs Horror Factor. Reduce by half in sunlight (round down).

Magic: None.

Psionics: None.

Alliances and Allies: Preys on lesser denizens of the Shadow Dimension, including injured or sleeping Shadow Beasts and Wraiths. Even tamed Shadow Behemoths used for hunting or riding are prickly and may snap at their master, or attack and devour him if he becomes seriously injured and unconscious. Only Shadow Lords are regarded as too dangerous to attack, even when helpless. Shadow Lords often use them as guard dogs, pets, and creatures in their arenas.

Enemies: Pretty much any creature that it can kill and eat is a source of food, so anything that moves is potential prey. Only creatures that prove to be too powerful are left alone, but these bold predators might try taking a few bites before giving up and backing down or running off. Puny, little humans and D-Bees are likely to be seen as easy prey.

Shadow Lord

Of all the creatures in the Shadow Dimension, the de-facto rulers are the Shadow Lords. Demonic beings who command legions of Shadow Beasts and have carved out areas they claim as their dominion. There is a constant power struggle among Shadow Lords, with many wars fought over territory. The winner of such battles takes command of the loser's minions and rules the land until someone comes to challenge him for it.

The Shadow Lords are, themselves, some sort of wicked, supernatural creatures composed of shadow and strange, black energy. They are sentient and have a humanoid form, but appear as dark, ghostly specters composed of dark shadows and mist. They always appear to be a dark, shadow-like figure in a semi-visible state even when exposed to direct sunlight. Their body shape is humanoid, but that's where the similarities end. They are mostly a black silhouette, like a semi-transparent ghost made of darkness. There are few visible features on the face or anywhere. The eyes appear as a single, long, red slit going across the bridge of the nose. When one speaks, the same red glow emanates from his mouth — fangs and pointed teeth silhouetted in the red light. It is almost as if a fire or blazing red energy burns inside the Shadow Lord.

The fingers are long and end in sharp talon-like claws. Their bodies are tall and thin, suggesting they are emaciated. At first glance, the shadows seem to be wearing some type of tattered or jagged cloak, cape or cowl, but closer inspection reveals they are really multiple tendrils that are part of the body, capable of lashing out in an instant to strike their enemies and pull visitors closer. Some Shadow Lords wear a bit of jewelry; a crown and/or a mantle or necklace of gold, and perhaps gold armbands or bracers. Gold seems to be the favored precious metal. The voice of a Shadow Lord sounds like a raspy whisper from someone across a room or from beyond the grave. Dogs howl in their presence, cats hiss and bare claws, horses whinny and show fear.

Shadow Lords are as intelligent as any human, and all of them seem to have a lust for violence and bloodletting. Whether this is a desire to attain power and acknowledgment among their own kind as well as lesser beings, like mortals, is unknown. In their native dimension, each Shadow Lord holds dominion over a small kingdom. If they were not intent on wiping each other out to take absolute control of the Shadow Dimension, they might actually pose a threat to the outside world. Most shadow kingdoms, whether they are the size of a city, state or province, or much larger, are ruled by one, supreme Shadow Lord, with a few dozen submissive Shadow Lords serving as his generals, enforcers and council. There are a few kingdoms where several Shadow Lords rule together like the *Obsidian Council*, but this is the exception, not the rule. Such unholy unions are gatherings of less experienced Shadow Lords who see strength in numbers (for now) or who have united against a common foe. Over time, most gatherings of Shadow Lords dissolve in treachery, with several

C. WALTON

backstabbing each other as they try to seize dominion and more power over their "partners."

Many believe Shadow Beings are some sort of archaic and forgotten demon, with the Shadow Lord being the most powerful of them. Some think they are creatures of magic, and some claim all Shadow Dimension creatures are a type of Elemental, hence their own unique Shadow Magic and manifestation as a sort of living, thinking shadow. However, unlike Elementals which are forces of nature, all intelligent Shadow Beings seem to be selfish, manipulative and wicked. Their personalities a reflection of their shadowy and deceitful essence. Mortals are wise to never trust a Shadow Lord for these reasons, especially when he seems to be friendly or accommodating. Such acts of kindness can only mean the monster wants something from the mortals or is trying to manipulate them in some scheme to cause conflict and bloodshed. The Shadow Lord's love of stirring up trouble and war is why many scholars, Atlanteans among them, believe they are ancient and forgotten chaos demons.

Shadow Lord NPC Monster

A Greater Chaos Demon, Non-Player Character

Alignment: Typically Miscreant (45%) or Diabolic (40%), but can be any evil alignment. None are known to be "good." The best alignment possible for a Shadow Lord is Anarchist, and that is rare in the extreme.

Attributes: I.Q. 1D6+16, M.E. 1D6+14, M.A. 1D6+18, P.S. 2D4+27 (Supernatural), P.P. 1D6+20, P.E. 1D6+20, P.B. 1D6+10, Spd 1D6+16.

M.D.C.: 2D6x100+800, reduce by half in sunlight. (In S.D.C. worlds, Shadow Lords have 2D6x100 Hit Points and 600 S.D.C., and are naturally ethereal in shadow, much the same as the spell. They must concentrate to take physical form in darkness, and when they do, they have a Natural A.R. of 14.) Shadow Lords become physical manifestations in sunlight with half their M.D.C. (or Hit Points and S.D.C., as the case may be).

Horror Factor: 15

Size: 7-10 feet (2.1 to 3 m) tall.

Weight: 300-500 pounds (135 to 225 kg); weightless when ethereal.

Average Life Span: Unknown and believed to be immortal.

P.P.E.: 1D6x100 + P.E. attribute number plus 20 per level of experience.

Natural Abilities: Supernatural P.S. and P.E. in darkness only (becomes Robotic P.S. in sunlight), can see in total darkness, nightvision 5,000 feet (1,524 m), can turn invisible in darkness and shadows, impervious to cold, heat, and fire, Bio-Regeneration 1D4x10 M.D.C. per melee round, destroyed tendrils regrow in 1D6 minutes (each has 1D6x10+16 M.D.C.), and magically understands and speaks all languages at 96%. Shadow Lords are cannibals, like Shadow Wraiths, and may attack and feed on their own kind when easier prey is not available.

Ethereal Natural State of Being in Shadows and Darkness (special): The Shadow Lord is the stuff of magic and shadows. They take physical form in darkness only when they will to do so, but are forced into physical form in sunlight. This ability works like the *Ethereal in Shadow*, except is the Shadow Lord's natural state and always on. **Note:** The Shadow Lord can speak in his raspy whisper while ethereal (unlike those using the Ethereal in Shadow spell), but must take physical form to cast spells and to make physical attacks.

As an Ethereal shadow, the Shadow Lord is immune to most physical attacks. Bullets, spears, knives, explosive force, cold, heat, fire, and most energy blasts pass right through him without harm. Only lasers hurt, but inflict half their usual damage to an Ethereal shadow. The character does not register on most sensor systems either, including infrared and heat sensors. Motion detectors have a 50/50 chance of registering a fast moving Ethereal Shadow Lord, but not a slow one (Spd of 7 or less), or a character who is using the Prowl skill while Ethereal. There is no P.P.E. cost associated with this natural ability.

Multiple Limbs (special): Each Shadow Lord has two human arms and *1D6+4 tentacles* that come out from around the shoulder blades on the back. Each is prehensile, with a 10 foot (3 m) reach forward and back. Each pair of additional tentacles function as extra limbs and provide an extra attack per melee round. When not in use, the tentacles hang limp. Since the Shadow Lord is perceived as a shadow or silhouette, especially from a distance, the hanging tentacles create the illusion of being a robe, cloak or cape even when they move en mass. It is not until the black tentacles begin to spread out that people present realize they are tentacles.

Shadow Walk (special): Same as the Shadow Magic spell, but is an ability that can be performed at will. The shadow must be six feet (1.8 m) tall/long or bigger. Maximum range: 4,000 feet (1,219 m), line of sight. If he can see the shadow, he can move there. There is no P.P.E. cost associated with this natural ability.

Track by Scent (special): Can track by scent at 60% (+10% to follow blood scent), and can smell blood up to one mile (1.6 km) away unless the wind is blowing away from the creature.

Summon Denizens of the Shadow Plane (special): The Shadow Lord has the ability to command legions of shadow denizens. Hundreds and even thousands of Shadow Beasts flock to the banner of powerful and charismatic Shadow Lords. These creatures see and respect power and often want to be with the most powerful Shadow Lord in the land. When one Lord is toppled, his minions are likely to fall on bended knee to swear allegiance to their new master.

From those Shadow Beasts, Shadow Wraiths and monsters counted among his minions, a Shadow Lord can instantly summon 2D6 Shadow Beasts, Shade Hunters or Shadow Behemoths once per day. In the alternative, he can summon 1D6 Shadow Wraiths. All are loyal and obedient servants who serve their master until he is slain and they have proof of his death.

Vulnerabilities/Penalties: Light is the enemy of all shadow beings. When the Shadow Lord is exposed to *true sunlight*, or even the Globe of Daylight spell, all combat bonuses, number of attacks per melee, speed, and M.D.C. (or Hit points and S.D.C. depending on environment) are reduced by half. However, the Globe of Daylight and sunlight does not hurt nor blind this powerful being, nor hold him at bay. Sunlight and the Globe of Daylight do force him to become solid, and he can be hit/injured by weapons that could not harm the Shadow Lord when he was ethereal.

Weapons made of light, Holy Weapons, Greater Rune Weapons of good alignment, demon slaying weapons, and silver-plated weapons inflict double damage to the Shadow Lord. S.D.C. silver-plated weapons do M.D. damage point for point, so if the weapon normally does 2D6 S.D.C. damage, it inflicts 2D6 M.D. to shadow creatures, even Shadow Lords. Moreover, even when the Shadow Lord is Ethereal, silver-plated weapons and weapons made of light can still damage him! Such weapons, including lasers, inflict half their normal damage to the Ethereal Shadow Lord.

The physical manifestation is vulnerable to all types of attacks, weapons, spells and psionics, all inflicting their normal damage.

Vulnerable to psionics and some magic when in shadow and Ethereal, but not those that are physical attacks or inflict physical damage.

R.C.C. Equivalent Skills: Barter 70%, Climb 98%/98%, Detect Ambush 65%, Dowsing 80%, Escape Artist 60%, Gambling 80%, Gemology 70%, Intelligence 80%, Land Navigation 90%, Lore: D-Bees 60%, Lore: Dimensions 70%, Lore: Faeries & Creatures of Magic 60%, Lore: Magic 88/68/53%, Lore: Demons and Monsters 80%, Philosophy 70%, Prowl 70% (plus bonuses for Ethereal), Tailing 80%, Wilderness Survival 90%, Paired Weapons, and two W.P.s of choice, typically Blunt and Sword, but can be any. Skills advance at 2% per level of experience. Tends to rely upon brute strength, cunning and magic. Has little use for technology.

Equivalent Level of Experience: 1D6+4 or as set by the Game Master.

Attacks per Melee: Eight, +1 for each pair of tentacles (3-5 pair) for 11-13 attacks total! Reduce by half in sunlight. Step into a shadow where this being lurks, and he fights at full strength regardless of the light that may be all around him. Shadow Lords instinctively use their tendrils, and are effective with them in combat, attacking or defending. This enables the Shadow Lord to attack up to four targets at once.

Mega-Damage: As per Supernatural P.S., typically 4D6 M.D. full strength punch or tentacle strike (or 2D4 M.D. for Robotic P.S. in sunlight), power punch does 1D6x10 M.D., but counts as two attacks. Tentacle strikes are the same as a punch, but can also parry and entangle. Tentacles cannot power punch. Claw strike does 1D4x10 M.D., a power claw strike does 1D6x10+12 M.D. but counts as two attacks. A bite does 2D6+2 M.D., or the Shadow Lord may use weapons or magic.

R.C.C. Bonuses (in addition to any likely attribute bonuses): +4 on Perception Rolls and initiative in darkness, +4 to strike and dodge, +6 to parry, +6 to pull punch, +3 to roll with impact, +2 to save vs magic, +6 to save vs mind control (but may pretend to fall under someone's control to get the upper hand on them), +6 to save vs Horror Factor and +2 to save vs Shadow Magic. Reduce by half in sunlight; round up.

Magic: Knows ALL Shadow Magic spells! In addition, a Shadow Lord knows a range of Ley Line Walker/Wizard spell invocations. Roll 1D6 to determine how many spell levels are known. If a one is rolled, the creature knows ALL level one spell invocations. If a two is rolled, he knows ALL wizard spells from levels one and two. If a three is rolled, it means the Shadow Lord knows all spells from levels 1-3, and so on. The most powerful Shadow Lords know 1D6+4 additional spell invocations from any level up to level 15.

Reduce P.P.E. cost of ALL Shadow Magic spells cast by the Shadow Lord by Half (special): Nobody knows Shadow Magic better than the Shadow Lords. Their affinity to darkness means Shadow Lords cast all Shadow Magic spells (but only Shadow Magic spells) at *half* the listed P.P.E. cost (round down), but only when in darkness/shadow. Full cost in sunlight, overcast skies or when bathed in bright artificial light. The normal duration of the spell is also doubled!

Psionics: None.

Alliances and Allies: Armies of Shadow Beasts and other shadow creatures obey Shadow Lords as their superior and master. Evil or foolish humans, D-Bees and other beings may choose to serve one for any number of reasons, but they will never be more than a pawn, henchman or lieutenant among the Shadow Lord's minions. Mortals are also sometimes enslaved and forced to serve Shadow Lords. Humans should consider all Shadow Lords to be an evil Greater Demon or lesser deity, and deal with the creatures accordingly.

A Shadow Lord may consider "helping" or working with mortals as a benefactor or partner, but only if it leads to war, death and disaster, or something else he wants (including revenge, power, entertainment, etc.). A Shadow Lord may assist or throw in with others as a supposed ally if they share a mutual goal, such as revenge, war or just about anything, but such allies should be prepared for betrayal. This godlike fiend may also, for a time, help someone simply because it strikes his fancy, or out of pretense when he is really using them as pawns or cannon fodder in one of his own plans.

The Shadow Lord always sees himself as superior to mortals and most demons and gods. However, as an archaic demon, Shadow Lords can be tricked, lured into serving or forced to serve a more powerful Demon Lord, dark god, or Alien Intelligence. Present-day deities and Lords of Hell consider Shadow Lords and all denizens of shadows as primitive and pathetic lesser beings seldom worthy of bothering with. It is best to leave them in the shadows and to their own meaningless lives.

Enemies: Creatures and Gods of Light and their priests and worshipers. Shadow Lords also have a disdain for Atlanteans, Lemurians, humans and most other life forms, especially heroes and Champions of Light. Actually, they do not care for other species of demons and dark gods much either, as they lust for their position and power.

Note: Shadow Lords are, for the most part, haughty, arrogant creatures who consider themselves above everyone. As such, they look down on most other life forms, particularly mortal creatures, and rarely, if ever, show them any kind of respect. If they do, it is most likely a ruse so they can take advantage of them, or for some other ulterior motive.

Shadow Guidelines

When playing or using any of the Shadow Beings or Shadow Mages, for that matter, the Game Master needs to know how shadows work and when they are most available. Conditions can vary dramatically depending on the time of day. G.M.s should use their best judgment, but it helps to paint a scene that the players can relate to. What follows is an optional guide for specific times of the day and common conditions in which shadows are plentiful or washed out, and when Shadow Beings and Mages are at full or reduced strength.

Light, visibility and depth of shadows vary with the time of year, time of day, location and other conditions. Light and the periods of shadow are longest during late spring and summer. This list can be used as a guideline.

Dawn: This is the 20 minutes before and 40 minutes after the sun is just beginning to peek above the horizon to create twilight conditions (same as overcast sky) and there are NO shadows. Shadow creatures function at half strength.

2-3 Hours after Dawn: Shadows are at their longest, especially in the first hour after sunrise. As the day approaches noon, the shadows get smaller and smaller. Shadow Beings function at half strength, unless they are safe inside one of the many long, deep shadows.

Mid-Day: From noon till 3:00 P.M. shadows are small and more or less directly under people and not very noticeable. Shadow creatures function at half strength and there are few if any shadows large enough to conceal them.

2-3 Hours before Dusk: Shadows are deep and long again, the same as after dawn. Shadow Beings function at half strength unless they are safe inside one of the many long, deep shadows.

Dusk: This is the 40 minutes of twilight before the sun sets and 20 minutes after, and there are NO shadows. Same as overcast. Shadow Beings function at half strength.

Overcast Sky: This may be caused by the time of day (see dusk and dawn) or from cloud cover or rainy conditions in which the sun is completely obscured and its light diffused by the clouds. There are no shadows or the few that exist are much too light and barely noticeable to be of any use. People can still see clearly, but the light is dim and washed out. Shadow Beings function at half strength in overcast conditions and cannot find shadows outdoors dark enough to be of any use to them (or to Shadow Mages or Shadow Assassins).

Night: While not ideal for creating true shadows, it is dark and comforting for beings who thrive in darkness. Shadow Mages and all Shadow Beings function at full strength. This is the time for the denizens of shadows and all creatures of the night.

Moon Covered by Clouds: No moon or stars. Pitch black and difficult for humans to see without a light source. Shadow Beings function at full strength.

Moon and Starlight in a Clear Sky: As long as the moon is at least half to two-thirds full, there will be some moonlight and obvious shadows surrounded by deeper and larger areas of darkness. Humans can see okay in patches of areas lit by moonlight, but the shadows there are deep and dark, as is the larger, surrounding darkness which is pitch black. Shadow Beings function at full strength in the darkness, shadows and moonlight.

Full Moon and Clear Sky: A full moon or mostly full moon creates a night landscape that is surprisingly bright and filled with many deep, long shadows cast by trees and objects for Shadow Beings and Mages to lurk. Shadow Beings function at full strength in the darkness, shadows and moonlight. The full moon simply means their potential victims may see the monsters or villains coming as they step from one shadow into the dim moonlight and into another.

Full Moon and Cloudy Sky: A full moon or mostly full moon is swallowed by the clouds to create a consuming darkness, foreboding landscape with peaks of moonlight. Where the moonlight peeks through there is a dark twilight effect with a few deep shadows, but the rest of the area is pitch black. Shadow Beings function at full strength in the darkness, shadows and moonlight.

Moon Sliver on a Clear Night: A crisp night is as dark as pitch. It is an overwhelming darkness everywhere. There is no light except that cast by artificial or magical means. Difficult for humans to see. Shadow Beings function at full strength.

Rainy Night: No moon or stars. Pitch black and difficult for humans to see without a light source. Shadow Beings function at full strength.

Nighttime Fog: A mist covers the ground to create twilight conditions (same as overcast) in the smothering darkness. There are few deep shadows in the fog, but plenty of grey shapes in the moving mist. Since it is nighttime, it is still dark enough that Shadow Beings function at full strength and are +10% to Prowl. Worse, visibility for humans is terrible, even with a light source, making them unable to see more than 1D6 feet (0.3 to 1.8 m) ahead of themselves.

Daytime Fog: A mist covers the ground to create twilight conditions (same as overcast). There are NO shadows, but since it is daytime, it is still bright enough that Shadow Beings function at half strength. Visibility for humans is terrible, making them unable to see more than 1D6 feet (0.3 to 1.8 m) ahead.

Daytime Rain: Whether a light rain or a downpour, the sky is cloudy and overcast, and rain makes a dreary, wet scene. It creates a twilight condition where there are NO shadows, but it is daytime and still bright enough that Shadow Beings function at half strength. Visibility for humans is poor, making them unable to see more than a half a mile (0.8 km). This condition typically lasts for 2D6x10 minutes to 2D6 hours.

Daytime Night Sky Storm: This is no oridinary rainstorm. The clouds are so thick and black that it creates a darkness equal to the beginning of nightfall. This black and menacing storm front lasts for 1D4x10 minutes and is likely to be accompanied by 3D6+10 minutes of torrential rain, and high winds (2D4x10 mph/32 to 128 km); tornado conditions. There are no shadows during the 1D4x10 period, but it is dark enough that Shadow Beings function at full strength as if it were night.

Palladium Books® Check List

The Rifter® Series
___ 173 The Rifter® #73 – $13.95
___ 174 The Rifter® #74 – $13.95
___ 175 The Rifter® #75 – $13.95
___ 176 The Rifter® #76 – $13.95
___ 177 The Rifter® #77 – $13.95
___ 178 The Rifter® #78 – $13.95 (Spring)

Splicers®   Note: Sourcebooks coming soon.
___ 200 Splicers® RPG – $23.95

Dead Reign®
___ 230 Dead Reign® RPG – $22.95
___ 231 SB 1: Civilization Gone™ – $12.95
___ 232 SB 2: Dark Places™ – $12.95
___ 233 SB 3: Endless Dead™ – $16.95
___ 234 SB 4: Fear the Reaper™ – $12.95
___ 235 SB 5: Graveyard Earth™ – $12.95
___ 236 SB 6: Hell Followed™ – $20.95

Rifts® Novels
___ 301 Sonic Boom™ – $9.95
___ 302 Deception's Web™ – $9.95
___ 303 Treacherous Awakenings™ – $9.95
___ 304 Tales of the Chi-Town 'Burbs™ – $12.95
___ 305 Rifts® Path of the Storm™ – $12.95

Weapons Books
___ 401 Weapons and Armor™ – $8.95
___ 402 Weapons and Castles™ – $8.95
___ 403 Weapons and Assassins™ – $9.95
___ 404 Weapons & Castles of the Orient™ – $9.95
___ 409 Exotic Weapons™ – $9.95
___ 410 European Castles™ – $9.95

Palladium Fantasy RPG®
___ 450 The Palladium Fantasy RPG® – $26.95
___ 4500IIC Palladium Fantasy RPG® 30th
       Anniversary Hardcover – $50.00
___ 451 Dragons & Gods™ – $24.95
___ 453 Old Ones™ 2nd Ed. – $24.95
___ 454 Monsters & Animals™ 2nd Ed. – $24.95
___ 455 Adventures on the High Seas™ – $24.95
___ 458 Island at the Edge of the World™ – $20.95
___ 459 Yin-Sloth Jungles™ – $20.95
___ 462 Western Empire™ – $24.95
___ 463 Baalgor Wastelands™ – $24.95
___ 464 Mount Nimro™ – $20.95
___ 465 Eastern Territory™ – $24.95
___ 466 Library of Bletherad™ – $20.95
___ 467 Northern Hinterlands™ – $24.95
___ 468 Land/Damned 1: Chaos Lands™ – $24.95
___ 469 LoD 2: Eternal Torment™ – $24.95
___ 470 LoD 3: The Citadel – $24.95 (coming)
___ 471 Wolfen Empire™ – $20.95
___ 472 Mysteries of Magic™ One: Heart of
       Magic – $16.95
___ 474 Bizantium/Northern Islands™ – $20.95
___ 475 Garden of the Gods™ – $16.95 (coming)

Heroes Unlimited™ / After the Bomb®
___ 500-2 Heroes Unlimited™, 2nd Ed. – $26.95
___ 5000HC Heroes Unlimited™ 30th Anniver-
       sary Hardcover – $50.00
___ 501 Villains Unlimited™ Revised – $24.95
___ 503 After the Bomb® RPG – $24.95
___ 505 Road Hogs™ (After the Bomb® II) –
       $9.95
___ 507 Mutants Down Under™ (AB III) – $9.95
___ 511 Mutants of the Yucatan™ (AB IV) – $9.95
___ 513 Mutants in Avalon™ (AB V) – $16.95
___ 514 Mutants in Orbit™ (AB VI) – $16.95
___ 515 Aliens Unlimited™ – $24.95
___ 516 Heroes Unlimited™ G.M.'s Guide –
       $24.95
___ 517 Century Station™ – $24.95
___ 518 Gramercy Island™ – $24.95
___ 519 Aliens Unlimited Galaxy Guide™ –
       $24.95
___ 520 Mutant Underground™ – $16.95
___ 521 Powers Unlimited® One – $16.95
___ 522 Powers Unlimited® Two – $16.95
___ 523 Powers Unlimited® Three – $16.95
___ 525 Revised Ninjas & Superspies™ – $20.95
___ 526 Mystic China™ – $24.95
___ 527 Armageddon Unlimited™ – $20.95

Robotech® RPG
___ 550 Robotech® The Shadow Chronicles®
       RPG (manga size) – $16.95
___ 550HC Robotech® The Shadow Chroni-
       cles® Deluxe Hardcover RPG – $30.95
___ 5500HC Robotech® The Shadow Chroni-
       cles® Gold Ed. Hardcover RPG – $70.00
___ 551 Robotech® Macross® Saga Source-
       book – $16.95
___ 552 Robotech® The Masters Saga™
       Sourcebook (NEW in 8½ x 11) – $20.95
___ 553 Robotech®: Expeditionary Force
       Marines Sourcebook – $20.95
___ 554 Robotech® The New Generation™
       Sourcebook – $16.95
___ 555 Robotech® Genesis Pits Sourcebook –
       $16.95

Robotech® RPG Tactics™ (New!)
___ 55100 Robotech® RPG Tactics™ – $99.95
___ 55105 Robotech® RPG Tactics™ Rule-
       book – $20.00
___ 55101 UEDF Dice Pack – $12.00
___ 55102 Zentraedi Dice Pack – $12.00
___ 55201 UEDF Valkyrie Wing – $36.95
___ 55202 UEDF Destroid Pack – $32.95
___ 55203 UEDF Spartan Pack – $32.95
___ 55401 Zentraedi Regult Battlepods – $36.95
___ 55402 Zentraedi Artillery Battlepods – $36.95
___ 55403 Zentraedi Glaug Command – $36.95

Rifts® Chaos Earth®
___ 660 Rifts® Chaos Earth® RPG – $20.95
___ 661 Rifts® CE Creatures of Chaos™ – $12.95
___ 662 Rifts® CE The Rise of Magic™ – $12.95
___ 665 Rifts® Chaos Earth® First Responders™
       – $16.95 (coming)
___ 666 Rifts® Chaos Earth® Resurrection™
       – $20.95

Beyond the Supernatural™
___ 700 Beyond the Supernatural™, 2nd Ed.
       – $24.95
___ 702 Tome Grotesque™ – $20.95 (coming)
___ 703 Beyond Arcanum™ – $24.95 (coming)

Nightbane®
___ 730 Nightbane® RPG – $24.95
___ 731 Nightbane®: Between the Shadows™
       – $20.95
___ 732 Nightbane®: Nightlands™ – $20.95
___ 733 Nightbane®: Through the Glass
       Darkly™ – $20.95
___ 735 Nightbane® Survival Guide™ – $20.95

Rifts®
___ 800HC Rifts® RPG Ultimate Edition – $39.95
___ 801 Rifts® Sourcebook One Revised – $20.95
___ 802-E Rifts® World Book 1: Vampire King-
       doms™, Revised – $24.95
___ 803 Rifts® Conversion Book One™ – $24.95
___ 804 Rifts® WB 2: Atlantis™ – $20.95
___ 805 Rifts® Sourcebook 2: Mechanoids™
       – $16.95
___ 807 Rifts® WB 3: England™ – $20.95
___ 808 Rifts® WB 4: Africa™ – $20.95
___ 809 Rifts® Dimension Book 1: Worm-
       wood™ – $20.95
___ 810 Rifts® WB 5: Triax™ – $24.95
___ 811 Rifts® Pantheons of the Megaverse®
       – $24.95
___ 812 Rifts® Sourcebook 3: Mindwerks™
       – $16.95
___ 813 Rifts® Mercenaries™ – $20.95
___ 814 Rifts® WB 6: South America – $20.95
___ 815 Rifts® WB 7: Underseas™ – $24.95
___ 816 Rifts® DB 2: Phase World® – $24.95
___ 817 Rifts® DB 3: Phase World® Source-
       book – $16.95
___ 818 Rifts® WB 8: Rifts® Japan™ –
       $24.95
___ 819 Rifts® WB 9: South America Two™
       – $24.95
___ 820 Rifts® WB 10: Juicer Uprising™ –
       $20.95
___ 821 Rifts® WB 11: Coalition War Cam-
       paign™ – $24.95
___ 822 Rifts® WB 12: Psyscape™ – $20.95
___ 825 Rifts® WB 13: Lone Star™ – $20.95

___ 826 Rifts® WB 14: New West™ – $24.95

___ 827 Rifts® WB 15: Spirit West™ – $24.95

___ 828 Rifts® Sourcebook 4: Coalition Navy™ – $16.95

___ 829 Rifts® WB 16: Federation of Magic™ – $20.95

___ 830 Rifts® DB 4: Skraypers™ – $20.95

___ 831 Rifts® Index Volume Two™ – $16.95

___ 832 Rifts® WB 17: Warlords of Russia™ – $24.95

___ 833 Rifts® WB 18: Mystic Russia™ – $20.95

___ 834 Rifts® WB 19: Australia 1 – $24.95

___ 835 Rifts® WB 20: Canada™ – $24.95

___ 836 Rifts® WB 21: Splynn Dimensional Market™ – $24.95

___ 837 Rifts® WB 22: Free Quebec™ – $24.95

___ 838 Rifts® WB 23: Xiticix Invasion™ – $20.95

___ 839 Rifts® Coalition Wars®: Sedition™ – $20.95

___ 840 Rifts® Coalition Wars®: Coalition Overkill™ – $16.95

___ 841 Rifts® Coalition Wars®: Sorcerers' Revenge™ – $16.95

___ 842 Rifts® Coalition Wars®: Cyber-Knights™ – $16.95

___ 843 Rifts® Coalition Wars®: Shadows of Evil™ – $16.95

___ 844 Rifts® Coalition Wars®: Final Siege™ – $24.95

___ 845 Rifts® Game Master Guide™ – $26.95

___ 846 Rifts® Aftermath™ – $24.95

___ 847 Rifts® DB5: Anvil Galaxy™ – $20.95

___ 848 Rifts® Book of Magic™ – $26.95

___ 849 Rifts® Adventure Guide™ – $24.95

___ 850 Rifts® Bionics Sourcebook™ – $16.95

___ 851 Rifts® DB 6: Three Galaxies™ – $20.95

___ 852 Rifts® Dark Conversions™ – $24.95

___ 853 Rifts® Chi-Town 'Burbs™ – $9.95

___ 854 Rifts® The Tolkeen Crisis™ – $12.95

___ 855 Rifts® The Black Vault™ – $9.95

___ 856 Rifts® The Vanguard™ – $9.95

___ 857 Rifts® WB 24: China One™ – $20.95

___ 858 Rifts® WB 25: China Two™ – $20.95

___ 859 Rifts® DB 7: Megaverse Builder™ – $16.95

___ 860 Rifts® DB 8: Naruni Wave Two™ – $16.95

___ 862 Rifts® WB 26: Dinosaur Swamp™ – $20.95

___ 863 Rifts® MercTown™ – $20.95

___ 865 Rifts® Merc Ops™ – $20.95

___ 866 Rifts® WB 27: Adventures in Dinosaur Swamp™ – $20.95

___ 867 Rifts® Mercenary Adventure Sourcebook – $12.95

___ 868 Rifts® WB 28: Arzno™ – $20.95

___ 869 Rifts® WB 29: Madhaven™ – $16.95

___ 870 Rifts® John Zeleznik Coloring Book – $5.95

___ 871 Rifts® Machinations of Doom™ – $18.95

___ 872 Rifts® DB 10: Hades™ – $24.95

___ 873 Rifts® DB 11: Dyval™ – $24.95

___ 874 Rifts® WB 30: D-Bees of North America™ – $24.95

___ 875 Rifts® DB12: Dimensional Outbreak – $24.95

___ 876 Rifts® Megaverse® in Flames™ – $24.95

___ 876HC Rifts® Megaverse® in Flames™ Gold Hardcover Edition – $50.00

___ 877 Rifts® Heroes of the Megaverse® – $16.95

___ 878 Rifts® Sourcebook: Shemarrian Nation™ – $16.95

___ 880 Phase World®: Fleets of the Three Galaxies™ – $16.95

___ 881 Rifts® WB 31: Triax™ Two – $24.95

___ 883 Rifts® DB 14: Thundercloud Galaxy™ – $20.95

___ 884 Rifts® Vampires Sourcebook™ – $20.95

___ 885 Rifts® WB 32: Lemuria™ – $24.95

___ 886 Rifts® Black Market™ – $24.95

___ 886HC Rifts® Black Market™ Hardcover Gold Edition – $60.00

___ 887 Rifts® WB 33: Northern Gun™ One – $24.95

___ 888 Rifts® WB 34: Northern Gun™ Two – $26.95

___ 889 Rifts® Sourcebook: Coalition States, Heroes of Humanity™ – $20.95

___ 890 Rifts® World Book: Secrets of the Atlanteans™ – $24.95

___ 891 Rifts® World Book: Sovietski™ – $24.95 (coming)

___ 892 Rifts® Sourcebook: The Disavowed™ – $16.95 (coming)

___ 893 Rifts® CS: Heroes of Humanity™ Arsenal Sourcebook – $16.95 (coming)

___ 894 Rifts® Haunted Tech™ – $16.95 (coming)

___ 2510 Rifts® & The Megaverse® Art Book – $22.95

___ 2510-HC Rifts® & The Megaverse® Art Book, Hardcover – $50.00

___ 2510-CML Rifts® & The Megaverse® Art Book, Collector's Masterwork Edition – $125.00

Miscellaneous Products

___ 600 Deluxe Revised RECON® RPG – $22.95

___ 2537 Gamer Coffee Mug – $10.00

___ 2539 Rifts® Dice Bag – Black – $8.00

___ 2545 Dead Reign™ Coffee Mug – $10.00

___ 2554 Palladium Bookmarks, Set One – $5.00

___ 2555 Palladium Bookmarks, Set Two – $5.00

___ 2561 Property of Chi-Town Library Pencil – $0.50 each

___ 2562 Future Visions™ – The Artistry of Charles Walton II – $13.95

___ 2566 Glitter Boy Mouse Pad – $9.95

___ 2567 Old Ones Mouse Pad – $9.95

___ 2568 Zombie Graveyard Mouse Pad – $9.95

___ 2575 Rifts Poker Cards 1 (full color) – $11.99

___ 2576 Rifts Poker Cards 2 (line art) – $11.99

Note: T-shirts and other products can be found online: www.palladiumbooks.com

Rifts® Miniatures

___ MI8002 Xiticix Pack – $18.00

___ MI8004 Coalition Dog Pack – $18.00

___ MI8005 Men of Magic Pack #1 – $18.00

___ MI8006 Cyborgs Pack #1 – $18.00

___ MI8007 Simvan & Ostrosaurus Pack – $18.00

___ MI8008 Coalition Skelebots Pack #1 – $18.00

___ MI8009 Coalition SAMAS Pack #1 – $22.00

___ MI8010 Coalition Sky Cycle Pack – $22.00

___ MI8011 Coalition Dog Pack #2 – $18.00

___ MI8015 Damaged Skelebots Pack #1 – $12.00

___ MI8016 Cyber-Adventurers Pack – $18.00

___ MI8017 Rogues & Scout Pack #1 – $18.00

___ MI8018 Brodkil & Witchling Pack – $18.00

___ MI8019 Damaged Skelebots Pack #2 – $18.00

___ MI8020 Psi-Stalkers & Scouts Pack #1 – $18.00

___ MI8021 Shadow Beast – $12.00

___ MI8022 Mystic Knight – $6.00

___ MI8023 Lord Magus – $6.00

___ MI8024 High Magus – $6.00

___ MI8025 Coalition Psi-Stalker – $6.00

___ MI8026 Coalition Dog Boy in DPM-D1 Armor – $6.00

___ MI8027 Coalition Dog Boy #2 $6.00

___ MI8028 Coalition Dog Boy #3 – $6.00

___ MI8029 Coalition Dog Boy #4 – $6.00

___ MI8030 Coalition Dog Boy #5 – $6.00

___ MI8031 Glitter Boy – $20.00

___ MI8032 Glitter Boy Pilot – $6.00

___ MI8033 Kydian Overlord – $20.00

___ MI8034 Dragonsaurus – $10.00

___ MI8035 Slaver and Slave (Atlantis) Set – $10.00

___ MI8036 Crazy – $6.00

___ MI8037 Juicer #1 – $6.00

___ MI8038 Juicer #2 – $6.00

___ MI8039 Cyborg #1 – $12.00

___ MI8040 Cyborg #2 – $12.00

___ MI8041 Cyborg #3 – $6.00

___ MI8042 Coalition Officer – $6.00

___ MI8043 Coalition Grunt #1 – $6.00

___ MI8044 Coalition Grunt #2 – $6.00

___ MI8045 Coalition Grunt #3 – $6.00

www.palladiumbooks.com